W9-CQG-359

Silver Burdett & Ginn

MATHEMATICS

AUTHORS

SENIOR SERIES AUTHORS
Lucy J. Orfan • Bruce R. Vogeli

SENIOR PROBLEM SOLVING AUTHORS
Stephen Krulik • Jesse A. Rudnick

Sadie C. Bragg • Ruth I. Champagne • Gerald A. Goldin • Edith E. Grimsley
Deborah B. Gustafson • John F. LeBlanc • William D. McKillip • Fernand J. Prevost

SILVER BURDETT & GINN   MORRISTOWN, NJ • NEEDHAM, MA

Atlanta, GA • Cincinnati, OH • Dallas, TX • Menlo Park, CA • Northfield, IL

ISBN 0-382-11523-6

Table of Contents

Theme: Communication

Working with Large Numbers

When its computer failed, the automatic packaging machine at the Acme Rice Factory put only 1 grain of rice in the first 1-pound box, 2 grains in the next box, 4 in the next, 8 in the next, and so on. The workers managed to shut the machine off after 30 boxes! How much rice did the machine try to put in the 30th box? How much rice did the machine try to package altogether?

WORKING TOGETHER

Work in a small group. Use a calculator.

1. Decide how you will compute the amount of rice that the machine tried to put in the 30th box.

2. Try your method and record your results.

3. Did your method work? How do you know? If it did not, discuss why and try another method.

1. Did the plan you devised take the limitations of your calculator into account? Explain.

2. Find the largest and the smallest positive numbers you can display on your calculator. Record your results.

3. Compare your results with those of other teams. Discuss any differences.

THINKING IT THROUGH

1. Why is it impossible to display the number of grains of rice in the 30th box on most calculators?

2. How many places long must a calculator display be to show this number?

3. In order to file a report with his company, the manager had to find out how much rice the machine fed to the 30 boxes during the computer failure. Devise a plan for computing the total number of grains of rice. Then compute.

4. If 1,200 grains of rice weigh one ounce, what will the manager require to clean up his factory—a garbage can, a tractor-trailer, or a 20-car freight train? Could this accident ever really happen?

Rounding Whole Numbers

To round a whole number, follow this flowchart.

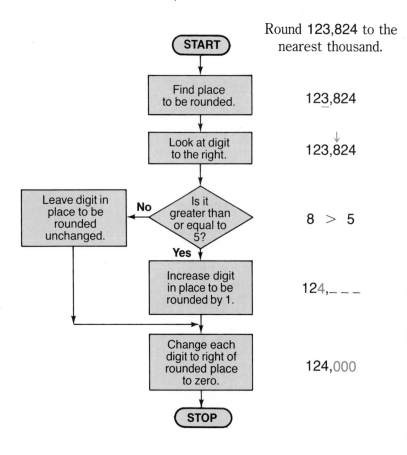

Round **123,824** to the nearest thousand.

Flowchart step	Example
START	
Find place to be rounded.	123,824
Look at digit to the right.	123,824
Is it greater than or equal to 5?	8 > 5
Increase digit in place to be rounded by 1.	124,_ _ _
Change each digit to right of rounded place to zero.	124,000
STOP	

More Examples

a. 17,542,508 rounded to the nearest million is 18,000,000.

b. 13,965 rounded to the nearest hundred is 14,000.

c. $5.35 rounded to the nearest dollar is $5.

CLASSWORK

Complete the chart below. Round each number to the places named.

		Nearest hundred	Nearest thousand	Nearest hundred thousand	Nearest million
1.	2,456,023				
2.	6,506,372				
3.	947,981				

PRACTICE

Round each number to the place named.

nearest ten	**1.** 43	**2.** 851	**3.** 675	**4.** 4,999
nearest thousand	**5.** 14,685	**6.** 998	**7.** 148,092	**8.** 395
nearest ten thousand	**9.** 736,553	**10.** 98,093	**11.** 8,732	**12.** 3,021
nearest hundred thousand	**13.** 843,147	**14.** 2,976,041	**15.** 71,071,089	**16.** 41,608
nearest million	**17.** 9,937,801	**18.** 453,762	**19.** 23,841,608	**20.** 176,206,000
nearest dollar	**21.** $4.95	**22.** $84.40	**23.** $399.69	**24.** $3.09

For each rounded number, what is the greatest possible original number? the least possible original number?

★ **25.** 4,000
(to nearest hundred)

★ **26.** 47,000
(to nearest thousand)

★ **27.** 1,000,000
(to nearest thousand)

APPLICATION

Rounded numbers are often used in newspaper headlines and articles. Use the following data to write your own headlines. Round each number to an appropriate place.

28. 84,426 people watched Valerie Brisco-Hooks win the women's 200-meter run at the 1984 Olympics in Los Angeles.

29. 179,264,395 Americans watched the 1984 Summer Olympics on TV.

★ **30.** A crowd of 9,023 fans went wild when Mary Lou Retton scored a 10 on her last event, the vault, giving her a gold medal in the women's all-around gymnastics competition.

5

Estimating Sums and Differences

The advertising manager of Radio KRPC needed an estimate of the station's earnings from commercials in September. The sales for airtime for the four weeks were $31,822; $9,656; $18,827; $24,263.

To estimate a sum or difference mentally, round each number to the greatest place of the greatest number, and then add or subtract.

$31,822		$30,000
9,656	round to	10,000
18,827		20,000
+ 24,263		+ 20,000
		$80,000

The sales totaled about $80,000.

To get a closer estimate, sometimes it is helpful to round to one more place to the right.

a. Estimate 2,645 − 389.

Round to the nearest thousand.

3,000	Estimate
− 0	too large
3,000	←

Round to the nearest hundred.

2,600	Closer
− 400	estimate
2,200	←

b. Estimate $438.23 + $44.65.

Round to the nearest hundred.

$400	Estimate
+ 0	too small
$400	←

Round to the nearest ten.

$440	Closer
+ 40	estimate
$480	←

c. Estimate 6,942 − 6,518.

Round to the nearest thousand.

7,000	Estimate
− 7,000	of zero
0	←

Round to the nearest hundred.

6,900	Closer
− 6,500	estimate
400	←

Classwork

Estimate each sum or difference. Try to estimate mentally.

1. 3,256
− 1,887

2. $58.63
+ 79.31

3. 54,936
− 45,201

4. $648.75
− 237.83

5. 349,762
+ 587,608

6. 157 + 76 + 298

7. 13,667 − 3,882

8. 246 + 38 + 304 + 197

Estimate each sum or difference. Try to estimate mentally.

1. 123 + 95	**2.** 668 − 359	**3.** 792 + 6,147	**4.** $7,235 − 6,968	**5.** 7,546 − 358
6. 43,013 + 4,529	**7.** $452.87 − 268.50	**8.** 12,198 − 3,555	**9.** 783,241 + 542,960	**10.** 2,467,049 − 1,990,454
11. 622 31 + 176	**12.** 3,412 4,072 + 1,861	**13.** 213 7,148 1,054 + 489	**14.** 2,126 218 1,583 + 917	**15.** 346,512 675,439 89,705 + 261,844

16. $712.98 + $850.01   **17.** 211,219 − 93,872   **18.** 42,364 − 4,967

Each number has been rounded to get an estimate. What is the least the actual sum or difference can be?

★ **19.** 400 + 600	★ **20.** 5,000 − 3,000	★ **21.** 7,000 0 + 4,000	★ **22.** 20,000 30,000 + 10,000	★ **23.** 800,000 − 500,000

APPLICATION

24. KRPC made the following sales of commercial airtime during the four weeks of October: $27,856; $18,223; $13,875; $21,097. Estimate the total sales.

★ **25.** The graph at the right shows the year's total sales for all commercial airtime sold by KRPC. Estimate the total sales.

★ **26.** About how much more did ABC Computers spend than Best Airlines? About how much more did Ultrasound Stereos spend than Beacon Jewelers?

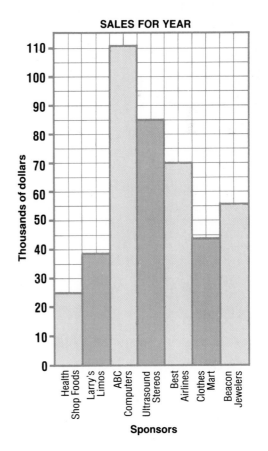

SALES FOR YEAR

7

Adding and Subtracting

A magic square appears in the upper right corner of this engraving. In a magic square the sum of each row, column, and diagonal is the same.

16	3	2	13
5	10	11	8
9	6		12
4	15	14	

Melancholy; an engraving by Albrecht Dürer, a sixteenth-century German artist

The sum for the magic square in the engraving is 34.

$$16 + 5 + 9 + 4 = 34$$

Find the missing addends.

Third column: $2 + 11 + \square + 14 = 34$

$$2 + 11 + 14 = 27$$

$$34 - 27 = 7$$

Check $2 + 11 + 7 + 14 = 34$

Fourth row: $4 + 15 + 14 + \square = 34$

$$4 + 15 + 14 = 33$$

$$34 - 33 = 1$$

Check $4 + 15 + 14 + 1 = 34$

Add the numbers along the diagonal to check that the sum is 34.

$$16 + 10 + 7 + 1 = 34$$

CLASSWORK

Add or subtract. Estimate to be sure each answer makes sense.

1. $\begin{array}{r} 3{,}847 \\ +\,1{,}659 \\ \hline \end{array}$

2. $\begin{array}{r} 6{,}019 \\ -\,3{,}543 \\ \hline \end{array}$

3. $\begin{array}{r} \$46.38 \\ 35.74 \\ 8.93 \\ +\quad 3.65 \\ \hline \end{array}$

4. $285{,}243 - 132{,}675$

5. $2{,}582 + 1{,}768 + 86$

6. $268{,}400 - 65{,}261$

8

PRACTICE

Add or subtract. Estimate to be sure each answer makes sense.

1.	9,005	**2.**	$13.79	**3.**	64,005	**4.**	$672.91	**5.**	423,574
	− 8,368		+ 16.24		− 39,127		+ 14.03		− 394,685

6.	786	**7.**	319	**8.**	3,149	**9.**	176,097	**10.**	4,005,756
	963		7		2,008		308,648		126,003
	+ 2,347		610		13,127		35,009		9,234,900
			+ 2,305		+ 863		+ 1,086,703		+ 675,459

11. $37.19 + $4.05 + $17.89   **12.** 7,431 − 998   **13.** 532,076 − 87,251

14. 47,152 + 6,590 + 119   **15.** $760.54 − $87.49   **16.** 10,219 + 176 + 1,269,746

Find each missing addend.

17. 36 + 27 + ☐ = 91   **18.** 457 + 338 + ☐ = 1,003

19. 43 + 7 + ☐ + 18 + 25 = 114   **20.** 1,886 + ☐ + 2,407 + 985 = 7,899

Complete each magic square and give the sum for each.

21.

508	753	410
		655
704		

22.

885		
	906	872
		927

23.

113			29
		78	99
		71	43
92		85	8

 ★ **24.** Choose four different digits. Form the greatest number possible. Form the least number possible. Use a calculator to subtract the least from the greatest. Repeat this procedure with the digits of the difference. Continue until you get 6,174.

APPLICATION

═══ MENTAL ARITHMETIC ═══

You can quickly find certain sums.

a. 98 + 98   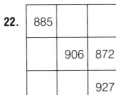 **Think** 98 is 2 less than 100.
100 + 100 = 200
200 − 4 = 196

b. 68 + 29   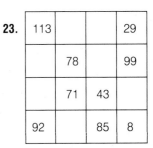 **Think** 29 is 1 less than 30.
68 + 30 = 98
98 − 1 = 97

Mentally find each sum or difference.

1. 198 + 198   **2.** 77 + 39   **3.** 89 + 89   **4.** 243 + 64   **5.** 342 + 98

6. 297 + 297 + 397   **7.** 148 + 207 + 148   **8.** 1,261 + 894

9

Problem Solving

FINDING FACTS FROM PICTURES AND TEXT

Problem solving is an important life skill. You can be a better problem solver if you follow the four-step plan shown below.

To launch a communications-satellite payload into orbit, a 2-stage Atlas-Centaur rocket might be used. The Atlas-Centaur rocket is 134 feet in height. How long is the part of the rocket that houses the satellite?

THINK **What is the question?**

How long is the part of the rocket that houses the satellite?

What are the facts?

Study the picture and the text to gather the facts.
The rocket is 134 feet in height.
The rocket has two stages—one 75 feet long, and one 32 feet long.

PLAN **How can the answer be found?**

Add the lengths of the two stages of the rocket. Then subtract that length from the total length of the rocket.

SOLVE **Carry out the plan. Do the work and find the answer.**

Stage 1 →   75 feet   134 feet (total length of rocket)
Stage 2 → + 32 feet   − 107 feet (length of 2 stages)
          107 feet   27 feet

The part of the rocket that houses the satellite is 27 feet long.

LOOK BACK **Has the question been answered? Is the arithmetic correct? Does the answer make sense?**

Check the total length by adding up.

        32 feet
     + 75 feet
      107 feet

Check subtraction by adding.

        27 feet
   + 107 feet
     134 feet

The answer is correct.

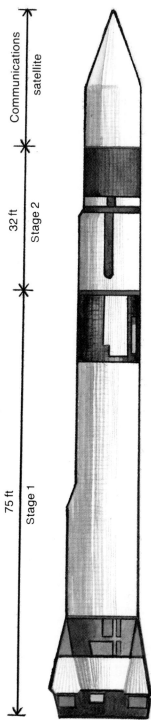

Communications satellite

32 ft — Stage 2

75 ft — Stage 1

Use Ginnie's telephone bill, shown at the right, to answer 1–4.

1. How much did Ginnie spend on long-distance calls?

2. What item on Ginnie's telephone bill cost $25.00?

3. How much more did the long-distance calls cost than the local service?

4. Ginnie spilled water on the bill. The amount of tax was erased. How much was it?

**Telephone Co.
July**

Local Service........	$ 12.00
Telephone Purchase..	$ 25.00
Long Distance.......	$ 83.00
Tax................	$
TOTAL.............	$128.00

Mr. and Mrs. Kagen and their three children are going to use the coupon shown at the right. Use it to answer 5–8.

5. What is the name of the museum the Kagens are going to visit?

6. How much will they save with the coupon?

7. The Kagens live in Ariel. If they leave their house at 2:15 P.M., when should they arrive at the museum?

8. Regular admission is $3 for adults and $2 for children. How much will the Kagens pay for admission with their coupon?

**COMMUNICATION WORLD
MUSEUM**

Just 12 minutes from Ariel

$1 OFF
Each Adult
Admission

50¢ OFF
Each Child
Admission

LIMIT: 5
persons with
this coupon

Present This Coupon
EXPIRES DEC. 31

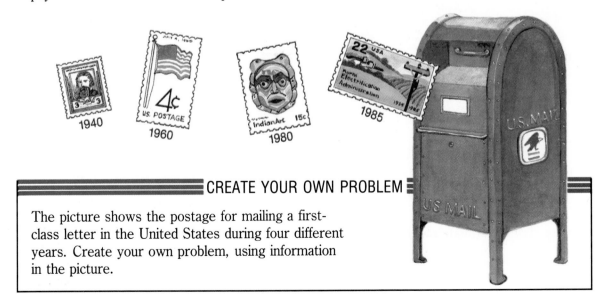

1940   1960   1980   1985

CREATE YOUR OWN PROBLEM

The picture shows the postage for mailing a first-class letter in the United States during four different years. Create your own problem, using information in the picture.

Estimating Products

The world's busiest phone is in a bus terminal in Chicago. On the average, 270 calls are made from the phone each day. About how many calls are made in a year?

To estimate a product, mentally do the following.

- Round each factor to its greatest place.

$$
\begin{array}{ccc}
270 & \longrightarrow & 300 \\
\times\,365 & \longrightarrow & \times\,400
\end{array}
$$

- Multiply the rounded factors.

Think $4 \times 3 = 12$

Then annex the same number of zeros as are in the rounded factors.

$$
\underset{\text{4 zeros}}{400} \times \underset{}{300} = \underset{\text{4 zeros}}{120{,}000}
$$

About 120,000 calls per year are made from the phone.

More Examples

a.
$$
\begin{array}{ccc}
226 & \longrightarrow & 200 \\
\times\,68 & \longrightarrow & \times\,70 \\
& & 14{,}000
\end{array}
$$

b.
$$
\begin{array}{ccc}
\$38.42 & \longrightarrow & \$\,40 \\
\times\quad 315 & \longrightarrow & \times\ 300 \\
& & \$12{,}000
\end{array}
$$

c.
$$
\begin{array}{ccc}
5{,}896 & \longrightarrow & 6{,}000 \\
\times\quad 92 & \longrightarrow & \times\quad 90 \\
& & 540{,}000
\end{array}
$$

CLASSWORK

Estimate. Try to estimate mentally.

1.
$$
\begin{array}{r}
52 \\
\times\,94
\end{array}
$$

2.
$$
\begin{array}{r}
\$8.19 \\
\times\,475
\end{array}
$$

3.
$$
\begin{array}{r}
8{,}764 \\
\times\,516
\end{array}
$$

4.
$$
\begin{array}{r}
23{,}165 \\
\times\quad 89
\end{array}
$$

5. 68×407

6. $7{,}223 \times 189$

PRACTICE

Estimate. Try to estimate mentally.

1. 23
    × 57

2. 82
    × 75

3. 148
    × 33

4. $2.72
    ×   46

5. 165
    × 121

6. 712
    × 265

7. 572
    × 483

8. $23.63
    ×   78

9. 9,165
    × 288

10. 4,525
    ×   289

11. 15,727
    ×   36

12. $123.30
    ×   57

13. 29,763
    ×   376

14. 4,129
    × 5,871

15. 46,351
    × 7,897

16. 57 × 42

17. 429 × $17.60

18. 7,349 × 319

19. 18,253 × 87

20. 8,163 × 2,819

21. 19,205 × 4,087

22. 83 × 46 × 74

23. 96 × 121 × 893

Use an estimate to choose the actual product.

24. 48 × 18
    a. 864
    b. 4,364
    c. 8,864

25. 197 × 23
    a. 471
    b. 4,531
    c. 9,641

26. 729 × 136
    a. 894
    b. 9,924
    c. 99,144

27. 63 × 487
    a. 3,481
    b. 30,681
    c. 425,071

For each estimated product, find the least possible actual product; the greatest possible actual product. Use a calculator.

★28.   50
      × 30
     ‾‾‾‾‾‾
     1,500

★29.   600
      × 70
     ‾‾‾‾‾‾
     42,000

★30. 1,000
      ×   700
     ‾‾‾‾‾‾‾
     700,000

★31.   8,000
        × 8,000
     ‾‾‾‾‾‾‾‾‾‾
     64,000,000

APPLICATION

32. Alexander Graham Bell spoke the first words over a telephone on March 10, 1876. By 1878 the first telephone exchange was opened in New Haven, Connecticut, with 21 phones. Today there are nearly 8,100,000 times as many phones in use in the United States. About how many phones are there in the United States today?

★33. If a pair of wires could handle only one call at a time, long-distance calls would be very expensive. But engineers have developed ways for many calls to travel on one pair of wires. In modern telephone cables there are 22 wires. Each pair of wires can handle as many as 13,200 calls at the same time. About how many calls can a cable handle in all?

LOGICAL THINKING

Put one number in each box to give the greatest product.

1 2 4 6 8 9

Multiplying

Some products are easy to find by following a pattern. But not all patterns continue unendingly. Be careful about drawing conclusions from just a few examples!

$9 \times 9 = 81$

$9 \times 98 = 882$

$9 \times 987 = 8,883$

$9 \times 9,876 = 88,884$

$9 \times 98,765 = ?$

Find $9 \times 98,765$.

$$
\begin{array}{r}
{\scriptstyle 7\,6\ 5\,4} \\
98,765 \\
\times \qquad 9 \\
\hline
888,885
\end{array}
$$

More Examples

a. $312 \times 221 = 68,952$

$213 \times 122 = 25,986$

b. $411 \times 102 = 41,922$

$114 \times 201 = 22,914$

c. $113 \times 223 = 25,199$

$311 \times 322 = ?$ ◀ Watch out!

Sun and Moon by Maurits C. Escher

Find 322×311.

$$
\begin{array}{r}
311 \\
\times 322 \\
\hline
622 \\
6\,22 \\
93\,3 \\
\hline
100,142
\end{array}
$$

CLASSWORK

detail, collection Haags Museum, The Hague

Multiply. Estimate to be sure each answer makes sense.

1. $\begin{array}{r}1,308 \\ \times \quad 64 \\ \hline\end{array}$	**2.** $\begin{array}{r}596 \\ \times 205 \\ \hline\end{array}$	**3.** $\begin{array}{r}\$40.96 \\ \times \quad 973 \\ \hline\end{array}$	**4.** $\begin{array}{r}16,085 \\ \times \quad 27 \\ \hline\end{array}$	**5.** $\begin{array}{r}82,716 \\ \times \quad 514 \\ \hline\end{array}$

6. 211×203 **7.** 112×302 **8.** $1,741 \times 7,105$ **9.** $\$510.25 \times 95$

14

Multiply. Estimate to be sure each answer makes sense.

1.	2.	3.	4.	5.
76 × 28	97 × 39	102 × 14	311 × 19	$4.26 × 28

6.	7.	8.	9.	10.
4,096 × 78	$33.21 × 84	20,642 × 59	516 × 124	873 × 219

11.	12.	13.	14.	15.
278 × 517	5,608 × 407	$96.58 × 726	27,136 × 945	2,183 × 6,057

16. 178 × 980   **17.** 2,114 × 56   **18.** 368 × 3,480   **19.** 14 × 9 × 24

20. 3,563 × 7,174   **21.** $236.20 × 4,057   **22.** 54,482 × 7,425   **23.** 352 × 43 × 75

Compare. Replace with <, >, or =.

24. 16 × 34 × 27 3,256 × 24   **25.** 28,792 × 356 356 × 28,792

26. 8,562 × 9,687 29,078 × 2,653   **27.** 3,564 × 28 108 × 21 × 44

28. 25 × 4 × 83 256 × 0 × 125   **29.** 8 × 125 × 365 435 × 250 × 4

 Use a calculator to multiply.

★ **30.** Choose any two-digit number. Multiply by 13. Multiply the result by 21. Multiply that result by 37. Choose another two-digit number and repeat the multiplication with that number. Repeat with another two-digit number. In each case, what is the relationship between the original number and the last product?

APPLICATION

Use a calculator to find each answer.

1. 15,873 × 7	**2.** 4 × 4	**3.** (1 × 8) + 1	**4. a.** 36 × 84
15,873 × 14	34 × 34	(12 × 8) + 2	63 × 48
15,873 × 21	334 × 334	(123 × 8) + 3	**b.** 32 × 46
15,873 × 28	3,334 × 3,334	(1,234 × 8) + 4	23 × 64
15,873 × 35	33,334 × 33,334	(12,345 × 8) + 5	**c.** 35 × 21
			53 × 12

Exponents

According to an old Chinese proverb,
A picture is worth 10,000 words.

Can you write 10,000 using exponents?

An **exponent** tells how many times the base is used as a factor.

$$\overset{\text{exponent}}{\underset{\text{base}}{10^{4}}} = \underset{\text{factors}}{10 \times 10 \times 10 \times 10}$$

$$10^{4} = 10,000$$
Read ten to the fourth power

A picture is worth 10^{4} words.

More Examples

	Read	Factors	Standard Form
2^3	two to the third power or two **cubed**	$2 \times 2 \times 2$	8
5^2	five to the second power or five **squared**	5×5	25
1^5	one to the fifth power	$1 \times 1 \times 1 \times 1 \times 1$	1

CLASSWORK

Write each using exponents.

1. $8 \times 8 \times 8 \times 8$ **2.** $1 \times 1 \times 1$ **3.** $3 \times 3 \times 3 \times 3 \times 3$ **4.** 9

Write each as a product of factors. Then write the number in standard form.

5. 3^2 **6.** 5^3 **7.** 10^5 **8.** 7^1 **9.** 6^4 **10.** 1^6

Write each using exponents.

1. $3 \times 3 \times 3$ **2.** $2 \times 2 \times 2 \times 2 \times 2$ **3.** 9×9

4. 1×1 **5.** $4 \times 4 \times 4 \times 4$ **6.** 12

Write each as a product of factors.

7. 6^3 **8.** 3^6 **9.** 7^4 **10.** 8^2 **11.** 4^1 **12.** 5^5

Write each number in standard form.

13. 4^2 **14.** 7^2 **15.** 18^2 **16.** 25^2 **17.** 1^8

18. 3^3 **19.** 8^4 **20.** 9^3 **21.** 6^7 **22.** 4^5

23. 6×10^5 **24.** $(3 \times 10^4) + (4 \times 10^3) + (7 \times 10)$

Make each sentence true.

25. $9^{\square} = 81$ **26.** $13^2 = \square$ **27.** $2^{\square} = 32$ **28.** $\square^3 = 64$

What is a **squumber**? The number 2025 is a squumber. To show that 2025 is a squumber, first separate it into 2 two-digit numerals: 20 25. Then follow these steps.

$$20 + 25 = 45 \qquad 45^2 = 2025$$

Which of the numbers below are squumbers?

⋆**29.** 3025   ⋆**30.** 8607   ⋆**31.** 5025   ⋆**32.** 9801

APPLICATION

CALCULATOR

Use a calculator to find the standard form for each number.

1. 8^7 **2.** 3^{14} **3.** 5^{10} **4.** 2^{25}

5. 37^5 **6.** 45^4 **7.** $15^6 + 27^4$ **8.** $42^4 + 68^3$

Make each sentence true.

9. $92^{\square} = 71,639,296$ **10.** $6^{\square} = 60,466,176$

11. $\square^4 = 2,401$ **12.** $\square^3 = 15,625$

Mixed Practice

1. $542 + 89 + 157$

2. $\begin{array}{r} 5,409 \\ -\ 3,875 \end{array}$

3. $\begin{array}{r} 48 \\ \times\ 63 \end{array}$

4. $\begin{array}{r} 855 \\ 3,762 \\ 57 \\ +\ 934 \end{array}$

5. 356×45

6. $\begin{array}{r} 1,500,752 \\ -\ 847,544 \end{array}$

7. $\begin{array}{r} 348,175 \\ 2,071,988 \\ +\ 577,047 \end{array}$

8. $545,062 - 66,055$

9. 2^9

10. $\begin{array}{r} 7,836 \\ \times\ 34 \end{array}$

11. 10^6

12. $29 + 68 + 113 + 44$

13. 5^4

14. $\begin{array}{r} 800,341 \\ -\ 398,765 \end{array}$

15. $58 + 409 + 8 + 26$

Dividing

In the average home in Riverton, the TV was on 2,563 hours last year. How many hours a week was this, to the nearest hour? (52 wk = 1 yr)

Step 1

Decide where to place the first quotient digit.

$$52 \overline{)2{,}563}$$

Step 2

Round the divisor and estimate the first quotient digit. Then divide.

50
$$\begin{array}{r} 5 \\ 52\overline{)2{,}563} \\ 2\ 60 \end{array}$$

↑ How many 5's in 25?

260 > 256
Trial quotient too great.
Try next lower digit.

Step 3

Continue to divide.

50
$$\begin{array}{r} 49 \\ 52\overline{)2{,}563} \\ 2\ 08 \quad (4 \times 52) \\ \hline 483 \\ 468 \ (9 \times 52) \\ \hline 15 \end{array}$$

Check (52 × 49) + 15 = 2,563

Since the remainder, 15, is less than half the divisor, round the quotient to 49. The TV was on 49 hours a week.

You can also check division by estimating. Mentally do the following.

Step 1

If the divisor has more than one digit, round it to its greatest place.

50
$$52\overline{)2{,}563}$$

Step 2

Find the first digit of the quotient. Write zeros for the other places.

50
$$\begin{array}{r} 50 \\ 52\overline{)2{,}563} \end{array}$$

The answer 49 is reasonable, since it is about 50.

Another Example

30
$$\begin{array}{r} 20 \\ 34\overline{)7{,}004} \\ 6\ 8 \\ \hline 20 \end{array}$$

?
$$34\overline{)20}$$

Since 34 > 20, write 0 in the quotient and continue dividing.

$$\begin{array}{r} 206 \\ 34\overline{)7{,}004} \\ 6\ 8 \\ \hline 204 \\ 204 \end{array}$$

Check

Multiply 34 × 206 = 7,004

Estimate
30
$$\begin{array}{r} 200 \\ 34\overline{)7{,}004} \end{array}$$

CLASSWORK

Divide. Be sure to check the answers.

1. $80\overline{)3{,}697}$

2. $60\overline{)5{,}863}$

3. $94\overline{)\$82.72}$

4. $500\overline{)136{,}550}$

5. $72\overline{)42{,}415}$

6. $85\overline{)5{,}197}$

7. 49,552 ÷ 163

8. $342\overline{)\$7{,}325.64}$

Divide. Check the answers by multiplying or by estimating.

1. $25\overline{)3{,}724}$

2. $43\overline{)8{,}195}$

3. $\$65.28 \div 16$

4. $74\overline{)5{,}646}$

5. $97\overline{)13{,}502}$

6. $63\overline{)12{,}192}$

7. $85\overline{)24{,}374}$

8. $63\overline{)\$191.52}$

9. $19\overline{)4{,}418}$

10. $16{,}932 \div 83$

11. $47\overline{)35{,}049}$

12. $81\overline{)\$253.53}$

13. $200\overline{)8{,}125}$

14. $280\overline{)\$92.40}$

15. $19{,}057 \div 300$

16. $360\overline{)22{,}305}$

17. $64\overline{)51{,}297}$

18. $72\overline{)\$504.72}$

19. $448\overline{)53{,}791}$

20. $10{,}052 \div 324$

21. $384\overline{)416{,}917}$

22. $416\overline{)836{,}576}$

23. $282\overline{)943{,}835}$

24. $687\overline{)4{,}278{,}523}$

Estimate which quotient is greater, a or b.

★ 25. a. $25\overline{)\$375.46}$

b. $326\overline{)\$647.85}$

★ 26. a. $84\overline{)55{,}786}$

b. $534\overline{)226{,}562}$

★ 27. a. $62\overline{)143{,}960}$

b. $584\overline{)1{,}668{,}760}$

APPLICATION

28. If the TV is on 2,373 hours a year in the average home in the United States, how many hours a day is this, to the nearest hour?

29. Keep a record for a week of the number of hours the TV in your home is on each day. On the average, how many hours a day was the TV on that week? Is it more or less than the average in **28**?

★ 30. This year many of the people in Riverton participated in a TV study. They gave up watching TV for the month of November. The table below shows how they spent their leisure time over the month. On the average, how many hours a day did each person spend doing each activity? Round to the nearest hour.

	Reading	Hobbies	Sports	Family Games	Studying	Parties
Total hours spent for month	176,580	270,990	174,570	129,438	92,544	68,472
Number of people who did activity	2,943	3,011	2,645	2,397	964	1,902

Problem Solving

SKILLS AND STRATEGIES REVIEW

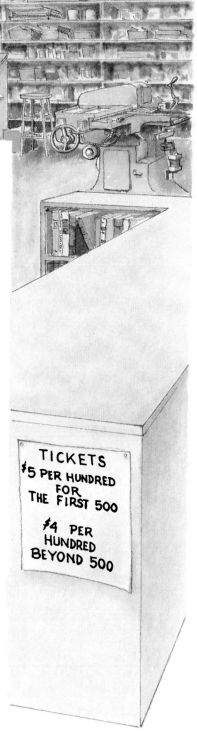

Paul and Julie have just opened the Baker Copy Center. Use the information in the picture to solve.

1. Arlene ordered 100 tickets for her class's Columbus Day dance. How much did she pay?

2. Gerry ordered 300 tickets for the junior high school Halloween dance. How much did they cost?

3. Mrs. Lewis ordered 700 tickets. How much did she pay?

4. Mr. Antonelli ordered 1,200 tickets for the high school Winter Holiday dance. How much did the tickets cost?

5. Sally needed 23 invitations for her party. Mike needed 32 invitations for his party. How much more will Mike pay than Sally?

6. The Center is open Monday through Friday from 9:00 A.M. to 5:00 P.M.. How many hours will it be open in October?

7. Julie and Paul signed a two-year lease for their shop. The first year will cost them $11,460. The second year they will pay $975 per month. What will they pay in rent for the first two years?

8. Julie has an order to print 100 copies of a 48-page magazine for the eighth grade of the local junior high school. Paul checked the paper supply and found that they had 9 reams of paper. (A ream contains 500 sheets.) Do they have enough paper to do the job?

★ 9. Mrs. Brown ordered 850 tickets for the charity softball game. How much did she pay?

20

Problem Solving
WHAT IF . . .?

The Baker Copy Center prints the local newspaper.

1. What town does the paper serve?

2. What is the date of this paper?

3. How often is the paper published?

4. What is the current circulation?

5. What is the price of the paper?

6. Where is the paper printed?

What if the Milltown Gazette doubles its circulation?

7. What will the new circulation be?

8. How much will the paper cost?

9. It costs Paul and Julie $.11 per copy to print the paper. What will it cost per week to print the paper?

10. How much will Paul and Julie make per week on the paper?

Paul pays $5.00 to have 100 sheets of paper folded by hand.

What if he buys a paper-folding machine for $1,875?

11. How many sheets of paper must be folded to recover the cost of the machine?

★ 12. How many weeks of the new circulation does this represent? On the average the Gazette is 32 pages long. (Each sheet of paper forms 4 pages.)

Paul and Julie buy their high-quality newsprint from the Acme Paper Mills. The paper comes only in boxes of 100 sheets. They pay $.02 per sheet.

What if the New Deal Paper Company offers to sell them paper of the same quality, in 100-sheet boxes, at the following price scale?

first 100 sheets	$.03 per sheet
second 100 sheets	$.02 per sheet
each additional 100 sheets	$.01 per sheet

★ 13. How many sheets will Paul and Julie have to buy from the New Deal Paper Company to save money?

CHAPTER REVIEW

Write each number in standard form. pages 16–17

1. $(6 \times 10^4) + (8 \times 10^2) + (6 \times 10) + 3$ 2. 408 billion

3. $(2 \times 10^6) + (8 \times 10^4) + (5 \times 10^3) + (6 \times 10^2) + 6$

4. 10^3 5. 5^2 6. 15^2 7. 2^4 8. 3^3 9. 4^5

Round each number to the nearest hundred; nearest ten thousand; nearest million. pages 4–5

10. 2,998,635   11. 6,129,462   12. 79,643,704   13. 802,983   14. 247,028

Estimate. pages 6–7, 12–13, 18–19

15. 365×429 16. $475 + 514$ 17. $8,429 \div 92$ 18. $4,096 - 2,824$ 19. $54\overline{)12,000}$

20. $\begin{array}{r} 3,782 \\ \times\ \ \ 512 \\ \hline \end{array}$ 21. $78\overline{)34,060}$ 22. $\begin{array}{r} 49,285 \\ \times\ \ \ \ \ \ 62 \\ \hline \end{array}$ 23. $\begin{array}{r} 54,925 \\ -\ 46,876 \\ \hline \end{array}$ 24. $28\overline{)3,480}$

Add, subtract, multiply, or divide. Check the answers. pages 8–9, 14–15, 18–19

25. $5,058 + 2,697$ 26. $3,113 - 946$ 27. $12,416 + 5,369$ 28. 187×59

29. $\begin{array}{r} 324 \\ 2,189 \\ +\ 4,235 \\ \hline \end{array}$ 30. $\begin{array}{r} 510,020 \\ -\ 328,763 \\ \hline \end{array}$ 31. $\begin{array}{r} 10,327 \\ \times\ \ \ \ \ 815 \\ \hline \end{array}$ 32. $\begin{array}{r} 4,596 \\ 13,728 \\ +\ 28,310 \\ \hline \end{array}$

33. $\begin{array}{r} 462 \\ \times\ 357 \\ \hline \end{array}$ 34. $\begin{array}{r} \$9.12 \\ \times\ \ \ 238 \\ \hline \end{array}$ 35. $\begin{array}{r} 5,609 \\ \times\ \ \ \ 84 \\ \hline \end{array}$ 36. $\begin{array}{r} 653,282 \\ -\ \ 85,697 \\ \hline \end{array}$

37. $306 \times 8,243$ 38. $1,404 \div 9$ 39. $86\overline{)7,935}$ 40. $142 \times 9,103$

41. $\$178.15 - \$85.48$ 42. $329\overline{)239,504}$ 43. $37\overline{)\$284.53}$ 44. 70×503

Write each using exponents. pages 16–17

45. 8×8 46. $4 \times 4 \times 4 \times 4$ 47. $6 \times 6 \times 6 \times 6 \times 6$ 48. 12×12

Solve. pages 10–11, 20–21

The pony express operated in the United States from 1860 to 1861 between Missouri and California. It cost $10 an ounce to send mail on the pony express. In 1984 it cost 20¢ for the first ounce and 17¢ for each additional ounce up to 12 ounces.

49. How much did it cost to send an 8-oz package on the pony express?

50. How much more or less expensive was it to send an 8-oz package in 1984?

Round each number to the place named.

1. 349 to the nearest hundred

2. 24,963,702 to the nearest million

3. 1,078,461 to the nearest thousand

4. 3,959 to the nearest hundred

Choose the best estimate for each.

5. 2,178 + 1,406 + 986

  a. 4,000

  b. 7,000

  c. 10,000

6. 2,786 × 318

  a. 90,000

  b. 900,000

  c. 9,000,000

7. 30,962 ÷ 43

  a. 7

  b. 70

  c. 700

Write each as a product of factors. Then write the number in standard form.

8. 4^3

9. 9^2

10. 10^4

11. 3^5

Add, subtract, multiply, or divide. Check the answers.

12.
$$\begin{array}{r} \$174.19 \\ -81.17 \\ \hline \end{array}$$

13.
$$\begin{array}{r} 3,621 \\ 725 \\ +348 \\ \hline \end{array}$$

14.
$$\begin{array}{r} 43,157 \\ 8,219 \\ +73,902 \\ \hline \end{array}$$

15.
$$\begin{array}{r} 42,016 \\ \times872 \\ \hline \end{array}$$

16. 3,262 ÷ 47

17.
$$\begin{array}{r} 476,019 \\ -137,493 \\ \hline \end{array}$$

18. 47 × 6,098

19. $98\overline{)21,063}$

Solve.

20. The editorial staff of *News Today* is buying 25 typewriters as advertised at the right. They will pay $500 as a cash down-payment. How much more money will they have to pay?

$180.⁰⁰ each
Buy 10 or more and
pay $155.⁰⁰ each.

Write in order from least to greatest.

$6^3 + 2^8$; $3^5 + 125$; $12^3 - 786$; $2^5 \times 3^3$; $8^4 - 5^5$;   18,050 ÷ 38

═ EXPLORE ═

SIGN LANGUAGE

Many people use sign language to communicate. Below are the
signs for the numbers 0 to 10. (Your palm faces the person
you are talking to.) Practice these signs.

0

1

2

3

4

5

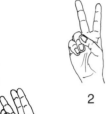
6

7

8

9

10

To form the signs for the numbers 30 to 99, combinations of
these signs are used. Here are four examples.

32

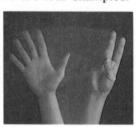
56

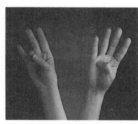
74

89

**The signs for *plus*, *minus*, and *times* appear below. Sign
each expression in 1–10. Have a classmate sign the answer.**

+ (plus)

− (minus)

× (times)

1. 31 + 42   2. 48 + 35   3. 68 − 59   4. 75 − 36   5. 8 × 7

6. 34 × 2   7. 86 − 54   8. 9 × 5   9. 32 + 59   10. 61 + 35

11. Find a book that tells the signs for the numbers 11 to 29; for 100.

BINARY AND HEXADECIMAL NUMBERS

Shown in this place-value chart is the decimal number 7,306. The digits 0, 1, 2, 3, 4, 5, 6, 7, 8, and 9 are used in decimal numbers (base 10).

10^4	10^3	10^2	10^1	1
	7,	3	0	6

The binary number 1001 is shown below. Only the digits 0 and 1 are used in **binary numbers** (base 2).

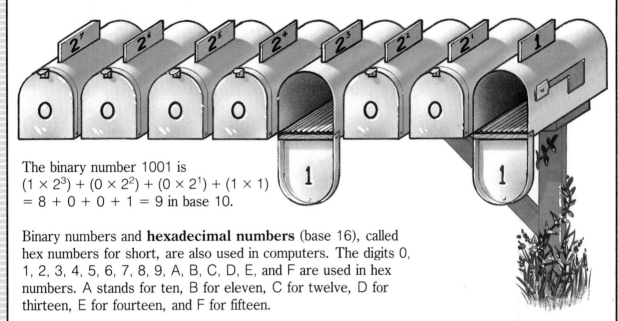

The binary number 1001 is
$(1 \times 2^3) + (0 \times 2^2) + (0 \times 2^1) + (1 \times 1)$
$= 8 + 0 + 0 + 1 = 9$ in base 10.

Binary numbers and **hexadecimal numbers** (base 16), called hex numbers for short, are also used in computers. The digits 0, 1, 2, 3, 4, 5, 6, 7, 8, 9, A, B, C, D, E, and F are used in hex numbers. A stands for ten, B for eleven, C for twelve, D for thirteen, E for fourteen, and F for fifteen.

The hex number 4B7 is
$(4 \times 16^2) + (B \times 16^1) + (7 \times 1) =$
$(4 \times 256) + (11 \times 16) + (7 \times 1) =$
$1,024 + 176 + 7 = 1,207$ in base 10.

16^4	16^3	16^2	16^1	1
		4	B	7

The examples at the right show that a four-digit binary number can be written as a one-digit hex number. Similarly, an eight-digit binary number can be written as a two-digit hex number.

Binary	Hex	Decimal
0111	7	7
1011	B	11
0111 1011	7B	123
1011 0111	B7	183

Write a hex number and a decimal number for each binary number.

1. 1101   **2.** 0110   **3.** 1111

4. 0100   **5.** 0010   **6.** 1010

7. 1110 1001   **8.** 1100 1011   **9.** 1101 0101

10. 0011 1011   **11.** 1000 0111   **12.** 1111 1111

13. 0101 1010 1101   **14.** 0011 0001 1011   **15.** 0111 1110 1001

The keyboard of a calculator has 3 kinds of keys.

Control keys ⬚C⬚ ⬚CE⬚ ⬚=⬚ ⬚M+⬚ ⬚CM⬚ ⬚RM⬚

Number entry keys ⬚0⬚ ⬚1⬚ ⬚2⬚ ⬚3⬚ ⬚4⬚ ⬚5⬚
⬚6⬚ ⬚7⬚ ⬚8⬚ ⬚9⬚ ⬚·⬚

Function keys ⬚+⬚ ⬚−⬚ ⬚×⬚ ⬚÷⬚ ⬚%⬚

Compare the keys on your calculator with the keys shown above.

You can do repeated operations on some calculators using the equal key (⬚=⬚).

Find 5 × 5 × 5.

Press ⬚5⬚ ⬚×⬚ ⬚5⬚ ⬚×⬚ ⬚5⬚ ⬚=⬚ ⟶ $\boxed{125.}$

or **Press** ⬚5⬚ ⬚×⬚ ⬚5⬚ ⬚=⬚ ⬚=⬚ ⟶ $\boxed{125.}$

Find 64 ÷ 2 ÷ 2 ÷ 2.

Press ⬚6⬚ ⬚4⬚ ⬚÷⬚ ⬚2⬚ ⬚÷⬚ ⬚2⬚ ⬚÷⬚ ⬚2⬚ ⬚=⬚ ⟶ $\boxed{8.}$

or **Press** ⬚6⬚ ⬚4⬚ ⬚÷⬚ ⬚2⬚ ⬚=⬚ ⬚=⬚ ⬚=⬚ ⟶ $\boxed{8.}$

▶To use the ⬚=⬚ key for repeated multiplication or division, enter the same number of equal signs as there are multiplication or division signs.

Find **8 × 8 × 8 × 8**. **Press** ⬚8⬚ ⬚×⬚ ⬚8⬚ ⬚=⬚ ⬚=⬚ ⬚=⬚ ⟶ $\boxed{4096.}$
3 multiplication signs   3 equal signs

Find **72 ÷ 3 ÷ 3**. **Press** ⬚7⬚ ⬚2⬚ ⬚÷⬚ ⬚3⬚ ⬚=⬚ ⬚=⬚ ⟶ $\boxed{8.}$
2 division signs   2 equal signs

WITH A CALCULATOR

Use the ⬚=⬚ key on your calculator to find the value of each.

1. 5 × 5 × 5 × 5   **2.** 3 × 3 × 3 × 3 × 3   **3.** 9 × 9 × 9 × 9 × 9

4. 4 × 4 × 4 × 4 × 4   **5.** 1,000 ÷ 10 ÷ 10   **6.** 100,000 ÷ 10 ÷ 10 ÷ 10

7. 729 ÷ 3 ÷ 3 ÷ 3 ÷ 3   **8.** 624 ÷ 2 ÷ 2 ÷ 2 ÷ 2   **9.** 1,000 ÷ 5 ÷ 5

10. Find a rule for using the ⬚=⬚ key for repeated subtraction.

11. Find a rule for using the ⬚=⬚ key for repeated addition.

INTRODUCING THE COMPUTER

A computer system includes **hardware** and **software.**
Hardware, or machinery, includes the following:

- an **input** device, such as a keyboard, for entering information into the computer

- a **central processing unit (CPU)** where all calculations are performed

- **memory**, which stores all information and instructions

- an **output** device, such as a monitor or printer, for getting information out of the computer

Some contents of memory are destroyed when the computer is turned off. To prevent this, programmers save their programs on floppy disks. Later the programs can be loaded into memory from the floppy disk. So a floppy disk can be used for both input and output.

Software consists of computer **programs.** A program is a set of instructions that tells the CPU what to do. Many languages are available for writing programs. FORTRAN, Pascal, and Logo are just a few. BASIC is the language used by most home computers.

The table shows the BASIC translations for some mathematics symbols.

Mathematics Symbol	BASIC Symbol	Example
+	+	25 + N
−	−	18 − A
×	*	A * B
÷	/	16/N

A **PRINT** statement is used to tell a computer to output words or numbers.

input PRINT 8 * 9
output 72

input PRINT 72/8
output 9

input PRINT " 15 + 9 = "; 15 + 9
output 15 + 9 = 24

When quotation marks are used, the computer outputs exactly what is in the quotation marks.

AT THE COMPUTER

Input the commands. Write each output.

1. PRINT 27 * 54
2. PRINT 119 - 82
3. PRINT 72/6
4. PRINT 9 * 6
5. PRINT "10 * N"
6. PRINT "18 + 6"
7. PRINT "BEGIN"
8. PRINT "5 * 9 = "; 5 * 9
9. PRINT "200 - 54 = "; 200 - 54

MAINTAINING SKILLS

Choose the correct answers. Write A, B, C, or D.

1. What is the standard form?
$(5 \times 10^6) + (1 \times 10^4) + (7 \times 10^2) + (3 \times 1)$

  A 510,703   C 5,100,703
  B 5,010,703   D not given

2. Compare. 386,190 ⬭ 368,190

  A >   C =
  B <   D not given

3. Round 2,906,154 to the nearest hundred.

  A 2,906,200   C 2,907,000
  B 2,906,100   D not given

4. Round 906,154 to the nearest ten thousand.

  A 900,000   C 910,000
  B 1,000,000   D not given

5. Estimate. 61,256 + 887 + 4,033

  A 72,000   C 66,000
  B 11,000   D not given

6. Estimate. 7,611 − 593

  A 6,000   C 8,000
  B 7,000   D not given

7.   84,760
   + 46,034

  A 130,794   C 120,794
  B 38,726   D not given

8. $3,223.56
   −   495.89

  A $3,719.45   C $2,838.77
  B $2,727.67   D not given

9. Estimate. 85 × 2,532

  A 27,000   C 270,000
  B 180,000   D not given

10. 26 × 5,911

  A 47,288   C 153,686
  B 143,686   D not given

11. What is 9^5 as a product of factors?

  A $9 \times 9 \times 9 \times 9 \times 9$ C $9 \times 5 \times 5$
  B $9 \times 9 \times 9 \times 9$ D not given

12. $113.46 ÷ 62

  A $1.83   C $1.85
  B $18.30   D not given

13. $390\overline{)856{,}451}$

  A 21,960 R11   C 2,196 R11
  B 2,196   D not given

Use the picture for 14 and 15.

Yearly Magazine Subscription Rates		
The Pen Pal	12 issues	$15.00
World Weekly	52 issues	$109.20
Tourist Times	40 issues	$140.00
Aerospace Journal	6 issues	$24.00
Museum News	12 issues	$33.00

14. What would it cost to subscribe for a year to *The Pen Pal* and *Tourist Times*?

  A $124.20   C $173.00
  B $249.20   D not given

15. How much more does *Aerospace Journal* cost per issue than *World Weekly*?

  A $14.20   C $2.56
  B $1.90   D not given

Place Value

In 1796, Americans used the coins shown at the right.

Decimals are used to record values between whole numbers. The numbers 0.01, 0.005, 2.50, 0.05, 0.25, 0.10, and 0.50 are decimals.

This table shows the decimal places to the right of ones place. Each place has a value 10 times that of the place to its right. The value of each place can be written using exponents.

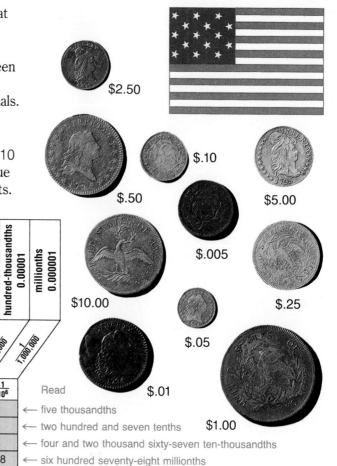

$2.50

$.10

$.50

$5.00

$.005

$10.00

$.25

$.05

$.01

$1.00

hundreds 100	tens 10	ones 1	tenths 0.1	hundredths 0.01	thousandths 0.001	ten-thousandths 0.0001	hundred-thousandths 0.00001	millionths 0.000001
100	10	1	$\frac{1}{10}$	$\frac{1}{100}$	$\frac{1}{1,000}$	$\frac{1}{10,000}$	$\frac{1}{100,000}$	$\frac{1}{1,000,000}$
10^2	10^1	1	$\frac{1}{10^1}$	$\frac{1}{10^2}$	$\frac{1}{10^3}$	$\frac{1}{10^4}$	$\frac{1}{10^5}$	$\frac{1}{10^6}$
		0.	0	0	5			
2	0	0.	7					
		4.	2	0	6	7		
		0.	0	0	0	6	7	8

Read

← five thousandths

← two hundred and seven tenths

← four and two thousand sixty-seven ten-thousandths

← six hundred seventy-eight millionths

Decimals can also be written in expanded form.

$$4.2067 = (4 \times 1) + (2 \times 0.1) + (6 \times 0.001) + (7 \times 0.0001)$$

$$= (4 \times 1) + \left(2 \times \frac{1}{10^1}\right) + \left(6 \times \frac{1}{10^3}\right) + \left(7 \times \frac{1}{10^4}\right)$$

CLASSWORK

Write the decimal for each.

1. eight and seven hundredths

2. $(3 \times 10) + (7 \times 0.1) + (5 \times 0.001)$

3. $\left(6 \times \frac{1}{10}\right) + \left(8 \times \frac{1}{100}\right) + \left(2 \times \frac{1}{10,000}\right)$

4. one hundred and twenty-five thousandths

Give the value of the digit 4 in each number. Then write each number in expanded form using exponents.

5. 0.064

6. 17.403609

7. 300.04

8. 9.03045

PRACTICE

Match each phrase in column A with the correct decimal in column B. Then give the value of the digit 4 in each number and write each number in expanded form using exponents.

A

1. sixty-eight and forty-nine hundredths

2. six thousand, eight hundred and forty-nine ten-thousandths

3. 5 and 402 hundred-thousandths

4. five hundred and forty-two ten-thousandths

5. 68 and 49 thousandths

6. five hundred forty-two ten-thousandths

7. six thousand eight hundred forty-nine ten-thousandths

8. five and four hundred two thousandths

B

a. 500.0042

b. 5.402

c. 6,800.0049

d. 0.6849

e. 68.49

f. 0.0542

g. 5.00402

h. 68.049

Write the decimal for each.

9. $3 \times \frac{1}{10}$

10. $\left(1 \times \frac{1}{10^1}\right) + \left(9 \times \frac{1}{10^3}\right)$

11. $(6 \times 10^3) + \left(5 \times \frac{1}{10^1}\right) + \left(3 \times \frac{1}{10^3}\right)$

12. $\frac{2}{100} + \frac{3}{1,000}$

13. $9 + 0.08 + 0.0001$

14. $\left(4 \times \frac{1}{10^2}\right) + \left(6 \times \frac{1}{10^3}\right) + \left(7 \times \frac{1}{10^6}\right)$

15. $(3 \times 1) + (4 \times 0.1) + (5 \times 0.001)$

16. $20 + 1 + \frac{5}{10} + \frac{3}{1,000} + \frac{6}{10,000}$

Write each as a decimal.

17. $\frac{23}{100}$

18. $\frac{72}{100}$

★19. $6\frac{45}{10,000}$

★20. $126\frac{746}{100,000}$

APPLICATION

Today Americans often use checks instead of coins or bills. The dollar amount is written in words, and the amount of cents is written as a fraction.

Write the amount of each check as a decimal.

21.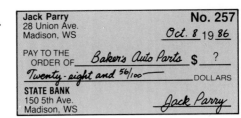

22.

★23. Besides the two checks above, Jack wants to write checks for the following amounts: $39.86; $15.28; $47.75; $97.55. He has $458.93 in his checking account. Does he have enough money to cover all six checks?

Comparing and Ordering Decimals

List the peaks in order from highest to lowest.

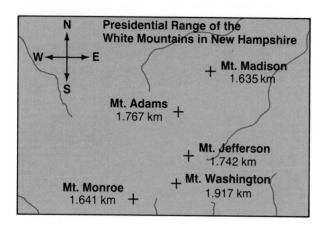

To compare two decimals, start at the left and find the first place where the decimals differ.

$$1.635 \bullet 1.767$$
$$\underset{6 < 7}{}$$
$$1.635 < 1.767$$

$$1.742 \bullet 1.917$$
$$\underset{7 < 9}{}$$
$$1.742 < 1.917$$

$$1.641 \bullet 1.635$$
$$\underset{4 > 3}{}$$
$$1.641 > 1.635$$

In order from highest to lowest, the peaks are as follows.

Mt. Washington		Mt. Adams		Mt. Jefferson		Mt. Monroe		Mt. Madison
1.917 km	>	1.767 km	>	1.742 km	>	1.641 km	>	1.635 km

When the numbers of decimal places in two decimals are different, annex zeros to compare.

$$1.91732 \bullet 1.917$$
$$1.91732 \bullet 1.91700$$
$$\underset{3 > 0}{}$$
$$1.91732 > 1.917$$

> 1.917 = 1.91700

CLASSWORK

Replace each ● with <, >, or =.

1. 15.290 ● 15.209

2. 0.0127 ● 0.01273

3. 4.63 ● 4.630

4. 24.78 ● 24.76

5. 116.458 ● 116.4580

6. 0.0071 ● 0.007

List in order from least to greatest.

7. 0.216; 0.22; 0.2164; 0.209

8. 5.6; 5.601; 5.06; 5.061; 5.610

32

PRACTICE

Replace each ● with <, >, or =.

1. 0.32 ● 0.34

2. 0.49 ● 0.493

3. 2.63 ● 2.6300

4. 7.09 ● 7.089

5. 108.03 ● 108.003

6. 0.056 ● 0.56

7. 3.17 ● 3.16

8. 46.00 ● 46

9. 0.38 ● 0.83

10. 47.03 ● 47.026

11. 57.32 ● 573.2

12. 0.061 ● 0.1

13. 4.2 ● 4.231

14. 0.0085 ● 0.00850

15. 0.100332 ● 0.100322

List in order from least to greatest.

16. 2.54; 2.45; 2.5; 2.454063

17. 0.062; 0.059; 0.618; 0.06

18. 0.628; 4; 23.1; 1.3; 0.098

19. 0.048; 0.48; 4.8; 40.008; 0.408

Use the list below to answer 20–22.

0.132   0.1308   0.1329   0.1313   0.1332   0.1322   0.13   0.1306

20. List the decimals that are between 0.131 and 0.133.

21. List the decimals that are between 0.1305 and 0.1325.

22. List the decimals that are between 0.13055 and 0.13085.

Use each set of digits to write the least possible decimal. Then use each set to write the greatest possible decimal less than 1.

★ **23.** 6, 4, 1, 0

★ **24.** 3, 0, 9, 6, 0

★ **25.** 1, 0, 8, 0, 5, 4, 0

APPLICATION

| HIKING TRAILS IN THE WHITE MOUNTAINS ||
Name	Distance (km)
Artist's Bluff	2.402
Basin-Cascades	4.803
Lonesome Lake	5.203
Mt. Willard	4.003
Tuckerman Ravine	6.404

26. List the trails in order from the shortest to the longest.

★ **27.** Which trail is 8 tenths kilometer longer than the Mt. Willard trail?

★ **28.** Which trail is 4 tenths kilometer longer than the Basin-Cascades trail?

33

Rounding Decimals

Organized baseball began in 1846 when the Knickerbockers played the New York Nine in Hoboken, New Jersey. Today baseball is the national pastime. People keep track of the records of their favorite players. One season, Yankee Dave Winfield had a batting average of 0.2826475. Round Winfield's average to the nearest thousandth.

To round decimals, follow this flowchart.

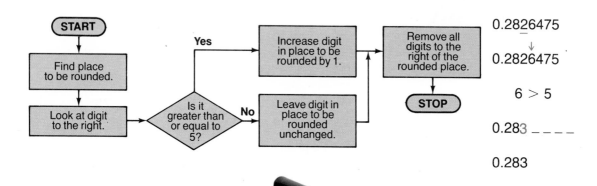

0.2826475
↓
0.2826475

6 > 5

0.283 _ _ _ _

0.283

Dave Winfield's batting average was 0.283.

More Examples

a. 0.547 rounded to the nearest one is 1.

b. 3.145 rounded to the nearest tenth is 3.1.

c. 0.00596 rounded to the nearest ten-thousandth is 0.0060.

d. $5.372 rounded to the nearest cent is $5.37.

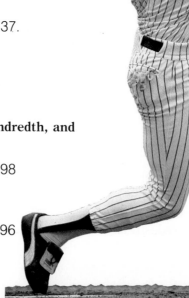

CLASSWORK

Round each to the nearest one, nearest hundredth, and nearest hundred-thousandth.

1. 0.934518   **2.** 4.398076   **3.** 0.006298

Round to the nearest cent.

4. $16.034   **5.** $.895   **6.** $205.996

Round to the place named.

nearest one	**1.** 0.63	**2.** 49.864	**3.** 0.0459
nearest tenth	**4.** 4.026	**5.** 21.3791	**6.** 0.984
nearest hundredth	**7.** 51.8312	**8.** 0.00346	**9.** 5.99861
nearest thousandth	**10.** 9.99964	**11.** 2.0453	**12.** 0.00465
nearest hundred-thousandth	**13.** 11.696513	**14.** 0.638997	**15.** 0.0196375
nearest cent	**16.** $4.443	**17.** $.996	**18.** $12.6782

Round 246.3799515 to the place named.

19. nearest one   **20.** nearest tenth   **21.** nearest hundredth

22. nearest thousandth   **23.** nearest ten-thousandth   **24.** nearest hundred-thousandth

25. nearest millionth   **26.** nearest ten   **27.** nearest hundred

APPLICATION

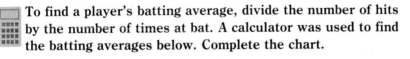 To find a player's batting average, divide the number of hits by the number of times at bat. A calculator was used to find the batting averages below. Complete the chart.

	Player	Number of Hits	Number of Times at Bat	Average Displayed on Calculator	Batting Average Rounded to Thousandths
28.	Don Mattingly	207	603	0.3432835	
29.	Darryl Strawberry	131	522	0.2509578	
★**30.**	Ken Griffey	109	399		

LOGICAL THINKING

Use the clues to name each number.

1. If you round the number to the nearest one, you get 4.
If you round the number to the nearest tenth, you get 4.0.
If you round the number to the nearest hundredth, you get 4.00.
It is the least such number.

★**2.** If you round the number to the nearest tenth, you get 0.0.
If you round the number to the nearest hundredth, you get 0.02.
If you round the number to the nearest thousandth, you get 0.019.
It is the greatest such number.

DON MATTINGLY OF-1B

Estimating Sums and Differences

The Chen family is going camping in the Blue Ridge Parkway National Park. Mrs. Chen used vacation costs from last year to estimate their expenses for this trip.

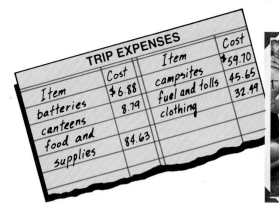

TRIP EXPENSES

Item	Cost	Item	Cost
batteries	$6.88	campsites	$59.70
canteens	8.79	fuel and tolls	45.65
food and supplies	84.63	clothing	32.49

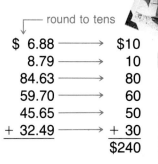

Estimate with decimals as you did with whole numbers. Mentally do the following.

- Round each number to the greatest nonzero place of the greatest number.

- Then add or subtract.

```
                       ┌─ round to tens
                       ▼
        $  6.88  ────→   $10
           8.79  ────→     10
          84.63  ────→     80
          59.70  ────→     60
          45.65  ────→     50
        + 32.49  ────→   + 30
                         $240
```

The Chens will spend about $240.

To get a closer estimate, remember to round to one more place to the right.

a. Estimate 15.63 − 3.865.

```
    20   Estimate        16    Closer
  −  0   too large     −  4    estimate
    20  ←───            12   ←───
```

b. Estimate 134.376 + 47.2.

```
   100   Estimate       130    Closer
  +  0   too small     + 50    estimate
   100  ←───            180   ←───
```

CLASSWORK

Estimate.

1.
```
  $5.97
   3.51
 +  .76
```

2.
```
   4.1052
 − 1.2149
```

3.
```
  14.061
 − 7.876
```

4.
```
   0.968
   0.98
 + 1.043
```

5.
```
  $26.78
 − 18.43
```

6. 4.78 + 12.286 + 8.61 + 9.486

7. 163.4 + 74.9 + 16.2 + 98.7

PRACTICE

Estimate.

1.	3.152 − 1.0637	**2.**	26.34 + 18.637	**3.**	49.814 − 11.9	**4.**	$476.95 − 216.98	**5.**	2.264 − 0.8615

6.	$1.29 2.14 1.83 + 3.62	**7.**	$2.03 1.08 1.44 + 5.75	**8.**	$ 4.33 8.52 26.42 + 11.88	**9.**	2.871 0.9543 7.0164 + 0.737	**10.**	11.431 9.1074 23.06 + 5.718

11. $12.10 + $10.50 + $2.12

12. 3.46 + 0.891 + 1.41

13. 7.432 − 5.961

14. 0.569 + 1.08 + 2.2

15. 9.281 − 4.0156

16. 18.28 − 4.0482

17. 18.5 + 7.612 + 26.818 + 11.14

18. 0.645 + 2.51 + 0.9 + 1.311 + 1.25

 Estimate each sum. Then use a calculator to find the actual sum. Use the estimate to check the calculator display.

★**19.**	6.309 0.83 7.4 + 0.9541	★**20.**	0.8635 0.9542 0.1734 + 1.0043	★**21.**	75.64 34.079 8.33 21.067 + 3.08	★**22.**	0.54371 1.00634 0.87402 0.93781 + 2.01346

APPLICATION

23. The distance from Smoky Summit to Shenandoah Point is 2.2 miles. Estimate the distance the Chens would hike if they went from the ranger station to Smoky Summit, to Shenandoah Point, and on back to the station.

24. The Chens can hike about 1 mile in half an hour. How long would it take them to make the trip in **23**?

25. Estimate which hike would be shorter, from Lookout Mountain to the ranger station to Shenandoah Point, or from Valley View to the ranger station to Smoky Summit.

★**26.** Name a hike that would take the Chens
    a. about 2 hours.
    b. about 3 hours.
    c. about $2\frac{1}{2}$ hours.

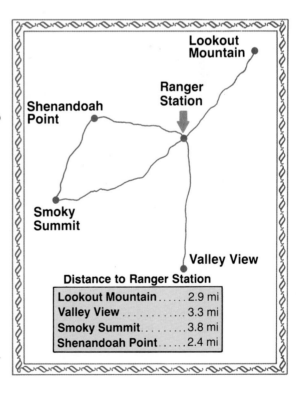

Distance to Ranger Station

Lookout Mountain	2.9 mi
Valley View	3.3 mi
Smoky Summit	3.8 mi
Shenandoah Point	2.4 mi

Adding and Subtracting Decimals

3.86	0.5	2
1.8	3	4.015
2.407	0.19	?

Start →

The sum of the numbers along the red path is 12. What is the missing number?

$$3.86 + 0.5 + 3 + 4.015 + ? = 12$$

Add and subtract as with whole numbers. Be sure to align the decimal points. Annexing zeros may help you align the points.

```
  3.860
  0.500
  3.000
+ 4.015
-------
 11.375
```

```
          9 9
      1 10 10 10
   1 2 . 0 0 0
 − 1 1 . 3 7 5
 -------------
     0 . 6 2 5
```

The missing number is 0.625.

You can estimate to be sure your answer makes sense, or you can add to check the accuracy of your answer.

Estimate.

3.86	⟶	4
0.5	⟶	1
3.	⟶	3
+ 4.015	⟶	+ 4
		12

Add.

```
   0.625
+ 11.375
--------
  12.000 = 12
```

CLASSWORK

Add or subtract. Check each answer.

1.
```
  0.86
  0.31
+ 2.41
```

2.
```
$214.08
   8.63
    .94
+ 72.00
```

3.
```
  8.78
− 5.93
```

4.
```
 23.4
− 9.86
```

5. $4 + 0.6 + 0.835 + 2.3$

6. $67 − 46.23$

PRACTICE

Add or subtract. Check each answer.

1. $\begin{array}{r} 1.9034 \\ -\ 0.66 \\ \hline \end{array}$
2. $\begin{array}{r} 1.784 \\ +\ 2.416 \\ \hline \end{array}$
3. $\begin{array}{r} 0.09351 \\ -\ 0.087 \\ \hline \end{array}$
4. $\begin{array}{r} 13 \\ -\ 6.5437 \\ \hline \end{array}$

5. $\begin{array}{r} 75.819 \\ -\ 31.729 \\ \hline \end{array}$
6. $\begin{array}{r} \$\ 2.17 \\ 10.32 \\ +\ \ 6.09 \\ \hline \end{array}$
7. $\begin{array}{r} 22.31 \\ 84.152 \\ 6.036 \\ +\ 17.01 \\ \hline \end{array}$
8. $\begin{array}{r} 74.9 \\ 26.3 \\ 9.88 \\ +\ 5 \\ \hline \end{array}$

9. $1.06 - 0.583$ 10. $2 - 0.865$ 11. $24.6 - 13.893$

12. $3.012 + 52 + 0.596 + 18.05$

13. $14.768 + 108.73 + 8.713 + 0.6755$

Name the missing numbers.

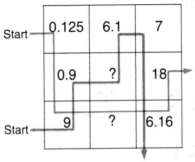

14. The sum along the red path is 55.5.

15. The sum along the blue path is 36.06.

Place a decimal point in each addend to make each sentence true.

★16. $64 + 735 + 93 = 23.05$ ★17. $237 + 153 + 303 = 20.7$

★18. $75 + 625 + 83 = 15.3$ ★19. $725 + 625 + 2125 = 10$

APPLICATION

John Steinbeck wrote a book about his travels around the states with his dog Charley. Here is some of their journey.

20. They drove 80 km from New York to Ohio. How far was it from Springfield, Penn. to the Ohio border?

★21. They began in Long Island and traveled 1,920 km to northern Maine, then 2,030 km to Niagara Falls, and 180 km to Pennsylvania. How far had they traveled when they reached Ohio?

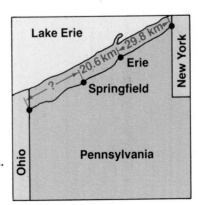

Mixed Practice

1. $765 + 849$

2. 47×614

3. $15\overline{)780}$

4. $\begin{array}{r} 25,409 \\ +\ 38,796 \\ \hline \end{array}$

5. $\begin{array}{r} 146,705 \\ -\ \ 98,947 \\ \hline \end{array}$

6. $\begin{array}{r} 4,605 \\ \times\ \ \ 246 \\ \hline \end{array}$

7. $2,143 + 847$

8. $24\overline{)7,596}$

9. $8\overline{)45,362}$

10. $\begin{array}{r} 36,781 \\ 5,063 \\ +\ 57,908 \\ \hline \end{array}$

11. 408×352

12. $5,018 - 748$

13. $\begin{array}{r} 26,043 \\ \times\ \ \ \ \ 78 \\ \hline \end{array}$

14. $\begin{array}{r} 6,475,014 \\ -\ 3,807,568 \\ \hline \end{array}$

15. $76\overline{)49,652}$

39

Problem Solving

TOO MUCH OR TOO LITTLE INFORMATION

There are facts that are not needed in some problems. Other times there is too little information to solve a problem. You must be able to decide which facts are needed and which are extra.

THINK
PLAN
SOLVE
LOOK
BACK

Texas is the second largest state in the United States. It has an area of 692,397 square kilometers. Texas became independent of Mexico in 1836. It remained an independent nation for 9 years. Then it was admitted to the United States as a state. In what year did Texas become a state?

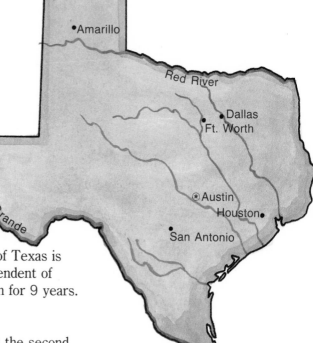

THINK   **What is the question?**

In what year did Texas become a state?

What are the facts?

Texas is the second largest state. The area of Texas is 692,397 square kilometers. It became independent of Mexico in 1836. It was an independent nation for 9 years.

Are there extra facts?

Yes. The area of Texas and the fact that it is the second largest state are extra facts.

PLAN   **How can the answer be found?**

To find the year that Texas was admitted to the United States, add 9 years to 1836.

$$1836 + 9 = n$$

SOLVE   **Carry out the plan. Then answer the question.**

$$\begin{array}{r} 1836 \\ +9 \\ \hline 1845 \end{array}$$

Texas became a state in 1845.

LOOK BACK   **Has the question been answered? Does the answer make sense?**

Check the facts again. The answer is correct.

If there is enough information, solve the problem. If there is extra information, tell what is extra and solve the problem. If there is not enough information, tell what is missing.

1. Oklahoma was admitted as a state in 1907. It was the forty-sixth state. How many states were admitted to the United States before Oklahoma?

2. Oil or natural gas has been found in 72 counties in Oklahoma. Eighteen wells were drilled on the state capital grounds. How many wells were drilled in Oklahoma?

3. Rhode Island has always been the smallest state. It is about 77 km long and 60 km wide. It could fit 200 times into Texas and nearly 500 times into Alaska. About how many more times can Rhode Island fit into Alaska than into Texas?

4. Block Island in the Atlantic Ocean is a 22-km ferry ride from Rhode Island. The lighthouse on the island is on a cliff that loses 0.8 m per year to erosion. The lighthouse could topple by the year 2000. How tall is the lighthouse?

5. In May 1858, Minnesota became the thirty-second state to gain admission to the United States. Known as the "Land of 10,000 Lakes," Minnesota actually has more than 15,000 lakes. About how many more lakes does Minnesota have than its nickname implies?

6. Minnesota has one of the largest open-pit mines in the world. The mine is about 4.8 km long and 1.6 km wide. It is deeper than a 50-story building is high. How much longer is the mine than it is wide?

7. Alaska, admitted in 1959, was the largest state to enter the Union. It covers 1,527,464 square kilometers. Delaware, the first to join the Union, is the second smallest state. It covers 5,328 square kilometers. How long after Delaware joined the Union did Alaska join?

★ 8. In Alaska there is a totem pole made in three parts. It is 14.7 m tall and 3.4 m in diameter. Without the top part it stands 10.4 m tall. The bottom part is 4.9 m tall. Which part is the tallest?

═══ CREATE YOUR OWN PROBLEM ═══

For each set of facts, write a problem. Then solve it.

1. Area of the Great Lakes

Lake Huron	59,570 square kilometers
Lake Ontario	19,520 square kilometers
Lake Michigan	57,990 square kilometers
Lake Erie	25,730 square kilometers
Lake Superior	82,380 square kilometers

2. The highest point in Texas is Guadalupe Peak, 2,667 m high. The lowest point in Texas is the Gulf of Mexico, at sea level.

Estimating Products

In 1896 in Detroit, Michigan, Henry Ford built his first gas-powered automobile. By the time his automobile became popular, gasoline cost about $.25 a gallon.

Ms. Tallchief stopped for gas today in Detroit. About how much will she pay in all?

To estimate a product, mentally do the following.

Step 1	Step 2

Round each factor to its greatest nonzero place.

Then multiply.

$$
\begin{array}{r} \$1.169 \\ \times\quad 7.6 \end{array}
\quad \text{round to} \quad
\begin{array}{r} \$1 \\ \times\ 8 \end{array}
\quad
\begin{array}{r} \$1 \\ \times\ 8 \\ \hline \$8 \end{array}
$$

Ms. Tallchief will pay about $8.

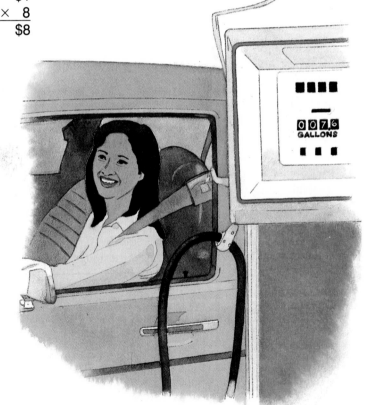

More Examples

a.
$$
\begin{array}{r} 0.985 \\ \times\ 82.391 \end{array}
\quad \text{round to} \quad
\begin{array}{r} 1.0 \\ \times\ 80 \\ \hline 80 \end{array}
$$

b.
$$
\begin{array}{r} 188.8 \\ \times\ 2.64 \end{array}
\quad \text{round to} \quad
\begin{array}{r} 200 \\ \times\ 3 \\ \hline 600 \end{array}
$$

c.
$$
\begin{array}{r} \$68.73 \\ \times\ 7.96 \end{array}
\quad \text{round to} \quad
\begin{array}{r} \$70 \\ \times\ 8 \\ \hline \$560 \end{array}
$$

CLASSWORK

Estimate.

1.
$$\begin{array}{r} 3.141 \\ \times\quad 85 \end{array}$$

2.
$$\begin{array}{r} \$74.29 \\ \times\ 0.982 \end{array}$$

3.
$$\begin{array}{r} 7.38 \\ \times\ 36.4 \end{array}$$

4.
$$\begin{array}{r} 66.003 \\ \times\ 11.35 \end{array}$$

5.
$$\begin{array}{r} 81.67 \\ \times\ 3.25 \end{array}$$

6. 8.6×4.325

7. 5.21×8.763

8. $1.2 \times 63 \times \$17.98$

PRACTICE

Estimate.

1. $\begin{array}{r} 4.32 \\ \times\ \ \ \ 6 \\ \hline \end{array}$

2. $\begin{array}{r} 5.64 \\ \times\ \ 8.1 \\ \hline \end{array}$

3. $\begin{array}{r} 73.2 \\ \times\ \ 5.6 \\ \hline \end{array}$

4. $\begin{array}{r} \$6.75 \\ \times\ \ 49.2 \\ \hline \end{array}$

5. $\begin{array}{r} 2.39 \\ \times\ 8.88 \\ \hline \end{array}$

6. $\begin{array}{r} 2.913 \\ \times\ 0.971 \\ \hline \end{array}$

7. $\begin{array}{r} 47.25 \\ \times\ \ 3.96 \\ \hline \end{array}$

8. $\begin{array}{r} 85.90 \\ \times\ \ 1.43 \\ \hline \end{array}$

9. $\begin{array}{r} \$37.95 \\ \times\ \ \ \ \ \ 72 \\ \hline \end{array}$

10. $\begin{array}{r} 6.75 \\ \times\ 5.302 \\ \hline \end{array}$

11. $\begin{array}{r} 2.543 \\ \times\ \ \ \ 93 \\ \hline \end{array}$

12. $\begin{array}{r} 11.096 \\ \times\ \ \ 1.73 \\ \hline \end{array}$

13. $\begin{array}{r} \$11.34 \\ \times\ \ \ 5.96 \\ \hline \end{array}$

14. $\begin{array}{r} 0.984 \\ \times\ 1.972 \\ \hline \end{array}$

15. $\begin{array}{r} 43.2 \\ \times\ 0.993 \\ \hline \end{array}$

16. $2.84 \times \$3.25$

17. 27×9.016

18. 573.6×19.58

19. 4.8×63.27

20. 4.16×0.98

21. $4.76 \times 1.85 \times 3.31$

22. $6.43 \times 19.31 \times 28.4$

23. $0.956 \times 38.7 \times 76.14$

24. $9.164 \times 7.862 \times 12.405$

Use an estimate to help select the correct answer.

25. 4.68×8.41
  a. 3.93588
  b. 39.3588
  c. 393.588

26. 11.4×6.71
  a. 764.94
  b. 7.6494
  c. 76.494

27. 0.97×17.3
  a. 16.781
  b. 167.81
  c. 1.6781

28. 6.85×45.6
  a. 3.1236
  b. 31.236
  c. 312.36

The following products were found on a calculator. Use estimation to help determine which products are correct.

★ 29. $\begin{array}{r} 0.9875 \\ \times\ \ \ 3.62 \\ \hline \end{array}$
  $\boxed{8.7545}$

★ 30. $\begin{array}{r} 26.35 \\ \times\ \ 7.34 \\ \hline \end{array}$
  $\boxed{193.409}$

★ 31. $\begin{array}{r} 4.136 \\ \times\ \ \ 6.8 \\ \hline \end{array}$
  $\boxed{48.3248}$

★ 32. $\begin{array}{r} 143.5 \\ \times\ 2.106 \\ \hline \end{array}$
  $\boxed{202.211}$

APPLICATION

Estimate.

33. A gas station has 3 tanks that each hold 6,000 gallons. Each day the station serves about 85 customers an average of 9.3 gallons each. How often are the tanks refilled?

6.6	3.96	0.35
1.78	0.88	6.59
0.874	7.2	7.62

Gasoline 25¢ a gallon

LOGICAL THINKING

1. Which two numbers on the billboard give the greatest product? the least product?

2. Which three numbers give the greatest product? the least product?

Multiplying Decimals

The face of Abraham Lincoln on Mount Rushmore is nearly 74 times as large as Lincoln's actual face. His face was about 0.25 meter long. How far will Roger and Eve have to climb to escape down Lincoln's face?

Multiply 74 × 0.25.

Cary Grant and Eva Marie Saint as Roger Thornhill and Eve Kendall in the movie *North by Northwest* by Alfred Hitchcock

Step 1

Multiply as with whole numbers.

$$
\begin{array}{r}
0.25 \\
\times 74 \\
\hline
100 \\
175 \\
\hline
1850
\end{array}
$$

They would have to climb about 18.5 meters.

Step 2

The number of decimal places in the answer equals the total number of decimal places in the factors.

$$
\begin{array}{r}
0.25 \\
\times 74 \\
\hline
18.50
\end{array}
$$
← 2 places
← 2 places

Estimate to be sure the answer makes sense.

$$
\begin{array}{r}
0.25 \longrightarrow 0.3 \\
\times 74 \longrightarrow \times 70 \\
\hline
21.0
\end{array}
$$

The answer is about 21, so the decimal point is correctly placed.

More Examples

a.
$$
\begin{array}{r}
3.5 \\
\times 8.3 \\
\hline
1\ 05 \\
28\ 0 \\
\hline
29.05
\end{array}
$$
← 2 places

← 2 places

b.
$$
\begin{array}{r}
27.3 \\
\times 0.86 \\
\hline
1\ 638 \\
21\ 84 \\
\hline
23.478
\end{array}
$$
← 3 places

← 3 places

c.
$$
\begin{array}{r}
0.018 \\
\times 2.3 \\
\hline
54 \\
36 \\
\hline
0.0414
\end{array}
$$
← 4 places

← 4 places

Annex a zero so there are enough places.

CLASSWORK

Multiply. Estimate to be sure each answer makes sense.

1.
$$
\begin{array}{r}
3.75 \\
\times 2.4 \\
\hline
\end{array}
$$

2.
$$
\begin{array}{r}
0.123 \\
\times 0.026 \\
\hline
\end{array}
$$

3.
$$
\begin{array}{r}
0.012 \\
\times 4.07 \\
\hline
\end{array}
$$

4.
$$
\begin{array}{r}
8.3057 \\
\times 321 \\
\hline
\end{array}
$$

5. 0.4 × 32.8

6. 0.25 × 0.0684

PRACTICE

Multiply. Estimate to be sure each answer makes sense.
Round the answers to 2, 8, and 12 to the nearest cent.

1.	4.97	2.	$16.38	3.	3.89	4.	0.012	5.	7,239
	× 0.2		× 2.1		× 0.25		× 3.5		× 0.45

6.	0.002	7.	7.841	8.	$52.68	9.	9.328	10.	0.0017
	× 0.01		× 35		× 0.421		× 0.005		× 0.23

11. 0.16 × 574   12. 0.03 × $4.36   13. 0.06 × 1.003   14. 0.0091 × 0.047

15. 83 × 0.17 × 74.2   16. 7.3 × 0.02 × 6.15   17. 0.069 × 0.357 × 0.02

Find each output.

Rule: Multiply by 8.06.

	Input	Output
18.	0.05	
19.	0.0694	
20.	3.9	

Rule: Multiply by 0.319.

	Input	Output
21.	7.82	
22.	0.354	
23.	74.7	

Rule: Multiply by 0.076.

	Input	Output
24.	8,953	
25.	0.043	
26.	25.8	

Name the numbers.

★ 27. The sum of two decimals is 1.4. Their product is 0.48. What are the two decimals?

★ 28. The sum of two decimals is 3.8. Their product is 3.25. What are the two decimals?

★ 29. The sum of two decimals is 6. Their product is 8.75. What are the two decimals?

APPLICATION

=== MENTAL ARITHMETIC ===

1. 14 × 2	2. 7 × 0.3	3. 8 × 15
14 × 0.2	70 × 0.3	8 × 1.5
14 × 0.02	700 × 0.3	8 × 0.15
14 × 0.002	7,000 × 0.3	8 × 0.015
4. 4.5 × 20	5. 40 × 7.5	6. 3.4 × 5
4.5 × 2	4 × 7.5	34 × 0.5
4.5 × 0.2	0.4 × 7.5	340 × 0.05
4.5 × 0.02	0.04 × 7.5	3,400 × 0.005

Dividing Decimals by Whole Numbers

Divide with decimals as you did with whole numbers. Place the decimal point in the quotient above the point in the dividend.

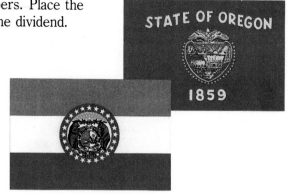

```
       12.74
26)331.24
    26
    ──
    71
    52
    ──
    19 2
    18 2
    ────
     1 04
     1 04
     ────
```

Multiply to check.
$26 \times 12.74 = 331.24$

Another way to check your division is to estimate. Mentally do the following.

Step 1	Step 2	Step 3	Step 4
Round the divisor.	Place the point in the quotient.	Find the first quotient digit.	Write zeros for all other quotient digits to the left of the point.

$$30 \quad 26\overline{)331.24}$$

$$30 \quad 26\overline{)331.24}$$

$$30 \quad 26\overline{)331.24}^{\,1\,.}$$

$$30 \quad 26\overline{)331.24}^{\,10.}$$

The answer 12.74 is reasonable, since it is about 10.

Sometimes you may have to annex zeros to the dividend to complete the division.

```
     0.8
8)6.5
  6 4
  ───
    1
```
← Annex zeros to continue.

```
     0.8125
8)6.5000
  6 4
  ───
   10
    8
  ───
   20
   16
  ───
   40
   40
  ───
```

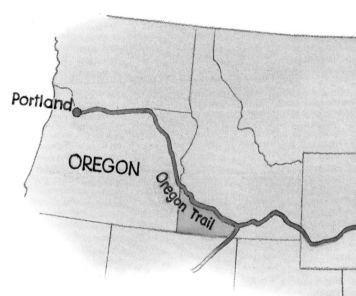

Portland

OREGON

Oregon Trail

Check

Multiply. $8 \times 0.8125 = 6.5$

Estimate. $8\overline{)6.5}^{\,0.8}$

CLASSWORK

Divide. Check each answer.

Remember $\frac{11}{4}$ means $11 \div 4$.

1. $9\overline{)31.5}$

2. $25\overline{)3.35}$

3. $\frac{11}{4}$

4. $0.645 \div 15$

5. $64\overline{)2.4}$

Divide. Check the answers to **1–8** by multiplying. Check
the answers to **9–20** by estimating.

1. $8\overline{)48.16}$ **2.** $6\overline{)\$44.22}$ **3.** $5\overline{)2.067}$ **4.** $4\overline{)0.9374}$

5. $65\overline{)149.5}$ **6.** $22\overline{)0.3036}$ **7.** $89\overline{)\$1,100.04}$ **8.** $35\overline{)22.295}$

9. $6.4 \div 25$ **10.** $38\overline{)52.25}$ **11.** $20\overline{)1.25}$ **12.** $175 \div 56$

13. $2.544 \div 60$ **14.** $\frac{9}{16}$ **15.** $75\overline{)4.53}$ **16.** $337\overline{)91.327}$

17. $144\overline{)\$224.64}$ **18.** $\frac{1.5}{125}$ **19.** $238\overline{)63.07}$ **20.** $\frac{468}{288}$

The answers below are estimates. Correct any inaccurate estimates.

21. $\overset{0.4}{37\overline{)1.628}}$ **22.** $\overset{\$.09}{73\overline{)\$68.62}}$ **23.** $\overset{5}{46\overline{)264.04}}$ **24.** $\overset{\$60}{62\overline{)\$389.98}}$

25. $\overset{0.003}{215\overline{)0.06235}}$ **26.** $\overset{0.2}{537\overline{)10.203}}$ **27.** $\overset{0.005}{472\overline{)2.5016}}$ **28.** $\overset{0.5}{732\overline{)360.876}}$

Find each quotient.

★ **29.** $\dfrac{6.4 \times 1.3}{8}$ ★ **30.** $\dfrac{5.76}{4 \times 0.5}$ ★ **31.** $\dfrac{2.14 + 3.5}{3}$ ★ **32.** $\dfrac{7.8 \times 0.35}{14 \times 5}$

Fort Laramie

1,000 km

Independence

MISSOURI

APPLICATION

In the 1840s, pioneers like George William
Bush and his family traveled the Oregon Trail
to reach the Oregon country.

33. Traveling about 10 hours a day, the wagon
trains covered about 25 km. On the
average, how far did they go per hour?

34. How many days would it take a wagon
train to go from Independence, Missouri,
to Fort Laramie, Wyoming?

35. If you traveled by car today from
Independence to Fort Laramie, going 80 km
per hour, how long would the trip take?

★ **36.** How many days would it take a wagon train
to go the 3,222-km length of the Oregon
Trail? How long would it take by car?
Round both answers to the nearest one.

Dividing Decimals

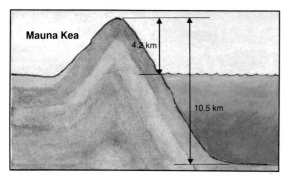

Mauna Kea

4.2 km

10.5 km

Mauna Kea in Hawaii is the world's highest mountain if it is measured from its base on the ocean floor. What part of Mauna Kea is above sea level?

$$\frac{4.2}{10.5} \longrightarrow 10.5\overline{)4.2}$$

To divide by a decimal, follow these steps.

Step 1 Make the divisor a whole number by multiplying by a power of 10.

$$10\,5.\overline{)4.2}$$

Step 2 Multiply the dividend by the same power of 10. Place the decimal point in the quotient.

$$105\overline{)4\,2.}$$

Step 3 Divide as with whole numbers.

$$\begin{array}{r} 0.4 \\ 105\overline{)42.0} \\ \underline{42\,0} \end{array}$$

0.4 of Mauna Kea is above sea level.

CLASSWORK

Divide. Check each answer.

1. $2.4\overline{)0.072}$

2. $2.1\overline{)16.8}$

3. $0.36\overline{)837}$

4. $\dfrac{18}{12.5}$

5. $19.68 \div 12.3$

6. $14.57 \div 3.875$

Mauna Loa in Hawaii as it erupts

PRACTICE

Divide. Check the answers to 1–8 by multiplying. Check the answers to 9–20 by estimating.

1. $0.4\overline{)17.28}$
2. $0.6\overline{)\$3.72}$
3. $0.5\overline{)356}$
4. $0.8\overline{)0.15}$

5. $0.23\overline{)1.5088}$
6. $0.133 \div 1.9$
7. $0.03\overline{)675}$
8. $0.57\overline{)3.6765}$

9. $2.5\overline{)\$20.10}$
10. $5.2\overline{)\$314.60}$
11. $0.2816 \div 0.04$
12. $0.35\overline{)0.9625}$

13. $117 \div 0.45$
14. $0.051\overline{)0.6426}$
15. $\dfrac{2,345}{6.7}$
16. $\dfrac{6.225}{0.025}$

17. $\dfrac{41}{3.2}$
18. $2.54\overline{)2.2225}$
19. $17.25 \div 55.2$
20. $38.7\overline{)126.162}$

Use an estimate to help select the correct answer.

21. $0.234\overline{)1.32093}$
  a. 5.645
  b. 56.45
  c. 564.5

22. $6.75\overline{)3,029.4}$
  a. 44.88
  b. 448.8
  c. 4,488

23. $12.56\overline{)816.4}$
  a. 0.65
  b. 6.5
  c. 65

24. $10.08 \div 0.18$
  a. 0.56
  b. 5.6
  c. 56

Find each missing digit.

25.
```
        ■ ■.■
7.■)3 2 7.■ ■
    3 ■ 4
    2 3 ■
    ■ ■ 8
      7 ■
      ■ ■
```

★26.
```
              ■ 0.■ 1
0.4 5 3)9.2 4 ■ ■ ■
        9 ■ ■
        ■ ■ ■ ■
        ■ ■ 1 2
          ■ ■ ■
          ■ ■ ■
```

★27.
```
                 0.■ ■ ■ ■
5 7.■)■ ■.3 5 ■ ■ 6
      4 5 ■ ■
      ■ ■ 9 ■
      2 ■ ■ 8
      ■ ■ 3 ■
      ■ ■ ■ ■
      ■ ■ 1 6
      ■ ■ ■ ■
```

APPLICATION

28. Mauna Loa in Hawaii is the world's largest volcano. It is about 9.1 km high. It rises 4.2 km above the sea. To the nearest tenth, what part of Mauna Loa is above sea level?

29. At its widest point Mauna Loa is almost 120 km wide. About how many times wider is Mauna Loa than it is high? Estimate.

★ 30. Mt. Waialeale on the island of Kauai is the wettest spot on the earth. It rains an average of 11.7 m a year. How many meters is that per month? per week?

★ 31. In 1948 it rained a record 15.77 m on Mt. Waialeale. It rains about 0.96 of the days of the year there. On the average, how much did it rain each day in 1948? Round to the nearest hundredth.

49

Rounding Quotients

Peter Vidmar competed in the 1984 Olympics in Los Angeles, California. What would Peter's average score be if the judges gave him these scores for a total of 78.65 points? Round to the nearest hundredth.

CALIFORNIA REPUBLIC

| 9.90 | 9.65 | 9.85 | 9.95 | 9.85 | 9.90 | 9.75 | 9.80 |

To round a quotient, divide to one more place than the place to which you are rounding.

$$
\begin{array}{r}
9.831 \\
8\overline{)78.650} \\
\underline{72} \\
6\;6 \\
\underline{6\;4} \\
25 \\
\underline{24} \\
10 \\
\underline{8} \\
2
\end{array}
$$

9.831 **rounds to** 9.83

← To round to hundredths, divide to thousandths.

Vidmar's score would be 9.83.

Another Example

Round 12 ÷ 7.2 to the nearest tenth.

$$
\begin{array}{r}
1.66 \\
7.2.\overline{)12\,0.00} \\
\underline{7\;2} \\
4\;80 \\
\underline{4\;32} \\
4\;80 \\
\underline{4\;32} \\
48
\end{array}
$$

1.66 **rounds to** 1.7

← To round to tenths, divide to hundredths.

CLASSWORK

Divide. Round to the nearest hundredth; to the nearest thousandth. Estimate to be sure each answer makes sense.

1. $3\overline{)2.78}$ **2.** $3 \div 0.7$ **3.** $1.8\overline{)3.75}$ **4.** $37\overline{)2.639}$ **5.** $\frac{16}{9}$ **6.** $\frac{2.5}{9.7}$

PRACTICE

Divide. Round to the place named. Check each answer.

nearest tenth

1. $9\overline{)46.7}$
2. $37\overline{)9.18}$
3. $3,568 \div 23$
4. $\frac{7}{9}$
5. $0.7\overline{)21.73}$
6. $7.3\overline{)2.35}$

nearest hundredth

7. $97.1 \div 4.8$
8. $7.4\overline{)\$453.08}$
9. $0.54\overline{)1.1923}$
10. $\frac{2}{3}$
11. $29\overline{)\$1,759}$
12. $\frac{78.516}{34}$

nearest thousandth

13. $43\overline{)7.156}$
14. $56 \div 99$
15. $3.14\overline{)78.54}$
16. $\frac{5}{6}$
17. $0.575\overline{)294}$
18. $\frac{0.028}{5}$

Find each output. Round to the nearest hundredth.

Rule: Divide by 6.

	Input	Output
19.	75	
20.	3.4	
21.	0.156	

Rule: Divide by 0.25.

	Input	Output
22.	56.4	
23.	0.68	
24.	1.123	

Rule: Divide by 17.2.

	Input	Output
25.	8.52	
26.	26	
27.	0.952	

Find the next two terms in each sequence.

★ 28. 1,814.4; 302.4; 50.4; ____; ____
★ 29. 1,409.4; 469.8; 156.6; ____; ____
★ 30. 6.4; 9.6; 14.4; ____; ____
★ 31. 2.3; 4.8; 7.3; ____; ____
★ 32. 2.7; 10.8; 1.8; 7.2; ____; ____
★ 33. 19.53125; 7.8125; 3.125; 1.25; ____; ____

APPLICATION

ESTIMATION

Estimate each answer. Then use a calculator to find the actual answer. Round to the nearest hundredth. Use the estimate to check the answer.

1. $\dfrac{\$2.67 \times 6.8}{7}$

2. $\dfrac{52.2}{5.2 \times 4.5}$

3. $\dfrac{914}{86} \times 0.12$

4. $\dfrac{9.59 + 8.67}{38}$

★ 5. $\dfrac{46.4 + 12.62}{95 \times 0.22}$

★ 6. $\dfrac{3.6 - 0.793}{28.7 - 10.7}$

51

Powers of 10 and Scientific Notation

1 million = 1,000,000 = 10^6

7.2 million = 7.2×10^6

▶The exponent or the number of zeros in a power of 10 tells how many places to move the decimal point when multiplying or dividing by a power of 10.

When multiplying by a power of 10, move the decimal point to the right.

a. $7.2 \times 10^6 = 7{,}200{,}000$
6 places

b. $0.21415 \times 1{,}000 = 214.15$
3 places

When dividing by a power of 10, move the decimal point to the left.

c. $5{,}436 \div 10^3 = 5{,}436. \div 10^3 = 5.436$
3 places

d. $0.425 \div 100 = 0.00425$
2 places

7.2×10^6 is written in scientific notation. To express a number in **scientific notation,** write it as this product:
(a number from 1 to 10) × (a power of 10).

Examples

Standard Form	Number from 1 to 10	Power of 10	Scientific Notation
597,500,000	5.97500000 / 8 places	10^8	5.975×10^8
47,326	4.7326 / 4 places	10^4	4.7326×10^4

└ Multiply to change to standard form. ┘

CLASSWORK

Find each product or quotient.

1. 3.467×10^5

2. 0.653×100

3. $8.9 \div 10^3$

4. $671.2 \div 10{,}000$

Write in scientific notation.

5. 6.84 million

6. 354,000

7. 45,060,000

8. 15,230,000,000

Find each product or quotient.

1. 34.5×100

2. $2.14 \times 1{,}000$

3. $0.264 \div 100$

4. 3.56×10^4

5. 4.18×10^4

6. $458.2 \div 10^3$

7. $0.009 \times 10{,}000$

8. $8.04 \div 1{,}000$

9. 6.23×10^6

10. $0.052 \times 100{,}000$

11. $3{,}416 \div 10^5$

12. $23{,}400 \div 10^4$

13. 6.56×10^{10}

14. 3.041×10^8

15. $0.0032 \times 100{,}000$

16. $915.4 \div 10^5$

17. $0.143 \div 10^3$

18. $3{,}622 \div 10{,}000$

Write in scientific notation.

19. 82,300

20. 50,700

21. 173,400

22. 406,300

23. 5,320,000

24. 22,200,000

25. 307,000,000

26. 9,146,000,000

Complete the chart.

		Standard Form	Scientific Notation
27.	7.24 million		
28.	82.61 billion		
29.	$1{,}319.4 \times 10$		
30.	29.5×10^6		
★ **31.**	$416 \times 10^5 \times 10^3$		
★ **32.**	0.782 million $\times$ 6.3 million		

APPLICATION

33. Write the size of Alaska—590,000 square miles—in scientific notation.

★ **34.** To the nearest cent, how much did Seward pay per square mile for Alaska?

=== CALCULATOR ===

Calculators often display the numbers 100,000,000 and greater in **E notation** (exponential notation). The display at the right shows 34,750,000 in E notation.

E notation

$3.475 \quad 07$

scientific notation
3.475×10^7

Find each product. Write the answer in scientific notation. Then write the answer as it is displayed on your calculator.

1. $3{,}297.8 \times 1{,}000{,}000$

2. $42{,}589 \times 10{,}000{,}000$

3. $63{,}548 \times 9{,}658$

4. $76{,}532 \times 52{,}109$

5. $789{,}563 \times 2{,}014{,}576$

6. $3{,}251{,}176 \times 2{,}005{,}583$

Problem Solving

SKILLS AND STRATEGIES REVIEW   Grand Tour

The Americana Travel Agency advertised a grand tour of the United States. The tour included visits to famous places around the country.

Use the picture at the right and the table below to solve 1–6.

1. There were 37 people on the trip. How much did the agency collect?

2. What is the average cost per day for one person?

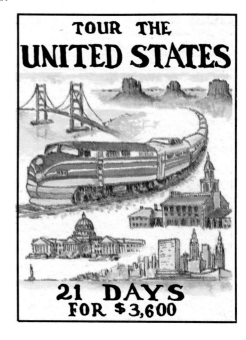

POPULATION OF THE CITIES ON THE TOUR

City	Population
Chicago, Ill.	3,005,072
San Francisco, Calif.	678,974
Los Angeles, Calif.	2,968,579
New York, N.Y.	7,071,639
Philadelphia, Pa.	1,688,210
Washington, D.C.	638,432

3. Arrange the population figures in order from greatest to least. Write the cities in that order.

4. What is the combined population of San Francisco and Los Angeles?

5. How much greater is the population of San Francisco than that of Washington, D.C.?

6. Which two cities have the greatest difference in population? What is the difference?

7. Death Valley, California, is the driest spot in the nation. The average annual rainfall is just over 1 inch. How much below the average California rainfall is that of Death Valley?

8. The average annual rainfall in Mount Waialeale, Hawaii, is 460 inches. How much greater is it than the average rainfall in Death Valley?

9. In California the people on the tour saw a bristlecone pine, the oldest living plant in the nation. They also saw the tallest living plant, the Howard Libbey redwood tree. It is 365 feet tall. How much taller is the Howard Libbey redwood than the bristlecone pine?

★ 10. Yellowstone National Park in Wyoming was a favorite among the tourists. The oldest national park in the United States, it takes up about 3,472 square miles of the total area of the state. The area of San Francisco is 46 square miles. To the nearest tenth, how many times greater is the area of Yellowstone Park?

The group stopped at a souvenir shop that sold T-shirts. Any state motto could be printed on the shirt. The cost of the printing was $.25 per letter. Punctuation counted as a letter.

11. *Virtue, Liberty, and Independence* is the state motto of Pennsylvania. How much would it cost to print the motto?

12. The motto of Texas is *Friendship.* How much would it cost to print the motto?

13. The T-shirts cost $5.00 in addition to the printing. *Eureka: I Have Found It* is the motto of California. How much would a shirt with the California motto cost?

JOIN FLY AWAY'S MILEAGE CLUB

FLY 10,000 MILES WITH FLY AWAY AIRLINES AND GET ONE FREE ROUND-TRIP TICKET TO ANY OF FLY AWAY'S DESTINATIONS.

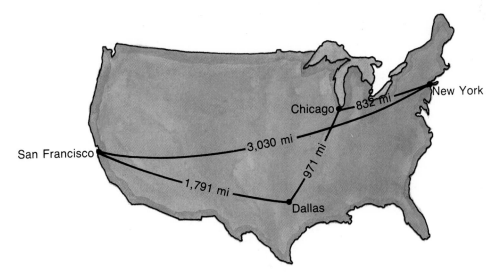

14. The tour group traveled part of the time by airplane. It went from New York to Chicago to Dallas to San Francisco. If the group had traveled nonstop from New York to San Francisco, how many miles would have been saved?

15. Many members of the tour group belong to the Mileage Club of Fly Away Airlines. How many times would a person have to fly nonstop between New York and San Francisco to become eligible for the 10,000-mile award?

16. How many round-trip flights between Chicago and Dallas would a person have to make to earn 5,000 miles of credit in the mileage club?

★ 17. If a 500-mile bonus were given for every 1,200 miles actually flown, how many round-trip flights between New York and Chicago would have to be flown to earn 2,500 bonus miles?

Write the decimal for each. Give the value of the digit 7 in each number. pages 30–31

1. sixty and thirty-seven hundredths

2. seven hundred nine thousandths

3. seven hundred and nine thousandths

4. 700 ten-thousandths

5. $(4 \times 1) + \left(7 \times \frac{1}{10^1}\right)$ 6. $(1 \times 10) + \left(7 \times \frac{1}{10^2}\right)$ 7. $(5 \times 1) + (6 \times 0.1) + (7 \times 0.001)$

Replace each ⬤ with <, >, or =. pages 32–33

8. 0.75 ⬤ 0.77   9. 2.01 ⬤ 2.010   10. 15.3 ⬤ 15.296   11. 0.901 ⬤ 0.91

Round to the nearest one, nearest hundredth, and nearest ten-thousandth. pages 34–35

12. 5.21467   13. 0.59843   14. 1.154968

Estimate. pages 36–37, 42–43, 46–47

15. $\begin{array}{r} 38.7 \\ \times\, 0.65 \end{array}$ 16. $\begin{array}{r} \$75.89 \\ \times\quad 0.75 \end{array}$ 17. $\begin{array}{r} 0.675 \\ +\, 0.531 \end{array}$ 18. $\begin{array}{r} \$26.78 \\ -\, 18.35 \end{array}$ 19. $5.7\overline{)1.983}$

Add, subtract, multiply, or divide. When dividing, round to the nearest hundredth where necessary. Check the answers. pages 38–39, 44–53

20. $\begin{array}{r} \$152.08 \\ 28.76 \\ +\quad 19.42 \end{array}$ 21. $\begin{array}{r} 158.734 \\ -\, 86.507 \end{array}$ 22. $\begin{array}{r} 5.487 \\ \times\, 1{,}000 \end{array}$ 23. $\begin{array}{r} 6.28 \\ \times\, 0.35 \end{array}$ 24. $\begin{array}{r} 27 \\ -\, 5.067 \end{array}$

25. $\begin{array}{r} 24.97 \\ \times\quad 3.06 \end{array}$ 26. $\begin{array}{r} \$75.09 \\ -\, 47.86 \end{array}$ 27. $0.7\overline{)0.04}$ 28. $\begin{array}{r} 1.09 \\ \times\, 0.84 \end{array}$ 29. $24\overline{)\$768.24}$

30. 89.7×10^6 31. $7.41 \div 10{,}000$ 32. $0.092 \times 100{,}000$

33. $74.2 + 1.63 + 0.548$ 34. $3.76 \div 0.8$ 35. $35 \div 100$

Write each in scientific notation. pages 52–53

36. 8,025,000   37. 15,674   38. 2,390,000,000

Solve. pages 40–41, 54–55

Randy and Mark traveled 150 miles to Yosemite National Park in California to go on a 5-day hiking trip. They hiked 5.2 miles the first day, 4.8 miles the second, 7.3 miles the third, 8.5 miles the fourth, and 6.6 miles the fifth.

39. How far did they hike altogether?

40. On the average, how far did they hike each day? Round to the nearest tenth mile.

Write the decimal for each.

1. six hundred and seventy-five thousandths
2. $(5 \times 1) + (4 \times 0.01) + (8 \times 0.0001)$
3. $(4 \times 10) + (1 \times 1) + \left(5 \times \frac{1}{10^1}\right) + \left(6 \times \frac{1}{10^3}\right)$

Replace each ⬤ with <, >, or =.

4. 3.911 ⬤ 3.91
5. 0.7506 ⬤ 0.750600

Round to the nearest tenth and to the nearest thousandth.

6. 8.17436
7. 0.389748

Choose the best estimate.

8. $0.617 + 0.295 + 0.67$
   a. 1.6
   b. 3.5
   c. 6.3

9. 68.7×0.376
   a. 0.28
   b. 2.8
   c. 28

10. $3.685 \div 0.84$
    a. 0.04
    b. 0.4
    c. 4

Add, subtract, multiply, or divide. When dividing, round to the nearest hundredth where necessary. Check the answers.

11.
$$\begin{array}{r} \$122.98 \\ 68.02 \\ + \quad 17.31 \\ \hline \end{array}$$

12.
$$\begin{array}{r} 164.397 \\ - \quad 95.088 \\ \hline \end{array}$$

13.
$$\begin{array}{r} 1.756 \\ \times \, 0.004 \\ \hline \end{array}$$

14.
$$\begin{array}{r} 89.2 \\ 13.2 \\ + \quad 16.3 \\ \hline \end{array}$$

15.
$$\begin{array}{r} 123.019 \\ \times \qquad 200 \\ \hline \end{array}$$

16. 0.0127×10^4

17. $65\overline{)149.5}$

18. $32.19 \div 10^3$

19. 0.375×10^5

20. $0.015\overline{)1.17049}$

21. $\$183.74 - 17.99$

Write each in scientific notation.

22. 13,010,000
23. 680,095,000,000

Solve. If there is too little information, tell what is missing.

24. In 1803 the United States paid France $15,000,000 for the Louisiana Purchase. How much did the Louisiana Purchase cost per acre?

25. The first oil well was dug in Titusville, Pennsylvania, in 1859. How much did 500 barrels cost in each year shown in the table?

Year	Price/Barrel
1859	$20
1862	$.10
1973	$2.40
1980	$32

Adrian worked for fifteen days. He was paid $.01 the first day, $.02 the second day, $.04 the third day, $.08 the fourth day, and so on. How much did he earn in all?

CHROMATIC NUMBERS

When you color a map, bordering regions must have different colors.

Some maps can be colored using only 2 colors.

Some maps require 3 colors.

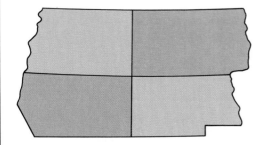

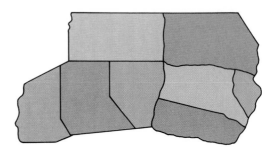

The **chromatic number** of a map is the minimum number of colors needed to color a map.

1. Copy each map at the right and color it. The chromatic number of map **A** is 3. What is the chromatic number of map **B**?

A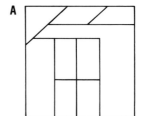

B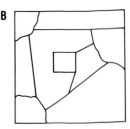

2. No map ever requires 5 colors. Only recently were mathematicians able to prove that this is true, although they had suspected it for a long time. Copy the map below of the United States, and color it. How many colors did you need?

ANCIENT NUMERATION SYSTEMS

The decimal number system is a place-value system based on powers of 10. Some ancient civilizations used place-value systems that were not based on powers of 10.

	1	2	3	4	5	6	7	8	9	10
Babylonian numbers (2,000 B.C.)	T	TT	TTT	TTTT	TTT / TT	TTT / TTT	TTTT / TTT	TTTT / TTTT	TTTTT / TTTT	⟨

For numbers less than 60, the Babylonians grouped by tens. For numbers greater than or equal to 60, they used a form of place value based on powers of 60.

Babylonian	Decimal
⟨ ⟨ ⟨ TTTT ⟨ ⟨	54
TTT ⟨ TTT / TTT ⟨⟨ T / ⟨	$(3 \times 60^2) + (16 \times 60) + (31 \times 1) = 11{,}791$

The Mayans used a vertical place-value system (read from bottom to top) based on powers of 20. However, instead of 20^2, the value of the third place was 18×20, or 360, the number of days in a solar year.

Mayan numbers (A.D. 400)

0	1	5
⊖	•	—

Mayan	Decimal
• • •	8
• / ⊖ / • • / =	$(1 \times 20 \times 18 \times 20) + (0 \times 18 \times 20) + (7 \times 20) + (10 \times 1) = 7{,}350$

Write the decimal number for each Babylonian or Mayan number.

1. ⟨ ⟨ ⟨ TTTT / TTT

2. ⟨ TTT TTTTT ⟨⟨ / TTTT ⟨

3. • • / • • • / • / = / ⊖

4. • • / ⊖ / =

5. • • • • / =

MAINTAINING SKILLS

Choose the correct answers. Write A, B, C, or D.

1. Compare. 4,019,743 ⬤ 4,090,743

   A >   C =
   B <   D not given

2. Round 3,719,843 to the nearest hundred thousand.

   A 3,700,000   C 4,000,000
   B 3,800,000   D not given

3. Estimate. 8,597 − 729

   A 8,000   C 6,000
   B 7,000   D not given

4.   6,009,716
   + 3,906,444

   A 9,916,150   C 9,916,160
   B 9,905,150   D not given

5.   3,900,000
   −   67,677

   A 3,832,233   C 3,823,323
   B 3,832,323   D not given

6. What is 11^2 in standard form?

   A 22   C 111
   B 121   D not given

7. What is 1^5 in standard form?

   A 5   C 10,000
   B 11,111   D not given

8.   8,719
   ×   23

   A 200,537   C 43,595
   B 20,537   D not given

9. $31\overline{)10,468}$

   A 337 R11   C 336 R52
   B 337 R21   D not given

10. 6.914 + 19.42 + 56.08

    A 82.414   C 82.44
    B 144.64   D not given

11. 13 − 4.71

    A 9.29   C 8.29
    B 17.71   D not given

12.   7.61
    × 0.03

    A 0.2283   C 2.283
    B 0.02283   D not given

13. $1.5\overline{)6.84}$

    A 0.456   C 45.6
    B 4.56   D not given

Solve.

14. Wilson Junior High School has 89 students in the orchestra, 113 students in the band, and 232 students in the chorus. How many students are in the band and orchestra combined?

    A 321   C 212
    B 202   D not given

15. How many more students are in the chorus than in the band?

    A 143   C 119
    B 121   D not given

Units of Length

There was ease in Casey's manner as he stepped into his place;
There was pride in Casey's bearing, and a smile on Casey's face;
And when, responding to the cheers, he lightly doffed his hat,
No stranger in the crowd could doubt 'twas Casey at the bat.

from "Casey at the Bat" by Ernest Thayer

A baseball bat is about 1 meter long.

The **meter (m)** is a unit of length in the metric system. So are the **millimeter (mm)**, **centimeter (cm)**, and **kilometer (km)**.

▶Very small lengths are measured in millimeters.

▶Small lengths are measured in centimeters.

▶Long distances are measured in kilometers.

Examples

a. The brim of Casey's hat measured about 4 mm thick.

b. Casey stood about 175 cm tall.

c. Had Casey not struck out, he would have run about 30 m to first base.

d. Some pitchers can throw a fast ball at speeds close to 160 km per hour.

10 mm = 1 cm	1,000 mm = 1 m
100 cm = 1 m	1,000 m = 1 km

CLASSWORK

Estimate the length of each. Then measure to the nearest centimeter or meter to check your estimates.

1. width of your thumb

2. your height

3. length of your desk

4. length of the classroom

5. length of your pencil

6. length of this book

Complete.

7. ___ m = 1 km

8. 1 cm = ___ mm

9. 5 m = ___ cm

10. 9 km = ___ m

11. ___ mm = 4 m

12. ___ cm = 30 mm

Which is the best estimate?

1. length of a car
   a. 5 mm   b. 5 cm   c. 5 m   d. 5 km

2. length of a pen
   a. 15 mm   b. 15 cm   c. 15 m   d. 15 km

3. George Washington's height
   a. 188 mm   b. 188 cm   c. 188 m   d. 188 km

4. width of a pencil point
   a. 1 mm   b. 1 cm   c. 1 m   d. 1 km

5. length of an Olympic-size pool
   a. 5 m   b. 50 m   c. 5 km   d. 50 km

6. distance from New York to Kansas City
   a. 18 m   b. 1,800 m   c. 18 km   d. 1,800 km

7. thickness of your math text
   a. 3 mm   b. 3 cm   c. 30 cm   d. 3 m

8. length of the George Washington Bridge
   a. 1 m   b. 10 m   c. 1 km   d. 10 km

Complete.

9. 1 m = ___ mm

10. 10 mm = ___ cm

11. 100 cm = ___ m

12. 2 km = ___ m

13. ___ cm = 7 m

14. 4 cm = ___ mm

15. ___ cm = 60 mm

16. 15,000 mm = ___ m

17. 8,000 m = ___ km

18. 9 m = ___ mm

19. ___ mm = 10 cm

20. ___ m = 24 km

21. 900 cm = ___ m

22. 150 cm = ___ m 50 cm

23. 4 m 65 cm = ___ cm

24. 358 cm = ___ m ___ cm   ★25. 5,008 m = 5 ___ 8 ___   ★26. 2,370 mm = ___ m ___ cm

List three objects that have the given measurement. Then verify your lists.

★27. between 1 m and 10 m   ★28. between 1 cm and 10 cm   ★29. between 1 mm and 10 mm

APPLICATION

MATH HISTORY

The metric system is a decimal system, just as our number and money systems are. It was created in France about 1790. Originally one meter was one ten-millionth (0.0000001, or $\frac{1}{10,000,000}$) the distance from the North Pole to the equator.

As more accurate ways of measuring are developed, the standard for a meter becomes more refined. Today one meter is 1,650,763.73 wavelengths of the orange-red light from krypton-86.

1. How many wavelengths long is 100 m?

★2. What is the distance from the North Pole to the equator in meters? in kilometers?

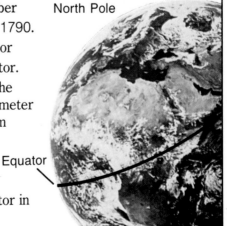

North Pole

Equator

Relating Units of Length

All metric prefixes name powers of 10. Some of the prefixes listed below are not commonly used, but you should recognize them and know their meanings.

Prefix	Symbol	Meaning	Unit of Length
kilo–	k	1,000	1 km = 1,000 m
hecto–	h	100	1 hm = 100 m
deka–	da	10	1 dam = 10 m
deci–	d	0.1	1 dm = 0.1 m
centi–	c	0.01	1 cm = 0.01 m
milli–	m	0.001	1 mm = 0.001 m

Use this table and the one above to find related units of length.

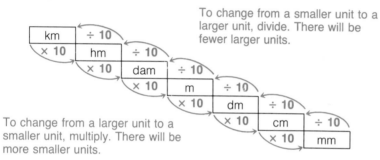

To change from a smaller unit to a larger unit, divide. There will be fewer larger units.

To change from a larger unit to a smaller unit, multiply. There will be more smaller units.

Examples

a. 7 cm = ____ m

1 cm = 0.01 m ⟶ 7 cm = 0.07 m

b. 1 m = ____ km   Smaller to larger, so divide.

1 m = (1 ÷ 10 ÷ 10 ÷ 10) km = 0.001 km

c. 35 dm = ____ mm   Larger to smaller, so multiply.

35 dm = (35 × 10 × 10) mm = 3,500 mm

CLASSWORK

Complete.

1. 1 ____ = 10 m

2. 1 dm = ____ m

3. ____ hm = 100 m

4. ____ dam = 1 m

5. 1 m = 10 ____

6. 12 dam = ____ m

7. 8 dm = ____ m

8. 70 dm = ____ km

9. 3.8 cm = ____ mm

Complete.

1. 1 ___ = 1,000 m

2. ___ m = 1 hm

3. 1 ___ = 0.01 m

4. ___ m = 1 mm

5. 1 ___ = 0.1 m

6. 10 m = ___ dam

7. 0.001 km = ___ m

8. ___ dm = 1 m

9. ___ m = 100 cm

10. 1 ___ = 0.1 dam

11. 0.01 hm = ___ m

12. 1 m = ___ mm

13. 12 cm = ___ m

14. 9 mm = ___ m

15. 4 dm = ___ m

16. ___ hm = 700 m

17. 5 ___ = 50 m

18. 10,000 m = 10 ___

19. 45 cm = ___ dm

20. 250 mm = ___ cm

21. 2,500 m = ___ km

22. ___ dm = 460 mm

23. 2.5 dm = ___ m

24. 5.65 m = ___ cm

25. 575 ___ = 57.5 cm

26. 6,070 ___ = 6.07 km

27. ___ mm = 74.6 dm

Replace each ● with <, >, or =.

28. 1,000 m ● 1 km

29. 1 cm ● 1 mm

30. 100 mm ● 1 m

31. 10 mm ● 1 cm

32. 1 km ● 100 m

33. 100 mm ● 1 cm

34. 10 cm ● 10 mm

35. 10 m ● 1,000 cm

36. 100 cm ● 100 m

★37. 25 cm ● 250 mm

★38. 345 cm ● 34.5 m

★39. 4.5 m ● 300 cm

APPLICATION

Doctors of sports medicine help prevent as well as treat injuries. They study all parts of the body, including the skeletal system, since a broken bone is a common sports injury.

Jane is in eighth grade. Her doctor measured the length of some of her bones as shown here.

Write the length or width of each bone in decimeters, centimeters and millimeters.

40. clavicle

41. humerus

42. radius

43. femur

44. tibia

45. phalange

Solve.

46. After a broken bone heals, it may be shorter than it was before it was broken. Jane broke her radius. How long was it after it healed?

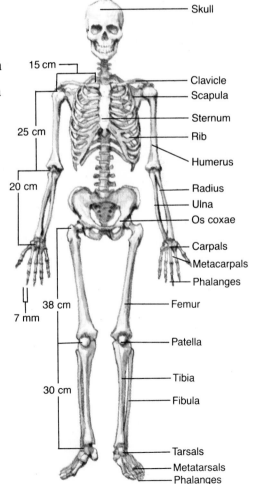

15 cm

25 cm

20 cm

38 cm

7 mm

30 cm

Skull

Clavicle

Scapula

Sternum

Rib

Humerus

Radius

Ulna

Os coxae

Carpals

Metacarpals

Phalanges

Femur

Patella

Tibia

Fibula

Tarsals

Metatarsals

Phalanges

Gram and Kilogram

The **kilogram (kg)**, **gram (g)**, **milligram (mg)**, and **metric ton (t)** are units of mass. It is common outside the field of science to use the word *weight* in place of *mass*.

▶Very light objects are measured in milligrams.

▶Light objects are measured in grams.

▶Heavy objects are measured in kilograms.

▶Very heavy objects are measured in metric tons.

$$1,000 \text{ mg} = 1 \text{ g}$$
$$1,000 \text{ g} = 1 \text{ kg}$$
$$1,000 \text{ kg} = 1 \text{ t}$$

To do well in sports, a proper diet is necessary.

Examples

Object	Weighs about
Vitamin tablet	1 g
Piece of chalk	10 g
Baseball	100 g

Object	Weighs about
Baseball bat	1 kg
Bowling ball	10 kg
Football player (adult)	100 kg

CLASSWORK

Estimate the weight of each. Then measure to the nearest gram or kilogram to check your estimate.

1. new pencil

2. paper clip

3. glass of water

4. this math book

5. pair of sneakers

6. calculator

Complete.

7. ____ g = 1 kg

8. 5,000 g = ____ kg

9. 1 g = ____ mg

10. 3,000 mg = ____ g

11. 8,000 kg = ____ t

12. 10 t = ____ kg

Estimate the weight—1 g, 10 g, 100 g, or 1 kg—of each object. Then order the objects from lightest to heaviest.

1. leotard, running shoes, wristband, shoelace

2. hockey stick, golf tee, Frisbee, whistle

3. plastic sandwich bag, lemon, pencil, loaf of bread

4. Ping-Pong paddle, pair of roller skates, pen, Ping-Pong ball

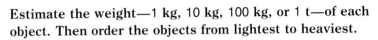

Estimate the weight—1 kg, 10 kg, 100 kg, or 1 t—of each object. Then order the objects from lightest to heaviest.

5. portable TV, camera, rowboat, yacht

6. Clydesdale horse, beagle, hawk, St. Bernard dog

7. football player, football, football helmet and shoes, football team

8. skateboard, inboard motorboat, motorcycle, bicycle

Complete.

9. 5 g = ___ mg

10. ___ g = 9 kg

11. 12 t = ___ kg

12. 6,000 g = ___ kg

13. ___ g = 7,000 mg

14. 2,000 kg = ___ t

15. ___ g = 15,000 mg

16. 35 kg = ___ g

17. 50 t = ___ kg

★ 18. 8 kg 700 g = ___ g

★ 19. 1 g + 2,000 mg = ___ g

★ 20. 50 t + 10,000 kg = ___ t

APPLICATION

MATH HISTORY

Mass is not the same as weight. In the metric system the unit of weight is the **newton (N)**. It is named after Sir Isaac Newton, who discovered the force of gravity in the mid-seventeenth century. Your mass is the same on any planet. But your weight varies depending on the gravitational pull of a planet.

Janell's weight is found by multiplying her weight on Earth by a given factor. Find Janell's weight on Venus, Mars, Jupiter, and the moon when her weight on Earth is 500 N.

mass   amount of matter in an object

weight   gravitational force on an object

	Venus	Mars	Jupiter	Moon
Factor to multiply times Janell's Earth weight	0.89	0.38	2.65	0.16
Janell's weight				

Milliliter and Liter

▶The **liter (L)** is a unit of capacity. A box 1 dm on a side holds 1 L.

▶Very small capacities are measured in **milliliters (mL)**. A box 1 cm on a side holds 1 mL.

▶Large capacities are measured in **kiloliters (kL)**. A box 1 m on a side holds 1 kL.

1,000 mL = 1 L   1,000 L = 1 kL

250 L

100 kL—

CLASSWORK

How would you measure each of these? Choose liter or milliliter.

1. gas for a car

2. glass of water

3. shampoo in a bottle

4. mustard for a sandwich

5. water in a bucket

6. can of juice

Complete.

7. 6,000 mL = ___ L

8. 9 L = ___ mL

9. 1 kL = ___ L

10. 3,000 L = ___ kL

11. ___ L = 24,000 mL

12. ___ kL = 2,000 L

PRACTICE

Complete. Use *L* or *mL*.

1. There are 500 ____ of water in the glass.

2. There are 4 ____ of juice in the jug.

3. Ms. Rios put 30 ____ of gasoline in her car.

4. Monique bought a 125-____ bottle of suntan lotion.

5. There are 5 ____ of soup in the spoon.

6. Marlon filled his fish tank with 17 ____ of water.

Complete.

7. 5 L = ____ mL

8. 7,000 L = ____ kL

9. ____ L = 9 kL

10. ____ L = 18,000 mL

11. 90,000 mL = ____ L

12. 145 kL = ____ L

★ 13. 5 L + 2,000 mL = ____ L

★ 14. 25 kL + ____ L = 40 kL

Estimate.

★ 15. How many liters of water do you normally use to take a bath? Do you use more or less to take a shower?

★ 16. What is the temperature of the water in which you bathe or shower?

APPLICATION

VISUAL THINKING

Beaker **A** is filled with water. Beakers **B** and **C** are empty. By pouring back and forth between the three beakers, separate the 100 mL of water so that there is 50 mL in one of the beakers. The first two pourings are shown in this table. Extend the table to find how many pourings are necessary.

MILLILITERS IN BEAKERS			
Beaker	A	B	C
Start	100	0	0
First Pouring	60	0	40
Second Pouring	60	40	0

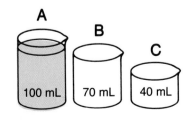

Mixed Practice

1. 75,642
    38,790
    + 68,465

2. 426
    × 785

3. 48,962,300
    − 37,985,463

4. 3.784
    36.91
    + 7.6382

5. 37)54,686

6. 38.9
    × 0.65

7. 4.8)0.6396

8. 54,608
    − 7,069

9. 2.86
    − 1.9384

10. 75)6.4125

11. 0.965
     3.47
     0.0684
     + 1.9

12. 7.456
     × 3.7

69

Relating Units

Each metric prefix is used with *meter, gram,* and *liter* to form names for other units of measure.

Prefix	Symbol	Meaning
kilo–	k	1,000
hecto–	h	100
deka–	da	10
deci–	d	0.1
centi–	c	0.01
milli–	m	0.001

$$1 \text{ km} = 1{,}000 \text{ m} \qquad 1 \text{ dm} = 0.1 \text{ m}$$
$$1 \text{ hL} = 100 \text{ L} \qquad 1 \text{ cg} = 0.01 \text{ g}$$
$$1 \text{ dag} = 10 \text{ g} \qquad 1 \text{ mL} = 0.001 \text{ L}$$

To change from a larger unit to a smaller unit, multiply. There will be more smaller units.

Move the decimal point to the right.

	× 10	× 10	× 10	× 10	× 10	× 10
kilometer	hectometer	dekameter	meter	decimeter	centimeter	millimeter
kilogram	hectogram	dekagram	gram	decigram	centigram	milligram
kiloliter	hectoliter	dekaliter	liter	deciliter	centiliter	milliliter
	÷ 10	÷ 10	÷ 10	÷ 10	÷ 10	÷ 10

Move the decimal point to the left.

To change from a smaller unit to a larger unit, divide. There will be fewer larger units.

Examples

a. 184 cm = ___ m   Smaller to larger, so divide.

184 cm = (184 ÷ 10 ÷ 10) m = 1.84 m = 1.84 m

b. 0.468 kg = ___ g   Larger to smaller, so multiply.

0.468 kg = (0.468 × 10 × 10 × 10) g = 0.468.g = 468 g

c. 36.5 mm = ___ cm   Smaller to larger, so divide.

36.5 mm = (36.5 ÷ 10) cm = 3.65 cm = 3.65 cm

CLASSWORK

Complete.

1. 1 ___ = 100 L

2. 1 cm = ___ m

3. 1 daL = ___ L

4. 754 m = ___ km

5. 0.687 L = ___ mL

6. 68 kg = ___ g

7. 100 mm = ___ cm

8. 6.2 cm = ___ mm

9. 4,230 mm = ___ dm

10. 4.76 g = 4,760 ___

PRACTICE

Complete.

1. 1 ____ = 10 m
2. 1 ____ = 0.001 g
3. ____ L = 1 kL
4. 1 dg = ____ g
5. 10 L = 1 ____
6. 100 cL = ____ L
7. 1.73 kg = ____ g
8. 0.74 km = ____ m
9. 9.7 cm = ____ m
10. 116 mg = 0.116 ____
11. 0.871 ____ = 8.71 dm
12. 386 kg = ____ g
13. ____ L = 3,896 mL
14. 0.0057 ____ = 5.7 mg
15. ____ L = 36.25 mL
16. 1,572 m = 1.572 ____
17. 27.2 m = ____ dm
18. 243,000 mg = ____ g
19. 6.5 ____ = 6,500 mL
20. 0.009 km = 9 ____
21. 1 L = 10 ____
22. ____ m = 0.0942 km
23. 411.6 g = 0.4116 ____
24. 1.94 m = ____ cm
25. 0.086 m = ____ mm
26. 39.7 cm = ____ mm
27. 14.5 ____ = 145 cm
28. ____ m = 10 dm
29. 1,746 mm = ____ cm
30. 3,996 mg = 3.996 ____
31. ____ t = 12,500 kg
32. ____ mg = 0.005 kg
33. 4,500 mm = 0.0045 ____
★ 34. 4.75 m = ____ m ____ dm ____ cm
★ 35. 3.67 m = 3 ____ 6 ____ 7 ____
★ 36. 0.806 kg = 8 ____ 6 ____
★ 37. 49.67 m = 4 ____ 9 ____ 6 ____ 7 ____

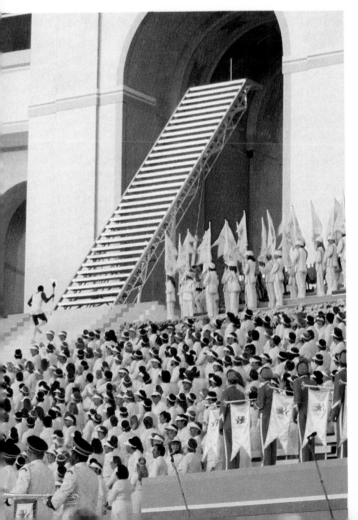

APPLICATION

Select the words that have a metric prefix, and give their meanings.

38. The modern Olympic Games were begun during the nineteenth century to promote world peace and friendship. They are held every four years.

39. For the first two decades, the Olympics were held only in the summer. Now there are Winter and Summer Olympic Games. The decathlon is just one of the events in the Summer Olympic Games.

40. Many countries use government funds to finance their athletes. In the United States, however, athletes are financed by contributions from companies and individuals. Every cent helps.

★ 41. The original Olympic Games were held in ancient Greece. They took place in the stadium at Olympia, which covered an area of about 2 hectares.

Precision and Greatest Possible Error

Kim Lee needs a bolt about 3 cm long to repair his racing bike. Both bolts below measure 3 cm to the nearest centimeter.

But, to the nearest millimeter, bolt **A** measures 34 mm, and bolt **B** measures 28 mm.

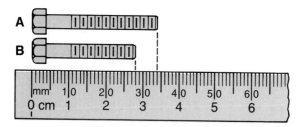

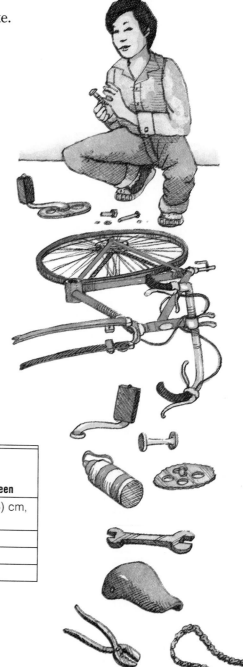

The measurements to the nearest millimeter are more precise. The smaller the unit to which you measure, the more **precise** the measurement.

All measurements are approximate. The difference between the approximate measurements of the bolts above and the actual measurements is called the *error of measurement*. The **greatest possible error (GPE)** of any measurement is one half the precision of the measurement. The actual measurement lies between the **measurement − GPE** and the **measurement + GPE**.

Measurement	Precision (measured to the nearest)	GPE	Actual measurement is between
3 cm	1 cm	0.5 cm	(3 − 0.5) cm and (3 + 0.5) cm, or 2.5 cm and 3.5 cm
34 mm	1 mm	0.5 mm	33.5 mm and 34.5 mm
33.8 mm	0.1 mm	0.05 mm	33.75 mm and 33.85 mm
300 g	100 g	50 g	250 g and 350 g

Classwork

Complete the chart below.

	Measurement	Precision	GPE	Actual measurement is between
1.	52 cm			
2.	6.3 L			
3.	640 kg			
4.	7.50 m			
5.	800 mg			

Complete the chart below.

	Measurement	Precision	GPE	Actual measurement is between
1.	84 m			
2.	325 mL			
3.	9.4 kg			
4.	4 L			
5.	4.0 L			
6.	2.735 kg			
7.	510 cm			
8.	145.0 m			
9.	100.45 dm			
10.	0.014 km			
11.	0.0035 kg			
12.	500 g			
★ 13.	500 g	1 g		
★ 14.	500 g	10 g		

Which measurement is more precise?

15. 12 km, 12,055 m

16. 424 mm, 42 cm

17. 424 cm, 42 mm

18. 0.508 kg, 0.58 kg

19. 4.06 km, 4.006 km

★ **20.** 1.723 g, 17.2 mg

★ **21.** 27.2 dm, 2,715 cm

★ **22.** 7.120 kL, 7,120 L

APPLICATION

CALCULATOR

Use a calculator to determine which measurement is more precise. Remember the fraction bar means to divide: $\frac{1}{3} \longrightarrow 1 \div 3$.

1. $\frac{1}{3}$ cm, 0.33333 cm

2. 6.14285 m, $\frac{43}{7}$ m

3. $\frac{5}{2}$ kg, 8.375 kg

4. 7.667 L, $\frac{17}{4}$ L

5. $\frac{18}{16}$ kL, $\frac{23}{9}$ kL

6. $\frac{34}{5}$ m, $\frac{13}{8}$ km

Problem Solving

SIMULATION

THINK
PLAN
SOLVE
LOOK
BACK

To solve a problem, sometimes a model of a real-world situation can be made. This model is called a **simulation**. Simulation makes it possible to study the problem on paper instead of actually having to act it out.

The holding pens for the bulls, horses, calves, and ponies at the rodeo are arranged as shown in the diagram below. Place the animals in the pens so that every row, every column, and both diagonals contain only one animal of each kind.

THINK   Place the animals in the pens so that each row, column, and diagonal contains only one animal of each kind.

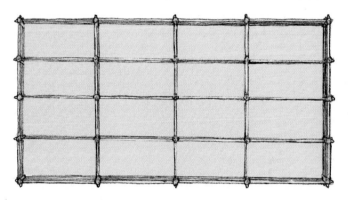

PLAN   Simulate the action by using slips of paper or bottle caps to represent the various animals. Arrange them until you have a correct solution.

SOLVE

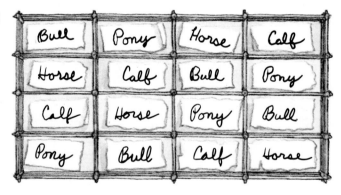

Bull	Pony	Horse	Calf
Horse	Calf	Bull	Pony
Calf	Horse	Pony	Bull
Pony	Bull	Calf	Horse

LOOK BACK   Does each row, column, and diagonal contain 4 different animals? Yes.

Is there any row, column, or diagonal that contains more than one of each kind of animal? No.

The answer is correct.

Use simulation to solve each problem. Using a drawing or small objects will be helpful.

1. During the warm-up drill before the start of the basketball game, the members of the Blue Jays stand in a circle. Each player tosses the ball to each one of the other players. How many times would the ball be tossed among 5 players?

2. The Blue Jays are getting new uniforms. The choices are shown at the right. How many different combinations of uniforms can the team select?

3. The coach at Roosevelt High School must inform all the basketball players that the time for practice has been changed. He tells 3 players, each of whom tells 2 more players, each of whom then tells 1 more player. How many players have been told about the time change?

★ 4. Alan, Bob, and Carl have a contest to decide which of them is the fastest runner. They will all run in each of 3 races. If one of them beats another in 2 of the 3 races, he will be considered the faster of the two. As a result of the races, it is determined that Alan is faster than Bob and that Bob is faster than Carl. Does this mean that Alan is faster than Carl?

=== CREATE YOUR OWN PROBLEM ===

Fill in the blanks with appropriate data from the list at the right. Then solve the problem.

Lian hiked ___ north, ___ east, ___ north, and ___ west. How far was she from where she started?

DATA		
47 km	3.5 km	39 km
2.5 km	74 cm	2.5 km
2 h	4 h	2.5 h
578 cm	2.8 km	67 km

Units of Time

When Fred P. Newton swam the Mississippi River from Minneapolis to New Orleans, he was in the water a total of 742 hours. How many days is this?

To change from a smaller to a larger unit, divide.

Change to days and hours.

```
        30 R22
   24)742
   ↑    72
        22
1 d = 24 h,   0
so divide    ──
by 24.       22
```

742 h = 30 d 22 h

Change to tenths of a day.

```
       30.91
  24)742.00
      72
      22 0
      21 6
      ───
        40
        24
```

742 h = 30.9 d

60 seconds (s) = 1 minute (min)
60 minutes = 1 hour (h)
24 hours = 1 day (d)
7 days = 1 week (wk)
52 weeks = 1 year (yr)
12 months (mo) = 1 year
365 days = 1 year
100 years = 1 century (c)

To change from a larger to a smaller unit, multiply.

4 h 15 min = (4 × 60) min + 15 min = 255 min

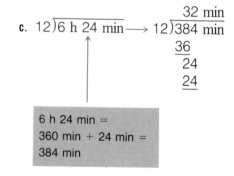

When adding, subtracting, multiplying, or dividing units of time, you may have to regroup.

a.
```
    4   38
    5̸ d 1̸4̸ h
  − 1 d 21 h
  ──────────
    3 d 17 h
```

```
5 d 14 h =
4 d + 1 d + 14 h =
4 d + 24 h + 14 h =
4 d 38 h
```

b.
```
    5 min   26 s
  ×            7
  ───────────────
   35 min 182 s, or
   38 min     2 s
          ↑
```

```
35 min 182 s =
35 min + 3 min 2 s =
38 min 2 s
```

c. 12)6 h 24 min ⟶
```
           32 min
      12)384 min
         36
         ──
         24
         24
         ──
```

```
6 h 24 min =
360 min + 24 min =
384 min
```

CLASSWORK

Complete.

1. 17 min 35 s = ___ s

2. 45 d = ___ wk ___ d

3. 256 min = ___ h (to the nearest tenth)

4.
```
  2 yr 3 mo
+ 3 yr 5 mo
```

5.
```
  28 min 26 s
− 19 min 35 s
```

6.
```
  3 d 17 h
×       5
```

7. 5)3 h 20 min

PRACTICE

Complete.

1. 100 s = ___ min ___ s
2. 270 min = ___ h ___ min
3. 5 min 25 s = ___ s
4. 2 h 35 min = ___ min
5. 125 h = ___ d ___ h
6. 37 d = ___ wk ___ d
7. 136 s = ___ min ___ s
8. 210 h = ___ d ___ h
9. 11 d 19 h = ___ h
10. 1,000 d = ___ yr ___ d
11. ___ wk = 3 yr 12 wk
12. ___ yr ___ mo = 72 mo
13. ___ yr = 6 c 35 yr
14. ___ yr ___ wk = 765 d
15. 192 d = ___ wk ___ d
16. 1 h 30 min 40 s = ___ s
17. 1,894 min = ___ d ___ h ___ min
18. 1,054 d = ___ yr ___ wk ___ d
19. 3 wk 5 d 10 h = ___ h

Find each to the nearest tenth.

20. 145 s = ___ min
21. ___ h = 349 min
22. 68 h = ___ d
23. ___ h = 295 min
★ 24. 3 h 51 min = ___ h
★ 25. 2 h 17 min 27 s = ___ h

Add, subtract, multiply, or divide.

26.
```
  22 min 16 s
−  9 min 34 s
```

27.
```
  6 h 17 min
×        4
```

28.
```
  14 h 47 min
+ 15 h 39 min
```

29.
```
  5 wk
− 2 wk 5 d
```

30.
```
  5 d 16 h
×      3
```

31.
```
  27 min 46 s
+ 43 min 33 s
```

32. 7)10 h 30 min

33. 8)5 d 16 h

34. 25)18 min 20 s

35.
```
  5 yr 3 wk 5 d
− 3 yr 6 wk 6 d
```

★ 36.
```
  6 d 42 min
×        3
```

★ 37.
```
  4 h 16 s
×     10
```

APPLICATION
Solve.

38. In the course of one day, how many times do the hands of a clock point in the same direction?

★ 39. It took Jon Erikson 38 h 27 min to swim across the English Channel three times. To the nearest tenth of an hour, how long did each crossing take on the average?

═══ LOGICAL THINKING ═══

It takes about 5 hours for a jet to fly coast-to-coast. One jet leaves San Francisco for New York at 9:40 A.M. EST, while another jet leaves New York for San Francisco at 11:00 A.M. EST. They pass each other at 1:00 P.M. EST. Which jet is closer to New York at that time?

Elapsed Time

Ships, airlines, and many countries use 24-hour time instead of 12-hour time to avoid confusion between A.M. and P.M.

12-hour time	24-hour time
7:30 A.M.	0730 ("oh seven thirty")
4:15 P.M.	1615 ("sixteen fifteen") ← Add 12 hours to 1 P.M. or later.
12:00 midnight	2400 ("twenty-four hundred") ←
12:27 A.M.	0027 ("oh oh twenty-seven") ← Subtract 12 hours from 12:01 A.M. to 12:59 A.M.

24-hour time	12-hour time
0935 ("oh nine thirty-five")	9:35 A.M.
1418 ("fourteen eighteen")	2:18 P.M. ← Subtract 12 hours from 1300 or later.
1900 ("nineteen hundred")	7:00 P.M. ←
0009 ("oh oh oh nine")	12:09 A.M. ← Add 12 hours to 0001 to 0059.

The *Liberty* finished this race in 3 hours 26 minutes. At what time did the *Liberty* finish?

Start time	12 h 10 min
Elapsed time	+ 3 h 26 min
Finish time	15 h 36 min

The *Liberty* finished at 1536, or 3:36 P.M.

Another Example

Find the elapsed time between 9:45 A.M. and 2:32 P.M.

Finish time	2:32 P.M.	14 h 32 min
Start time	− 9:45 A.M.	− 9 h 45 min
Elapsed time		4 h 47 min

CLASSWORK

1. Write 2:05 P.M. in 24-hour time.

2. Write 2012 in 12-hour time.

3. Find the elapsed time between 10:37 A.M. and 8:16 P.M.

4. Find the time 2 h 24 min before 1:20 P.M.

5. Find the time 4 h 56 min after 11:03 A.M.

America's Cup Race

START TIME

12:10 P.M.

78

Write the 24-hour time for each.

1. 5:35 A.M.
2. 3:38 P.M.
3. 4:05 A.M.
4. 7:48 P.M.
5. 1:24 A.M.
6. 12:03 A.M.
7. 11:30 P.M.
8. 5:00 P.M.

Write the 12-hour time for each.

9. 1235
10. 0345
11. 0915
12. 1700
13. 0900
14. 1932
15. 1517
16. 0006

Find each time.

17. 4 h 14 min after 6:19 A.M.
18. 6 h 23 min before 10:04 A.M.
19. 3 h 34 min after 6:47 P.M.
20. 5 h 35 min after 9:25 A.M.
21. 9 h 46 min before 5:12 P.M.
★ 22. 8 h 39 min after 11:33 P.M.
★ 23. 3 h 18 min before 1:09 A.M.
★ 24. 17 h 22 min before 2:48 A.M.

Find the elapsed time between the given times.

25. 4:24 A.M. and 10:16 A.M.
26. 6:30 P.M. and 11:27 P.M.
27. 11:24 A.M. and 8:21 P.M.
28. 7:21 A.M. and 11:24 P.M.
★ 29. 10:28 P.M. and 3:47 A.M.
★ 30. 1:45 P.M. and 11:20 A.M.

APPLICATION

The America's Cup race is the world's most famous sailboat competition. A boat from one nation challenges the defending champion. In 1983 the Australian boat *Australia II* challenged the United States boat *Liberty*.

31. What was the race time for *Liberty* in race 2?

32. What was the race time for *Australia II* in race 1?

★ 33. The winner of the cup must win four out of seven races. Which boat won the America's Cup in 1983?

Race	Boat	Start	Finish
1	Liberty	12:10:08	15:35:50
	Australia II	12:10:05	15:37:00
2	Liberty	12:10:08	15:58:14
	Australia II	12:10:13	15:59:47
3	Liberty	14:00:02	17:53:48
	Australia II	14:00:10	17:50:34
4	Liberty	12:10:07	15:39:24
	Australia II	12:10:13	15:40:07
5	Liberty	12:10:06	15:41:43
	Australia II	12:10:43	15:39:56
6	Liberty	12:10:14	15:45:01
	Australia II	12:10:21	15:41:36
7	Liberty	13:05:08	17:21:26
	Australia II	13:05:16	17:20:45

(times given in hours: minutes: seconds)

Problem Solving

SKILLS AND STRATEGIES REVIEW

Solve.

1. Today Janet ran 4 laps around the track in 5 min 3.4 s. Yesterday it took her 2.6 s longer. What was her time yesterday?

2. By next week, Janet's athletic trainer wants her to decrease today's time by 5 s. What would her time be then?

3. By the end of the next week, Janet had run each of the 4 laps as follows: 75.0 s, 74.7 s, 74.3 s, and 74.25 s. Did she reach her goal?

4. Michael and Joseph both weighed 65.95 kg when they started an exercise program 5 weeks ago. Michael now weighs 61.9 kg. Joseph now weighs 63.7 kg. What was Michael's average weekly weight loss?

Monroe County had its annual Spring Sports Day. One of the events was a cross-country minithon. The runners ran 1,200 m north, 750 m east, 1,675 m south, 900 m west, and 475 m north.

5. When they finished, where were they relative to their starting point?

6. How many kilometers long was the course they ran?

The winner of the minithon ran the race in 15 min 12 s. The second-place runner finished in 15 min 22 s. The third-place runner's time was 15 min 48 s.

7. How much faster did the winner run the course than the second-place runner? than the third-place runner?

8. How long did it take each of the first-, second-, and third-place runners to run 1 kilometer?

Some of the other events were the relay race, the Hot Potato contest, and the bike race.

9. Last year's winning team set a record of 51.7 s in the 4-person relay race. This year the 4 legs of the relay were run by the winners in the following times: 12.8 s, 13.3 s, 13.1 s, and 12.4 s. Did this year's team break the record?

10. Alex, Bonnie, Chan Lee, and Darlene were in a Hot Potato contest. They stood in a circle and passed a potato. The potato passed from Chan Lee to Darlene to Alex to Bonnie to Chan Lee and so on. The potato was passed 11 times. Who was the last to receive the potato?

11. Twenty-four cyclists started their bike race at 11:35 A.M. The winning time was 2 h 15 min. What time did the winner cross the finish line?

12. The second-place cyclist in the bike race was 7 minutes behind the winner. What time did the second-place cyclist cross the finish line?

13. Carmen spent ten weeks training for the cycling event. The first week she rode her bike 3 km each day. She increased her distance by 0.5 km each week thereafter. How far did she ride her bike each day on her fifth week of training? How far did she ride each day on her tenth week of training?

★ 14. While they waited for their events, Amelia, Bob, Carol, and Daryl had a Frisbee toss. Amelia had a yellow Frisbee, Bob had a blue one, Carol had a red one, and Daryl had a white one. The Frisbees were tossed between the following people: Amelia and Bob, Carol and Daryl, Amelia and Carol, and Daryl and Bob. Finally, Carol and Bob exchanged Frisbees, and so did Daryl and Amelia. Who had the red frisbee at the end?

CHAPTER REVIEW

Which is the best estimate? pages 62–63, 66–69

1. distance from Seattle to St. Louis   **a.** 2,700 cm   **b.** 2,700 m   **c.** 2,700 km

2. weight of a basketball   **a.** 1 mg   **b.** 1 g   **c.** 1 kg

3. milk in a full carton   **a.** 1 mL   **b.** 1 L   **c.** 100 L

4. length of this book   **a.** 25 cm   **b.** 25 mm   **c.** 25 m

Complete. pages 64–65, 70–71

5. 1 dm = ___ m

6. 1 ___ = 100 m

7. 40 mm = ___ cm

8. 1,000 L = 1 ___

9. 32 kg = ___ g

10. 200 cm = ___ m

11. 1.5 kg = ___ g

12. 574 mg = ___ g

13. 10 L = 1 ___

14. 27.2 dm = ___ cm

15. 2,940 m = ___ km

16. ___ mm = 7.4 cm

17. 6 d = ___ h

18. 7 min 26 s = ___ s

19. 75 d = ___ wk ___ d

20. 286 min = ___ h ___ min

21. 123 wk = ___ yr ___ wk

22. 84 h = ___ d (to the nearest tenth)

Give the precision and the GPE for each. pages 72–73

23. 262 mg

24. 1.2 km

25. 16.00 L

26. 0.012 g

Add, subtract, multiply, or divide. pages 76–77

27.   3 h 41 min
     + 1 h 26 min

28.   5 min 16 s
     − 2 min 38 s

29.   4 d 15 h
     ×   6

30.   10 min
     − 3 min 19 s

31.   7 wk 4 d
     + 8 wk 3 d

32. 32)‾18 d 16 h

33.   6 h
     − 2 h 28 min

34.   10 h 27 min
     ×   5

Find each time. pages 78–79

35. 0637 hours in 12-hour time

36. 6 h 15 min before 3:15 P.M.

37. 1:43 P.M. in 24-hour time

38. 1302 hours in 12-hour time

39. 4 h 57 min after 11:16 A.M.

40. 5 h 43 min before 11:22 P.M.

41. the elapsed time between 3:57 A.M. and 9:06 A.M.

Solve. pages 74–75, 80–81

42. One year the members of the winning team in the Olympic 1,600-m relay had the following times: 45.8 s, 44.9 s, 44.5 s, 44.3 s. What was their total time? What was their average time?

43. A penny is rolled around a second penny, starting as shown. Will Lincoln's head be facing up or down when the penny is rolled halfway around?

CHAPTER TEST

Which is the best estimate?

1. height of a basketball net   **a.** 3 cm   **b.** 3 m   **c.** 3 km

2. distance from Chicago to New York   **a.** 1,200 cm   **b.** 1,200 m   **c.** 1,200 km

3. weight of a racketball racket   **a.** 300 g   **b.** 300 kg   **c.** 300 t

4. weight of this book   **a.** 1 mg   **b.** 1 g   **c.** 1 kg

5. capacity of the fuel tank in a car   **a.** 60 mL   **b.** 60 L   **c.** 600 L

6. capacity of a soup spoon   **a.** 5 mL   **b.** 5 L   **c.** 50 L

Complete.

7. 1 dam = 10 ___

8. 0.01 g = 1 ___

9. 4 dm = ___ m

10. 2.3 m = ___ cm

11. 72 L = ___ mL

12. 9,675 g = ___ kg

13. 7.5 cm = ___ mm

14. 0.923 g = ___ mg

15. 128 h = ___ d ___ h

16. 9 h 21 min = ___ min

17. To the nearest tenth, 266 min is ___ h.

18. The elapsed time between 8:56 A.M. and 2:17 P.M. is ___ h ___ min.

Give the precision and the GPE for each.

19. 463 g

20. 16.200 km

Add, subtract, or multiply.

21.   16 h 27 min
   − 6 h 51 min

22.   4 wk 3 d
   + 6 wk 5 d

23.   12 h 25 min
   ×   3

Solve.

24. Janet Lynn jogs 5 km every day. From her home she jogs 750 m north, 1,250 m west, 350 m south, 500 m east, 275 m south, 500 m west, and 125 m south. At that point, where is she relative to her home? How much farther does she have to jog?

25. Janet Lynn jogs for 30 min. After she gets back home, it takes her 50 min to eat, shower, get dressed, and walk to the train station. Her train leaves at 7:50 A.M. One morning she got a late start and did not begin jogging until 6:35 A.M. Did she make her train?

4 × (2 h 15 min) + 5 × (3 h 17 min) = ___ d (to the nearest tenth)

PUZZLE PIECES

Can you put these pieces together so that they fit into the
triangle? Trace them and cut them out. Use a ruler to check
the measurements of each of your pieces.

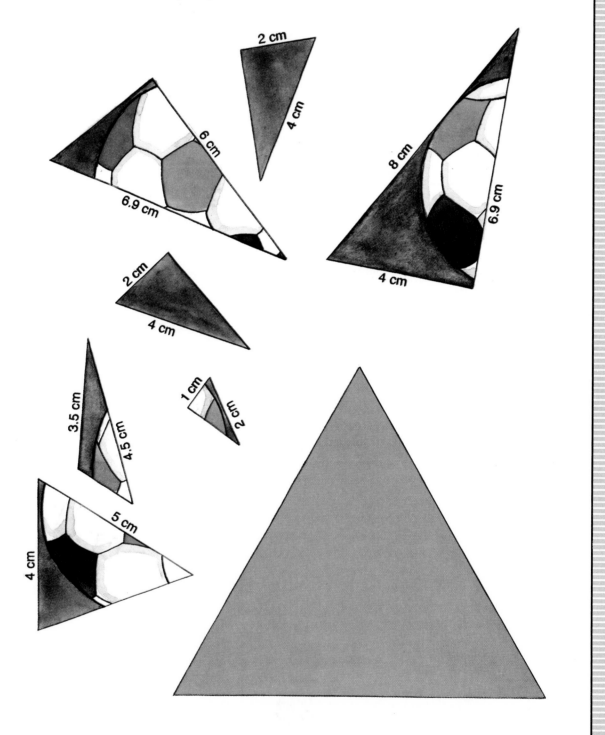

SIGNIFICANT DIGITS AND ACCURACY

The **significant digits** in a measurement are those digits that tell the number of times the unit to which you measured is used.

Examples

Measurement	Measured to the Nearest (Precision)	Number of Units	Significant Digits	Number of Significant Digits
4.6 m	0.1 m	46 (0.1 m)	4, 6	2
302 g	1 g	302 (1 g)	3, 0, 2	3
0.085 kg	0.001 kg	85 (0.001 kg)	8, 5	2
50.40 L	0.01 L	5,040 (0.01 L)	5, 0, 4, 0	4
450 km	10 km	45 (10 km)	4, 5	2

The more significant digits in a measurement, the more **accurate** the measurement.

Listed in order from most accurate to least accurate, the measurements above are as follows.

50.40 L ⟵ 4 significant digits

302 g ⟵ 3 significant digits

4.6 m, 0.085 kg, 450 km ⟵ 2 significant digits

Complete this chart.

	Measurement	Measured to the nearest (Precision)	Number of Units	Significant Digits	Number of Significant Digits
1.	49.6 m				
2.	5,000 km				
3.	1.300 km				
4.	106.250 m				
5.	0.05 m				
6.	250 m				
7.	78,590 km	1 km			

8. List the measurements above in order from least accurate to most accurate.

9. List the measurements above in order from least precise to most precise.

FLOWCHARTS

The step-by-step procedure used to solve a problem is called
an **algorithm.** A computer programmer often begins by
making a **flowchart** to represent the steps of the algorithm.

Each symbol in a flowchart has a meaning.

 is used for start or stop.

is used for input
or output.

is used for operations
and directions.

is used for a decision.

This flowchart shows how to do a countdown for
a rocket launching. The flowchart uses a **loop.**
A loop is used to *repeat* steps in an algorithm.
Follow the arrows to count down from 10.

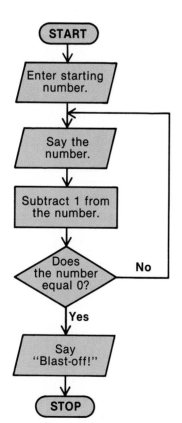

This is a loop.

Follow the flowchart to complete the input-output chart.

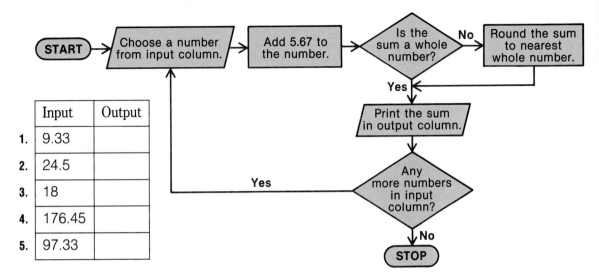

	Input	Output
1.	9.33	
2.	24.5	
3.	18	
4.	176.45	
5.	97.33	

Copy the flowchart. Write each step in the correct place.

6. how to be a good base runner

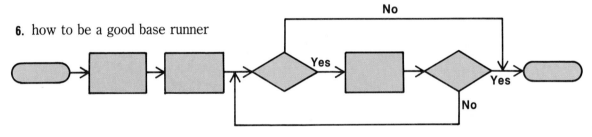

Reach first base safely.   Are you home?   STOP   Is there time to run to next base?

Run to next base.   Hit the ball.   START

Solve.

7. The steps are given for a flowchart showing how to count odd numbers. Put the steps in order and construct the flowchart.

Let the number equal 1.   START

Say the number.   Add 2.

8. What step does not appear in the flowchart showing how to count odd numbers? Does the loop in the flowchart ever come to an end?

Make a flowchart for each.

9. how to make peanut butter sandwiches

10. how to add 46.78 and 32.21

11. how to convert one metric unit to another

12. how to write a number in scientific notation

MAINTAINING SKILLS

Choose the correct answers. Write A, B, C, or D.

1. Estimate. 48,090 + 1,139

  A 49,000   **C** 61,000
  B 50,000   **D** not given

2. 42 × 63,000

  A 264,600   **C** 264,046
  B 26,460,000   **D** not given

3. 34$\overline{)52{,}739}$

  A 155 R5   **C** 1,551
  B 1,551 R5   **D** not given

4. Round 367.1059 to the nearest hundred.

  A 400   **C** 300
  B 380   **D** not given

5. Round 376.1059 to the nearest tenth.

  A 376.2   **C** 376
  B 376.11   **D** not given

6. Round 376.1059 to the nearest thousandth.

  A 376.105   **C** 376.2
  B 376.106   **D** not given

7.   0.4791
  − 0.0948

  A 0.3653   **C** 0.3843
  B 0.3657   **D** not given

8. 7 ÷ 1.25

  A 5.6   **C** 0.56
  B 56   **D** not given

9. What is 29,000,000 in scientific notation?

  A 29×10^6 **C** 2.9×10^7
  B 2.9×10^6 **D** not given

10. Complete. 0.84 kg = ___ g

  A 8,400   **C** 840
  B 84   **D** not given

11.   6 d 7 h
  ×   9

  A 56 d 15 h   **C** 54 d 15 h
  B 54 d 16 h   **D** not given

12. What is the precision of 300 g?

  A 100 g   **C** 1 mg
  B 1 g   **D** not given

13. What is the elapsed time between 10:30 P.M. and 1:24 A.M.?

  A 3 h 54 min   **C** 3 h 6 min
  B 2 h 54 min   **D** not given

Solve. If there is not enough information, tell what information is missing.

14. The Hikers' Club went on a 14-day trip to Colorado. Each member paid $650 for the trip. What was the total cost of the trip?

  A $6,500   **C** $9,100
  B need number of   **D** not given
     club members

15. The club camped at an elevation of 11,624 feet. The next day they walked for 6 hours to reach an elevation of 10,160 feet. How many feet did they ascend or descend?

  A descended 244 feet
  B ascended 1,464 feet
  C descended 1,464 feet
  D not given

Theme: Rivers

Exploring Areas of Polygons

First read the newspaper article shown at the right. Then work in a small group on the following activities.

1. Discuss and decide what the mayor meant by "waste."

2. Sketch as many different regular polygons as you can that could be cut from the city's old token, without too much waste.

3. Devise a method for estimating the waste involved for each of the regular polygons you sketched. Use it to arrange the polygons in order of decreasing waste.

CITY COUNCIL STALEMATE ON TOKEN DESIGN

(Aug. 28) The city council met last night for the seventeenth time to debate the shape of new tokens for the city buses. To save the city money, the council suggested using the existing tokens. The plan is to convert each round token in use to a token shaped like a regular polygon. "Chop them into triangles," Councilman Simso recommended pointedly. "Squares would be better," Councilwoman Danz replied. Mayor Tirola was concerned about wasting the pieces chopped off the edges. "My administration is against waste of any kind," the Mayor said.

The meeting was not lacking in excitement. At one point a delegation of college students presented samples of the 17-sided token that they prefer. Later, a group of eighth-grade students from the Kennedy School giggled when the Council passed a resolution to adopt the polygon that minimizes waste.

SHARING YOUR THINKING

Compare your results with those of another group.

1. How did you estimate the amount of waste if the token is square?

2. How are the square and octagonal tokens related? What do you notice about the amount of waste in each case?

3. What can you say about the amount of waste from a 16-sided polygon compared with that from a 32-sided polygon?

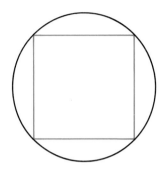

THINKING IT THROUGH

1. Write a statement explaining how the amount of waste is related to the number of sides of the polygon. Write a statement explaining how the area of a regular polygon is related to the area of a circle.

2. Why do you think some eighth graders giggled when the council voted to adopt the polygon with the least amount of waste?

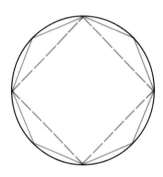

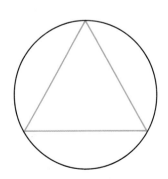

Exploring Areas of Irregular Polygons

For some polygons, such as triangles, rectangles, squares, parallelograms, and trapezoids, there are formulas to find areas. For other polygons, you need to use special methods for finding area.

WORKING TOGETHER

Work in a group. Use a sheet of centimeter-grid paper and a ruler. Select four points, one on each edge of the grid paper, and join them with segments to form a quadrilateral. No point should be at a corner of the paper.

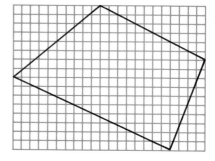

1. Calculate the total area of the grid paper.

2. Find the areas of any triangular regions that were formed.

3. Devise a method for finding the area of the quadrilateral. Record its area.

One group made a mistake and chose a fifth point not on an edge of their grid paper.

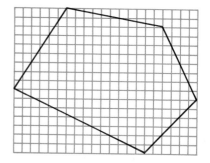

4. Decide how your method for finding the area of a quadrilateral could be extended to find the area of a pentagon.

5. Experiment to test your method.

6. Do you think your method would work for any polygon? Explain.

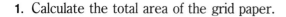
SHARING YOUR THINKING

Compare your results with those of other groups.

1. Did any group form a regular quadrilateral? Could you form a regular quadrilateral on your grid paper, in the way described above? Explain.

2. Did any group form a rectangle? a parallelogram? a trapezoid? Could you form any of these figures on your grid paper? Explain.

3. What if you were given a polygon larger than one sheet of grid paper. Discuss how you could use your method to find its area.

When you draw a polygon on a rectangular piece of grid paper, the triangles you use to help find the area of the polygon are right triangles. Do you need to use triangles outside the polygon or can you partition the polygon itself into right triangles?

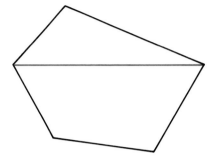

Work in a group of four to find out.

1. Each member of your group should draw a different polygon. Draw the longest diagonal that you can for your polygon. Are any right triangles formed? Will drawing a diagonal always form at least one triangle? Explain.

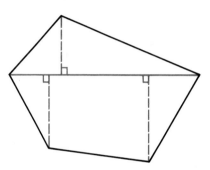

2. From each vertex of the polygon, not on the diagonal, draw a segment perpendicular to the diagonal. Are any right triangles formed? Will at least one right triangle always be formed? Explain.

3. Is your polygon now partitioned into right triangles only? If not, what can you do to create other right triangles?

4. Two members of your group should draw and investigate a pentagon. The other two should draw and investigate a hexagon.

   • Trace each figure. Save the copy.

   • Partition each polygon into right triangles.

   • Measure carefully and then calculate the area of your partitioned polygon.

   • Trade traced polygons with the other two people in your group. Calculate the area of this new partitioned polygon.

5. Can a polygon always be partitioned into right triangles only? Explain why this method of partitioning polygons is important in finding the area of an irregular polygon.

Properties

Jenny and Barbara will travel by canoe from Chester to Whitehorse, a distance of 12 km. They will make a rest stop in Milltown or Pennton. The distance they travel will be the same, no matter where they stop.

ADDITION PROPERTIES
(for all numbers a, b, and c)

Commutative Property

$$a + b = b + a$$
$$9 + 3 = 3 + 9$$

Associative Property

$$a + (b + c) = (a + b) + c$$
$$5 + (6 + 4) = (5 + 6) + 4$$

Identity Property

$$a + 0 = a \qquad 0 + a = a$$
$$75 + 0 = 75 \qquad 0 + 75 = 75$$

MULTIPLICATION PROPERTIES
(for all numbers a, b, and c)

Commutative Property

$$a \times b = b \times a$$
$$5 \times 7 = 7 \times 5$$

Associative Property

$$a \times (b \times c) = (a \times b) \times c$$
$$2 \times (4 \times 3) = (2 \times 4) \times 3$$

Identity Property

$$a \times 1 = a \qquad 1 \times a = a$$
$$27 \times 1 = 27 \qquad 1 \times 27 = 27$$

Zero Property

$$a \times 0 = 0 \qquad 0 \times a = 0$$
$$19 \times 0 = 0 \qquad 0 \times 19 = 0$$

Distributive Property of Multiplication Over Addition

$$a(b + c) = (a \times b) + (a \times c)$$
$$2(3 + 5) = (2 \times 3) + (2 \times 5)$$

A number beside parentheses means multiply by that number.

CLASSWORK

Name the property illustrated.

1. $6 \times 5 = 5 \times 6$ **2.** $8 + 0 = 8$ **3.** $12 + 8 = 8 + 12$

4. $1 \times 84 = 84$ **5.** $9 \times 1 = 1 \times 9$ **6.** $12 \times 0 = 0$

7. $(20 \times 5) \times 4 = 20 \times (5 \times 4)$ **8.** $7(9 + 4) = (7 \times 9) + (7 \times 4)$

Name the property illustrated.

1. $9 \times 7 = 7 \times 9$ **2.** $0 + 100 = 100$ **3.** $(9 + 8) + 7 = 9 + (8 + 7)$

4. $1 \times 109 = 109$ **5.** $204 + 3 = 3 + 204$ **6.** $5(8 + 4) = (5 \times 8) + (5 \times 4)$

7. $21 \times 1 = 21$ **8.** $129 \times 0 = 0$ **9.** $(5 \times 8) \times 9 = 5 \times (8 \times 9)$

10. $8 \times 1 = 1 \times 8$ **11.** $16 + 0 = 16$ **12.** $(2 + 3) + 4 = 2 + (3 + 4)$

13. $0 \times 15 = 0$ **14.** $25 + 143 = 143 + 25$ **15.** $(2 \times 3) + (2 \times 4) = 2(3 + 4)$

Make each sentence true. Name the property used.

16. $25 \times \square = 25$ **17.** $16 + 13 = \square + 16$ **18.** $(2 + 3) + 7 = 2 + (\square + 7)$

19. $\square + 67 = 67$ **20.** $29 \times \square = 1 \times 29$ **21.** $(3 \times \square) \times 8 = 3 \times (9 \times 8)$

22. $38 \times \square = 0$ **23.** $36 \times 45 = 45 \times \square$ **24.** $5(6 + \square) = (5 \times 6) + (5 \times 12)$

25. $0 + \square = 81$ **26.** $68 \times 0 = \square$ **27.** $146 \times \square = 146$

Write *true* or *false* for each statement.

28. If the product of two numbers is 0, then one of the numbers must be 0.

29. When a number is divided by 1, the quotient is that number.

30. When a number is divided by itself, the quotient is that number.

31. When a number is subtracted from 0, the difference is that number.

32. Zero divided by any number greater than 0 is 0.

★**33.** Any number divided by 0 is equal to that number.

★**34.** Subtraction is commutative.

★**35.** Division is commutative.

★**36.** Subtraction is not associative.

★**37.** Division is associative.

APPLICATION

=====MENTAL ARITHMETIC=====

Use the properties to help you mentally compute each answer.

1. $30 + (70 + 18)$ **2.** $(15 \times 8) + (15 \times 2)$ **3.** $(19 \times 5) \times 200$

4. $8 + 9 + 2 + 1 + 6$ **5.** $13 + 6 + 7 + 14$ **6.** $9 + 7 + 4 + 1 + 3 + 6$

7. $(6 \times 15) + (6 \times 35)$ **8.** $(640 + 391) + 360$ **9.** $(25 \times 68) \times 40$

10. $(27 \times 14) + (27 \times 6)$ ★**11.** 21×19 ★**12.** 38×42

Order of Operations

The Spences, Rodrigos, and O'Neills went rafting together. How much did they pay?

4 adults + 6 children

$4 \times 23 + 6 \times 15$

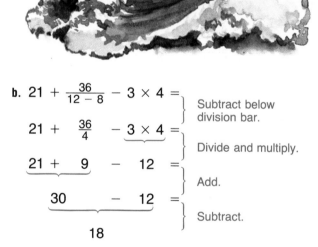

5 Hours of Rafting Fun on the Lehigh River	
Adults	$23
Children	$15

To find the value of an expression with more than one operation, follow this order.

1. Do work with exponents.

2. Do all multiplication and division as they occur from left to right.

$4 \times 23 + 6 \times 15 =$

3. Do all addition and subtraction as they occur from left to right.

$92 + 90 =$

182

The value of the expression $4 \times 23 + 6 \times 15$ is 182. They paid $182 to go rafting.

When parentheses or a division bar appear, first follow the order of operations inside the parentheses, or above or below the division bar.

a. $3 + 2(8 + 3^2) =$

$3 + 2(8 + 9) =$ Simplify exponent.

$3 + 2 \times 17 =$ Add in parentheses.

$3 + 34 =$ Multiply.

37 Add.

b. $21 + \dfrac{36}{12 - 8} - 3 \times 4 =$ Subtract below division bar.

$21 + \dfrac{36}{4} - 3 \times 4 =$ Divide and multiply.

$21 + 9 - 12 =$ Add.

$30 - 12 =$ Subtract.

18

CLASSWORK

Find the value of each expression.

1. $9 \times 3 + 1$

2. $8(5 + 1)$

3. $27 + 4 - 8 \times 3$

4. $4^2 \div 8$

5. $20 - (12 - 8 \div 2) \times 2$

6. $320 \div (8 + 8 \times 3)$

7. $32 - 3 \times 2^3 - \dfrac{16 - 4}{3}$

8. $6 \times 7 - \dfrac{5 + 4}{3} \times 8$

9. $29 - 2 \times 3^2 + 28 \div 7$

PRACTICE

Find the value of each expression.

1. $3 + 4 - 6$

2. $18 - 7 \times 2$

3. $37 + 8 - 29$

4. $35 \div 5 - 3$

5. $2^2 - 1$

6. $15 - (3 + 4)$

7. $48 \div (12 \div 3)$

8. $4(3 + 9)$

9. $75 - 3 \times 25$

10. $3^2 + 15 \times 2$

11. $\frac{12 \times 8}{6} \times (4 + 4)$

12. $139 - \frac{27 + 54}{3}$

13. $252 \div 7 \div 6$

14. $8 \times \frac{24 - 6}{9}$

15. $(3 + 42) \div 9$

16. $48 \div 2^3 - \frac{21 - 11}{2}$

17. $32 \times 17 - 135$

18. $14 \times (3^2 + 37)$

19. $5^2 - 8 \times 2 + \frac{15}{3}$

20. $\frac{8 + 14}{5 + 6} \times (7 - 4)$

21. $(86 - 245 \div 7) \times 5$

22. $15 \times 8 + 35 \div 5$

23. $15 \times (8 + 35) \div 5$

24. $(15 \times 8 + 35) \div 5$

25. $4^2 + 9 \times 6 - 4$

26. $(4^2 + 1) \times 6 - 4$

27. $4^2 + 9 \times (6 - 4)$

28. $47 - 81 \div 9 + 36(3 + 2)$

29. $\frac{42 + 6^2}{2^4 - 2 \times 5}$

30. $(18 + 9) \times 3 \div 9 - \frac{4^2}{2}$

Use parentheses to make each sentence true.

★**31.** $3 + 5 \times 8 - 2 = 62$

★**32.** $42 \div 3 + 4 = 6$

★**33.** $5 \times 8 - 4 \times 2 = 40$

★**34.** $3^2 - 3 \times 8 - 15 \div 3 = 11$

★**35.** $48 \div 8 \div 2 + 4 = 1$

★**36.** $24 \div 2 + 2 \times 5 = 2$

APPLICATION

37. On the rafting trip Mrs. Spence sat behind Rob O'Neill, Mr. Rodrigo sat behind his son Mark, and Mark sat in front of Rob O'Neill. In what order, front to back, were these four people seated on the raft?

LOGICAL THINKING

Write each expression. You may use addition, subtraction, multiplication, division, exponents, and parentheses.

Example Use four 3's to name seven. $3 + 3 + 3 \div 3 = 3 + 3 + 1 = 7$

1. Use four 5's to name six.

2. Use four 5's to name ten.

3. Use four 4's to name twenty.

4. Use three 6's to name thirty.

5. Use three 3's to name twenty-four.

6. Use five 5's to name one hundred.

★**7.** Use four 4's to name each number from zero to ten.

Expressions

Dockworkers can load 11 tons of cargo per minute onto this container ship.

The expression $11 \times y$, or $11y$, represents the amount of cargo the workers can load in y minutes. The variable y represents the number of minutes. A **variable** is a symbol that represents a number in an expression or an equation.

To find the number of tons the workers can load in 15 minutes, **evaluate** $11y$ for $y = 15$.

$$11y =$$
$$11 \times 15 =$$
$$165$$

Substitute 15 for y to find a value of $11y$.

The dockworkers can load 165 tons in 15 minutes.

More Examples

Write an expression for each. Then evaluate the expression.

a. sixteen less than a number t

$$t - 16$$
Let $t = 20$. $20 - 16 = 4$

b. two times a number x, plus seven

$$2x + 7$$
Let $x = 9$. $2 \times 9 + 7 =$
$$18 + 7 = 25$$

CLASSWORK

Evaluate each expression. Let $x = 4$ and $y = 28$.

1. $3x - 4$
2. $2y$
3. $\frac{y}{4}$
4. $9 - x$
5. $\frac{y - x}{6}$

Write an expression for each.

6. twelve more than a number y

7. the product of eight and a number d

Evaluate each expression. Let $a = 5$, $b = 4$, $c = 15$, and $d = 7$.

1. $c - 9$ **2.** $d + 12$ **3.** $5 + b$ **4.** $4a$

5. $3d$ **6.** $\frac{c}{3}$ **7.** $2b + 3$ **8.** $14 - 2a$

9. a^2 **10.** ab **11.** $(d - 7) \times a$ **12.** $\frac{bd}{7}$

13. $\frac{2a - b}{3}$ **14.** $25 - a + b$ **15.** $a + c - b^2$ **16.** $16 + c - (b + 7)$

Find each output.

Input	Output
x	$3(x - 4)$
17. 7	
18. 12	
19. 35	

Input	Output
y	$2y^2$
20. 5	
21. 8	
22. 10	

Input	Output
f	$\frac{36 - 2f}{4}$
23. 4	
24. 12	
25. 18	

Write an expression for each.

26. thirteen times a number b

27. a number n plus fourteen

28. fifty less than a number y

29. a number r divided by ten

30. the product of five and a number c

31. the sum of twice a number y and five

★ **32.** the product of a number n and six, minus nine

★ **33.** ten less than a number x divided by three

Write as a word expression.

34. $3a$ **35.** $n + 6$ **36.** $15 - b$ **37.** $\frac{p}{5}$ **38.** $\frac{8}{c}$

★ **39.** $7p - 2$ ★ **40.** $9(c + 3)$ ★ **41.** $\frac{m + n}{2}$ ★ **42.** $\frac{12}{c + d}$ ★ **43.** $36 - 2x + 5$

APPLICATION

Write an expression for each. Use x for the variable. Then evaluate the expression.

44. Dockworkers can load 2 tons of cargo per minute onto a regular cargo ship.
  a. How many tons can they load in one hour?
  b. How many tons can they load in 2 hours 30 minutes?

★ **45.** How many more tons does a supertanker carry than these other ships?
  a. a container ship
  b. a LASH ship
  c. a tanker

Type of Ship	Capacity (in tons)
Container	11,000
LASH	24,000
Tanker	2,000
Supertanker	450,000

Equations and Formulas

Sacagawea traveled 3,000 miles with the expedition from her Mandan village to the Pacific coast. How far had the expedition traveled before she joined them?

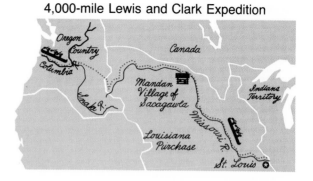

4,000-mile Lewis and Clark Expedition

Write an equation. An **equation** is a number sentence with an equal sign (=).

3,000 plus some number n is 4,000.

$$3,000 + n = 4,000$$

To **solve** an equation, find a value for the variable that makes the sentence true. This value is a **solution.**

Use 1,000 as a value for n in $3,000 + n = 4,000$.

$$3,000 + 1,000 = 4,000$$

1,000 is the solution. The expedition had traveled 1,000 miles before Sacagawea joined them.

A **formula** is an equation. Evaluate each formula for the given value.

a. $p = c + 200$ (Let $c = 125$.)
$p = 125 + 200$
$p = 325$

b. $60h = m$ (Let $h = 7$.)
$60 \times 7 = m$
$420 = m$

detail, courtesy of the Montana Historical Society

CLASSWORK

Substitute the given value in the equation. Then tell whether it is a solution.

1. $x + 17 = 29$ (Let $x = 12$.) **2.** $18y = 126$ (Let $y = 7$.) **3.** $2y - 48 = 15$ (Let $y = 59$.)

Write an equation for each.

4. Twenty more than a number c is fifty.

5. The product of five and a number y is ten.

Evaluate each formula.

6. $s = n - 10$, for $n = 38$

7. $24d = h$, for $d = 5$

Substitute the given value in the equation. Then tell whether it is a solution.

1. $9y = 63$ (Let $y = 7$.)
2. $t - 10 = 10$ (Let $t = 10$.)
3. $3n - 68 = 49$ (Let $n = 39$.)
4. $\frac{n}{14} = 8$ (Let $n = 112$.)
5. $y - 57 = 0$ (Let $y = 57$.)
6. $2x + 5 = 39$ (Let $x = 20$.)
7. $\frac{w}{15} = 9$ (Let $w = 165$.)
8. $x + 11 = 14$ (Let $x = 3$.)
9. $35 = 20 + y$ (Let $y = 55$.)
10. $2(13-x)=18$ (Let $x=4$.)
11. $10(n - 2) = 9$ (Let $n = 10$.)
12. $4(m + 5) = 80$ (Let $m = 15$.)

Write an equation for each.

13. A number n plus four is nine.

14. Thirty-two less than a number x is ten.

15. A number t divided by twelve is equal to twenty.

16. Eleven less than the product of eight and a number x is thirty-seven.

★ 17. Seven times the sum of a number c and fifteen is one hundred thirty-three.

★ 18. One hundred forty-three divided by the sum of a number b and six is eleven.

Evaluate each formula for the given values.

19.

t	$c = 2t + 3$
4	
12	
18	

20.

a	$h = 8 + \frac{18 - a}{2}$
4	
12	
17	

21.

s	$A = s^2$
7	
15	
36	

★ 22.

r	t	$d = rt$
35	2	
55	4	
60	2.5	

★ 23.

t	f	$s = 7t + 3f$
2	1	
3	2	
5	0	

★ 24.

B	h	$V = Bh$
2	3.5	
4	7.2	
8.3	10	

APPLICATION

Write an equation for each. Substitute the given values in the equation to find the solution.

25. The Lewis and Clark Expedition took 28 months to make the round trip from St. Louis to the Pacific coast and back. Nine months were spent wintering over. How many months were spent traveling? Use the values 10, 15, 19, and 21.

★ 26. Forty-five people started out from St. Louis on the expedition. Among them were Lewis and Clark, Clark's servant York, 23 volunteers from the army, and 9 boatmen. The rest were interpreters, hunters, and carpenters. How many were interpreters, hunters, and carpenters? Use the values 7, 10, 13, and 16.

Slant Indian Village, Mandan, North Dakota

Problem Solving

PATTERNS

Sometimes recognizing a pattern will help you solve a problem.

THINK
PLAN
SOLVE
LOOK
BACK

1. Lois needs three more squares to complete this design on a sail. What colors will she use for the missing squares?

1   2   3   4

What are the facts?

She uses 4 colors. Each square has 2 colors.

5   6   7   8

How can the answer be found?

Look for a pattern. Notice that diagonally the squares along any row from lower left to upper right are all the same. Also, in the vertical columns the top half of each square matches the bottom half of the square above it.

9   10   11   12

Carry out the plan.

Since squares 13, 7, and 4 are , square 10 must be .

Since squares 14 and 8 are , square 11 must be .

Since square 12 is yellow on the bottom, square 16 must be yellow on top. All squares with yellow on top have green on the bottom.

So square 16 is .

13   14   15   16

How can the solution be checked?

Check to see that each kind of square appears in every row and in every column.

2. Find the next two numbers in this sequence.
1, 3, 6, 10, 15, ___, ___.

How can the answer be found?

Look for a pattern.

    3 = 1 + 2   10 = 1 + 2 + 3 + 4
    6 = 1 + 2 + 3   15 = 1 + 2 + 3 + 4 + 5

Continue the pattern, and find the missing numbers.

    1 + 2 + 3 + 4 + 5 + 6 = 21
    1 + 2 + 3 + 4 + 5 + 6 + 7 = 28

The sequence is 1, 3, 6, 10, 15, 21, 28.

PRACTICE

Complete each pattern.

1.

2. A, C, E, G, ___, ___, ___

3.

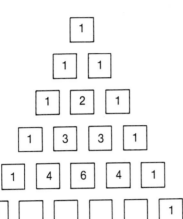

4.

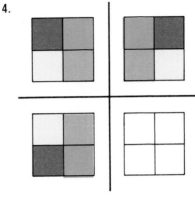

5. 1, 2, 4, 8, ___, ___

6. 1, 1, 2, 3, 5, 8, ___, ___

7. 1, 3, 9, 27, ___, ___

8. 1, 4, 9, 16, ___, ___, ___

Solve.

9. For the pattern at the right, what is the order of colors in the third row?

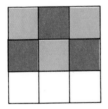

10. How many squares are in the pattern?

11. John Holder is a piano tuner. He knows that middle C on the piano has a frequency of 256 cycles of vibrations per second. Each time he moves down one octave, the frequency is one half as many cycles per second. Find the frequency when he plays C three octaves below middle C.

★ 12. Amy has a 20-gallon fish tank. The water evaporates at the rate of 1.5 gallons each week. She adds 2 gallons of water every other week. Amy added water today and the tank is now holding 16 gallons. How much water will be in the tank six weeks from today?

=== CREATE YOUR OWN PROBLEM ===

1. Make up a number pattern using addition. Start with 1. Write the first five numbers of the pattern. Have a classmate write the next three numbers.

2. Make up a color pattern using squares and the colors red, blue, and yellow. Show the first five squares of the pattern. Have a classmate show the next three squares.

Inverse Operations

Evaporation and precipitation are inverse processes in the water cycle.

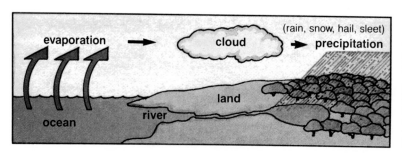

Addition and subtraction are **inverse operations**.

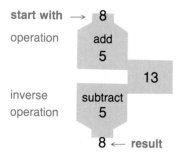

start with → 8

operation | add 5

13

inverse operation | subtract 5

8 ← result

Multiplication and division are **inverse operations**.

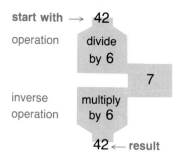

start with → 42

operation | divide by 6

7

inverse operation | multiply by 6

42 ← result

More Examples

a.

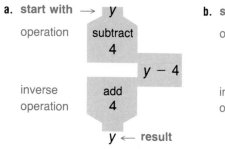

start with → y

operation | subtract 4

$y - 4$

inverse operation | add 4

y ← result

b.

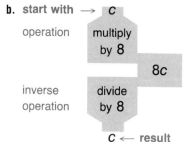

start with → c

operation | multiply by 8

$8c$

inverse operation | divide by 8

c ← result

CLASSWORK

Name the inverse of each operation.

1. add 7   **2.** divide by 5   **3.** subtract 2   **4.** multiply by 9

5. divide by 12   **6.** subtract 16   **7.** add 24   **8.** twice a number

An operation has been performed on each variable. Write the inverse operation.

9. $c - 6$ **10.** $5n$ **11.** $7 + y$ **12.** $\frac{x}{3}$ **13.** $d + 12$

PRACTICE

Name the inverse of each operation.

1. add 8   **2.** multiply by 3   **3.** subtract 7   **4.** divide by 9

5. subtract 14   **6.** add 19   **7.** multiply by 15   **8.** divide by 21

9. increase by 14   **10.** decrease by 5   **11.** add 0   **12.** double a number

An operation has been performed on each variable. Write the inverse operation.

13. $n + 7$ **14.** $c - 4$ **15.** $8d$ **16.** $\frac{c}{3}$ **17.** $x - 6$

18. $8 + c$ **19.** $5x$ **20.** $\frac{n}{10}$ **21.** $y - 15$ **22.** $20 + d$

23. $14n$ **24.** $x - 32$ **25.** $\frac{t}{18}$ **26.** $c + 18$ **27.** $\frac{r}{30}$

Complete each sentence.

28. $23 + 4 - 4 = \square$ **29.** $\frac{3 \times 8}{3} = \square$

30. $19 - 7 + 7 = \square$ **31.** $10 - 10 + 16 = \square$

32. $\frac{72}{8} \times 8 = \square$ **33.** $5 \times 14 \div 5 = \square$

34. $n - 12 + 12 = \square$ **35.** $\frac{9x}{9} = \square$

36. $\frac{c}{15} \times 15 = \square$ **37.** $8 - 8 + y = \square$

38. $20d \div 20 = \square$ **39.** $t + 24 - 24 = \square$

★**40.** $2d - 5 + 5 = \square$ ★**41.** $2 + 3n - 2 = \square$

★**42.** $\frac{n - 6}{5} \times 5 = \square$ ★**43.** $\frac{3(x - 4)}{3} = \square$

★**44.** $\frac{5n - 2 + 2}{5} = \square$ ★**45.** $\frac{2(c + 4 - 4)}{2} = \square$

APPLICATION

CALCULATOR

Use the $\boxed{+}$, $\boxed{-}$, $\boxed{\times}$, $\boxed{\div}$, or $\boxed{=}$ keys to make each sentence true.

1. $15 \,\square\, 7 \,\boxed{-}\, 15 \,\boxed{=}\, 7$ **2.** $24 \,\square\, 3 \,\boxed{\div}\, 24 \,\boxed{=}\, 3$

3. $9 \,\boxed{+}\, 7 \,\square\, 7 \,\square\, 9 \,\boxed{=}\, 14$ **4.** $18 \,\boxed{\times}\, 9 \,\square\, 9 \,\square\, 2 \,\boxed{=}\, 36$

5. $8 \,\square\, 6 \,\boxed{\times}\, 10 \,\square\, 10 \,\boxed{=}\, 14$ **6.** $6 \,\boxed{-}\, 6 \,\square\, 8 \,\square\, 9 \,\boxed{=}\, 72$

7. $12 \,\square\, 7 \,\boxed{\div}\, 12 \,\square\, 8 \,\boxed{=}\, 15$ **8.** $24 \,\square\, 8 \,\boxed{+}\, 8 \,\square\, 6 \,\boxed{=}\, 5$

★**9.** $9 \,\square\, 8 \,\boxed{\div}\, 9 \,\square\, 6 \,\square\, 3 \,\boxed{=}\, 10$ ★**10.** $2 \,\square\, 18 \,\boxed{-}\, 18 \,\square\, 3 \,\boxed{+}\, 3 \,\boxed{=}\, 33$

Addition and Subtraction Equations

It took Huck and Jim 13 days to go from St. Petersburg, Missouri, to Cairo, Illinois. After 5 days they had reached St. Louis, Missouri. How long did it take them to get from St. Louis to Cairo?

$$d + 5 = 13$$

To solve the equation $d + 5 = 13$, find the value of the variable.

▶Always do the same thing to both sides of an equation to keep the sentence balanced.

$d + 5 = 13$	Use the inverse of adding 5 to solve.
$d + 5 - 5 = 13 - 5$	Subtract 5 from *both* sides of the equation.
$d = 8$	Solution

Check

$8 + 5 = 13$	Replace *d* with 8 in the original equation.

The Adventures of Huckleberry Finn by Mark Twain

It took 8 days to go from St. Louis to Cairo.

More Examples

a.

$y - 8 = 19$	Use the inverse of subtracting 8 to solve.
$y - 8 + 8 = 19 + 8$	Add 8 to *both* sides.
$y = 27$	Solution

Check

$27 - 8 = 19$	Replace *y* with 27 in the original equation.

b.

$1.7 + n = 3.1$	Use the inverse of adding 1.7 to solve.
$1.7 - 1.7 + n = 3.1 - 1.7$	Subtract 1.7 from *both* sides.
$n = 1.4$	Solution

Check

$1.7 + 1.4 = 3.1$	Replace *n* with 1.4 in the original equation.

CLASSWORK

First tell what must be done to both sides of the equation. Then solve it. Check each solution.

1. $x + 9 = 24$
2. $14 + a = 14$
3. $y - 12 = 37$
4. $18 = x - 10$
5. $41 = y + 20$
6. $n - 2.5 = 0$
7. $44 = x - 0$
8. $3.5 + n = 7.9$

**First tell what must be done to both sides of the equation.
Then solve it. Check each solution.**

1. $x + 11 = 20$ 2. $y + 15 = 27$ 3. $n - 19 = 7$ 4. $b - 12 = 8$

5. $y + 19 = 19$ 6. $t - 43 = 86$ 7. $32 + a = 96$ 8. $119 = x + 43$

9. $31 = d + 0$ 10. $w - 2.7 = 2.7$ 11. $8.2 = 5.4 + y$ 12. $r - 35 = 0$

13. $175 = n + 100$ 14. $7.2 = b - 1.8$ 15. $x + 144 = 144$ 16. $p - 121 = 168$

17. $1 = m - 78$ 18. $0 + t = 0$ 19. $9.7 = 5.6 + x$ 20. $2.4 = c - 2.4$

21. $1 = d + 0$ 22. $38 + n = 49$ 23. $6 = a - 3.5$ 24. $x + 37 = 62$

★ 25. $n - 27 = 54 + 18$ ★ 26. $112 - 84 = s - 17 + 18$ ★ 27. $12 \times 5 = x + 17$

Write an equation for each sentence. Then solve it.

28. A number n decreased by 19 is 35.

29. Nine increased by a number x is 25.

30. The sum of a number b and 45 is 108.

31. A number y decreased by 0.4 is 8.6.

32. A number n increased by 7.4 is 12.

33. Ninety-eight is equal to a number b decreased by 32.

★ 34. The sum of a number x and 36 is the sum of 26 and 53.

★ 35. A number c increased by 23 equals 87 decreased by 19.

★ 36. Fifty-five less than a number n is equal to the product of 25 and 18.

★ 37. One hundred forty-three divided by 13 equals a number y decreased by 37.

APPLICATION

Write an equation for each. Then solve it.

38. Huck and Jim's trip from St. Petersburg to Cairo was about 300 miles long. The trip from St. Petersburg to St. Louis was about 125 miles long. How far was it from St. Louis to Cairo?

★ 39. The Mississippi, the longest river in the United States, flows 2,350 miles from its source in Minnesota to its mouth in the Gulf of Mexico. Its widest point is at Cairo, Illinois, where it is 4,500 feet across. How much more or less than a mile across is it at Cairo?

Multiplication and Division Equations

Ben Carleo works for the Fish and Game Commission. During one four-day period, he released 1,424 trout into the Snake River. On the average, how many did he release each day?

$$4t = 1,424$$

To solve $4t = 1,424$, find the value of the variable.

▶Always do the same thing to both sides of an equation to keep the sentence balanced.

$4t = 1,424$ — Use the inverse of multiplying by 4 to solve.

$\frac{4t}{4} = \frac{1,424}{4}$ — Divide *both* sides of the equation by 4.

$t = 356$ — Solution

Check

$4 \times 356 = 1,424$ — Replace *t* with 356 in the original equation.

On the average, Ben released 356 fish each day.

More Examples

a. $\frac{d}{6} = 15$ — Use the inverse of dividing by 6 to solve.

$\frac{d}{6} \times 6 = 15 \times 6$ — Multiply *both* sides by 6.

$d = 90$ — Solution

Check

$\frac{90}{6} = 15$ — Replace *d* with 90 in the original equation.

b. $c \times 12 = 10.8$ — Use the inverse of multiplying by 12 to solve.

$\frac{c \times 12}{12} = \frac{10.8}{12}$ — Divide *both* sides by 12.

$c = 0.9$ — Solution

Check

$0.9 \times 12 = 10.8$ — Replace *c* with 9 in the original equation.

CLASSWORK

First tell what must be done to both sides of the equation.
Then solve it. Check each solution.

1. $4x = 40$
2. $\frac{a}{7} = 5$
3. $9 = \frac{x}{0.7}$
4. $13n = 13$
5. $96 = 12y$
6. $19 = n \div 11$
7. $a \times 2.5 = 22.5$
8. $1 = \frac{n}{21}$

PRACTICE

First tell what must be done to both sides of the equation. Then solve it. Check each solution.

1. $2x = 32$

2. $8x = 72$

3. $\frac{n}{6} = 9$

4. $36 = 9y$

5. $b \times 20 = 12$

6. $\frac{t}{5} = 8$

7. $38c = 38$

8. $y \div 10 = 10$

9. $1.4 = \frac{x}{9}$

10. $\frac{a}{7} = 15$

11. $55 = b \times 5$

12. $6a = 12.6$

13. $80 = 16c$

14. $7.5 = 7.5y$

15. $1 = \frac{m}{4.3}$

16. $28 = \frac{w}{10}$

17. $22 = y \div 7$

18. $14.4 = 12x$

★ **19.** $24x = 2 \times 36$ ★ **20.** $25y = 133 + 117$ ★ **21.** $2s^2 = 162$

Write an equation for each sentence. Then solve it.

22. Three times a number y is 48.

23. A number z divided by 7 is 36.

24. The product of a number t and 25 is 17.5.

25. A number n is divided by 1.9. The quotient is 34.

26. Nine times a number c equals 153.

27. Seventeen is the quotient of a number z and 13.

★ **28.** The product of 12 and 15 is equal to a number x divided by 3.

★ **29.** The product of a number n and 16 equals the product of 32 and 12, divided by 4.

APPLICATION

30. Ben released fish over a 7-day period. He released 295, 325, 305, 335, and 315 fish the first five days. Following this pattern, how many fish did he release on days 6 and 7?

LOGICAL THINKING

You have a message for Jim Kirk, but you must figure out his telephone number first. The first three digits are 555. The remaining four can be found by using the following information. The sum of the four digits is his age, twenty-two. The first digit is three times the third. The second digit is two less than the fourth. The fourth digit is twice the third. What is Jim Kirk's telephone number?

Mixed Practice

1. $34.6 + 7.95 + 162.1$

2.
$$3{,}462 \times 507$$

3.
$$684{,}903 - 487{,}006$$

4. $7.5\overline{)364.2}$

5.
$$\$345.67 \\ 56.78 \\ + \ 89.34$$

6.
$$0.6987 \times 34.3$$

7.
$$48.6 \\ - 17.891$$

8. $54\overline{)3{,}375}$

9. $3{,}006 - 1{,}848$

10.
$$36{,}482 \\ 409{,}806 \\ 43{,}064 \\ + 270{,}857$$

11. $0.28\overline{)101.0352}$

12.
$$\$5.38 \times 256$$

CHAPTER REVIEW

Name the property illustrated. pages 94–95

1. $8 + 6 = 6 + 8$

2. $3(4 + 5) = (3 \times 4) + (3 \times 5)$

3. $17 \times 0 = 0$

4. $(5 \times 7) \times 9 = 5 \times (7 \times 9)$

Evaluate each expression. Let $a = 19$, $b = 11$, and $d = 6$. pages 96–99

5. $24 + 6 - 7 \times 3$

6. $4^2 \div 2$

7. $32 \div 8 \times 5 + 7$

8. $(135 - 87) \div 3$

9. $b - 9$

10. $2d + 1$

11. $25 - a + b$

12. d^2

13. $\frac{d}{3}$

14. $a \times d - b$

15. ad

16. $\frac{a + b}{2}$

Substitute the given value in the equation. Then tell whether it is a solution. pages 100–101

17. $x + 6 = 10$ (Let $x = 4$.)

18. $\frac{t}{5} = 35$ (Let $t = 7$.)

19. $2x - 1 = 7$ (Let $x = 4$.)

First tell what must be done to both sides of the equation. Then solve it. Check each solution. pages 106–109

20. $x + 8 = 17$

21. $y - 13 = 9$

22. $4x = 20$

23. $\frac{n}{6} = 7$

24. $m - 49 = 0$

25. $18 = \frac{x}{7}$

26. $6x = 102$

27. $35 + a = 35$

28. $18 = 18n$

29. $119 = a - 12$

30. $\frac{m}{15} = 1$

31. $21 = a + 9$

32. $y + 1.3 = 2.1$

33. $\frac{a}{0.8} = 1.5$

34. $0.6m = 4.2$

35. $6.5 = x - 1.8$

Write an equation for each sentence. Then solve it. pages 106–109

36. The sum of a number b and 16 is 41.

37. The product of 7 and a number y is 175.

38. Twelve less than a number n equals 68.

39. A number x divided by 0.3 is 7.

40. Twenty more than a number x is 56.

41. Twice a number c is 138.

Solve. pages 102–103

42. Fur traders could row up the Mississippi 1,500 km from New Orleans to St. Louis at about 15 km per day. How long did the trip take?

43. A steamboat going up the Mississippi picked up 1 passenger at the first stop, 3 at the second, 5 at the third, 7 at the fourth, and so on. How many passengers got on at the twelfth stop? How many passengers were on the boat after the twelfth stop?

Name the property illustrated.

1. $(5 + 3) + 4 = 5 + (3 + 4)$ **2.** $5(6 + 7) = (5 \times 6) + (5 \times 7)$

Evaluate each expression. Let $x = 9$ and $y = 5$.

3. $48 \div 6 \times 3 + 9$ **4.** $129 \div (21 - 18)$ **5.** $2x - 1$ **6.** $\frac{x + y}{2}$ **7.** y^2

Name the inverse of each operation.

8. divide by 7   **9.** subtract 5   **10.** add 3.6

Solve each equation.

11. $x + 6 = 15$ **12.** $9 = x - 18$ **13.** $\frac{x}{4} = 8$ **14.** $9x = 72$

15. $x - 14 = 11$ **16.** $\frac{x}{25} = 1$ **17.** $53 + y = 53$ **18.** $21y = 63$

19. $x + 1.9 = 2.7$ **20.** $y - 6 = 0$ **21.** $1.5x = 4.5$ **22.** $\frac{y}{0.3} = 7$

Solve. Use the graph at the right. Write an equation for 23 and 24.

23. How much longer than the Arkansas is the Missouri?

24. On a canoe trip down the Hudson, Lee and Paul averaged 25 km a day. At this rate, how long would it take them to canoe down the entire river?

25. As she traveled along the Rio Grande, Cocheta saw each flag below. Following this pattern, what would the next flag be?

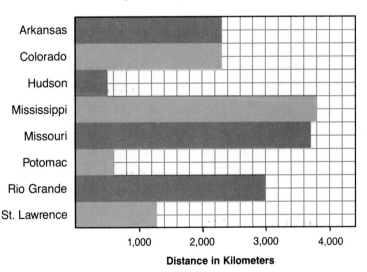

Length of U.S. Rivers to the Nearest 100 km

If you traveled the length of all the rivers in the graph above, about how far would you have traveled? Traveling at the rate of 50 km a day, how long would it take to travel the length of all the rivers?

EXPLORE

ORDER OF OPERATIONS

Even though the same keystroke sequence has been pressed,
different calculators may display different answers.

A calculator with an **arithmetic** operating
system performs the operations in the order
in which they are entered.

A calculator with an **algebraic** operating
system performs the operations according to
the rules for the order of operations.

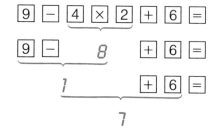

$$9 - 4 \times 2 + 6 =$$
$$5 \quad \times 2 + 6 =$$
$$10 \quad + 6 =$$
$$16$$

Use this keystroke sequence to find out which operating
system the calculator you use has. If the display is 110, it has an
arithmetic system. If the display is 70, it has an algebraic system.

$$5 + 8 \times 9 - 7 =$$

**Find the display for each of the following on the calculator
you use. Then find the display for a calculator that uses the
other operating system. Tell which answer is correct
according to the rules for the order of operations.**

1. $6 + 4 \times 5 - 3$

2. $6 + 8 \div 2 - 7$

3. $32 - 6 \times 4 + 10$

4. $36 - 12 \div 6$

5. $9 + 24 \div 3 - 11$

6. $25 - 10 \div 5 - 2$

7. $36 \div 2 - 6 \div 3$

8. $42 \div 7 - 6 \div 2$

9. $9 \times 8 - 56 \div 8$

10. $8 \times 3 + 7 \times 5$

11. $7 \times 6 - 3 + 4 \times 5$

12. $16 + 28 \div 4 - 5 \times 3$

13. $64 - 8 \times 3 \div 6 + 10$

14. $16 + 32 \div 8 \times 3 - 5 \times 2$

15. $45 \div 9 + 3 \times 7 - 16 \div 2$

16. $54 \div 6 - 4 \times 2 + 35 \div 5$

ALGEBRA

The word *algebra* comes from the Arabic word *al-jabr,* which was part of the title of a ninth century Arabic book, *hisab al-jabr wa'l muqabalah.* It was written by the mathematician al-Khowarazmi. The title means "the science of reuniting and equating."

Mathematical relationships are often difficult to understand when expressed in words. But the same relationships when expressed using algebra can be understood and simplified. Algebra often makes it easy to solve difficult problems—problems great ancient mathematicians could not solve.

Can you find a value for each x below?

1. $x = 4 + 2(5^2 + 3) + 12 - 6 \div 3$

2. $3x + 7 = 16$ 3. $\frac{x}{3^2} = 2.7$ 4. $2^x = 2^3$

5. The product of 8 and 9 equals the quotient of a number x divided by 4.

6. $x = \frac{25 - 4}{49 \div 7}$ 7. $x = 3^2 + 4^2$ 8. $5x^2 = 80$

9. Five times a number x when decreased by 2 equals 17 increased by 6.

10. $31 - x = 27$ 11. $\frac{144}{x} = 48$ 12. $x^2 = 10^2 - 8^2$

CUMULATIVE REVIEW

Choose the correct answers. Write A, B, C, or D.

1. What is 26 billion in standard form?

   A 26,000,000,000   C 2,600,000,000
   B 26,000,000   D not given

2. What is the standard form?
   $(2 \times 10^5) + (3 \times 10^4) + (7 \times 10^2) + (5 \times 10)$

   A 230,750   C 237,075
   B 23,075   D not given

3. What is 8^3 in standard form?

   A 24   C 512
   B 64   D not given

4. 97,006 + 981 + 14,703

   A 112,689   C 101,690
   B 112,690   D not given

5.   261,703
    −   5,918

   A 265,785   C 255,785
   B 255,795   D not given

6. $176.12
    ×   100

   A $17,612.00   C $176,120.00
   B $1,761.20   D not given

7. 57)1,083

   A 18 R48   C 19 R3
   B 19   D not given

8. What is the decimal for $\frac{9}{100}$?

   A 9.0   C 0.09
   B 0.9   D not given

9. What is the decimal for $2 + \left(3 \times \frac{1}{10}\right)$?

   A 3.2   C 3.02
   B 2.03   D not given

10. Compare. 7.681 ⬤ 7.6805

    A >   C =
    B <   D not given

11. Compare. 31.42 ⬤ 31.24

    A >   C =
    B <   D not given

12. Estimate. 29.704 − 11.693

    A 30   C 40
    B 20   D not given

13. Estimate. 316.49 × 2.93

    A 900   C 600
    B 800   D not given

14. Divide and round to the nearest hundredth. $\frac{17}{3}$

    A 5.33   C 5.66
    B 5.67   D not given

15. Divide and round to the nearest hundredth. 5.4)62

    A 1.15   C 11.49
    B 11.48   D not given

16. Complete. 30 cm = ___ mm

    A 0.3   C 3
    B 300   D not given

17. Complete. ___ g = 5 kg

    A 0.05   C 50
    B 5,000   D not given

18. Complete. 2.4 L = 2,400 ___

    A mL   C hL
    B L   D not given

CUMULATIVE REVIEW

Choose the correct answers. Write A, B, C, or D.

19. Complete. 6 ___ = 600 mm

    A dam   **C** cm
    B dm   **D** not given

20. Estimate the height of a barn.

    A 10 m   **C** 20 km
    B 20 cm   **D** not given

21. Estimate the capacity of a bucket.

    A 30 mL   **C** 30 L
    B 3 kL   **D** not given

22.   1 wk 6 d
    + 3 wk 5 d

    A 4 wk 4 d   **C** 5 wk 4 d
    B 5 wk 1 d   **D** not given

23. $4\overline{)3\text{ h }20\text{ min}}$

    A 50 min   **C** 1 h 50 min
    B 1 h 5 min   **D** not given

24. What addition property is used?
    16 + 0 = 16

    A associative   **C** distributive
    B commutative   **D** not given

25. What multiplication property is used?
    10 × 3 = 3 × 10

    A identity   **C** associative
    B commutative   **D** not given

26. What is the value of $2^4 + 14 \div 2$?

    A 15   **C** 22
    B 23   **D** not given

27. What is the value of
    $(9 \times 2 + 7) \div 5 + 17$?

    A 22   **C** 33
    B 25   **D** not given

28. What is an expression for a number r plus six?

    A 4 − 6   **C** 6r
    B r + 6   **D** not given

29. What is an expression for the sum of five times a number x and two?

    A $2x + 5$ **C** $5x + 2$
    B $2 + x + 5$ **D** not given

30. What must you do to both sides of this equation to solve it? $36 = w + 9$

    A subtract 9   **C** add 9
    B subtract 36   **D** not given

31. What must you do to both sides of this equation to solve it? $\frac{x}{7} = 8$

    A divide by 7   **C** multiply by 7
    B multiply by 8   **D** not given

32. Solve this equation. $m − 16 = 8$

    A $m = 8$ **C** $m = 2$
    B $m = 24$ **D** not given

33. Solve this equation. $0.3y = 1.5$

    A $y = 5$ **C** $y = 0.45$
    B $y = 0.5$ **D** not given

34. Solve this equation. $x + 83 = 112$

    A $x = 198$ **C** $x = 29$
    B $x = 31$ **D** not given

35. Solve this equation. $7 = \frac{c}{4.6}$

    A $c = 32.2$ $c = 11.6$
    B $c = 3.22$ **D** not given

36. Solve this equation. $b − 5.5 = 4.9$

    A $b = 11.4$ **C** $b = 0.6$
    B $b = 10.4$ **D** not given

Choose the correct answers. Write A, B, C, or D.

Use the picture for 37–39.

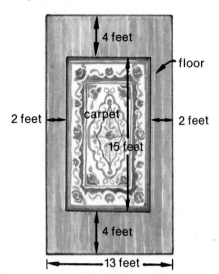

37. How wide is the carpet?

   A 13 feet   **C** 9 feet
   B 11 feet   **D** not given

38. How long is the floor?

   A 23 feet   **C** 19 feet
   B 15 feet   **D** not given

39. How much wider is the floor than the carpet?

   A 2 feet   **C** 4 feet
   B 9 feet   **D** not given

Solve each problem. If there is not enough information, tell what information is missing.

40. The population of Los Angeles is about 3,000,000. The combined population of Los Angeles and Philadelphia is about 4,000,000. Which city has the greater population and by how much?

   A Los Angeles by 1,000,000
   B need population of Philadelphia
   C Philadelphia by 2,000,000
   D not given

41. Memphis is 480 miles from Houston. Omaha is 790 miles from Houston. Akron is 620 miles from Memphis. How much farther is it from Memphis to Akron than from Memphis to Houston?

   A 140 miles
   B need distance from Akron to Houston
   C 310 miles
   D not given

Solve.

42. Daryl is making a quilt from squares of material. The quilt has 9 rows of 6 squares. The corner squares and the two center squares in the middle row are white. Each square sharing a side with a white square is gold. Of the remaining squares, one half are blue and one half are pink. How many squares are gold?

   A 6   **C** 14
   B 22   **D** not given

43. How many squares of Daryl's quilt are blue?

   A 26   **C** 13
   B 17   **D** not given

Find the pattern. What are the next two numbers?

44. 7, 11, 15, 19, ___, ___

   A 23, 27   **C** 23, 25
   B 21, 23   **D** not given

45. 5, 10, 20, 40, ___, ___

   A 80, 160   **C** 80, 120
   B 60, 80   **D** not given

46. 2, 2.6, 3.2, 3.8, ___, ___

   A 4.2, 4.8   **C** 4.0, 4.6
   B 4.4, 5.0   **D** not given

Factors

Jim, Tom, and Sharon are playing a game called Cartel. Jim wants to spend $12 for trucks. Oil tankers cost $6 and car carriers cost $4. How many of either truck can he buy?

$$6\overline{)12}4\overline{)12}$$
$$23$$

Jim can buy either 2 oil tankers or 3 car carriers.

When 12 is divided by 6 or by 4, the remainder is 0. So 12 is divisible by 6 and also by 4. The numbers 6 and 4 are factors of 12.

A number is divisible by each of its factors.

The rules below can be used to check quickly for divisibility.

A number is divisible by	2	if the last digit is 0, 2, 4, 6, or 8.
	3	if the sum of the digits is divisible by 3.
	4	if the number formed by the last 2 digits is divisible by 4.
	5	if the last digit is 0 or 5.
	6	if the number is even, and the sum of the digits is divisible by 3.
	8	if the number formed by the last 3 digits is divisible by 8.
	9	if the sum of the digits is divisible by 9.

The factors of 12 are 1, 2, 3, 4, 6, and 12.

The factors of 16 are 1, 2, 4, 8, and 16.

The common factors of 12 and 16 are 1, 2, and 4.

The **greatest common factor (GCF)** of 12 and 16 is 4.

CLASSWORK

Write the factors of each.

1. 15   **2.** 24   **3.** 18   **4.** 16   **5.** 17   **6.** 42

Write the common factors. Then find each GCF.

7. 26, 39   **8.** 15, 32   **9.** 18, 45   **10.** 20, 35, 55

PRACTICE

Complete each chart, using the rules for divisibility.

	Number	Divisible by		
		3	6	9
1.	186	yes		no
2.	294			
3.	10,026			
4.	7,910			
5.	1,234,515			

	Number	Divisible by		
		4	5	8
6.	816	yes	no	
7.	1,035			
8.	10,636			
9.	12,060			
10.	1,030,040			

Write the factors of each.

11. 12   **12.** 32   **13.** 60   **14.** 13   **15.** 25   **16.** 100

Write the common factors.

17. 8, 12   **18.** 16, 24   **19.** 16, 32   **20.** 6, 7

21. 36, 60   **22.** 27, 45   **23.** 9, 45, 60   ★**24.** 119, 167, 179

Find the GCF for each.

25. 4, 10   **26.** 12, 18   **27.** 24, 27   **28.** 8, 9

29. 48, 60   **30.** 13, 104   **31.** 28, 42, 98   ★**32.** 175, 250, 400

APPLICATION

33. Sharon spent her money on real estate. Houses cost $8 and warehouses cost $10. If she spent $1,040 on houses, how many houses did she buy? How many warehouses could she have bought instead?

★**34.** Tom bought freight cars for a train line and spent $35. Jim bought some, too, and spent $40. How much at most could the freight cars have cost?

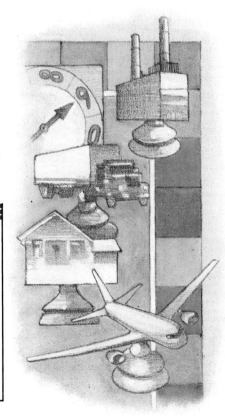

LOGICAL THINKING

During a recent census a woman told the census taker that she had three children. When asked their ages, she replied, "The product of their ages is 72. The sum of their ages is the same as my house number." The census taker ran to look at the house number. "I still can't tell," she complained. The woman replied, "Oh, that's right. I forgot to tell you that the oldest one likes the game Cartel." The census taker immediately wrote down the ages of the three children. How old were they?

Prime Factors

Marie works for the Appalachian Quilt Company. She has made 23 squares so far. Using these 23 squares, can she make a rectangular quilt having more than 1 row?

The only factors of 23 are 1 and 23.

The quilt could have only 1 row of 23 squares. Marie cannot make a quilt, using 23 squares.

23 is a prime number.

▶A **prime number** is a whole number greater than 1 whose only factors are 1 and itself. Examples of prime numbers: 2, 3, 5, 7, 11, 13, 17, 19, 23

▶A **composite number** is a whole number greater than 1 that is not prime. Examples of composite numbers: 4, 6, 8, 9, 10, 12, 14, 15, 16, 18, 20

The numbers 0 and 1 are neither prime nor composite.

Every composite number can be written as the product of two or more prime numbers. This product, or **prime factorization,** can be found by dividing by prime numbers until the quotient becomes prime.

Find the prime factorization of 60.

$$\begin{array}{r} 30 \\ 2\overline{)60} \end{array} \qquad \begin{array}{r} 15 \\ 2\overline{)30} \end{array} \qquad \begin{array}{r} 5 \\ 3\overline{)15} \end{array} \qquad 60 = 2 \times 2 \times 3 \times 5$$

A factor tree can also be used.

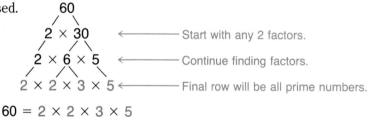

Start with any 2 factors.

Continue finding factors.

Final row will be all prime numbers.

$$60 = 2 \times 2 \times 3 \times 5$$

Use exponents when a factor is repeated. $60 = 2^2 \times 3 \times 5$

CLASSWORK

Write *prime* or *composite* for each.

1. 16 **2.** 27 **3.** 31 **4.** 39 **5.** 47 **6.** 99

Write the prime factorization for each. Use exponents.

7. 18 **8.** 44 **9.** 76 **10.** 84 **11.** 136 **12.** 204

Find all the prime numbers from 1 to 100.

1. Follow these steps, using the Sieve of Eratosthenes.

   a. Write all the whole numbers from 1 to 100 in rows of six.

   b. Cross out 1, since 1 is not prime.

   c. Circle 2. Cross out all the numbers divisible by 2.

   d. Circle 3. Cross out all the numbers divisible by 3.

   e. Circle the next number after 3 that is not crossed out. Cross out all the numbers divisible by that number.

   f. Continue until all the numbers are either circled or crossed out. All the prime numbers less than 100 will be circled.

Find the prime factorization for each, using a factor tree.

2. 10	3. 63	4. 78	5. 66	6. 105	7. 162

Write the prime factorization for each, using exponents.

8. 20	9. 40	10. 27	11. 52	12. 24	13. 45
14. 50	15. 125	16. 90	17. 96	18. 81	19. 100
20. 120	21. 135	22. 225	23. 363	★24. 528	★25. 1,024

Find each number, given the prime factorization.

26. $2^2 \times 3^2$	27. 5^3	28. $2^4 \times 3$	29. 7×2^2	★30. $2^4 \times 3^2 \times 5^2$	★31. 3^8

APPLICATION

===== MATH HISTORY =====

The mathematician Christian Goldbach (1690–1764) made a famous conjecture, or guess, about prime numbers. Goldbach's Conjecture states: Every even number greater than 2 can be expressed as the sum of two prime numbers; every odd number greater than 7 can be expressed as the sum of three prime numbers. For centuries, mathematicians have tried unsuccessfully to disprove Goldbach's Conjecture.

Write each even number as the sum of two primes.

1. 24	2. 10	3. 52	4. 112

Write each odd number as the sum of three primes.

5. 15	6. 27	7. 35	8. 57

Multiples

A toy company manufactures miniature cars on an assembly line. Every third car is painted white, and every fourth car has a number on it. How often is a numbered white car made?

To find the multiples of a number, multiply the number by every whole number.

	× 0	× 1	× 2	× 3	× 4	× 5	× 6	× 7	× 8	...
Multiples of 3	⓪	3	6	9	⑫	15	18	21	㉔	...
Multiples of 4	⓪	4	8	⑫	16	20	㉔	28	32	...

... means the list
continues indefinitely.

The common multiples of 3 and 4 are 0, 12, 24, ...

▶The **least common multiple (LCM)** of two or more numbers is the least nonzero number that is a multiple of each number.

The LCM of 3 and 4 is 12. So every 12th car will be a numbered white car.

Find the LCM of 10 and 12.

To find the LCM of two numbers, list the multiples of the greater number. The first nonzero number that is a multiple of both is the LCM.

The multiples of 12 are 0, 12, 24, 36, 48, 60, 72, . . .

60 is the first nonzero number that is also a multiple of 10.

So 60 is the LCM of 10 and 12.

CLASSWORK

Write the first five multiples of each.

1. 5   **2.** 6   **3.** 8   **4.** 15   **5.** 20   **6.** 25

Find the LCM for each.

7. 4, 9   **8.** 6, 8   **9.** 5, 10   **10.** 8, 10   **11.** 3, 7, 14

122

Write the first four common multiples.

1. 3, 6   2. 3, 5   3. 8, 12   4. 12, 16

Find the LCM for each.

5. 4, 6   6. 8, 4   7. 3, 5   8. 8, 16

9. 6, 16   10. 8, 32   11. 10, 25   12. 12, 24

13. 15, 20   14. 18, 54   15. 35, 70   16. 16, 18

17. 2, 4, 5   18. 4, 12, 20   19. 10, 20, 30   20. 2, 3, 5

Complete. Follow the rule if given.

Rule: Divide by 7.

	Input	Output
21.	0	
22.		1
23.	14	

Rule: Multiply by 3.

	Input	Output
24.		0
25.	1	
26.		6

Find the rule.

27.	Input	Output
	3	15
	4	20
	5	25

Show that the product of the numbers equals the product of their GCF and their LCM.

★ 28. 6, 8   ★ 29. 12, 16   ★ 30. 15, 36   ★ 31. 10, 25

APPLICATION

32. If every fourth car has a number and every fifth car has a painted stripe, how often does a numbered car with a stripe appear?

33. Tanya had $9 to spend. Striped cars cost $3. White cars cost $4. If she spent all of her money, which kind did she buy?

34. Numbered toy cars come 3 in a box. White cars come 2 in a box. At least how many boxes of each are needed to have an equal number of each kind?

★ 35. Every third car is white; every fourth car is numbered; every fifth car is striped. How often will a miniature car appear that is white, numbered, and striped?

CALCULATOR

1. 2, 4, 8, 16, . . . is a sequence of the powers of 2. That is, 2, 4, 8, 16, . . . can be written 2^1, 2^2, 2^3, 2^4, ... Use a calculator to find the 26th number in the sequence. Enter 2 and multiply by 2 twenty-five times.

2. Find the 15th number in the sequence: 3, 9, 27, 81, . . .

3. Find the 13th number in the sequence: 4, 16, 64, 256, . . .

Greatest Common Factor and Least Common Multiple

Use prime factorization to find the GCF and the LCM of two or more numbers.

Find the GCF and LCM of 8 and 36.

First find the prime factorization of each.

$$8: 2\overline{)8} \quad 2\overline{)4} \qquad 8 = 2^3$$
$$ \quad {}^4 \qquad {}^2$$

$$36: 2\overline{)36} \quad 2\overline{)18} \quad 3\overline{)9} \quad 36 = 2^2 \times 3^2$$

PEPPERS 8 FOR 2^{00}

CORN 3 DOZ. FOR 5^{00}

The GCF is the product of the common prime factors. If there are no common prime factors, the GCF is 1.

$$8 = \boxed{2} \times \boxed{2} \times 2$$
$$36 = \boxed{2} \times \boxed{2} \times 3 \times 3$$
$$2 \times 2 = 4$$

The GCF of 8 and 36 is 4.

The LCM is the product of the highest power of each prime factor.

$$8 = \boxed{2^3}$$
$$36 = 2^2 \times \boxed{3^2}$$
$$2^3 \times 3^2 = 72$$

The LCM of 8 and 36 is 72.

More Examples

Find the GCF and LCM of each.

a. $9 = 3^2 \qquad 4 = 2^2$

$\quad$ GCF = 1

$\quad$ LCM = $3^2 \times 2^2 = 36$

b. $8 = 2^3 \qquad 32 = 2^5$

$\quad$ GCF = $2^3 = 8$

$\quad$ LCM = $2^5 = 32$

c. $20 = 2^2 \times 5 \qquad 56 = 2^3 \times 7$

$\quad$ GCF = $2^2 = 4$

$\quad$ LCM = $2^3 \times 5 \times 7 = 280$

CLASSWORK

Find the GCF and the LCM of each.

1. $6 = 3 \times 2$
   $9 = 3 \times 3$

2. $10 = 2 \times 5$
   $16 = 2 \times 2 \times 2 \times 2$

3. $45 = 3^2 \times 5$
   $30 = 2 \times 3 \times 5$

4. 8, 9

5. 3, 12

6. 24, 18

7. 50, 25

Find the GCF of each.

1. $10 = 2 \times 5$
   $35 = 5 \times 7$

2. $30 = 2 \times 3 \times 5$
   $70 = 2 \times 5 \times 7$

3. $36 = 2 \times 2 \times 3 \times 3$
   $90 = 2 \times 3 \times 3 \times 5$

Find the LCM of each.

4. $16 = 2^4$
   $25 = 5^2$

5. $18 = 2 \times 3^2$
   $12 = 2^2 \times 3$

6. $20 = 2^2 \times 5$
   $60 = 2^2 \times 3 \times 5$

Find the GCF and the LCM of each.

7. 12, 18   8. 8, 32   9. 18, 30   10. 14, 49

11. 12, 15   12. 24, 36   13. 25, 40   14. 10, 21

15. 6, 16   16. 12, 16   17. 12, 28   18. 30, 40

19. 75, 90   20. 2, 4, 10   21. 3, 5, 7   ★22. 28, 35, 56

Write *true* or *false*.

23. The sum of two even numbers is even.

24. The sum of two odd numbers is odd.

25. The product of two even numbers is even.

26. The product of two odd numbers is odd.

27. Every even number is a multiple of 2.

28. Every multiple of 16 is a multiple of 8.

★29. Every multiple of 8 is a multiple of 16.

★30. Every whole number is a factor of 0.

APPLICATION

LOGICAL THINKING

A farmer once led a herd of Shetland ponies and a flock of Indian Runner ducks into the barnyard. At least how many of each animal passed through the gate if the total number of duck heads and duck feet was the same as the total number of pony heads and pony feet?

Problem Solving

DIVIDE AND CONQUER

Complicated problems can often be solved by dividing them into smaller, simpler problems to be solved one at a time. The results can then be combined to solve the original problem.

Pete is a checker in Dixon's Market. Mrs. Rosen bought groceries valued at $41.80. She had the following manufacturers' coupons, worth twice their face value: 4 at 20¢ each, 3 at 25¢ each, and 1 at 50¢. She had the following store coupons, worth their face value: 2 at 12¢ each and 1 at 25¢. How much did Pete collect for the groceries?

What is the question?

How much did Pete collect for the groceries?

What are the facts?

$41.80 worth of groceries
Manufacturers' coupons: 4 at 20¢; 3 at 25¢; 1 at 50¢
Store coupons: 2 at 12¢; 1 at 25¢
Manufacturers' coupons are worth twice their face value.
Store coupons are worth their face value.

How can the answer be found?

Divide the problem into smaller problems.

Step 1 Find the total value of the manufacturers' coupons and double it.

Step 2 Find the total value of the store coupons.

Step 3 Find the total value of all the coupons.

Step 4 Subtract the value of the coupons from the original cost of the groceries.

Follow the steps in order and find the answer.

Step 1	Step 2	Step 3	Step 4
4 at 20¢ = 80¢	2 at 12¢ = 24¢	$4.10	$41.80
3 at 25¢ = 75¢	+ 1 at 25¢ = 25¢	+ .49	− 4.59
+ 1 at 50¢ = 50¢	49¢	$4.59	$37.21
$2.05			

2 × $2.05 = $4.10

Pete collected $37.21 for the groceries.

Is your arithmetic correct?

Use addition to check. The answer is correct.

Solve each problem.

1. Yvette worked last summer mowing lawns. She mowed each lawn once a week. She received $5 for each of 7 lawns, $6 for each of 3 lawns, and $10 for each of 2 lawns. How much did she earn each week?

2. Ramón delivers groceries. He charges 50¢ a bag for deliveries within 5 blocks of the store and 75¢ a bag beyond 5 blocks. One day he delivered 8 bags 2 blocks away and 5 bags 7 blocks away. How much did he earn?

Ferris Junior High School is having a fair next week. Use the graph below to answer 3–8.

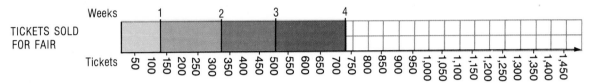

3. How many tickets for the fair have been sold each week?

4. Were more tickets sold the first two weeks or the last two weeks? How many more?

5. The tickets are selling for $1.75 each. How much more was collected the fourth week than the second week?

6. How much money was collected in all by the end of the fourth week?

7. The students want to raise at least $2,000. How many more tickets must they sell to meet this goal?

8. By the day of the fair, the students had sold 525 more tickets. For every ticket they sold, the town council gave $.25. How much money did the students raise in all?

Use the sign at the right to answer 9–11.

9. Mona bought 3 albums and 2 cassettes. She paid $2.19 in tax. How much did she pay in all for her purchases?

10. Manuel bought 2 albums, 2 LP stereo records, and 1 disc. He paid $2.96 in tax. How much did he pay in all?

11. Janine bought 3 cassettes and 3 albums. Two of the albums were each marked down to $2.00 less than the sale price. She paid $2.15 in tax. How much did she pay in all?

S & J Music Store SALE!

Item	Sale Price
Albums	$9.99
LP Stereo	$6.99
Compact discs	$15.39
Cassettes	$3.29

═ CREATE YOUR OWN PROBLEM ═

What questions can you ask about the information in this circle graph? Write three.

TYPICAL DAY FOR AN EIGHTH GRADER

School 6 Hours
Other
Sleep 8 Hours

Simplest Form

Navaho rugs are prized for their designs. The girl has completed $\frac{6}{8}$ of her rug. Her instructor has completed $\frac{3}{4}$ of a rug she is weaving.

numerator
↓   ↓
$\frac{3}{4}$ and $\frac{6}{8}$ are equivalent fractions. $\frac{3}{4} = \frac{6}{8}$
↑   ↑
denominator

To find an equivalent fraction, multiply or divide the numerator and denominator by the same nonzero number.

$$\frac{3}{5} = \frac{3 \times 6}{5 \times 6} = \frac{18}{30} \qquad \frac{12}{21} = \frac{12 \div 3}{21 \div 3} = \frac{4}{7}$$

► Equivalent fractions have cross products that are equal.

 $\frac{4}{6} = \frac{8}{12}$ $4 \times 12 = 6 \times 8$

Cross products can be used to find equivalent fractions.

$$\frac{6}{10} = \frac{n}{15} \quad 6 \times 15 = 10 \times n$$
$$90 = 10 \times n$$
$$9 = n \qquad \text{So } \frac{6}{10} = \frac{9}{15}.$$

► A fraction is in **lowest terms,** or **simplest form,** when the GCF of its numerator and denominator is 1. Two numbers are *relatively prime* if their GCF is 1.

To write a fraction in simplest form, divide the numerator and denominator by their GCF.

Write $\frac{9}{15}$ in simplest form.

The GCF of 9 and 15 is 3. $\frac{9 \div 3}{15 \div 3} = \frac{3}{5}$

The GCF of 3 and 5 is 1. So $\frac{3}{5}$ is in simplest form.

CLASSWORK

Replace each ● with = or ≠ (not equal). Use cross products.

1. $\frac{4}{10}$ ● $\frac{40}{100}$ 2. $\frac{40}{100}$ ● $\frac{2}{5}$ 3. $\frac{3}{5}$ ● $\frac{2}{3}$ 4. $\frac{5}{10}$ ● $\frac{3}{6}$ 5. $\frac{1}{12}$ ● $\frac{10}{125}$

Find each value of *n*.

6. $\frac{3}{4} = \frac{n}{16}$ 7. $\frac{3}{2} = \frac{9}{n}$ 8. $\frac{n}{15} = \frac{4}{20}$ 9. $\frac{5}{n} = \frac{6}{12}$ 10. $\frac{n}{8} = \frac{11}{4}$

Write each in simplest form.

11. $\frac{15}{20}$ 12. $\frac{18}{10}$ 13. $\frac{8}{27}$ 14. $\frac{85}{100}$ 15. $\frac{36}{45}$ 16. $\frac{7}{28}$

128

PRACTICE

Replace each ⬭ with = or ≠.

1. $\frac{2}{4}$ ⬭ $\frac{5}{10}$ **2.** $\frac{6}{9}$ ⬭ $\frac{4}{6}$ **3.** $\frac{3}{10}$ ⬭ $\frac{30}{100}$ **4.** $\frac{7}{12}$ ⬭ $\frac{8}{13}$

5. $\frac{6}{8}$ ⬭ $\frac{4}{3}$ **6.** $\frac{1}{6}$ ⬭ $\frac{4}{24}$ **7.** $\frac{16}{40}$ ⬭ $\frac{7}{15}$ **8.** $\frac{3}{20}$ ⬭ $\frac{12}{80}$

Find each value of n.

9. $\frac{15}{20} = \frac{n}{4}$ **10.** $\frac{25}{100} = \frac{1}{n}$ **11.** $\frac{9}{12} = \frac{6}{n}$

12. $\frac{5}{2} = \frac{n}{18}$ **13.** $\frac{17}{n} = \frac{5}{10}$ **14.** $\frac{n}{20} = \frac{15}{50}$

Write in simplest form.

15. $\frac{9}{12}$ **16.** $\frac{21}{24}$ **17.** $\frac{20}{16}$ **18.** $\frac{10}{45}$ **19.** $\frac{49}{49}$

20. $\frac{64}{32}$ **21.** $\frac{27}{64}$ **22.** $\frac{25}{75}$ **23.** $\frac{18}{30}$ **24.** $\frac{40}{25}$

25. $\frac{36}{28}$ **26.** $\frac{13}{78}$ **27.** $\frac{108}{36}$ **28.** $\frac{42}{10}$ **29.** $\frac{49}{63}$

30. $\frac{66}{99}$ **31.** $\frac{36}{48}$ **32.** $\frac{70}{100}$ ★**33.** $\frac{143}{209}$ ★**34.** $\frac{168}{1,000}$

Write four fractions that name each point on the number line below.

35. A   **36.** B   **37.** C   **38.** D   **39.** E

Which letter on the number line corresponds to each fraction?

★**40.** $\frac{12}{48}$ ★**41.** $\frac{27}{72}$ ★**42.** $\frac{198}{264}$ ★**43.** $\frac{280}{320}$

APPLICATION

Are equal parts red for each pair of rugs?

44.    **45.** 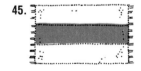   **46.**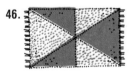

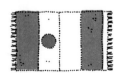   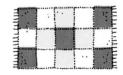   

1. 86,397 + 9,568

2. 15,682 − 5,095

3.   293,178
              15,286
         +   29,980

4.   17,006
         −   5,298

5.   63,198
         ×   7

6.   3,279
         ×   36

7. $42\overline{)2,365,482}$

8. $18\overline{)90,432}$

9. 16.8 + 412 + 0.09

10. 56 − 3.825

11. 31.7 − 0.63

12.   15.9
         ×   0.6

13. 0.08 × 0.04

14. $5\overline{)1.8}$

15. $0.6\overline{)0.228}$

Estimate.

16. 325.71 + 96.015

17. 62.91 − 8.016

18. 518.16 × 3.2

19. $5.2\overline{)1,563.81}$

Fractions and Mixed Numbers

Mike, Alberto, Ron, and Marita earn money playing in an orchestra. They practice $3\frac{1}{2}$ hours every week. Each practice session is $\frac{1}{2}$ hour long. So they have 7 half-hour sessions weekly.

$$3\frac{1}{2} = \frac{7}{2}$$

A mixed number or a whole number can be written as an improper fraction.

a. Multiply and then add to find the numerator for a mixed number.

$$3\frac{1}{2} = \frac{6+1}{2} = \frac{7}{2}$$ $\frac{7}{2}$ is an **improper fraction,** since the numerator is greater than or equal to the denominator.

b. Write 4 as a fraction with 6 as the denominator.

$$4 = \frac{4}{1} \times \frac{6}{6} = \frac{24}{6}$$

An improper fraction can be written as a mixed number or a whole number.

c. $\frac{23}{4} \longrightarrow$ $\begin{array}{r} 5 \\ 4\overline{)23} \\ \underline{20} \\ 3 \end{array} = 5\frac{3}{4}$ **d.** $\frac{27}{9} = 27 \div 9 = 3$

Find each value of n.

e. $7\frac{13}{10} = 8\frac{n}{10}$

$$7\frac{13}{10} = 7 + \frac{13}{10}$$

$$= 7 + 1\frac{3}{10}$$

$$= 8\frac{3}{10} \quad \text{So } n = 3.$$

f. $9\frac{1}{3} = 8\frac{n}{3}$

$$9\frac{1}{3} = 8 + 1 + \frac{1}{3}$$

$$= 8 + \frac{3}{3} + \frac{1}{3}$$

$$= 8\frac{4}{3} \quad \text{So } n = 4.$$

CLASSWORK

Write each as an improper fraction, a whole number, or a mixed number.

1. $7\frac{5}{8}$ **2.** $\frac{27}{10}$ **3.** $8\frac{1}{2}$ **4.** $\frac{72}{9}$ **5.** $9\frac{3}{4}$ **6.** $\frac{13}{4}$

Find each value of n.

7. $7 = \frac{n}{5}$ **8.** $5\frac{2}{3} = 4\frac{n}{3}$ **9.** $4\frac{9}{6} = 5\frac{3}{n}$ **10.** $5 = \frac{5}{n}$ **11.** $9\frac{2}{3} = n\frac{5}{3}$ **12.** $7 = \frac{n}{1}$ **13.** $4 = 3\frac{n}{7}$

Write each as an improper fraction.

1. $1\frac{7}{10}$
2. $3 = \frac{\square}{1}$
3. $5\frac{2}{3}$
4. $7\frac{4}{9}$
5. $6\frac{3}{4}$
6. $5\frac{5}{6}$

7. $10\frac{7}{8}$
8. $4 = \frac{\square}{3}$
9. $12\frac{1}{2}$
10. $4\frac{3}{8}$
11. $20\frac{2}{5}$
12. $13\frac{1}{6}$

Write each as a mixed number or a whole number.

13. $\frac{25}{5}$
14. $\frac{33}{10}$
15. $\frac{18}{7}$
16. $\frac{40}{8}$
17. $\frac{59}{7}$
18. $\frac{62}{5}$
19. $\frac{26}{4}$

20. $\frac{12}{12}$
21. $\frac{17}{8}$
22. $\frac{78}{9}$
23. $\frac{27}{3}$
24. $\frac{75}{2}$
25. $\frac{100}{6}$
26. $\frac{133}{5}$

Find each value of x.

27. $1\frac{4}{5} = \frac{x}{5}$
28. $3\frac{5}{5} = x$
29. $5\frac{9}{5} = 6\frac{x}{5}$
30. $8\frac{5}{9} = 7\frac{x}{9}$

31. $6 = 5\frac{x}{8}$
32. $5\frac{2}{9} = 4\frac{11}{x}$
33. $7\frac{7}{3} = x\frac{1}{3}$
34. $11\frac{x}{8} = 9\frac{22}{8}$

35. $4\frac{11}{3} = 7\frac{x}{3}$
36. $9\frac{1}{6} = 8\frac{7}{x}$
37. $10\frac{x}{5} = 11\frac{2}{5}$
38. $11\frac{28}{10} = 13\frac{x}{10}$

Replace each □ with the missing mixed number.

★ **39.** $4{,}500{,}000 = \square$ million
★ **40.** $1{,}250{,}000 = \square$ million
★ **41.** $6{,}750{,}000 = \square$ million

APPLICATION

42. Mike practices alone $2\frac{1}{2}$ hours each week, $\frac{1}{2}$ hour a day. How many days a week does he practice alone?

43. Sometimes Janeen sings with the orchestra. For a performance she practices $\frac{1}{2}$ hour each day for 9 days. How many hours does she practice? Give the answer as a mixed number.

44. For playing at a benefit, the 4 musicians received $150. They divided the money evenly. How much money did each one receive? Give the answer both as a mixed number and as dollars and cents.

★ **45.** The benefit committee had $250 to spend. One half was spent on the orchestra and $\frac{1}{4}$ was spent on food. How much money was left to spend on decorations? Give the answer as dollars and cents.

Comparing Fractions

Sarah is a cabinetmaker. She must drill a hole for a $\frac{5}{16}$-inch dowel. Will a $\frac{3}{8}$-inch drill bit make a large enough hole?

Compare $\frac{5}{16}$ and $\frac{3}{8}$.

To compare unlike fractions, rename them as like fractions. Then compare the numerators.

- Find the least common denominator (LCD).

  $\frac{5}{16}$ and $\frac{3}{8}$ **Think**   The LCM of 16 and 8 is 16, so 16 is the LCD of $\frac{5}{16}$ and $\frac{3}{8}$.

- Write as like fractions.

  $\frac{5}{16}$ $\frac{3}{8} = \frac{6}{16}$

- Compare the numerators.

  $5 < 6$, so $\frac{5}{16} < \frac{6}{16}$ and $\frac{5}{16} < \frac{3}{8}$.

A $\frac{3}{8}$-inch drill bit makes a large enough hole.

More Examples

a. Compare $8\frac{2}{3}$, $8\frac{5}{6}$, and $8\frac{3}{4}$.

Since the whole numbers are the same, compare the fractions.

The LCD of $\frac{2}{3}$, $\frac{5}{6}$, and $\frac{3}{4}$ is 12.

$\frac{2}{3} = \frac{8}{12}$ $\frac{5}{6} = \frac{10}{12}$ $\frac{3}{4} = \frac{9}{12}$

$\frac{8}{12} < \frac{9}{12} < \frac{10}{12}$, so $8\frac{2}{3} < 8\frac{3}{4} < 8\frac{5}{6}$.

b. Compare $\frac{3}{5}$ and $\frac{3}{10}$.

Since the numerators are the same, compare the denominators. The fraction with the *lesser* denominator is the *greater* fraction.

$5 < 10$, so $\frac{3}{5} > \frac{3}{10}$.

CLASSWORK

Write as like fractions.

1. $\frac{5}{2}, \frac{3}{4}$ 2. $\frac{1}{3}, \frac{3}{8}$ 3. $\frac{1}{6}, \frac{5}{9}$ 4. $\frac{9}{10}, \frac{1}{4}$ 5. $\frac{1}{2}, \frac{3}{10}, \frac{7}{100}$

Compare. Use <, >, or = for each ⬤.

6. $\frac{1}{2}$ ⬤ $\frac{2}{3}$ 7. $\frac{13}{4}$ ⬤ $\frac{11}{5}$ 8. $\frac{4}{7}$ ⬤ $\frac{4}{9}$ 9. $2\frac{4}{5}$ ⬤ $2\frac{8}{10}$ 10. $8\frac{2}{3}$ ⬤ $9\frac{1}{4}$

132

Write as like fractions.

1. $\frac{3}{2}, \frac{5}{4}$

2. $\frac{1}{8}, \frac{3}{4}$

3. $\frac{3}{10}, \frac{2}{5}$

4. $\frac{7}{6}, \frac{1}{4}$

5. $\frac{1}{3}, \frac{1}{4}$

6. $\frac{5}{6}, \frac{2}{9}$

7. $\frac{7}{16}, \frac{5}{12}$

8. $\frac{7}{12}, \frac{5}{18}$

9. $\frac{1}{2}, \frac{2}{3}, \frac{5}{6}$

10. $\frac{1}{6}, \frac{3}{4}, \frac{2}{5}$

Compare. Use <, >, or = for each ●.

11. $\frac{3}{8}$ ● $\frac{7}{8}$

12. $\frac{9}{10}$ ● $\frac{7}{10}$

13. $\frac{5}{6}$ ● $\frac{10}{12}$

14. $\frac{3}{4}$ ● $\frac{3}{7}$

15. $\frac{2}{2}$ ● $\frac{3}{3}$

16. $\frac{5}{12}$ ● $\frac{2}{3}$

17. $\frac{2}{11}$ ● $\frac{2}{5}$

18. $\frac{7}{8}$ ● $\frac{1}{2}$

19. $\frac{3}{5}$ ● $\frac{9}{10}$

20. $\frac{7}{10}$ ● $\frac{1}{2}$

21. $2\frac{1}{3}$ ● $2\frac{1}{2}$

22. $8\frac{3}{5}$ ● $6\frac{3}{5}$

23. $1\frac{1}{4}$ ● $1\frac{2}{5}$

24. $10\frac{2}{7}$ ● $9\frac{3}{7}$

25. $6\frac{1}{3}$ ● $6\frac{3}{8}$

Write in order from least to greatest.

26. $\frac{1}{2}, \frac{1}{3}, \frac{1}{4}$

27. $\frac{1}{5}, \frac{1}{3}, \frac{1}{4}$

28. $4\frac{3}{8}, 4\frac{5}{12}, 4\frac{1}{3}$

★ 29. $\frac{1}{30}, \frac{2}{3}, \frac{7}{12}, \frac{11}{15}, \frac{5}{6}$

APPLICATION

30. Sarah has drilled two holes in a piece of wood. One is $\frac{1}{8}$ inch in diameter and the other is $\frac{3}{16}$ inch in diameter. She has a bolt with a $\frac{5}{32}$-inch diameter. Will the bolt fit through both holes?

★ 31. Sarah has 3 bolts for 3 holes that she has drilled. The bolts measure $\frac{15}{64}, \frac{1}{8}$, and $\frac{9}{32}$ inches in diameter. Choose the bolt that best fits each hole.

Holes (inches)	Bolts
$\frac{5}{16}$	
$\frac{1}{4}$	
$\frac{5}{32}$	

USING CROSS PRODUCTS

Another way to compare fractions is to use cross products. Study these examples. Then use <, >, or = for each ●.

$\frac{1}{2}$ ● $\frac{5}{10}$

$\frac{3}{4}$ ● $\frac{7}{10}$

$\frac{1}{4}$ ● $\frac{5}{8}$

$1 \times 10 = 2 \times 5$

$3 \times 10 > 4 \times 7$

$1 \times 8 < 4 \times 5$

So $\frac{1}{2} = \frac{5}{10}$.

So $\frac{3}{4} > \frac{7}{10}$.

So $\frac{1}{4} < \frac{5}{8}$.

1. $\frac{3}{4}$ ● $\frac{3}{5}$

2. $\frac{3}{10}$ ● $\frac{2}{5}$

3. $\frac{10}{16}$ ● $\frac{13}{24}$

4. $\frac{12}{18}$ ● $\frac{10}{15}$

Fractions and Decimals

Stockholders are owners of businesses. They buy and sell stock in companies. The prices (in dollars) of some stocks appear here. How much would one share of Light Computer cost at yesterday's high?

$28\frac{3}{4}$ dollars = $28.■■

Divide to change $\frac{3}{4}$ to a decimal.

$$\frac{3}{4} \longrightarrow 4\overline{)3.00} = 0.75$$

```
      0.75
  4)3.00
    2 8
      20
      20
       0
```

0.75 is a **terminating decimal.** The remainder is 0.

$\frac{3}{4} = 0.75$

One share of Light Computer cost $28.75 at yesterday's high.

Write $\frac{5}{6}$ as a decimal.

```
        0.833...
  6)5.000
    4 8
      20
      18
      20
```

$0.833\ldots = 0.83\frac{1}{3}$

0.833... is a **repeating decimal.** The remainder is never 0. If you continue to divide, the digits in the quotient continue to repeat.

$\frac{5}{6} = 0.833\ldots$, or $0.8\overline{3}$ A bar is used to show the digit or digits that repeat.

STOCK MARKET LISTINGS

STOCK	HIGH	LOW	CLOSE	CHANGE
Light Comptr	$28\frac{3}{4}$	$27\frac{1}{2}$	$27\frac{1}{2}$	$-1\frac{5}{8}$
LMO	$64\frac{7}{8}$	$63\frac{5}{8}$	$64\frac{3}{4}$	$+\frac{3}{8}$
Thrush	$29\frac{7}{8}$	29	$29\frac{1}{4}$	$-\frac{5}{8}$
Sando	$50\frac{3}{4}$	$48\frac{3}{8}$	$48\frac{3}{8}$	$+2\frac{1}{4}$

CLASSWORK

Write each as a decimal.

1. $\frac{3}{8}$

2. $3\frac{1}{2}$

3. $\frac{2}{3}$

4. $4\frac{1}{3}$

5. $1\frac{3}{10}$

6. $\frac{5}{8}$

7. $1\frac{1}{6}$

8. $\frac{3}{5}$

9. $\frac{7}{25}$

10. $\frac{3}{20}$

11. $6\frac{2}{15}$

12. $\frac{1}{9}$

Write each as a decimal.

1. $\frac{1}{2}$ 2. $\frac{1}{4}$ 3. $\frac{3}{4}$ 4. $\frac{1}{8}$ 5. $\frac{7}{8}$ 6. $\frac{4}{5}$ 7. $\frac{1}{3}$ 8. $\frac{1}{10}$

9. $\frac{1}{5}$ 10. $\frac{2}{5}$ 11. $\frac{5}{6}$ 12. $\frac{9}{10}$ 13. $\frac{1}{20}$ 14. $\frac{3}{20}$ 15. $\frac{5}{12}$ 16. $\frac{1}{25}$

17. $\frac{7}{10}$ 18. $\frac{1}{6}$ 19. $\frac{3}{11}$ 20. $\frac{1}{9}$ 21. $\frac{7}{20}$ 22. $\frac{7}{30}$ 23. $\frac{3}{16}$ 24. $\frac{8}{3}$

25. $\frac{20}{9}$ 26. $\frac{11}{8}$ 27. $2\frac{7}{10}$ 28. $5\frac{3}{2}$ 29. $1\frac{2}{9}$ 30. $11\frac{4}{9}$ 31. $4\frac{7}{50}$ 32. $6\frac{1}{12}$

Compare. Use <, >, or = for each ⬭.

★ 33. $\frac{3}{5}$ ⬭ 0.61   ★ 34. $\frac{2}{3}$ ⬭ 0.65   ★ 35. $\frac{1}{11}$ ⬭ 0.09091   ★ 36. $\frac{7}{12}$ ⬭ 0.584

APPLICATION

37. How much would one share of Sando stock at yesterday's closing price cost? Write the answer as a decimal.

38. How much did the price of LMO stock change from the day before? Write the answer as a decimal.

★ 39. Eight shares of LMO stock cost $517. What is the price per share? Is this price higher or lower than yesterday's high?

═══ CALCULATOR ═══

Use a calculator to find the decimal equivalent for each fraction. Write each as displayed on the calculator.

1. $\frac{1}{9}$ 2. $\frac{2}{9}$ 3. $\frac{3}{9}$ 4. $\frac{1}{99}$ 5. $\frac{2}{99}$ 6. $\frac{3}{99}$ 7. $\frac{1}{999}$ 8. $\frac{2}{999}$ 9. $\frac{3}{999}$

Use the patterns above to find the decimal equivalent for each of the following without using a calculator.

10. $\frac{4}{9}$ 11. $\frac{5}{9}$ 12. $\frac{5}{99}$ 13. $\frac{7}{99}$ 14. $\frac{8}{999}$

Problem Solving

SKILLS AND STRATEGIES REVIEW

Arlene Smith is an automobile saleswoman for Solomon Motors.

1. She sold this car to the Taylors for $1,000 off the sticker price. They paid $2,500 down and borrowed the rest. How much did they borrow?

2. The Taylors will pay back the money they borrowed in 48 monthly payments of $220 each. How much will they have paid in interest?

3. The Taylors went for a drive in their new car. They drove 2.3 km south, 4.2 km east, 4.6 km north, 5.0 km west, and 2.3 km south. Where were they relative to their starting point?

4. Joe Santora bought a second-hand van for $6,800. He has $2,500 in cash. He will borrow the rest from the bank. How much interest will he pay?

5. Joe took his van for a test drive. He drove 1.5 km east, 3.4 km south, 1.5 km west, and 0.7 km north. Where was he relative to his starting point?

Arlene has this graph in her office. It shows her sales for the first 5 months of the year. She is supposed to sell 20 cars a month.

6. How many more cars did she sell in May than in February and March combined?

7. By how many cars was she short of her quota during the first 3 months?

8. How many cars must she sell in June to bring her six-month sales up to her quota?

9. From June to December, Arlene sold 153 cars. Did she reach her quota for the year?

10. Arlene earns an average commission of $175 on each car she sells. What was her income for the year?

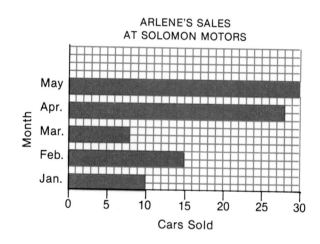

ARLENE'S SALES
AT SOLOMON MOTORS

11. How many more cars would she have had to sell to bring her income for the year to $50,000?

Problem Solving

WHAT IF . . . ?

This is Sandy's record of the number of hours she worked this week as a receptionist at Solomon Motors. She is paid $3.80 per hour.

Day	Mon.	Tues.	Wed.	Thurs.	Fri.	Sat.	Sun.
Hours	4	0	4	2	7	10	6

1. On which day did she work the longest?

2. Which day did she have off?

3. How much did she earn during the week?

4. On which days did she earn more than $22.80?

5. The company deducted $19.38 for taxes for the week. How much did Sandy take home?

What if Sandy's schedule for next week is the same as the one for this week, but she also works 5 additional hours Thursday?

6. How many hours will she work during the week?

7. How much will she earn for the week?

8. The company will deduct $22.23 for taxes. How much will Sandy take home?

What if Sandy receives a raise of $.30 per hour and works the same number of hours she worked the first week?

9. What will her salary be for the week?

10. The company will deduct $20.97 for taxes. How much will Sandy take home?

What if Sandy is paid double time for Sunday and works the same number of hours she did the first week?

11. How much will she earn for the week at $3.80 an hour?

12. How much will she earn for the week with the raise of $.30 an hour?

CHAPTER REVIEW

Write the factors of each number. Then find the GCF. pages 118–119

1. 7, 8   **2.** 10, 15   **3.** 21, 35   **4.** 32, 40

Write the first five multiples of each number. Then find the LCM. pages 122–123

5. 3, 7   **6.** 8, 16   **7.** 6, 9   **8.** 12, 30

Use prime factorization to find the GCF and LCM. pages 120–121, 124–125

9. 9, 16   **10.** 36, 54   **11.** 15, 20   **12.** 60, 75

Write each in simplest form. pages 128–129

13. $\frac{9}{12}$ **14.** $\frac{3}{15}$ **15.** $\frac{56}{14}$ **16.** $\frac{10}{25}$ **17.** $\frac{32}{27}$ **18.** $\frac{72}{100}$

Find each value of n. pages 128–129

19. $\frac{7}{8}=\frac{n}{16}$ **20.** $\frac{5}{n}=\frac{30}{24}$ **21.** $\frac{n}{12}=\frac{21}{36}$ **22.** $\frac{36}{48}=\frac{n}{4}$

Write each as a whole number or a mixed number. pages 130–131

23. $\frac{16}{9}$ **24.** $\frac{25}{5}$ **25.** $\frac{76}{8}$ **26.** $\frac{11}{3}$ **27.** $\frac{83}{6}$

Write each as an improper fraction. pages 130–131

28. $2\frac{2}{3}$ **29.** $3\frac{5}{8}$ **30.** $8=\frac{\square}{5}$ **31.** $10\frac{5}{6}$ **32.** $4\frac{2}{5}$

Compare. Use <, >, or = for each ⬤. pages 132–133

33. $\frac{7}{20}$ ⬤ $\frac{11}{20}$ **34.** $\frac{1}{8}$ ⬤ $\frac{1}{9}$ **35.** $\frac{5}{6}$ ⬤ $\frac{7}{8}$ **36.** $1\frac{3}{8}$ ⬤ $1\frac{5}{12}$

Write each as a decimal. pages 134–135

37. $\frac{7}{9}$ **38.** $\frac{8}{25}$ **39.** $1\frac{3}{16}$ **40.** $\frac{2}{3}$ **41.** $7\frac{1}{6}$

Solve. pages 126–127, 136–137

42. Jenna is making a square quilt. She has 81 squares. How many rows and columns will her quilt have?

43. Elena sold one of her quilts for $120. She had spent $40 for the materials. What fraction of the sale was profit?

Write the factors of each number. Then find the GCF. List the first five multiples of each number. Then find the LCM.

1. 5, 6

2. 8, 10

Use prime factorization to find the GCF and LCM.

3. 8, 32

4. 12, 16

Write each in simplest form.

5. $\frac{3}{18}$

6. $\frac{20}{25}$

7. $\frac{84}{12}$

8. $\frac{25}{49}$

Find each value of *n*.

9. $\frac{n}{5} = \frac{10}{25}$

10. $\frac{56}{14} = \frac{4}{n}$

11. $\frac{n}{15} = \frac{10}{50}$

12. $\frac{9}{15} = \frac{30}{n}$

Write each improper fraction as a whole number or a mixed number. Write each mixed number or whole number as an improper fraction.

13. $\frac{31}{12}$

14. $\frac{45}{5}$

15. $2\frac{7}{8}$

16. $7 = \frac{\square}{4}$

Compare. Use <, >, or = for each ⬤.

17. $\frac{7}{8}$ ⬤ $\frac{5}{6}$

18. $1\frac{9}{12}$ ⬤ $1\frac{3}{4}$

19. $\frac{1}{5}$ ⬤ $\frac{1}{4}$

Write each as a decimal.

20. $\frac{9}{20}$

21. $\frac{1}{3}$

22. $1\frac{3}{8}$

23. $3\frac{4}{11}$

Solve.

24. A dance committee had $50 to spend. The members bought rolls of crepe paper at $3.50 for a box of 10. How much did they buy and what was spent if $43 was left?

25. One share of Sando stock sold for $29\frac{7}{8}$ dollars at yesterday's high and $29\frac{1}{4}$ dollars at yesterday's closing. Which price was greater? Write each price as a decimal.

Marita paid $15 to have her violin repaired. It took 45 minutes. What was the charge per hour?

FRACTION RUMMY

Listed in the first column at the right are 13 fractions. Three equivalent fractions are given for each. For each of the 52 fractions, make a playing card like the ones below.

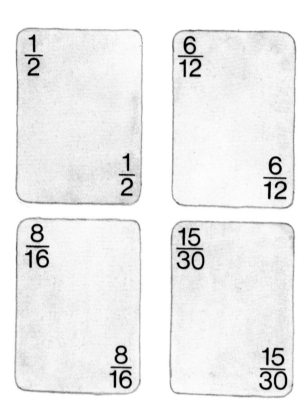

$\frac{1}{2}$	$\frac{6}{12}$	$\frac{8}{16}$	$\frac{15}{30}$
$\frac{1}{3}$	$\frac{4}{12}$	$\frac{9}{27}$	$\frac{12}{36}$
$\frac{2}{3}$	$\frac{8}{12}$	$\frac{10}{15}$	$\frac{14}{21}$
$\frac{1}{4}$	$\frac{3}{12}$	$\frac{4}{16}$	$\frac{5}{20}$
$\frac{3}{4}$	$\frac{9}{12}$	$\frac{15}{20}$	$\frac{18}{24}$
$\frac{1}{5}$	$\frac{4}{20}$	$\frac{5}{25}$	$\frac{7}{35}$
$\frac{3}{5}$	$\frac{9}{15}$	$\frac{12}{20}$	$\frac{18}{30}$
$\frac{1}{6}$	$\frac{2}{12}$	$\frac{3}{18}$	$\frac{4}{24}$
$\frac{5}{6}$	$\frac{10}{12}$	$\frac{20}{24}$	$\frac{25}{30}$
$\frac{1}{8}$	$\frac{2}{16}$	$\frac{3}{24}$	$\frac{5}{40}$
$\frac{3}{8}$	$\frac{6}{16}$	$\frac{9}{24}$	$\frac{18}{48}$
$\frac{5}{8}$	$\frac{10}{16}$	$\frac{20}{32}$	$\frac{25}{40}$
$\frac{7}{8}$	$\frac{14}{16}$	$\frac{21}{24}$	$\frac{35}{40}$

To play Fraction Rummy (2 to 4 players)

The dealer shuffles the cards and deals 7 cards to each player. The remaining cards are placed facedown. The top card, turned faceup, is put beside the deck as the discard pile.

Play begins to the left of the dealer. Each player in turn may take the top card from the deck or the top card from the discard pile. Each time a player picks up a card, he or she must also discard a card faceup on the discard pile.

When a player has 3 cards that name equivalent fractions, the player may lay them down on the table. Any player who has or draws the fourth card naming an equivalent fraction may lay it down during his or her turn.

The winner is the first player to play all his or her cards. If the cards in the deck are used up before someone wins, the discard pile is shuffled and placed facedown. Again the top card is turned faceup beside the deck, and play continues.

TWIN PRIMES

Prime numbers have fascinated people since about 500 B.C. Many questions have been posed concerning prime numbers. Some have been answered and others have not. Here are some questions that can be answered using the Sieve of Eratosthenes. Use the sieve to find the prime numbers from 1 to 300. Then answer each of the following.

1. Write the primes between each pair.

   a. 100 and 150   **b.** 180 and 230   **c.** 250 and 300

2. How many primes are there between 1 and 300?

3. As you go farther down the list of counting numbers, do prime numbers occur more often or less often?

4. List two primes that are consecutive counting numbers.

5. Can there be any other pairs of primes that are consecutive? Explain your answer.

6. **Twin primes** are pairs of primes whose difference is exactly 2. (3 and 5 are twin primes.) Find a pair of twin primes between each pair.

   a. 20 and 40   **b.** 170 and 190

   c. 200 and 240   **d.** 250 and 280

7. Do you think there is a finite number of primes? a finite number of twin primes?

COMPUTER

COMPUTER PROGRAMS AND FLOWCHARTS

A program is a set of instructions written in a computer language. Some programmers use the BASIC language, which uses statements, commands, and functions.

▶NEW clears the memory of the computer for a new program.

▶LET tells the computer to assign a value to a variable.

▶REM is a remark for the programmer. It is ignored by the computer.

▶PRINT tells the computer to print numbers or exactly what is inside quotation marks.

▶INPUT tells the computer to wait for 1 or more numbers, each named by a variable.

▶GOTO tells the computer to branch to another line of the program.

▶END signals the computer to stop the program.

▶RUN tells the computer to follow the program.

▶IF . . . THEN tells the computer to test an expression. It will follow the instructions after THEN only when the expression after IF is true. When the IF expression is false, the computer skips to the next line of the program.

▶INT(X) is a BASIC function that gives the greatest whole number that is not greater than X.

Examples

$INT(19.99) = 19$ $INT(7/2) = 3$

This flowchart and program will determine if a number is a whole number.

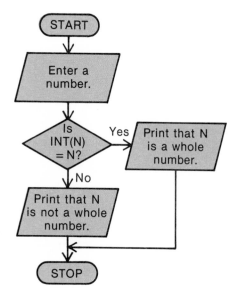

PROGRAM

```
10 REM PROGRAM TO DETERMINE
   IF A NUMBER IS A WHOLE NUMBER
20 PRINT "ENTER A NUMBER."
30 INPUT N
40 IF INT(N) = N THEN GOTO 70
50 PRINT N;" IS NOT A WHOLE
   NUMBER."
60 GOTO 80
70 PRINT N;" IS A WHOLE NUMBER."
80 END
```

OUTPUT

```
RUN
ENTER A NUMBER.
? 14
14 IS A WHOLE NUMBER.
RUN
ENTER A NUMBER.
? 23.8
23.8 IS NOT A WHOLE NUMBER.
```

This flowchart and program will determine if one number is a divisor of another. Line 50 uses the INT function to test the quotient for divisibility.

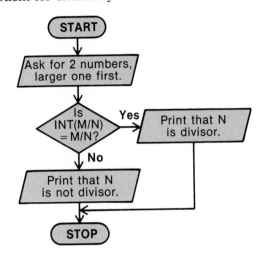

PROGRAM

```
10 REM PROGRAM TO DETERMINE
   DIVISIBILITY
20 PRINT "ENTER 2 NUMBERS, TYPE
   THE LARGER FIRST."
30 INPUT M
40 INPUT N
50 IF INT(M/N) = M/N THEN GOTO 80
60 PRINT N;" IS NOT A DIVISOR
   OF ";M
70 GOTO 90
80 PRINT N;" IS A DIVISOR OF ";M
90 END
```

Use the program to answer each question.

1. If M = 739310 and N = 13, what is the computer output?

2. What number is not allowed for variable N?

3. Suppose the computer output at line 50 is
   `19 IS NOT A DIVISOR OF 79000`
   What number was assigned to M? to N?

4. Tom always enters his smaller number first. Will the program still run correctly? Will the program ever go to line 80?

Write the computer output for each program below.

5.
```
10 LET N = 7.9 * 3.85
20 PRINT INT(N)
30 END
```

6.
```
10 LET A = 99.99
20 LET B = 5
30 PRINT INT(A/B)
40 END
```

7.
```
10 LET X = 22.93
20 LET Y = 2 * X + 1
30 PRINT INT(Y)
40 END
```

AT THE COMPUTER

Run the program at the top of this page to find if 291 is a divisor of each.

1. 18339   2. 131241   3. 217668   4. 5839   5. 1746

Use a flowchart to write a program for each. Then test your program on the computer.

6. Ask for a whole number. Divide it by 2. If the quotient is a whole number, print that the number is even. If the quotient is not a whole number, print that the number is odd.

★ 7. Ask for an odd number between 10 and 50. Divide it by 3, 5, and 7. If any quotient is a whole number, then print "COMPOSITE." If no quotient is a whole number, print "PRIME."

MAINTAINING SKILLS

Choose the correct answers. Write A, B, C, or D.

1. Compare. 3.1 ⬭ 3.01

    A >   **C** =

    B <   **D** not given

2. 0.762×10^5

    A 7.62   **C** 76,200

    B 7,620   **D** not given

3. $69.01 \div 10^4$

    A 6.901   **C** 6,901

    B 0.006901   **D** not given

4. What is the greatest possible error of the measurement 26 cm?

    A 5 cm   **C** 1 cm

    B 0.5 cm   **D** not given

5. What is the greatest possible error of the measurement 26.0 cm?

    A 0.01 cm   **C** 0.05 cm

    B 0.5 cm   **D** not given

6. Evaluate $(ab) \div 3$ for $a = 6$ and $b = 5$.

    A 30   **C** 10

    B 2   **D** not given

7. Evaluate $4a - 2b$ for $a = 6$ and $b = 5$.

    A 4   **C** 34

    B 22   **D** not given

8. Solve this equation. $d \div 9 = 18$

    A $d = 2$ **C** $d = 0.5$

    B $d = 162$ **D** not given

9. Solve this equation. $x - 7.2 = 9.1$

    A $x = 16.3$ **C** $x = 2.1$

    B $x = 1.9$ **D** not given

10. Solve this equation. $1.2y = 48$

    A $y = 4$ **C** $y = 40$

    B $y = 0.4$ **D** not given

11. What are the common factors of 15 and 20?

    A 1, 5   **C** 1, 3, 4, 5

    B 1, 3, 5   **D** not given

12. What is the LCM of 6, 11, and 12?

    A 132   **C** 12

    B 66   **D** not given

13. Compare. $\frac{5}{8}$ ⬭ $\frac{10}{16}$

    A >   **C** =

    B <   **D** not given

14. What is the decimal for $\frac{7}{8}$?

    A 0.875   **C** 0.925

    B 1.143   **D** not given

Find the pattern. What are the next two numbers?

15. 3, 9, 15, 21, ___, ___

    A 25, 31   **C** 27, 33

    B 24, 27   **D** not given

16. 1, 4, 16, 64, ___, ___

    A 128, 256   **C** 256, 512

    B 256, 1,024 **D** not given

17. 5.3, 4.8, 4.3, 3.8, ___, ___

    A 3.3, 2.8   **C** 3.3, 2.3

    B 2.8, 1.8   **D** not given

Theme: Pastimes that Lead to Careers

Adding and Subtracting Fractions and Mixed Numbers

Students' Favorite Activities

Jeremy's survey of the students at Clearview School shows that half the students prefer the performing clubs—dance ensemble, glee club, and drama club. The other half prefer either sports or the school newspaper. What part of the student body prefers the most popular activity?

Subtract $\frac{1}{2} - \frac{1}{8}$ to find what part of the student body prefers sports.

To add or subtract fractions, do the following.

• Write equivalent fractions using the LCD.

• Add or subtract the numerators.
  Write the answer in simplest form.

$$\begin{array}{r} \frac{1}{2} = \frac{4}{8} \\ -\frac{1}{8} = \frac{1}{8} \\ \hline \frac{3}{8} \end{array}$$

Think LCD of $\frac{1}{2}$ and $\frac{1}{8}$ is 8.

$\frac{3}{8}$ of the student body prefers sports.

To add mixed numbers, first add the fractions, then add the whole numbers. Write the answer in simplest form. Subtract mixed numbers similarly.

$$\begin{array}{r} 2\frac{3}{4} = 2\frac{3}{4} \\ 1\frac{1}{2} = 1\frac{2}{4} \\ +1\frac{1}{2} = 1\frac{2}{4} \\ \hline 4\frac{7}{4} = 5\frac{3}{4} \end{array}$$

SCHOOL
NEWS

CLASSWORK

Add or subtract. Write each answer in simplest form.

1. $\frac{5}{8}$
   $+\frac{7}{8}$

2. $\frac{2}{5}$
   $-\frac{1}{6}$

3. $\frac{7}{12}$
   $+\frac{1}{3}$

4. $6\frac{3}{8}$
   $+5\frac{1}{8}$

5. $10\frac{2}{3}$
   $-4\frac{1}{4}$

6. $5\frac{3}{4}$
   -2

7. $\frac{17}{12} - \frac{5}{6}$

8. $\frac{1}{2} + \frac{1}{3} + \frac{1}{4}$

9. $10\frac{3}{4} - 8\frac{2}{5}$

10. $3\frac{1}{2} + 5 + 1\frac{7}{10}$

146

PRACTICE

Add or subtract. Write each answer in simplest form.

1. $\dfrac{13}{16}$ $-\dfrac{7}{16}$

2. $\dfrac{5}{6}$ $+\dfrac{5}{6}$

3. $9\dfrac{3}{10}$ $+2\dfrac{7}{10}$

4. $14\dfrac{1}{2}$ -7

5. 12 $+9\dfrac{5}{6}$

6. $\dfrac{3}{4}$ $+\dfrac{1}{6}$

7. $9\dfrac{3}{5}$ $+2\dfrac{1}{10}$

8. $\dfrac{2}{3}$ $-\dfrac{3}{8}$

9. $\dfrac{1}{10}$ $+\dfrac{3}{4}$

10. $10\dfrac{5}{6}$ $-7\dfrac{2}{3}$

11. $\dfrac{4}{9} - \dfrac{1}{6}$

12. $\dfrac{3}{10} + \dfrac{17}{100}$

13. $10\dfrac{1}{3} - 5$

14. $11\dfrac{1}{2} + 5\dfrac{3}{8}$

15. $\dfrac{1}{2} + \dfrac{3}{8} + \dfrac{4}{5}$

16. $\dfrac{7}{8} - \dfrac{2}{5} - \dfrac{1}{4}$

17. $4\dfrac{1}{2} + 6\dfrac{7}{10} + 2\dfrac{2}{5}$

18. $14\dfrac{7}{8} - 5\dfrac{3}{4}$

A fraction with 1 as the numerator is a *unit fraction*. Write each of the following fractions as the sum of unit fractions. Use no unit more than once in a sum.

19. Write $\dfrac{5}{8}$ using two unit fractions.

20. Write $\dfrac{3}{10}$ using two unit fractions.

21. Write $\dfrac{13}{16}$ using three unit fractions.

★ 22. Write $\dfrac{3}{7}$ using three unit fractions.

Evaluate each expression for $a = 1\dfrac{1}{4}$, $b = \dfrac{3}{5}$, and $c = 2\dfrac{2}{3}$.

★ 23. $a + b - \dfrac{1}{3}$

★ 24. $c - a + b$

★ 25. $c + a - b$

★ 26. $c - b + \dfrac{8}{15}$

APPLICATION

27. Joan plans the layout for Clearview School's newspaper. This week she is using $\dfrac{1}{4}$ of the sports page for advertising and $\dfrac{3}{8}$ of the page for stories. How much space is left for pictures?

28. Josh wrote a story for the *Town Gazette* about students volunteering at the Senior Citizen Center. Last week Flo worked $2\dfrac{3}{4}$ h in the exercise room and $2\dfrac{1}{2}$ h in the crafts room. How long did she work in all?

LOGICAL THINKING

Three volumes of Shakespeare stand side by side on a bookshelf. Volume 1 is at the left and Volume 3 is at the right. The bindings are facing you. Each cover is $\dfrac{1}{4}$ inch thick and each book without its cover is $1\dfrac{1}{2}$ inches thick. If a bookworm ate its way directly from page 1 of Volume 1 to the last page of Volume 3, how far would it travel?

Renaming Before Subtracting

Grace is making costumes for the school musical. For the final costume she needs $2\frac{1}{2}$ yards of fabric. She has $1\frac{3}{4}$ yards. How much more fabric does she need?

Step 1

Write equivalent fractions using the LCD.

$$\begin{array}{r} 2\frac{1}{2} = 2\frac{2}{4} \\ -\ 1\frac{3}{4} = 1\frac{3}{4} \\ \hline \end{array} \quad \begin{array}{l}\textbf{Think}\\ \frac{2}{4} < \frac{3}{4}\end{array}$$

Step 2

Rename if you can't subtract.

$$\begin{array}{r} 2\frac{2}{4} = 1\frac{6}{4} \\ -\ 1\frac{3}{4} = 1\frac{3}{4} \\ \hline \end{array}$$

Step 3

Subtract. Write the answer in simplest form.

$$\begin{array}{r} 1\frac{6}{4} \\ -\ 1\frac{3}{4} \\ \hline \frac{3}{4} \end{array}$$

Grace needs another $\frac{3}{4}$ yard of fabric.

More Examples

a.
$$\begin{array}{r} 5\frac{1}{6} = 4\frac{7}{6} \\ -\ 2\frac{5}{6} = 2\frac{5}{6} \\ \hline 2\frac{2}{6} = 2\frac{1}{3} \end{array}$$

b.
$$\begin{array}{r} 7\ \ = 6\frac{3}{3} \\ -\ 3\frac{1}{3} = 3\frac{1}{3} \\ \hline 3\frac{2}{3} \end{array}$$

c.
$$\begin{array}{r} 12\frac{1}{4} = 12\frac{5}{20} = 11\frac{25}{20} \\ -\ 6\frac{2}{5} = 6\frac{8}{20} = 6\frac{8}{20} \\ \hline 5\frac{17}{20} \end{array}$$

Classwork

Subtract. Write each answer in simplest form.

1. $\begin{array}{r} 4\frac{1}{3} \\ -\ 1\frac{2}{3} \\ \hline \end{array}$

2. $\begin{array}{r} 7\frac{3}{10} \\ -\ 4\frac{4}{5} \\ \hline \end{array}$

3. $\begin{array}{r} 5 \\ -\ 1\frac{3}{4} \\ \hline \end{array}$

4. $\begin{array}{r} 8\frac{1}{6} \\ -\ 7\frac{3}{4} \\ \hline \end{array}$

5. $\begin{array}{r} 5\frac{1}{8} \\ -\ 1\frac{3}{4} \\ \hline \end{array}$

6. $4\frac{1}{4} - 1\frac{3}{4}$

7. $10\frac{2}{5} - 8\frac{3}{4}$

8. $2 - \frac{1}{2}$

9. $10 - 5\frac{1}{7}$

PRACTICE

Subtract. Write each answer in simplest form.

1. $\begin{array}{r} 12 \\ -\ 9\frac{5}{6} \\ \hline \end{array}$

2. $\begin{array}{r} 10 \\ -\ 6\frac{7}{8} \\ \hline \end{array}$

3. $\begin{array}{r} 13 \\ -\ 8\frac{2}{5} \\ \hline \end{array}$

4. $\begin{array}{r} 3\frac{1}{2} \\ -\ 1\frac{3}{4} \\ \hline \end{array}$

5. $\begin{array}{r} 16\frac{1}{3} \\ -\ 7\frac{5}{8} \\ \hline \end{array}$

6. $\begin{array}{r} 8 \\ -\ 2\frac{1}{3} \\ \hline \end{array}$

7. $\begin{array}{r} 12\frac{1}{2} \\ -\ 6\frac{3}{4} \\ \hline \end{array}$

8. $\begin{array}{r} 14\frac{3}{4} \\ -\ 5\frac{7}{8} \\ \hline \end{array}$

9. $14 - 5\frac{3}{4}$

10. $7\frac{2}{3} - 3\frac{4}{5}$

11. $5\frac{1}{9} - 3\frac{4}{9}$

12. $22\frac{3}{4} - 10\frac{5}{6}$

13. $12 - \frac{3}{8}$

14. $5\frac{1}{3} - 2\frac{3}{8}$

15. $9 - 8\frac{2}{5} + 4\frac{1}{10}$

16. $10\frac{2}{3} - 9\frac{3}{4} + 7\frac{1}{2}$

★17. $\left(5 - 2\frac{1}{8}\right) + \left(4\frac{1}{8} - 1\frac{2}{3}\right)$

★18. $6\frac{1}{5} - \left(4\frac{1}{3} - 1\frac{4}{5}\right)$

Find the missing numbers in each sequence.

★19. $9\frac{4}{5}$, $9\frac{1}{5}$, $8\frac{3}{5}$, $\square$, $\square$

★20. $6\frac{2}{3}$, 6, $5\frac{1}{3}$, $\square$, $\square$

★21. 12, $10\frac{7}{8}$, $9\frac{3}{4}$, $\square$, $\square$

★22. 10, $8\frac{2}{5}$, $6\frac{4}{5}$, $\square$, $\square$

APPLICATION

23. Paula has been attending the Chamber School of Design for $1\frac{1}{2}$ years to become a fashion designer. She must have 2 years of classroom training and 2 years of on-the-job training to graduate. How many more years must she complete in order to graduate?

★24. One of the outfits Paula designed was a woman's suit that requires $1\frac{5}{8}$ yards of fabric for the skirt, $2\frac{3}{4}$ yards for the jacket, and $2\frac{1}{2}$ yards for the slacks. There are $6\frac{1}{2}$ yards left on the bolt of fabric that Paula wants for the suit. Is there enough fabric?

Mixed Practice

1. $n + 1 = 9$

2. $x - 4 = 7$

3. $3x = 27$

4. $\frac{x}{2} = 7$

5. $y - 19 = 17$

6. $m + 6 = 6$

7. $15m = 75$

8. $17 = a + 8$

9. $\frac{x}{29} = 1$

10. $108 = m - 19$

11. $18 = \frac{x}{6}$

12. $15 + x = 16$

13. $8x = 104$

14. $107 = y - 9$

15. $\frac{x}{27} = 3$

16. $13x = 91$

17. $\frac{x}{3} = 18$

18. $x + 28 = 47$

19. $y - 39 = 5$

20. $14y = 28$

Counting Fractions

WORKING TOGETHER

Read the *Daily Lampoon* article at the right. Then work in a team.

1. Discuss what Unet Entirvul means by "all fractions between 0 and 1."

2. Imagine that your team has a very detailed number line and a magnifying glass! Discuss where you might begin on the number line to select fractions to add. How could you be sure you would not miss any?

3. Try to find a way to organize the fractions so that you can add them without missing or repeating any. Try your method.

4. Record the results of your explorations.

TYCOON OFFERS PRIZE!

Los Angeles   Aug. 29

Industrialist Unet Entirvul has offered a prize of $1 million to any mathematics student who adds up all the fractions between 0 and 1 correctly. At the press conference where he announced the prize, Mr. Entirvul said: "I tried to add them all up myself but I made a mistake somewhere between

$$\frac{1}{279{,}387{,}419} \quad \text{and} \quad \frac{2}{279{,}387{,}419}$$

Any student who adds them all up deserves the money, even if a calculator or a computer is used."

The son of a school teacher, Entirvul came to the United States in 1959 without a dollar in

1. Each group should report on the results of its explorations. What problems were encountered by groups that used a number line to organize the selection of addends? Did the method work?

2. Did any group use graph paper as a way to list all the fractions? One way to do this is to think of a fraction as an ordered pair—the denominator first, then the numerator:

$$\tfrac{1}{2} \longrightarrow (2,\ 1)$$

If you had a large enough piece of graph paper and enough time, could you plot *every* fraction in this way? Discuss.

3. Do you need to consider all fractions in order to win the prize? If not, which fractions need not be considered?

4. If you used the triangular arrangement at the right to list all the fractions, would you have a chance to win Mr. Entirvul's $1 million? Explain.

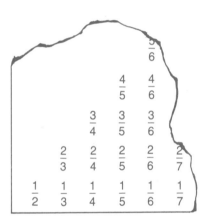

1. The nineteenth-century German mathematician Georg Cantor used a fraction graph to "count" all the fractions, including those greater than or equal to 1. How would Cantor's graph be different from the one above?

2. Cantor concluded that there were exactly enough whole numbers to "count" all the fractions.

   • What do you think Cantor meant by "counting"?

   • Why does Cantor's conclusion mean that there is no greatest fraction?

   • What does Cantor's conclusion say about Mr. Entirvul's offer of a prize?

Multiplying Fractions

Jon is a cadet member of the Civil Air Patrol (CAP). He has learned to fly and has helped on several search-and-rescue missions. There are 65 members in Jon's local CAP group. Two fifths are cadets (ages 13–18). How many cadets are in the group?

To multiply fractions, multiply numerators and multiply denominators. You can simplify factors before multiplying by dividing a numerator and a denominator by a common factor.

$$\frac{2}{5} \times 65 = \frac{2}{\overset{}{\underset{1}{\cancel{5}}}} \times \frac{\overset{13}{\cancel{65}}}{1} = \frac{2 \times 13}{1 \times 1} = \frac{26}{1} = 26$$

There are 26 cadets in Jon's group.

More Examples

a. $\frac{\overset{1}{\cancel{5}}}{\underset{2}{\cancel{6}}} \times \frac{\overset{3}{\cancel{9}}}{\underset{2}{\cancel{10}}} = \frac{1 \times 3}{2 \times 2} = \frac{3}{4}$

b. $7 \times \frac{4}{9} = \frac{7}{1} \times \frac{4}{9} = \frac{7 \times 4}{1 \times 9} = \frac{28}{9}$, or $3\frac{1}{9}$

c. Find $\frac{2}{3}$ of 9.

$\frac{2}{\underset{1}{\cancel{3}}} \times \frac{\overset{3}{\cancel{9}}}{1} = \frac{2 \times 3}{1 \times 1} = \frac{6}{1} = 6$

d. Find $\frac{1}{2}$ of $\frac{1}{4}$.

$\frac{1}{2} \times \frac{1}{4} = \frac{1 \times 1}{2 \times 4} = \frac{1}{8}$

CLASSWORK

Multiply. Write each answer in simplest form.

1. $\frac{7}{10} \times \frac{3}{5}$

2. $\frac{3}{4} \times \frac{1}{2}$

3. $15 \times \frac{2}{5}$

4. $\frac{5}{7} \times 21$

5. $\frac{1}{3} \times \frac{1}{4}$

6. $\frac{3}{4} \times 5$

7. $\frac{2}{3} \times \frac{3}{2}$

8. $\frac{5}{6} \times \frac{3}{8}$

Find each.

9. $\frac{7}{8}$ of 12

10. $\frac{1}{2}$ of $\frac{1}{8}$

11. $\frac{3}{4}$ of 16

12. $\frac{2}{5}$ of $\frac{15}{4}$

PRACTICE

Multiply. Write each answer in simplest form.

1. $\frac{3}{5} \times \frac{2}{3}$ 2. $\frac{1}{2} \times \frac{4}{5}$ 3. $\frac{5}{8} \times 16$ 4. $\frac{3}{8} \times \frac{4}{15}$

5. $8 \times \frac{5}{4}$ 6. $\frac{3}{10} \times 5$ 7. $\frac{2}{5} \times \frac{5}{2}$ 8. $\frac{2}{3} \times \frac{3}{8}$

9. $\frac{5}{12} \times \frac{4}{3}$ 10. $\frac{5}{8} \times \frac{4}{5}$ 11. $\frac{7}{8} \times 6$ 12. $\frac{5}{8} \times \frac{4}{9}$

13. $10 \times \frac{5}{6}$ 14. $\frac{4}{9} \times \frac{2}{3}$ 15. $\frac{2}{3} \times \frac{1}{5}$ 16. $\frac{4}{5} \times \frac{3}{2}$

17. $\frac{1}{2} \times \frac{3}{4} \times \frac{3}{8}$ 18. $\frac{3}{4} \times 4 \times \frac{2}{3}$ 19. $24 \times \frac{5}{6} \times \frac{3}{4}$ 20. $\frac{2}{3} \times \frac{3}{5} \times \frac{1}{4}$

★21. $\left(1 - \frac{3}{4}\right) \times \left(\frac{1}{2} + \frac{3}{8}\right)$ ★22. $\frac{1}{4} + \frac{5}{6} \times \frac{3}{4} - \frac{1}{2}$ ★23. $\left(\frac{2}{3} + \frac{1}{4}\right) \times \frac{2}{3} \times \frac{2}{11}$ ★24. $6 \times \frac{5}{4}\left(1 - \frac{4}{5}\right) + \frac{3}{2}$

Find each.

25. $\frac{2}{3}$ of $\frac{3}{4}$ 26. $\frac{1}{2}$ of 2   27. $\frac{5}{8}$ of $\frac{4}{5}$ 28. $\frac{4}{5}$ of 20   29. $\frac{7}{4}$ of $\frac{2}{3}$ 30. $\frac{4}{7}$ of 28

Find each output.

	Input	Output
	n	$\frac{2}{3}n$
31.	$\frac{4}{5}$	
32.	12	
33.	$\frac{1}{2}$	
34.	$\frac{5}{6}$	

	Input	Output
	n	$\frac{3}{2}n$
35.	$\frac{6}{7}$	
36.	$\frac{1}{3}$	
37.	$\frac{3}{5}$	
38.	$\frac{1}{2}$	

	Input	Output
	n	$2n + \frac{1}{4}$
★39.	$\frac{2}{3}$	
★40.	$\frac{1}{2}$	
★41.	$\frac{1}{6}$	
★42.	$\frac{7}{8}$	

APPLICATION

43. One year the national membership of CAP was about 63 thousand. About $\frac{3}{7}$ were cadets. About how many cadets were there in CAP?

★44. Jeff Kowalski, a pilot with a commercial airline, flew from New York to Pittsburgh and back. It took $\frac{3}{4}$ hour to get to Pittsburgh. With the help of the jet stream, the return trip took only $\frac{4}{5}$ the time. How long was the round trip?

Dividing Fractions

▶Two numbers whose product is 1 are **reciprocals**, or **multiplicative inverses**.

- $8 \times \frac{1}{8} = 1$

  8 and $\frac{1}{8}$ are reciprocals.

- $\frac{3}{5} \times \frac{5}{3} = 1$

  $\frac{3}{5}$ and $\frac{5}{3}$ are reciprocals.

Dividing by a number gives the same result as multiplying by its reciprocal.

$$40 \div 8 = 5 \qquad 40 \times \frac{1}{8} = 5$$

Dale develops her own film. Each roll of film takes $\frac{1}{8}$ bottle of developer solution. Her bottle of solution is $\frac{3}{4}$ full. How many rolls of film can Dale develop?

$$\frac{3}{4} \div \frac{1}{8} = n$$

To divide by a fraction, multiply by its reciprocal.

$$\frac{3}{4} \div \frac{1}{8} = \frac{3}{4} \times 8 = \frac{3}{\overset{}{\underset{1}{4}}} \times \frac{\overset{2}{8}}{1} = \frac{3 \times 2}{1 \times 1} = \frac{6}{1} = 6$$

Dale can develop 6 rolls of film.

More Examples

a. $\dfrac{3}{5} \div \dfrac{4}{15} = \dfrac{3}{\underset{1}{5}} \times \dfrac{\overset{3}{15}}{4} = \dfrac{3 \times 3}{1 \times 4} = \dfrac{9}{4}$, or $2\dfrac{1}{4}$

b. $\dfrac{2}{5} \div 4 = \dfrac{\overset{1}{2}}{5} \times \dfrac{1}{\underset{2}{4}} = \dfrac{1 \times 1}{5 \times 2} = \dfrac{1}{10}$

CLASSWORK

Find the reciprocal of each number.

1. $\frac{1}{2}$　　　2. $\frac{2}{7}$　　　3. 4　　　4. $\frac{5}{6}$　　　5. 9　　　6. $\frac{1}{6}$

Divide. Write each answer in simplest form.

7. $\frac{1}{2} \div \frac{1}{3}$　　　8. $12 \div \frac{1}{2}$　　　9. $\frac{3}{4} \div 6$　　　10. $\frac{2}{5} \div \frac{3}{8}$

PRACTICE

Find the reciprocal of each number.

1. $\frac{1}{3}$
2. 5
3. $\frac{2}{3}$
4. $\frac{7}{5}$
5. 20
6. $\frac{3}{4}$

7. $\frac{9}{10}$
8. $\frac{5}{12}$
9. $\frac{1}{8}$
10. 100
11. $\frac{1}{10}$
12. 7

Divide. Write each answer in simplest form.

13. $\frac{2}{3} \div \frac{8}{3}$
14. $\frac{5}{8} \div \frac{3}{8}$
15. $\frac{3}{8} \div \frac{5}{8}$
16. $5 \div \frac{1}{4}$

17. $\frac{1}{2} \div 2$
18. $\frac{3}{4} \div 3$
19. $\frac{2}{3} \div \frac{2}{3}$
20. $\frac{5}{12} \div \frac{5}{6}$

21. $\frac{6}{5} \div \frac{4}{15}$
22. $1 \div \frac{7}{8}$
23. $\frac{3}{4} \div \frac{6}{5}$
24. $20 \div \frac{4}{7}$

25. $\frac{4}{5} \div \frac{3}{10}$
26. $\frac{4}{5} \div \frac{4}{3}$
27. $\frac{1}{6} \div \frac{1}{4}$
28. $9 \div \frac{3}{4}$

Evaluate each expression for $a = \frac{1}{3}$ and $b = \frac{3}{4}$.

29. $a \div b$
30. $9 \div b$
★ 31. $\frac{7}{8} \div \left(a + \frac{5}{6}\right)$
★ 32. $b \times \left(a \div \frac{1}{6}\right)$

APPLICATION

33. To stop the developing process, film goes from developing solution to stop bath. Dale has $\frac{2}{3}$ bottle of stop bath left. She uses $\frac{1}{4}$ bottle for each roll of film. How many rolls can she develop?

34. The last step in the developing process is to put the film in a solution called a fixer. Dale has 3 bottles of fixer. She uses $\frac{1}{3}$ bottle for each roll of film. Dale has 8 rolls of film to develop. Does she have enough fixer?

★ 35. Carl is a motion picture photographer for the Lions football team. During the last quarter of a game, he discovers that he has only 10 minutes of film left. Each play lasts about 50 seconds. How many plays can he shoot with the remaining film? $\left(50 \text{ seconds} = \frac{50}{60}, \text{ or } \frac{5}{6}, \text{ minute}\right)$

Multiplying and Dividing Mixed Numbers

For their All-American Feast, the students in the Chefs' Club are preparing this recipe. They expect to feed 42 people, which is $10\frac{1}{2}$ times the number the recipe serves. How much flour will they need?

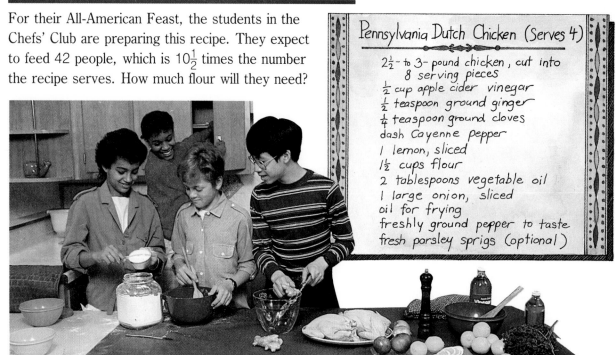

Pennsylvania Dutch Chicken (Serves 4)

$2\frac{1}{2}$- to 3- pound chicken, cut into
8 serving pieces
$\frac{1}{2}$ cup apple cider vinegar
$\frac{1}{2}$ teaspoon ground ginger
$\frac{1}{4}$ teaspoon ground cloves
dash Cayenne pepper
1 lemon, sliced
$1\frac{1}{2}$ cups flour
2 tablespoons vegetable oil
1 large onion, sliced
oil for frying
freshly ground pepper to taste
fresh parsley sprigs (optional)

To multiply with mixed numbers write the mixed numbers and the whole numbers as improper fractions. Then multiply the fractions.

Find $10\frac{1}{2}$ times the amount of flour.

$$10\frac{1}{2} \times 1\frac{1}{2} =$$

$$\frac{21}{2} \times \frac{3}{2} = \frac{21 \times 3}{2 \times 2} = \frac{63}{4} = 15\frac{3}{4}$$

The Chefs' Club will need $15\frac{3}{4}$ cups of flour.

To divide with mixed numbers, write the mixed numbers and the whole numbers as improper fractions. Then divide the fractions.

Find $9 \div 2\frac{7}{10}$.

$$9 \div 2\frac{7}{10} =$$

$$\frac{9}{1} \div \frac{27}{10} = \frac{\overset{1}{\cancel{9}}}{1} \times \frac{10}{\underset{3}{\cancel{27}}} = \frac{1 \times 10}{1 \times 3} = \frac{10}{3} = 3\frac{1}{3}$$

More Examples

a. $3 \times 2\frac{1}{2} = \frac{3}{1} \times \frac{5}{2} = \frac{15}{2}$, or $7\frac{1}{2}$

b. $2\frac{1}{4} \div \frac{3}{8} = \frac{9}{4} \div \frac{3}{8} = \frac{\overset{3}{\cancel{9}}}{\underset{1}{\cancel{4}}} \times \frac{\overset{2}{\cancel{8}}}{\underset{1}{\cancel{3}}} = 6$

CLASSWORK

Multiply or divide. Write each answer in simplest form.

1. $1\frac{3}{4} \times 3\frac{1}{2}$

2. $5 \div 2\frac{2}{3}$

3. $6 \times 2\frac{1}{6}$

4. $\frac{1}{3} \times 1\frac{1}{5}$

5. $2\frac{1}{3} \div 3\frac{1}{2}$

6. $3\frac{3}{10} \div 11$

7. $2\frac{5}{6} \div 5\frac{1}{10}$

8. $1\frac{1}{2} \times \frac{2}{3}$

Multiply or divide. Write each answer in simplest form.

1. $1\frac{1}{2} \times 2\frac{3}{4}$ 2. $2\frac{1}{3} \times 3$ 3. $1\frac{1}{4} \div 2\frac{1}{2}$ 4. $3\frac{1}{2} \div \frac{7}{8}$

5. $2 \div 2\frac{1}{4}$ 6. $1\frac{7}{8} \times 3\frac{2}{3}$ 7. $\frac{5}{6} \times 2\frac{2}{5}$ 8. $5 \div 3\frac{1}{8}$

9. $2\frac{2}{3} \div \frac{1}{3}$ 10. $4\frac{1}{5} \times 1\frac{1}{2}$ 11. $3\frac{1}{3} \times \frac{3}{4}$ 12. $\frac{1}{3} \div 2\frac{1}{3}$

13. $3\frac{3}{4} \times 6$ 14. $12 \times 2\frac{5}{6}$ 15. $5\frac{1}{3} \div 4$ 16. $4\frac{1}{2} \div 2\frac{1}{2}$

17. $5\frac{3}{7} \div 2\frac{3}{8}$ 18. $2\frac{1}{10} \times 3\frac{3}{4}$ 19. $5\frac{3}{5} \div 2\frac{1}{10}$ 20. $3\frac{3}{4} \times 6\frac{4}{5}$

21. $4\frac{3}{8} \times 4 \times 2\frac{2}{5}$ 22. $\frac{3}{5} \times 12 \times 7\frac{1}{2}$ 23. $3\frac{3}{4} \times 5\frac{1}{3} \times 2$

★24. $4\frac{1}{2} \div \left(8 \times 6\frac{3}{4}\right)$ ★25. $\left(4\frac{1}{5} \div 4\frac{2}{3}\right) \times 1\frac{1}{9}$ ★26. $\left(1\frac{1}{2} \times 3\frac{1}{6}\right) \div \frac{1}{4}$

APPLICATION

27. How much ginger and how much cloves will the Chefs' Club use in their recipe?

28. How much chicken and how much apple cider vinegar will the Chefs' Club use?

★29. Manny, a chef in a Boston restaurant, often prepares New England Fish Chowder. At home he prepares $\frac{1}{12}$ the restaurant recipe for his family. How much of each ingredient does he use at home? There are 32 tablespoons in a pound of butter. How many tablespoons of butter does Manny use at home?

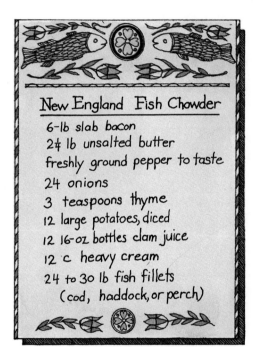

New England Fish Chowder

6-lb slab bacon
2¼ lb unsalted butter
freshly ground pepper to taste
24 onions
3 teaspoons thyme
12 large potatoes, diced
12 16-oz bottles clam juice
12 c heavy cream
24 to 30 lb fish fillets
(cod, haddock, or perch)

MENTAL ARITHMETIC

You can quickly find certain products using the distributive property.

$$3\frac{1}{8} \times 24 = \left(3 + \frac{1}{8}\right) \times 24 = (3 \times 24) + \left(\frac{1}{8} \times 24\right) = 72 + 3 = 75$$

1. $2\frac{1}{4} \times 16$ 2. $2\frac{1}{6} \times 42$ 3. $8\frac{1}{10} \times 50$ 4. $7\frac{1}{5} \times 10$

5. $3\frac{1}{4} \times 12$ 6. $1\frac{1}{9} \times 63$ 7. $5\frac{1}{4} \times 20$ 8. $3\frac{1}{8} \times 40$

Problem Solving

MAKING AND USING DRAWINGS

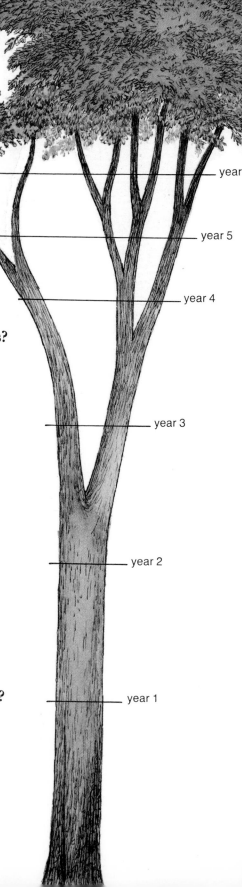

A drawing can be an important problem-solving tool. It can provide the answer to a problem. It can help you see a pattern that will provide the answer.

year 6

year 5

year 4

1. Marietta enjoys drawing. She hopes to be a professional artist some day. Her drawing at the right shows the way some trees split their branches during the growing season. How many branches does the tree have after the seventh growing season?

How many branches does the tree have after 7 seasons?

The facts are in the drawing. Count the number of branches there are after each growing season. Try to find a pattern.

year 3

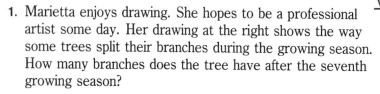

Season	1	2	3	4	5	6	7
Branches	1	1	2	3	5	8	☐

Notice that at the end of each growing season, the number of branches is the sum of the numbers for the two preceding seasons.

$$1 + 1 = 2 \qquad 1 + 2 = 3 \qquad 2 + 3 = 5 \qquad 3 + 5 = 8$$

Therefore, there will be $5 + 8 = 13$ branches at the end of the seventh growing season.

year 2

2. Harry and his dad like to build things around the house. They are making a staircase out of cinder blocks. They used 6 blocks to make a 2-step staircase. How many blocks would they need to make a 5-step staircase?

How many blocks would they use for a 5-step staircase?

They use 6 blocks to make a 2-step staircase.

There are two ways to solve the problem. Make a drawing and count the blocks, or make a series of drawings and look for a pattern. Pick the method you prefer. Solve the problem. Use the other method to check the answer.

year 1

Solve each problem.

1. Harry and his dad cut down a large tree to make room for a garden. It took them 12 min to cut through the trunk. How long will it take them to cut the rest of the trunk into 5 pieces if they work at the same rate?

2. Each branch of one tree in Harry's yard sprouts two new branches each season. After the first season, there were two branches. How many new branches were there after the fifth season?

3. A tennis tournament was held last week. There were 8 people in the tournament. Jeff beat Ira in match 1. Nancy defeated Lois in match 2. David defeated Elmer in match 3. Barbara beat Eleanor in match 4. In match 5 the winner of match 1 beat the winner of match 2. In match 6 the winner of match 4 beat the winner of match 3. In the final round, match 7, the winner of match 5 lost. Who was the champion?

4. The results of six baseball games are being posted on the bulletin board at the playground. The coach wants to tack up the six lists by placing one tack in each corner of each list. The corners will overlap. What is the least number of tacks the coach needs to tack up all six lists?

The Bike-Cycle Club uses the two routes shown on the map at the right.

5. The route along Montco Road (black route) is 10 miles long. How long is Lynn Road?

★ 6. How much longer is the route along Circle Road (red route) than the route along Montco Road?

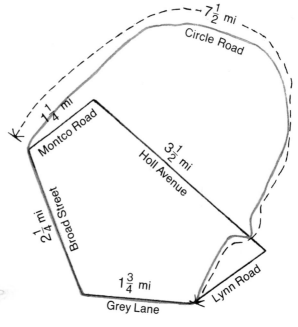

CREATE YOUR OWN PROBLEM

Tama used this drawing to solve a problem. Make up a problem she might have been solving.

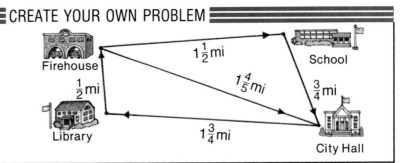

Decimals and Fractions

These teenagers designed Mini-Yosemite Park in San Francisco. How long did they make Golden Pine Trail? Write the length as a fraction.

To change a decimal to a fraction, follow these steps.

Step 1 Write the decimal as an equivalent fraction or mixed number with a denominator that is a power of 10.

$$0.5 = \frac{5}{10}$$

Step 2 Write the fraction in simplest form.

$$\frac{5}{10} = \frac{1}{2}$$

They made Golden Pine Trail $\frac{1}{2}$ mile long.

More Examples

a. $4.125 = 4\frac{125}{1,000}$

$\qquad$ **Think** $\frac{125 \div 125}{1,000 \div 125} = \frac{1}{8}$

$\qquad 4.125 = 4\frac{1}{8}$

b. $0.875 = \frac{875}{1,000}$

$\qquad$ **Think** $\frac{875 \div 125}{1,000 \div 125} = \frac{7}{8}$

$\qquad 0.875 = \frac{7}{8}$

c. $5.75 = 5\frac{75}{100}$

$\qquad$ **Think** $\frac{75 \div 25}{100 \div 25} = \frac{3}{4}$

$\qquad 5.75 = 5\frac{3}{4}$

d. $0.33\frac{1}{3} = \frac{33\frac{1}{3}}{100} = 33\frac{1}{3} \div 100$

$\qquad = \frac{100}{3} \div \frac{100}{1}$

$\qquad = \frac{100}{3} \times \frac{1}{100} = \frac{1}{3}$

$\qquad 0.33\frac{1}{3} = \frac{1}{3}$

CLASSWORK

Write each as a fraction or mixed number in simplest form.

1. 0.75

2. 8.625

3. 0.66

4. 0.1

5. 3.8

6. 5.25

7. 0.05

8. $0.16\frac{2}{3}$

PRACTICE

Write each as a fraction or mixed number in simplest form.

1. 0.9   **2.** 0.5   **3.** 0.125   **4.** 0.6

5. $0.33\frac{1}{3}$ **6.** 0.25   **7.** 3.45   **8.** 2.7

9. 0.875   **10.** 0.4   **11.** 1.15   **12.** 1.05

13. 2.375   **14.** 1.5   **15.** 8.04   **16.** 2.65

17. 3.625   **18.** 11.75   **19.** 2.125   **20.** 6.55

21. 7.16   **22.** 3.12   **23.** 1.36   **24.** 4.875

25. 1.6875   **26.** 0.3125   **27.** 2.4375   **28.** 0.004

29. 0.0825   **30.** $0.66\frac{2}{3}$ **31.** $0.83\frac{1}{3}$ ★ **32.** $0.08\frac{1}{3}$

Find each sum or product. Write as a fraction and as a decimal.

33. $\frac{1}{2} + 0.7 + \frac{1}{5}$ **34.** $\frac{4}{5} \times 0.25$ **35.** $\frac{5}{8} + 0.375 + 1.5$

36. $1.5 \times 2\frac{1}{4}$ **37.** $6\frac{1}{4} \times 4.2$ **38.** $1\frac{1}{3} + 2.75 + 0.83\frac{1}{3}$

Write each as a decimal without dividing.

★ **39.** $\frac{1}{50}$ ★ **40.** $\frac{7}{50}$ ★ **41.** $\frac{2}{25}$ ★ **42.** $\frac{8}{25}$ ★ **43.** $\frac{8}{125}$ ★ **44.** $\frac{21}{125}$

APPLICATION

45. Teresa is a park planner. Her plan for a Green Acres area calls for 0.35 of the trees to be pines. What fraction of the trees will be pines? Write the fraction in simplest form.

★ **46.** At the beginning of winter Teresa placed a bird feeding station every $0.66\frac{2}{3}$ miles along the trails. How many stations were there along a 6-mile trail?

CALCULATOR

A calculator displayed the following quotients. On a calculator use multiplication and subtraction to find the remainder. Then write the quotient as a mixed number.

1. $277 \div 8 = 34.625$ **2.** $1,245 \div 6 = 207.5$

3. $253 \div 2 = 126.5$ **4.** $783 \div 5 = 156.6$

5. $657 \div 12 = 54.75$ **6.** $459 \div 8 = 57.375$

Estimating with Fractions

X410 CLOSED FOR REPAIRS

NEXT FUEL STATION: 1,820,602 miles

"Oh no!" thought Mika. "Will my reserve fuel get me there?"

Estimate to find if Mika has enough fuel.

Mika can go 2,000,000 miles on $\frac{1}{2}$ tank.

Rounded to the nearest million, 1,820,602 is 2,000,000. So Mika has to go about 2,000,000 miles.

Mika has $\frac{3}{8}$ tank.

$$\frac{3}{8} + \frac{1}{4} = \frac{5}{8}$$

reserve

$\frac{5}{8} > \frac{1}{2}$, so she will make it.

To estimate when adding, subtracting, multiplying, or dividing fractions, round as you do with decimals. If the fraction is $\frac{1}{2}$ or greater, round to the next whole number. If it is less than $\frac{1}{2}$, leave the digit in the place to be rounded unchanged.

a.

	rounds to	
$2\frac{1}{2}$	rounds to	3
$+ 2\frac{1}{4}$	rounds to	$+ 2$
		5

b.

	rounds to	
$5\frac{1}{6}$	rounds to	5
$- 3\frac{7}{8}$	rounds to	$- 4$
		1

c. $9 \div 2\frac{7}{10}$ rounds to $9 \div 3 = 3$

d. $2\frac{1}{5} \times 7\frac{2}{3}$ rounds to $2 \times 8 = 16$

CLASSWORK

Tell whether each fraction is less than or greater than $\frac{1}{2}$.

1. $\frac{3}{4}$ **2.** $\frac{3}{5}$ **3.** $\frac{7}{16}$ **4.** $\frac{4}{9}$ **5.** $\frac{3}{8}$

Estimate each answer.

6.

$3\frac{3}{4}$
$+ 1\frac{1}{2}$

7.

$8\frac{1}{8}$
$- 4\frac{2}{3}$

8.

$9\frac{1}{6}$
$+ \frac{2}{3}$

9.

$9\frac{7}{8}$
$\times 1\frac{9}{10}$

10. $5\frac{1}{6} \times 2\frac{7}{10}$

11. $13\frac{5}{6} \div 2\frac{1}{5}$

PRACTICE

Without using paper and pencil, tell whether each fraction is less than or greater than $\frac{1}{2}$.

1. $\frac{7}{10}$ 2. $\frac{1}{4}$ 3. $\frac{1}{3}$ 4. $\frac{2}{3}$ 5. $\frac{4}{7}$

6. $\frac{5}{12}$ 7. $\frac{6}{11}$ 8. $\frac{2}{5}$ 9. $\frac{7}{8}$ 10. $\frac{11}{16}$

Estimate each answer.

11. $3\frac{2}{7}$
    $+ 5\frac{1}{5}$

12. $9\frac{2}{3}$
    $- 6\frac{5}{9}$

13. $\frac{4}{5}$
    $+ \frac{1}{8}$

14. $2\frac{3}{8}$
    $- 2\frac{1}{4}$

15. $\frac{5}{6}$
    $+ \frac{2}{3}$

16. $3\frac{4}{5} \times 2\frac{1}{10}$

17. $\frac{8}{9} - \frac{1}{6}$

18. $10 \div 1\frac{7}{8}$

19. $\frac{3}{4} \times \frac{7}{9}$

20. $5\frac{3}{7} + 6\frac{1}{9}$

21. $\frac{7}{8} \div \frac{5}{3}$

22. $9\frac{5}{7} \times 4\frac{2}{9}$

23. $\frac{9}{10} \div 2\frac{5}{6}$

Tell whether each fraction is closer to 0, $\frac{1}{2}$, or 1. (You may wish to convert to decimals.)

24. $\frac{5}{6}$ 25. $\frac{1}{10}$ 26. $\frac{9}{10}$ 27. $\frac{9}{16}$

28. $\frac{1}{16}$ 29. $\frac{5}{8}$ 30. $\frac{3}{7}$ 31. $\frac{4}{5}$

Estimate whether each answer is less than or greater than 1.

★ 32. $\frac{1}{2} + \frac{3}{5}$ ★ 33. $1\frac{1}{3} - \frac{1}{4}$ ★ 34. $\frac{9}{5} \times \frac{1}{2}$

★ 35. $1\frac{1}{3} \div \frac{1}{5}$ ★ 36. $\frac{2}{5} + \frac{1}{3}$ ★ 37. $\frac{6}{5} \times \frac{9}{8}$

APPLICATION

CALCULATOR

Estimate each answer. Then use a calculator to find the actual answer. Use the estimate to check the answer.

1. $\dfrac{3\frac{7}{8} + 4\frac{1}{4}}{1\frac{5}{8}}$

2. $\dfrac{5\frac{5}{8} \times 3\frac{3}{5}}{1\frac{1}{2}}$

3. $\dfrac{10 \div 1\frac{1}{4}}{\frac{1}{2}}$

4. $\dfrac{4\frac{7}{8} - 1\frac{3}{8}}{1\frac{1}{4}}$

5. $\dfrac{3\frac{1}{2} + 5\frac{1}{4}}{10 - 6\frac{1}{2}}$

6. $\dfrac{6\frac{1}{2} - 1\frac{1}{4}}{1\frac{1}{8}}$

163

Fraction Equations

Solve equations with fractions and mixed numbers the same way you solve equations with whole numbers.

a.
$$n + 1\frac{1}{2} = 2$$

Use the inverse of adding $1\frac{1}{2}$ to solve.

$$n + 1\frac{1}{2} - 1\frac{1}{2} = 2 - 1\frac{1}{2}$$

$$n = \frac{1}{2}$$

Check $\frac{1}{2} + 1\frac{1}{2} = 2$

b.
$$a - \frac{7}{8} = \frac{5}{8}$$

Use the inverse of subtracting $\frac{7}{8}$ to solve.

$$a - \frac{7}{8} + \frac{7}{8} = \frac{5}{8} + \frac{7}{8}$$

$$a = \frac{12}{8} = \frac{3}{2}, \text{ or } 1\frac{1}{2}$$

Check $1\frac{1}{2} - \frac{7}{8} = \frac{5}{8}$

c.
$$\frac{1}{8}b = \frac{3}{4}$$

Use the inverse of multiplying by $\frac{1}{8}$ to solve.

$$\frac{1}{8} \div \frac{1}{8} \times b = \frac{3}{4} \div \frac{1}{8}$$

$$b = \frac{3}{4} \div \frac{1}{8} = \frac{3}{4} \times \frac{8}{1} = 6$$

Check $\frac{1}{8} \times 6 = \frac{3}{4}$

d.
$$n \div \frac{1}{2} = 1\frac{1}{2}$$

Use the inverse of dividing by $\frac{1}{2}$ to solve.

$$n \div \frac{1}{2} \times \frac{1}{2} = 1\frac{1}{2} \times \frac{1}{2}$$

$$n = \frac{3}{2} \times \frac{1}{2} = \frac{3}{4}$$

Check $\frac{3}{4} \div \frac{1}{2} = \frac{3}{4} \times \frac{2}{1} = \frac{3}{2} = 1\frac{1}{2}$

CLASSWORK

Solve and check.

1. $n + \frac{1}{3} = \frac{5}{3}$

2. $y - \frac{1}{6} = \frac{5}{6}$

3. $\frac{1}{2}a = 6$

4. $y \div 4 = \frac{3}{5}$

5. $x + 3\frac{1}{8} = 5$

6. $x - 1\frac{3}{4} = 2\frac{5}{8}$

7. $b \div 1\frac{1}{3} = 2$

8. $s \times 1\frac{3}{4} = 7$

PRACTICE

Solve and check.

1. $x + \frac{1}{4} = \frac{3}{4}$

2. $y - \frac{4}{5} = \frac{4}{5}$

3. $x - \frac{1}{8} = \frac{7}{8}$

4. $\frac{1}{2} + n = \frac{3}{2}$

5. $\frac{1}{3}x = 2$

6. $\frac{3}{4}y = \frac{1}{4}$

7. $4n = \frac{1}{2}$

8. $y \div \frac{1}{2} = 4$

9. $x - \frac{2}{3} = 1$

10. $y - \frac{1}{3} = \frac{2}{3}$

11. $1\frac{1}{5} + n = 2\frac{3}{5}$

12. $3 + x = 7\frac{1}{2}$

13. $2\frac{1}{4} \times n = 3$

14. $\frac{7}{5}x = 21$

15. $x \div 4 = 3\frac{5}{8}$

16. $y \div \frac{5}{4} = \frac{8}{3}$

17. $y - 1\frac{1}{4} = 2\frac{5}{8}$

18. $1\frac{3}{4} + n = 2\frac{1}{8}$

19. $x + 2\frac{1}{5} = 3\frac{1}{10}$

20. $n - 4\frac{1}{3} = 5\frac{5}{6}$

21. $\frac{1}{10}n = 1\frac{3}{5}$

22. $2\frac{2}{3} \times n = 1\frac{2}{3}$

23. $n \div \frac{3}{8} = 2\frac{2}{3}$

24. $y \times 3\frac{3}{8} = 4\frac{1}{2}$

Write an equation for each sentence. Then solve it.

25. A number n plus $\frac{5}{6}$ equals $\frac{11}{6}$.

26. One half times a number y is $\frac{1}{5}$.

27. The sum of a number y and $2\frac{1}{3}$ equals $3\frac{2}{3}$.

28. A number a divided by 5 is $\frac{3}{5}$.

29. A number n minus $\frac{2}{3}$ is 0.

30. The product of a number y and 7 is $3\frac{1}{2}$.

★ **31.** The sum of $\frac{2}{5}$, $1\frac{1}{5}$, and a number n is $2\frac{1}{5}$.

★ **32.** A number y divided by 3 equals $\frac{2}{3}$ times $\frac{3}{5}$.

APPLICATION

Choose the appropriate equation to solve.

33. The student council at Storme School held a dance. They collected $300 from ticket sales. That was $2\frac{1}{2}$ times the cost of the dance. How much did the dance cost?

    a. $2\frac{1}{2} \times n = 300$ **b.** $n \div 2\frac{1}{2} = 300$

★ **34.** Marian is on the town council. She is organizing the town Independence Day celebration. She has $1,200 to spend. She will spend $\frac{1}{2}$ on food, $\frac{1}{3}$ on entertainment, and the rest on salaries for police officers, firefighters, and the first aid squad. How much will be spent on each item?

    a. $\frac{1}{2}x = \$1,200$ **b.** $\frac{1}{2} \times \$1,200 = x$

        $\frac{1}{3}y = \$1,200$ $\frac{1}{3} \times \$1,200 = y$

        $\frac{1}{4}z = \$1,200$ $\frac{1}{6} \times \$1,200 = z$

Length, Weight, Capacity

As its spring project the Fairview Garden Club is landscaping this section of land at the entrance to Fairview Junior High. Write the width in feet and inches. Then write it in yards and inches.

Length	Weight	Capacity
12 in. = 1 ft	16 oz = 1 lb	8 fluid ounces (fl oz) = 1 c
3 ft = 1 yd	2,000 lb = 1 ton (T)	2 c = 1 pt
5,280 ft = 1 mi		2 pt = 1 qt
1,760 yd = 1 mi		4 qt = 1 gal

To convert from a larger unit to a smaller unit, multiply.

$6\frac{2}{3}$ ft = ___ ft ___ in.

1 ft = 12 in.

$\frac{2}{3}$ ft = $\frac{2}{3}$ × (12 in.) = 8 in.

$6\frac{2}{3}$ ft = 6 ft 8 in.

To convert from a smaller unit to a larger unit, divide.

$6\frac{2}{3}$ ft = ___ yd ___ in.

3 ft = 1 yd

6 ft = (6 ÷ 3) yd = 2 yd

$6\frac{2}{3}$ ft = 2 yd 8 in.

The width is 6 ft 8 in., or 2 yd 8 in.

More Examples

a. $5\frac{1}{2}$ lb = ___ oz

1 lb = 16 oz

$5\frac{1}{2}$ lb = $5\frac{1}{2}$ × (16 oz)

$= \frac{11}{2} × \frac{16}{1}$ oz = 88 oz

b. 21 fl oz = ___ c ___ fl oz

8 fl oz = 1 c

$$21 \text{ fl oz} \rightarrow 8\overline{)21} \quad \begin{array}{r} 2 \text{ R5} \\ \underline{16} \\ 5 \end{array}$$

21 fl oz = 2 c 5 fl oz, or $2\frac{5}{8}$ c

CLASSWORK

Complete.

1. 15 ft 6 in. = ___ yd ___ in.

2. $2\frac{1}{2}$ mi = ___ ft

3. 28 in. = ___ ft ___ in.

4. $4\frac{1}{4}$ pt = ___ fl oz

5. 7,500 lb = ___ T

6. 57 oz = ___ lb ___ oz

7. $8\frac{1}{3}$ ft = ___ ft ___ in.

8. $9\frac{3}{4}$ ft = ___ yd ___ in.

9. 20 ft = ___ yd ___ ft

PRACTICE

Complete.

1. 48 in. = ___ ft

2. $5\frac{3}{4}$ ft = ___ ft ___ in.

3. $4\frac{2}{3}$ yd = ___ ft

4. 10,560 ft = ___ mi

5. $9\frac{1}{2}$ ft = ___ yd ___ in.

6. 8 in. = ___ ft

7. 64 in. = ___ ft ___ in.

8. 7 ft 8 in. = ___ in.

9. 5 yd 2 ft = ___ ft

10. 1,320 ft = ___ mi

11. 28 ft = ___ yd ___ ft

12. 108 in. = ___ yd

13. 3 lb = ___ oz

14. 96 oz = ___ lb

15. 5,000 lb = ___ T

16. 7 T = ___ lb

17. $5\frac{1}{4}$ lb = ___ lb ___ oz

18. 100 oz = ___ lb

19. 4 oz = ___ lb

20. 3 lb 12 oz = ___ oz

21. 114 oz = ___ lb ___ oz

22. 8 gal = ___ qt

23. 2 qt = ___ gal

24. 14 qt = ___ gal ___ qt

25. 4 fl oz = ___ c

26. 17 c = ___ qt ___ c

27. 3 qt 1 pt = ___ pt

28. 1 pt = ___ qt

29. 1 qt = ___ fl oz

30. 2 qt 1 pt 1 c = ___ c

31. 10 lb 4 oz = ___ lb

★ 32. 6 ft 4 in. = ___ yd

★ 33. $14\frac{2}{3}$ ft = ___ yd ___ ft ___ in.

Complete.

34. $111\frac{1}{2}$ gal = ___ qt

35. 26,400 ft = ___ mi

36. 440 yd = ___ mi

37. 39 lb 12 oz = ___ oz

38. 7 mi = ___ yd

39. 104 oz = ___ lb

APPLICATION

40. The Garden Club members are buying their supplies in a nursery that sells only quart containers of weed killer. How many containers do they need?

41. Nodin works at the nursery. He is bottling fertilizer for sale in pint containers. He has 12 gallons of fertilizer. How many pint containers does he need?

★ 42. Nodin uses the instructions below to mix the liquid fertilizer. How many cups of fertilizer crystals does he use with 10 gallons of water? (1 tablespoon (tbsp) = $\frac{1}{2}$ fl oz)

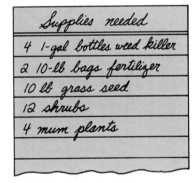

Supplies needed
4 1-gal bottles weed killer
2 10-lb bags fertilizer
10 lb grass seed
12 shrubs
4 mum plants

167

Working With Measurement

The Model Railroad Club is expanding their model railroad layout. Lee and Adelita are making trains. On one train the engine and coal car together are 1 ft 3 in. long. The engine alone measures 8 in. How long is the coal car?

$$\begin{array}{r} 1 \text{ ft } 3 \text{ in.} \\ - \qquad 8 \text{ in.} \\ \hline \end{array}$$ 3 in. < 8 in., so regroup to subtract.

$$\begin{array}{r} \overset{0}{\cancel{1}} \text{ ft } \overset{15}{\cancel{3}} \text{ in.} \\ - \qquad 8 \text{ in.} \\ \hline 7 \text{ in.} \end{array}$$ 1 ft = 12 in.
12 in. + 3 in. = 15 in.

The coal car is 7 in. long.

More Examples

a.
$$\begin{array}{r} 3 \text{ ft } 5 \text{ in.} \\ + 2 \text{ ft } 8 \text{ in.} \\ \hline 5 \text{ ft } 13 \text{ in.} \end{array} = 5 \text{ ft} + (1 \text{ ft} + 1 \text{ in.})$$
$$= 6 \text{ ft } 1 \text{ in.}$$
$$= 2 \text{ yd } 1 \text{ in.}$$

b.
$$\begin{array}{r} \overset{6}{\cancel{7}} \text{ yd} \overset{3 \text{ ft}}{} \\ - 3 \text{ yd } 2 \text{ ft} \\ \hline 3 \text{ yd } 1 \text{ ft} \end{array}$$

c.
$$\begin{array}{r} 1 \text{ pt } 1 \text{ c} \\ \times \qquad 5 \\ \hline 5 \text{ pt } 5 \text{ c} \end{array} = (2 \text{ qt} + 1 \text{ pt}) + (1 \text{ qt} + 1 \text{ c})$$
$$= 3 \text{ qt } 1 \text{ pt } 1 \text{ c}$$

d.
$$\begin{array}{r} 6 \text{ yd } 1 \text{ ft} \\ \times \qquad \frac{1}{2} \\ \hline 3 \text{ yd } \frac{1}{2} \text{ ft} \end{array} = 3 \text{ yd } 6 \text{ in.}$$

CLASSWORK

Add, subtract, or multiply.

1.
$$\begin{array}{r} 12 \text{ ft } 7 \text{ in.} \\ + \quad 8 \text{ ft } 9 \text{ in.} \\ \hline \end{array}$$

2.
$$\begin{array}{r} 8 \text{ yd} \\ - 4 \text{ yd } 2 \text{ ft} \\ \hline \end{array}$$

3.
$$\begin{array}{r} 2 \text{ T } 1{,}250 \text{ lb} \\ + 1 \text{ T } 1{,}000 \text{ lb} \\ \hline \end{array}$$

4.
$$\begin{array}{r} 4 \text{ gal} \\ - 1 \text{ gal } 2 \text{ qt} \\ \hline \end{array}$$

5.
$$\begin{array}{r} 2 \text{ lb } 6 \text{ oz} \\ \times \qquad 4 \\ \hline \end{array}$$

6.
$$\begin{array}{r} 4 \text{ ft } 3 \text{ in.} \\ \times \qquad 5 \\ \hline \end{array}$$

Add, subtract, multiply, or divide.

1. 2 ft 8 in.
   + 4 ft 2 in.

2. 5 ft 10 in.
   − 3 ft 7 in.

3. 2 gal 1 qt
   + 3 gal 2 qt

4. 8 lb 9 oz
   + 3 lb 11 oz

5. 3 qt
   − 1 qt 1 pt

6. 3 lb 3 oz
   − 1 lb 11 oz

7. 4 lb 13 oz
   + 2 lb 14 oz

8. 5 yd
   − 2 yd 2 ft

9. 12 oz
   × 8

10. 3 qt
    × 3

11. 2 ft 7 in.
    × 2

12. 3 lb 4 oz
    × 4

13. 5 yd
    − 2 yd 1 ft

14. 4 ft 10 in.
    + 3 ft 7 in.

15. 2 lb 9 oz
    × 3

16. 2 c
    −   6 fl oz

★ 17. 4)10 ft 8 in.

★ 18. 3)7 lb 5 oz

★ 19. 3)13 qt 1 pt

★ 20. 5)6 yd 2 ft

APPLICATION

21. The Model Railroad Club runs HO-scale trains which are $\frac{1}{87}$ the size of actual trains. An actual engine and coal car together are 103 ft 3 in. long. The coal car is 43 ft 6 in. long. How long is the actual engine?

22. Jana is an intern training in an architect's office. She is building a model of a performing arts center that will be $\frac{1}{48}$ the size of the actual building. The actual auditorium will be 40 ft high. How high should the model be?

VISUAL THINKING

Slim, Bobbi, Curly, Fred, and Jo-Jo are in these positions at the finish of a race.

> Slim is 20 yards behind Bobbi.
> Jo-Jo is 30 yards ahead of Slim.
> Curly is 50 yards behind Jo-Jo.
> Fred is 10 yards behind Curly.

Who is the winner? Who is second, third, fourth, and last?

Problem Solving

SKILLS AND STRATEGIES REVIEW   Summer Jobs

King's Land Amusement Park ran this advertisement.

SUMMER HELP NEEDED !

Clowns :	$3.35 an hour
Flume and Tramway operators :	$4.85 an hour
Restaurant servers and cashiers :	$3.75 an hour

Solve. Use the advertisement for 1–4.

1. Sarah worked as a clown for six weeks during the summer. She worked the following hours for the six weeks: $25\frac{1}{2}$, 31, 22, 29, $27\frac{1}{2}$, 25. How much did she earn?

2. For her costumes, Sarah had three blouses and two pairs of pants. They are shown at the right. How many different costumes could she put together?

3. Lorraine worked as an operator for the flume. She helped people onto a new log every 30 seconds. On the average, a log held 3 people. How many people rode on the flume every hour?

4. Larry worked as a server at one of the restaurants for two weeks. He worked $21\frac{1}{2}$ hours the first week and 26 hours the second week. Then he got a new job as an operator for the tramway. He worked the following hours for the next six weeks: $24\frac{1}{2}$, 28, $30\frac{1}{2}$, 26, 31, 24. How much did he earn?

The amphitheater at King's Land has six sections of seats. Each section has ten rows. There is 1 seat in the first row. There are 2 seats in the second row, 3 seats in the third row, and so on.

5. How many seats are in the amphitheater?

Mr. Krebs, the manager of King's Land, keeps records of daily attendance.

6. On the average day, 38 buses and 374 cars enter the park. Each bus holds an average of 45 people. Each car holds an average of 3 people. How many more people went to the park on Independence Day than on an average day?

7. Based on attendance records, Mr. Krebs determined that the park should be open Thursday through Sunday each week. The park is closed during the winter. How many days of the year is the park open?

Last Saturday the Morton family went to King's Land. After entering the park, they went on the flume, the tramway, and the safari, in that order. Then they ate lunch at the Mexican Restaurant. After lunch they rode on the Ferris wheel, then went to a dolphin show at the amphitheater, and finally rode on the flume again before they left.

8. How far did the Morton family walk if they always took the shortest route?

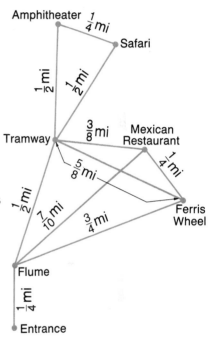

The Ferris wheel has 13 chairs numbered 1 to 13. The chairs are unloaded and loaded in the following order.

Stop 1: unload/load chair 2   Stop 2: unload/load chair 8

Stop 3: unload/load chair 1   Stop 4: unload/load chair 7

★9. Chair 11 will be unloaded and loaded on which stop?

★10. Which chair will be unloaded and loaded on stop 13?

SOMETHING EXTRA

THEN AND NOW

Here are two problems. One appeared in 1881 in *The Complete Arithmetic* by Henry B. Maglathin, published by Leach, Shewell, and Sanborn. One was written today. Try to solve them.

Then

Bought a cask of oil, containing $68\frac{1}{2}$ gallons, at 72 cents a gallon; $\frac{3}{8}$ having leaked out, the remainder was sold at 90 cents a gallon. Did I make or lose and how much?

Now

Paul has a lemonade stand at the Bound Brook Golf Course. He paid $5.86 for 6 gallons of lemonade. After one gallon spilled, he sold the rest at 25¢ for an 8-oz glass. How much did Paul make or lose?

CHAPTER REVIEW

Write each answer in simplest form. pages 146–157

1. $\frac{1}{3}$
$+\frac{3}{4}$

2. $\frac{2}{5}$
$-\frac{3}{10}$

3. $\frac{5}{6}$
$+\frac{2}{3}$

4. $\frac{5}{12}$
$+\frac{4}{3}$

5. $\frac{3}{4}$
$-\frac{3}{10}$

6. $7\frac{5}{6}$
$-3\frac{1}{6}$

7. $9\frac{2}{3}$
$+8\frac{2}{3}$

8. $12\frac{5}{12}$
$-8\frac{2}{3}$

9. $9\frac{3}{4}$
$+2\frac{5}{6}$

10. $4\frac{1}{8}$
$-1\frac{1}{2}$

11. $7 \times \frac{1}{7}$

12. $\frac{1}{2} \times \frac{3}{5}$

13. $\frac{3}{10} \times \frac{2}{9}$

14. $5 \div \frac{1}{3}$

15. $\frac{3}{8} \times \frac{5}{6}$

16. $\frac{3}{4} \div 9$

17. $1\frac{3}{7} \times 2\frac{5}{8}$

18. $1\frac{1}{2} \div 1\frac{2}{3}$

Write each decimal as a fraction in simplest form. pages 160–161

19. 0.3

20. 0.75

21. 0.16

22. 0.375

23. 0.8

Estimate. pages 162–163

24. $9\frac{2}{7} - 7\frac{1}{8}$

25. $\frac{1}{2} + \frac{1}{4}$

26. $6 \div 1\frac{3}{4}$

27. $2\frac{2}{3} \times 3\frac{1}{5}$

Solve and check. pages 164–165

28. $x + \frac{3}{2} = \frac{7}{2}$

29. $\frac{1}{4}n = \frac{5}{2}$

30. $y + 2\frac{1}{4} = 6$

31. $a \div 5 = 1\frac{3}{8}$

Complete. pages 166–167

32. $4\frac{1}{3}$ ft = ___ in.

33. 69 oz = ___ lb

34. 11 pt = ___ gal ___ qt ___ pt

Add, subtract, or multiply. pages 168–169

35.   5 ft 4 in.
$+$ 2 ft 9 in.

36.   4 lb 3 oz
$-$ 1 lb 8 oz

37.   3 qt 1 pt
$\times$ 2

38.   6 yd
$-$ 4 yd 2 ft

Solve. pages 158–159, 170–171

39. Jerry plans the layout for the *Silver Times*. He is using $\frac{1}{3}$ of the front page for pictures and $\frac{1}{2}$ of the page for stories. How much space is left for the index?

40. Grace is sewing pearls on the sleeves of a costume. Each sleeve is $10\frac{1}{2}$ in. around. She sews on a pearl every $1\frac{1}{2}$ in. How many pearls will she sew on each sleeve?

CHAPTER TEST

Write each answer in simplest form.

1. $\frac{5}{8} + \frac{7}{8}$

2. $\frac{2}{3} - \frac{3}{5}$

3. $\frac{2}{3} \times \frac{1}{2}$

4. $2\frac{3}{8} + 3\frac{1}{3}$

5. $1\frac{1}{2} \times 3\frac{1}{4}$

6. $\frac{5}{8} \div 2$

7. $5\frac{2}{5} - 3\frac{1}{2}$

8. $4 \div 1\frac{1}{2}$

9. $8 - 1\frac{1}{4}$

10. $3\frac{1}{3} \div 2\frac{2}{3}$

11. $3 \times \frac{7}{12}$

12. $9 + 1\frac{1}{8}$

Choose the best estimate.

13. $\frac{9}{5} \div \frac{7}{8}$
    a. $\frac{1}{2}$
    b. 1
    c. 2

14. $\frac{3}{4} + \frac{1}{6}$
    a. 0
    b. $\frac{1}{2}$
    c. 1

15. $4\frac{2}{9} \times 1\frac{1}{5}$
    a. 1
    b. 4
    c. 7

Solve and check.

16. $\frac{1}{6} + y = \frac{5}{6}$

17. $\frac{2}{5}y = \frac{2}{5}$

18. $y \div \frac{1}{2} = 4$

Write each decimal as a fraction in simplest form.

19. 0.6

20. 0.875

Complete.

21. $4\frac{1}{2}$ ft = ____ in.

22. $\begin{array}{r} 3 \text{ ft } 3 \text{ in.} \\ - 1 \text{ ft } 7 \text{ in.} \\ \hline \end{array}$

23. $\begin{array}{r} 1 \text{ gal } 2 \text{ qt} \\ \times \qquad 8 \\ \hline \end{array}$

Solve.

24. Anne plays in Clearview School's band. She practices the clarinet $\frac{3}{4}$ hour every weekday and $1\frac{1}{2}$ hours on Saturday and on Sunday. How many hours does she practice each week?

25. Lamont drove from Seabright to Clinton to Monroe to Franklin to Carson and back to Monroe. How far did he drive?

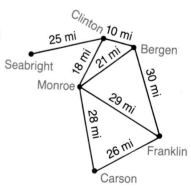

A $33\frac{1}{3}$-speed record rotates $33\frac{1}{3}$ times a minute. How many times will a $33\frac{1}{3}$-speed record rotate in 45 seconds?

FRACTION CIPHER

In a fraction cipher, a message is sent as a series of fractions.
A key word is used to scramble the alphabet. In the first code
below the key word NUNTIUS is used to scramble the alphabet.
In the second code the key word LEXICON is used. In any
code the digits below the letters can be arranged in any order.

Complete each message.

1	2	3	4	5	6	7	8
N U N	T I U S	A B C	D E F G H	J K L M	O P Q R V	W X Y	Z
4 8 9	3 6 7 9	5 6 7	5 6 7 8 9	6 7 8 9	3 6 7 8 9	6 7 8	9

Message

$\frac{2}{9}$ $\frac{4}{6}$ $\frac{1}{4}$ $\frac{4}{5}$ $\frac{7}{8}$ $\frac{6}{3}$ $\frac{1}{8}$ $\frac{6}{8}$ $\frac{4}{7}$ $\frac{6}{8}$ $\frac{2}{6}$ $\frac{4}{6}$ $\frac{1}{9}$ $\frac{4}{5}$ $\frac{3}{5}$ $\frac{5}{9}$ $\frac{4}{6}$ $\frac{2}{9}$ $\frac{2}{9}$ $\frac{3}{5}$ $\frac{4}{8}$ $\frac{4}{6}$

S

1	2	3	4	5	6	7	8
L E X	I C O N	A B D	F G H J K	M P Q	R S T U V	W X Y	Z
3 7 9	4 6 8 9	7 8 9	5 6 7 8 9	5 7 9	5 6 7 8 9	6 8 9	9

Message

$\frac{2}{4}$ $\frac{4}{9}$ $\frac{2}{9}$ $\frac{1}{7}$ $\frac{7}{6}$ $\frac{7}{9}$ $\frac{2}{8}$ $\frac{6}{8}$ $\frac{2}{6}$ $\frac{2}{8}$ $\frac{6}{8}$ $\frac{1}{3}$ $\frac{3}{9}$ $\frac{7}{6}$ $\frac{1}{7}$ $\frac{1}{3}$ $\frac{1}{3}$ $\frac{3}{9}$ $\frac{2}{8}$ $\frac{2}{9}$ $\frac{1}{7}$

I

**Make up your own code using fractions. Make up a key word to scramble
the alphabet. Then send a message to a friend, using this fraction cipher.**

COMPLEX AND CONTINUED FRACTIONS

A **complex fraction** has one or more fractions in the numerator, the denominator, or both.

$$\frac{\frac{2}{3}}{\frac{3}{5}}$$

To simplify a complex fraction, rewrite the fraction, using the $\div$ symbol.

$$\frac{2}{3} \div \frac{3}{5} = \frac{2}{3} \cdot \frac{5}{3} = \frac{10}{9}$$

Simplify each complex fraction.

1. $\dfrac{\frac{4}{5}}{\frac{2}{3}}$
2. $\dfrac{\frac{3}{10}}{\frac{4}{5}}$
3. $\dfrac{\frac{5}{3}}{2}$
4. $\dfrac{4}{\frac{2}{5}}$
5. $\dfrac{\frac{7}{8}}{\frac{9}{4}}$

A complex fraction such as $\dfrac{1}{2 + \dfrac{1}{1 + \frac{1}{3}}}$ is called a **continued fraction.**

This continued fraction can be simplified as shown below.

$$\frac{1}{2 + \dfrac{1}{1 + \frac{1}{3}}} = \frac{1}{2 + \dfrac{1}{\frac{4}{3}}} = \frac{1}{2 + \frac{3}{4}} = \frac{1}{\frac{11}{4}} = \frac{4}{11}$$

Simplify each continued fraction.

6. $\dfrac{1}{4 + \dfrac{1}{6 + \frac{1}{2}}}$

7. $\dfrac{1}{3 + \dfrac{1}{2 + \frac{1}{2}}}$

8. $\dfrac{1}{2 + \dfrac{1}{3 + \dfrac{1}{5 + \frac{1}{2}}}}$

Leap Year

Every four years an extra day must be added to the year because it takes the earth a little over 365 days—about $365\frac{1}{4}$ days—to orbit the sun. However, $365\frac{1}{4}$ is an approximation. The number of days it actually takes is

$$365 \; \cfrac{1}{4 + \cfrac{1}{7 + \cfrac{1}{1 + \cfrac{1}{3 + \cfrac{1}{4 + \cfrac{1}{1 + \cfrac{1}{1 + \frac{1}{2}}}}}}}}$$

FEBRUARY

SUN	MON	TUES	WED	THUR	FRI	SAT
		1	2	3	4	5
6	7	8	9	10	11	12
13	14	15	16	17	18	19
20	21	22	23	24	25	26
27	28	29				

By how much is the approximation in error?

MAINTAINING SKILLS

Choose the correct answers. Write A, B, C, or D.

1. $10.36 + 7.458 + 16.091$

   A 33.909 C 33.809

   B 33.799 D not given

2. $1.6\overline{)0.5}$

   A 3.125 C 0.3125

   B 0.03125 D not given

3. Complete. ___ cm = 1.7 m

   A 170 C 0.017

   B 17 D not given

4. Complete. 0.53 kg = ___ g

   A 53 C 5.3

   B 530 D not given

5. Make the sentence true.
   What addition property is used?
   $32 +$ ___ $= 32$

   A 0; commutative C 0; identity
   B 1; identity D not given

6. Make the sentence true.
   What multiplication property is used?
   $4 \times$ ___ $= 9 \times 4$

   A 9; identity C 9; distributive
   B 1; identity D not given

7. What is $\frac{12}{32}$ in simplest form?

   A $\frac{6}{16}$ C $\frac{1}{4}$

   B $\frac{3}{8}$ D not given

8. Compare. $\frac{1}{7}$ ⬤ $\frac{1}{3}$

   A $>$ C $=$
   B $<$ D not given

9. What is the decimal for $\frac{3}{8}$?

   A 2.6 C 0.325

   B 0.375 D not given

10. $5\frac{7}{9} - \frac{5}{8}$

    A $4\frac{11}{72}$ C $4\frac{45}{72}$

    B $5\frac{56}{72}$ D not given

11. $\frac{3}{8} + \frac{1}{3}$

    A $\frac{17}{24}$ C $\frac{4}{11}$

    B $\frac{4}{24}$ D not given

12. $1\frac{1}{8} \div 4\frac{3}{10}$

    A $\frac{172}{45}$ C $\frac{45}{172}$

    B $\frac{387}{80}$ D not given

13.   6 ft
    $-$ 3 ft 9 in.

    A 3 ft 3 in. C 2 ft 3 in.
    B 9 ft 9 in. D not given

Solve.

14. Charlene buys 3 cans of peas at $.35 per can, 5 cans of soup at $.49 per can, and a bag of flour for $1.29. How much change will she receive from a $10 bill?

    A $5.21 C $6.50
    B $4.79 D not given

15. Elmer's Electronics has a goal of 250 televisions sold each week. This week they have sold 37 on Monday, 41 on Tuesday, 20 on Wednesday, and 83 on Thursday. How many more must be sold to meet the goal?

    A 89 C 181
    B 69 D not given

Theme: Shapes in Nature Imitated by People

Angles

Objects made by people often imitate shapes in nature. The angles of the maple seed and the boomerang allow them to twirl in the air. The angle of the boomerang also allows it to return to the thrower.

Two rays with a common endpoint (the **vertex**) form an **angle**. Angles are classified according to their measures.

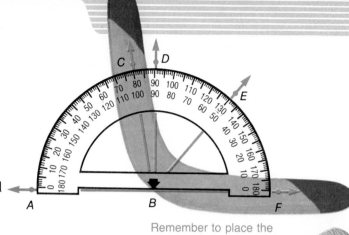

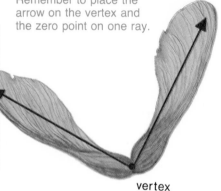

Remember to place the arrow on the vertex and the zero point on one ray.

vertex

ANGLES			
Kind	**Definition**	**Example**	**Measure of Example**
Acute	Measures less than 90°	∠ABC	80°
Right	Measures 90°	∠ABD	90°
Obtuse	Measures more than 90° but less than 180°	∠ABE	130°
Straight	Measures 180°	∠ABF	180°

▶Two angles are **supplementary** if the sum of their measures is 180°.

∠ABC and ∠CBF are supplementary angles.

$$80° + 100° = 180°$$

▶Two angles are **complementary** if the sum of their measures is 90°.

∠DBE and ∠EBF are complementary angles.

$$40° + 50° = 90°$$

CLASSWORK

Measure these angles. Then classify them as acute, right, or obtuse. Which pairs of angles are complementary? Which pairs of angles are supplementary?

1.

2.
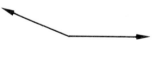

3.

4.

5.
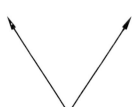

6.

Measure each angle. Then classify it as
acute, right, obtuse, or straight.

1. ∠DPE   **2.** ∠CPD   **3.** ∠BPD

4. ∠BPE   **5.** ∠CPE   **6.** ∠APE

7. ∠APF   **8.** ∠APC   **9.** ∠BPF

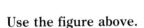

Use the figure above.

10. Name two pairs of complementary angles.

11. Name two pairs of supplementary angles.

Find the complement and the supplement of each.

12. 45°   **13.** 12°   **14.** 89°   **15.** 33°   ★ **16.** X

Draw each angle.

17. Draw ∠CDE with measure 15° greater than a right angle. What kind of angle is ∠CDE?

18. Draw ∠XYZ with measure 10° less than a right angle. What kind of angle is ∠XYZ?

19. Draw ∠PQR with measure 45° less than a right angle. What kind of angle is ∠PQR?

20. Draw ∠MNO with measure 90° greater than a right angle. What kind of angle is ∠MNO?

Use the figure at the right.

★ **21.** Without measuring, find a, b, c, and d.

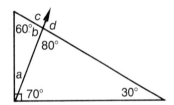

APPLICATION

═══ ESTIMATION ═══

Estimate the measure of each angle below. Then use a protractor and compare the actual measure with your estimate. (Hint: Use a right angle as a reference.)

1.   **2.**   **3.**

4.   **5.**   **6.**

Congruence

The congruent triangles in the spider web and in the bridge give them added strength.

▶ Two segments are **congruent** (≅) if they have the same length.
The length of $\overline{AC}$ equals the length of $\overline{DF}$ ($AC = DF$), so $\overline{AC} \cong \overline{DF}$.

▶ Two angles are congruent if they have the same measure.
The measure of angle A equals the measure of angle D ($m\angle A = m\angle D$), so $\angle A \cong \angle D$.

▶ Two figures are congruent if they are the same size and shape, that is, if the sides and angles of one are congruent to the sides and angles of the other.

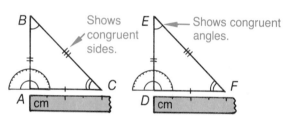

$\overline{AB} \cong \overline{DE}$ $\overline{BC} \cong \overline{EF}$ $\overline{AC} \cong \overline{DF}$

$\angle A \cong \angle D$ $\angle B \cong \angle E$ $\angle C \cong \angle F$

Therefore $\triangle ABC \cong \triangle DEF$.
$\llcorner \triangle$ means *triangle*.

Name congruent figures in the order of the corresponding parts. The **corresponding parts** are the parts that match.

CLASSWORK

Measure to determine if the figures in each pair are congruent. If so, name the congruent sides and congruent angles. Then state the congruence for the figures.

1.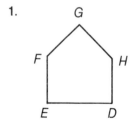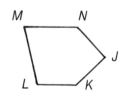

2.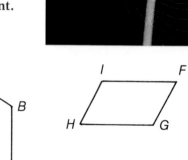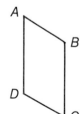

PRACTICE

Measure to determine if the figures in each pair are congruent. If so, name the congruent sides and congruent angles. State the congruence for the figures.

1.

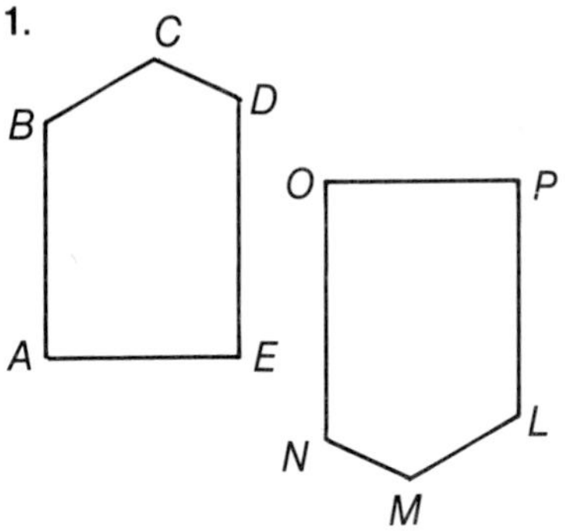

2.

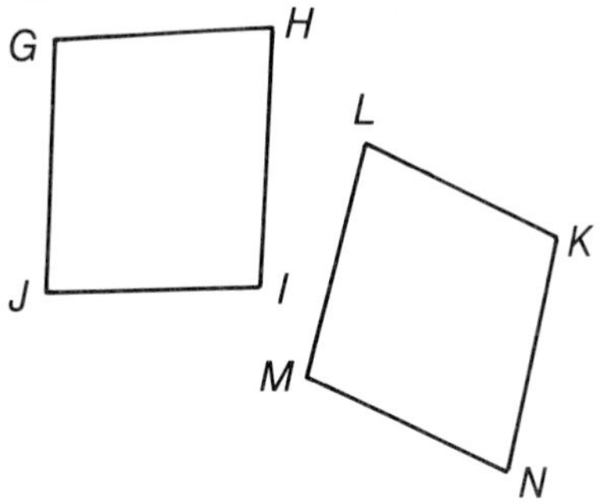

3.

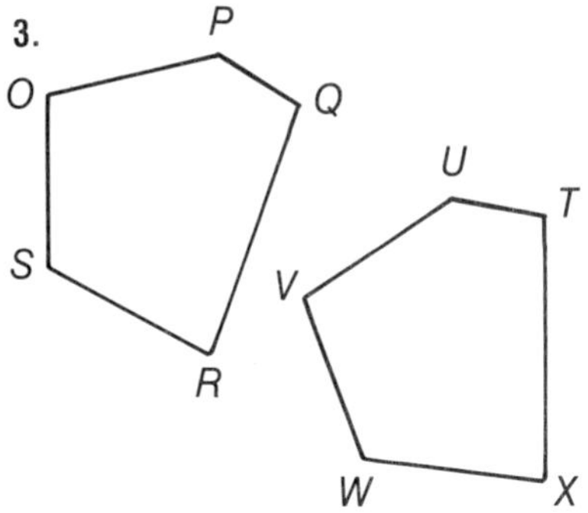

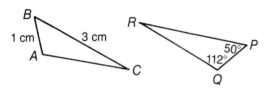

Find each of the following for △ABC ≅ △QPR.

4. ∠A ≅ ?

5. ∠B ≅ ?

6. ∠C ≅ ?

7. $\overline{AB}$ ≅ ?

8. $\overline{AC}$ ≅ ?

9. $\overline{BC}$ ≅ ?

10. length of $\overline{QP}$

11. length of $\overline{PR}$

12. m∠C

Use the figure at the right.

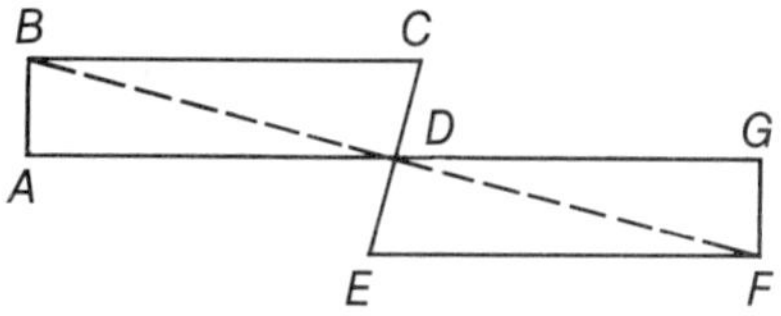

★ **13.** Name the congruent figures. *D* is the *midpoint* of $\overline{AG}$, of $\overline{BF}$, and of $\overline{CE}$. *AB* = *FG* and *BC* = *EF*.

APPLICATION

SYMMETRY

A plane figure has **line symmetry** if it can be folded into two congruent parts that match exactly. This figure has 4 lines of symmetry.

A plane figure has **point symmetry** if it can be rotated less than a full turn and still looks *exactly* like it did before it was turned. This figure has 6 positions about its point of symmetry where it looks exactly the same.

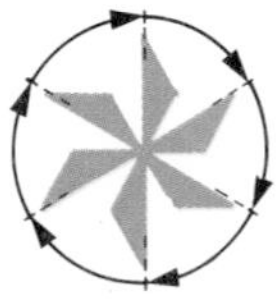

Which figures below have line symmetry? How many lines of symmetry does each have? Which have point symmetry? How many positions?

1.

2.

3.

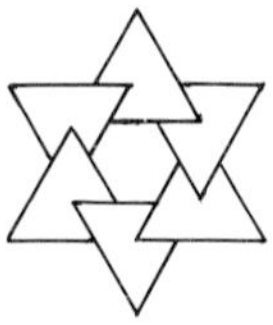

4.

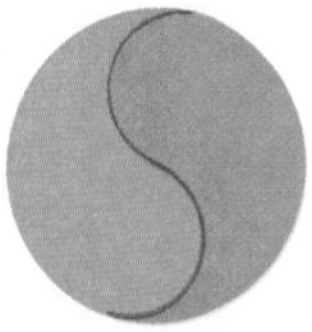

5.

Intersecting Lines

In the Rift Valley in Africa, papyrus grass stems intersect each other to give the stems strength against the wind.

Two lines can intersect to form four right angles. Such intersecting lines are **perpendicular** (⊥).

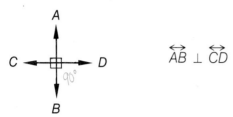

$$\overleftrightarrow{AB} \perp \overleftrightarrow{CD}$$

Two lines can also intersect to form two acute angles and two obtuse angles. The lines form pairs of adjacent angles that are supplementary.

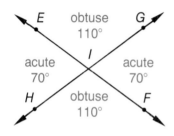

Adjacent angles have a common vertex and a common ray between them.

m∠EIG + m∠GIF = 180°   m∠GIF + m∠HIF = 180°

m∠HIF + m∠EIH = 180°   m∠EIH + m∠EIG = 180°

The intersecting lines also form two pairs of congruent angles, called **vertical angles.**

∠EIH ≅ ∠GIF   ∠EIH and ∠GIF are vertical angles.

∠EIG ≅ ∠HIF   ∠EIG and ∠HIF are vertical angles.

CLASSWORK

Without measuring, give the measure of each angle.

1. ∠PQS   2. ∠SQT   3. ∠TQR

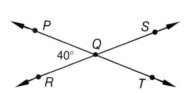

In the figure at the right, name all the following.

4. perpendicular lines

5. vertical angles

6. an angle that is a supplement of ∠QRS

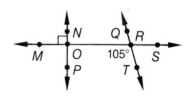

PRACTICE

In the figure at the right, $\overleftrightarrow{AB} \perp \overleftrightarrow{CD}$ and m∠CPE = 35°. Find the measure of each angle.

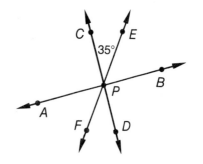

1. ∠APC **2.** ∠FPD **3.** ∠CPB

4. ∠APD **5.** ∠BPD **6.** ∠BPE

7. Name an angle that is congruent to ∠DPE.

8. Name an angle that is adjacent to ∠APF.

Use the figure at the right. Write *true* or *false* for each statement.

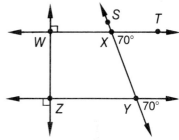

9. $\overleftrightarrow{WZ} \perp \overleftrightarrow{WX}$ **10.** $\overleftrightarrow{WX} \perp \overleftrightarrow{XY}$

11. m∠WZY = 90° **12.** m∠WXY = 100°

13. m∠XYZ = 110° **14.** m∠SXW = 110°

15. ∠TXY and ∠WXY are supplementary.

16. ∠SXT and ∠WXY are vertical angles.

17. ∠WXY and ∠XYZ are supplementary.

18. ∠TXY and ∠SXW are supplementary.

Use the figure at the right. $\overleftrightarrow{AB}$ and $\overleftrightarrow{CD}$ lie in plane *p*.

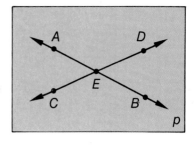

19. How many points do you need to draw a line? That is, how many points *determine* a line?

20. How many points do you need to draw two intersecting lines?

★ **21.** How many points determine a plane?

Copy the figure used in 9–18.

★ **22.** Draw a line through X perpendicular to $\overleftrightarrow{WX}$. Mark the point P at the intersection of $\overleftrightarrow{ZY}$.

★ **23.** In the figure in **22**, what is m∠PXY?

APPLICATION

The cables on the Brooklyn Bridge give it support. Without measuring, find each measure below.

24. a **25.** b **26.** c **27.** d **28.** e **29.** f

★ **30.** Find another example of intersecting lines in architecture. Sketch the intersection. Estimate the measure of each angle.

183

Parallel Lines

The wind has carved parallel lines in this sand dune.

Two lines in the same plane that never intersect are **parallel (∥).**

$$\overleftrightarrow{JK} \parallel \overleftrightarrow{LM}$$

A **transversal** is a line that intersects two or more lines at different points.

$\overleftrightarrow{NR}$ is a transversal.

Bruneau Sand Dunes State Park near Snake River, Idaho

Two parallel lines intersected by a transversal form pairs of congruent angles.

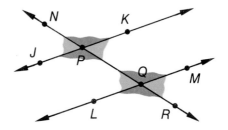

Corresponding Angles	Alternate Interior Angles	Alternate Exterior Angles
∠LQR ≅ ∠JPQ		
∠LQP ≅ ∠JPN	∠LQP ≅ ∠QPK	∠NPK ≅ ∠LQR
∠RQM ≅ ∠QPK	∠JPQ ≅ ∠PQM	∠JPN ≅ ∠RQM
∠MQP ≅ ∠KPN		

CLASSWORK

In the figure at the right, $\overleftrightarrow{BD} \parallel \overleftrightarrow{EG}$ and m∠CFE = 65°. Find the measure of each angle.

1. ∠ACB   **2.** ∠FCD   **3.** ∠CFG

4. ∠BCF   **5.** ∠EFH   **6.** ∠ACD

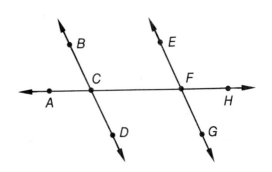

Name these angles in the figure at the right.

7. the alternate interior angles

8. the corresponding angles

PRACTICE

In the figure at the right, $\overleftrightarrow{PT} \parallel \overleftrightarrow{UX}$, $\overleftrightarrow{PT} \perp \overleftrightarrow{RZ}$, and m∠PSV = 45°. Find the measure of each angle.

1. ∠SVW   2. ∠UVY

3. ∠QST   4. ∠VST

5. ∠YVW   6. ∠UVS

7. ∠PSQ   8. ∠STW

9. ∠TWX   10. ∠STR

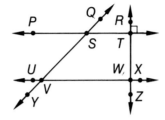

Use the figure above. Write *true* or *false* for each statement.

11. ∠PSV and ∠SVW are alternate interior angles.

12. ∠QST and ∠UVY are alternate exterior angles.

13. ∠TSV and ∠WVY are corresponding angles.

14. ∠TSV and ∠SVW are alternate interior angles.

15. ∠PSV and ∠UVY are corresponding angles.

16. ∠PSV and ∠QST are vertical angles.

17. ∠PSV and ∠SVU are supplementary angles.

18. ∠PSQ and ∠VST are supplementary angles.

19. $\overleftrightarrow{UX} \perp \overleftrightarrow{RZ}$

20. m∠VST + m∠STW = 215°

Sketch two intersecting planes.

★ 21. What geometric figure is the intersection of the planes?

★ 22. *Skew lines* are lines that do not intersect and are not in the same plane. Draw two skew lines in your sketch.

APPLICATION

Without measuring, find the measure of each angle.

23. ∠AHC   24. ∠DHI   25. ∠FIB

26. ∠HDF   27. ∠JFG   28. ∠DFJ

29. Is $\overleftrightarrow{CD} \parallel \overleftrightarrow{EF}$?   30. Is $\overleftrightarrow{AB} \parallel \overleftrightarrow{DG}$?

★ 31. Find pictures showing examples of parallel lines and parallel lines cut by transversals. Show that they are examples by drawing lines over the objects. Use these pictures to make a collage titled "Parallel Lines in Our World."

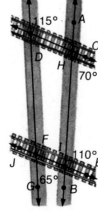

1. 5,078
   + 2,967

2. 4,113
   − 649

3. 2,609
   × 86

4. 16,810 ÷ 82

5. 248.1
   − 78.9

6. 9 + 10.8 + 1.7

7. $69.09
   − 48.96

8. 5.28
   × 0.35

9. 45 ÷ 100

10. 4.56 ÷ 0.8

Evaluate. Let $n = 4$.

11. $n + 8$

12. $15 - n$

13. $7n$

14. $4n - 2$

15. $3n + 9$

16. $(n + 2) + (n - 1)$

17. $6(n + 3)$

18. $6n + 3$

Polygons

Why do you think the polygons shown below are called regular polygons?

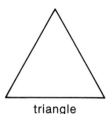
triangle

quadrilateral

pentagon

hexagon

Measure the sides and angles of each.

- What do you notice?
- How would you describe a regular polygon?
- What methods can you use to find the sum of the measures of the angles of a regular polygon?

WORKING TOGETHER

Work with a partner. Draw a triangle that is not regular. How can you find the sum of the measures of the angles?

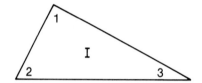

1. Use the triangle you have drawn. Number the angles as shown. Cut out the triangle and make two more copies.

   - Place the three triangles as shown.

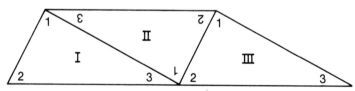

   - How can this model help you find the sum of the measures of the angles in a triangle?

2. Experiment with other triangles. Is the sum of the angle measures always the same?

SHARING YOUR THINKING

Discuss and solve.

1. Look at the triangles cut out by other classmates. Can they all be placed as shown?

2. If a triangle has an acute angle, how can you describe the sum of the measures of the other angles?

3. What is the sum of the two acute angles in a right triangle?

4. What is the measure of each angle of a regular triangle?

A. Draw any quadrilateral. Label it *ABCD*.

    1. How would you define a diagonal of a quadrilateral? of any polygon?

    2. How many diagonals does a quadrilateral have?

    3. Can you draw more than one diagonal from vertex *A* of your quadrilateral? Explain.

    4. Discuss how to find the sum of the angle measures of a quadrilateral.

B. Work in groups of three to find the sum of the angle measures of any polygon. Decide who will do each task.

    ● Draw a polygon.

    ● Draw all the diagonals from one vertex.

    ● Copy and complete the chart on the right.

Change roles and repeat the activity for other polygons.

INVESTIGATING POLYGONS		
	Triangle	Quadrilateral
Number of sides	3	4
Number of diagonals from one vertex	0	1
Number of triangles formed	1	2
Sum of angle measures	180°	

    1. What patterns can you discover from studying the data you recorded?

    2. Without drawing a diagram, find the sum of the angle measures of a decagon.

    3. Use what you have learned to write a formula for the sum of the angle measures of a polygon with *n* sides.

    4. Use a calculator and the results above to find the sum of the angle measures for a polygon with 9 sides; with 12 sides; with 20 sides.

    5. The sum of the measures of the angles of a polygon is 900°. How many sides does the polygon have?

Triangles

The faces of many crystals are triangular.

Here are 6 equilateral triangles made with 12 sticks. Form 3 equilateral triangles by moving 4 of the sticks.

 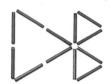

What is an equilateral triangle?

Triangles classified according to sides

No two sides congruent	scalene 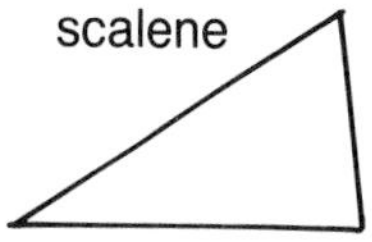
At least two sides congruent At least two angles congruent	isosceles 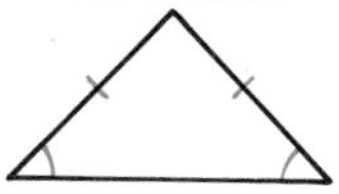
All three sides congruent All three angles congruent	equilateral 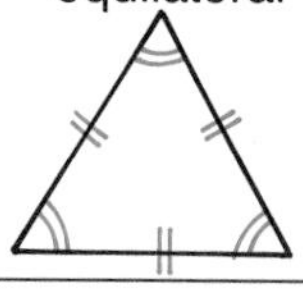

Triangles classified according to angles

One right angle	right 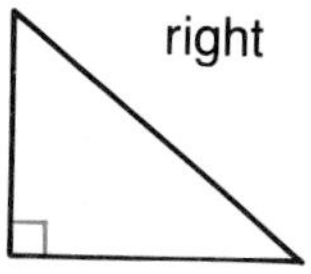
One obtuse angle	obtuse 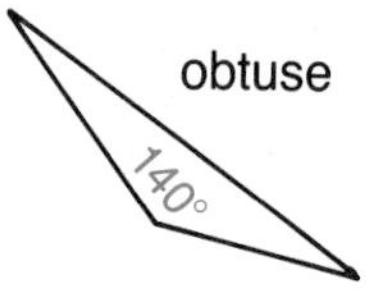 140°
All acute angles	acute 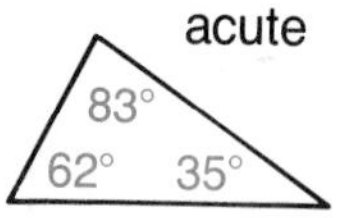 83° 62° 35°

CLASSWORK

For each triangle, find the missing measures.

1. isosceles
x
a   46°
4   5
b

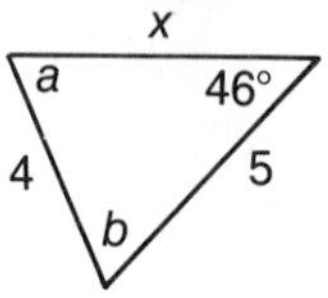

2. equilateral
15   b
a   x
y   c

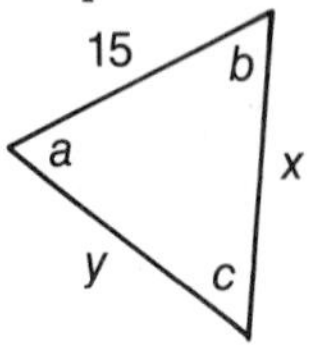

3. right
a   5
3
b   37°
4

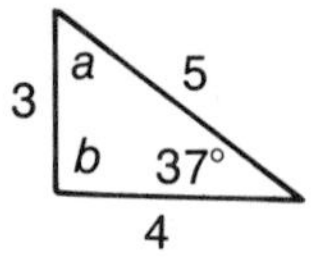

4. scalene
11   a   8
30°   40°
16

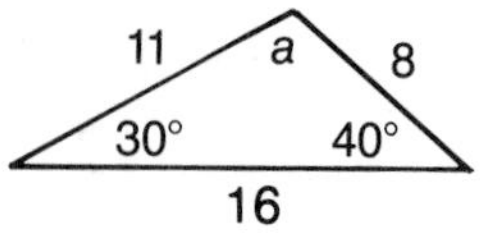

For each triangle, measure each side and each angle. Classify the triangle as right, acute, or obtuse; scalene, isosceles, or equilateral.

1.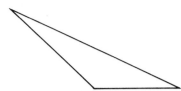

2.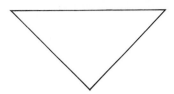

3.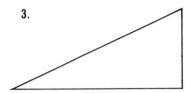

For each triangle, find the missing measures.

4. equilateral

5. right isosceles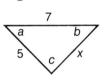

6. isosceles

★ 7. scalene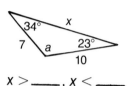

$x > $ _____, $x < $ _____

If possible, sketch each triangle. If not, explain why.

8. right scalene

9. obtuse equilateral

10. right isosceles

11. right equilateral

12. isosceles scalene

13. acute scalene

Classify each triangle as acute, right, or obtuse; scalene, isosceles, or equilateral.

★ 14. The vertices are A, B, and C. Side $\overline{AB}$ has the same length as side $\overline{BC}$. $m\angle A = m\angle C = 60°$.

★ 15. The vertices are X, Y, and Z. $m\angle X = 65°$ and $m\angle Y = 25°$.

APPLICATION

16. The shapes of these road signs imitate shapes found in nature. Triangular-shaped road signs mean "slow down and proceed with caution." What kind of triangle are these signs?

★ 17. What other kinds of polygons are shown in these pictures?

=== LOGICAL THINKING ===

You have 12 sticks in the following lengths: 3 are 2 units long, 3 are 3 units long, 3 are 4 units long, and 3 are 5 units long. How many different triangles can you make? What types of triangles can you make?

Quadrilaterals

Examples of quadrilaterals appear in nature as well as in things made by people.

Composition (1921) by the twentieth-century Dutch painter Piet Mondrian

Quadrilaterals have 4 sides and 4 angles. There are some special quadrilaterals.

trapezoid

parallelogram

In a trapezoid exactly one pair of opposite sides is parallel.

In a parallelogram both pairs of opposite sides are parallel. Opposite sides and opposite angles are congruent.

rhombus

rectangle

square

A rhombus is a parallelogram with all sides congruent.

A rectangle is a parallelogram with four right angles.

A square is a rectangle with all sides congruent.

CLASSWORK

1. In the figure at the right, name the opposite sides, the parallel sides, and the congruent sides.

2. Is *WXYZ* a trapezoid? a parallelogram? a rhombus? a rectangle? a square?

3. Which kinds of quadrilaterals are parallelograms? Which are rhombuses? Which are rectangles?

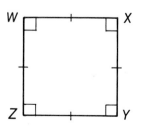

PRACTICE

For each quadrilateral below, name the parallel sides, the
congruent sides, and the congruent angles. Then name
the quadrilateral.

1.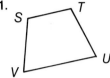

2.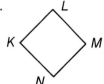

3.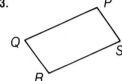

4.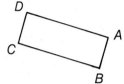

For each quadrilateral, find the missing measures.

5.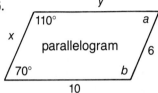

6.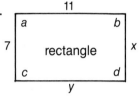

7.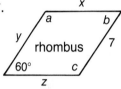

Write *true* or *false* for each statement.

8. A square is a rhombus.

9. A rectangle is a trapezoid.

10. The opposite angles of a parallelogram
are congruent.

11. The opposite sides of a trapezoid
are congruent.

12. A parallelogram is a rectangle.

13. A trapezoid is a parallelogram.

14. The opposite angles of a rectangle are
congruent.

15. A trapezoid sometimes has four right
angles.

★ 16. A parallelogram with one right angle is
a rectangle.

★ 17. A rectangle with congruent adjacent
sides is a square.

Name each quadrilateral.

★ 18. The vertices are A, B, C, and D.
Side $\overline{AD}$ is the same length as side $\overline{BC}$.
Side $\overline{AB}$ is parallel to side $\overline{CD}$. m∠A =
m∠B = 70°. m∠C = m∠D = 110°.

★ 19. The vertices are W, X, Y, and Z.
Side $\overline{WX}$ is the same length as side $\overline{ZY}$.
Side $\overline{WZ}$ is parallel to side $\overline{XY}$. m∠W =
m∠Y = 65°. m∠X = m∠Z = 115°.

APPLICATION

VISUAL THINKING

1. Remove 4 sticks to leave 5 squares.
2. Remove 8 sticks to leave 2 squares.
(The squares need not be the same size.)

Problem Solving

MAKING AND USING TABLES

Tables are useful for organizing information. The information is then easier to use to solve problems.

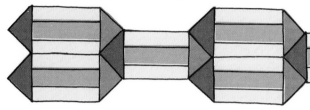

1. Kathy is making a mosaic design using triangles and rectangles. The table shows how many of each kind she uses. If she uses 27 rectangles, how many triangles will she need?

Triangles	2	4	6	8	10	
Rectangles	3	6	9	12	15	

How many triangles will she need?
Kathy uses 27 rectangles. In the table the row for triangles increases by 2. The row for rectangles increases by 3.

Continue the table until the row for rectangles shows 27.

Triangles	2	4	6	8	10	12	14	16	18
Rectangles	3	6	9	12	15	18	21	24	27

The table shows that Kathy will need 18 triangles.

Check to make sure the fractions are equivalent.

That is, $\frac{18}{27} = \frac{18 \div 9}{27 \div 9} = \frac{2}{3}$.

The answer is correct.

2. Two clocks in the steeple of the city hall show the same time at 2:00 P.M. One of these clocks runs correctly. The other one is running backwards. At what hour will they show the same time again?

Make a table to show the times for each clock.

Time on clock 1	2 P.M.	3 P.M.	4 P.M.	5 P.M.	
Time on clock 2	2 P.M.	1 P.M.	12 noon	11 A.M.	

Complete the table. Solve the problem.

Mr. Harwood is planting 7 groves of fruit trees. The table shows his plan. Copy and complete the table.

Grove	1	2	3	4	5	6	7
Apple	6	8	10	12	10	8	6
Peach	9	12					9
Pear	10	16	24				10
Total	25	36	49				25

1. How many peach trees are in grove 5?

2. How many pear trees are in grove 4?

3. How many apple trees should Mr. Harwood buy altogether?

4. How many peach trees should Mr. Harwood buy altogether?

5. How many trees does he need altogether?

6. How many of each tree will be in grove 6?

Jim and Louisa are making a game board from a square piece of wood. They take turns drawing lines as shown. Jim draws a horizontal line, then Louisa draws a vertical line. They continue until each has drawn 20 lines.

7. How many sections are there when they have each drawn 1 line?

8. How many sections are there when they have each drawn 2 lines?

9. How many sections will there be when they have each drawn 3 lines?

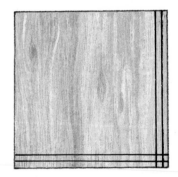

10. Make a table to show the number of lines and the number of sections there will be each time they both draw their lines.

11. How many sections will there be when they finish?

★ 12. How many lines must they each draw to have exactly 625 sections?

=== CREATE YOUR OWN PROBLEM ===

Use the data in this table to create your own problem.

	Jack	Mary	Clem
Regular Hexagons	3	6	9
Equilateral Triangles	6	12	18
Squares	4	8	12

Perimeter

At the right is a sketch of a botanical garden.
What is the distance around the path?

$$75 + 150 + 75 + 100 + 100 = 500$$

The distance around the path is 500 m.

The distance around a polygon is its
perimeter. You can use a formula to find
the perimeter of some polygons.

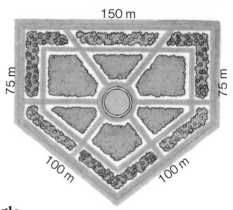

150 m

75 m

75 m

100 m

100 m

Square

The perimeter of a square is four times the
length of a side.

P = 4s

$P = 4 \times 5$
$\quad = 20$

The perimeter is 20 m.

s = 5 m

Rectangle

The perimeter of a rectangle is twice the length
plus twice the width.

P = 2l + 2w
= 2(l + w)

$P = 2(12 + 5)$
$\quad = 2 \times 17 = 34$

The perimeter is 34 m.

w = 5 m

l = 12 m

The formula $P = ns$ can be used to find the perimeter of any
regular polygon. In the formula, n is the number of sides and
s is the length of each side.

P = ns

$P = 5 \times 3.5$
$P = 17.5$

The perimeter is 17.5 cm.

3.5 cm

CLASSWORK

Find the perimeter of each figure.

1.
2 m   1 m
1 m
4 m   3 m

2.
2.5 cm

3.
5 km
2.5 km

4.
3 cm   9 cm
4 cm
3 cm   7 cm

5. an equilateral triangle with side 14 cm

6. a rectangle 7.2 cm by 5 cm

Find the perimeter of each figure.

1.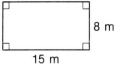
15 m, 8 m

2.
9 cm

3.
13 m, 12 m, 5 m

4.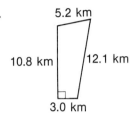
5.2 km, 10.8 km, 12.1 km, 3.0 km

5.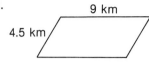
9 km, 4.5 km

6.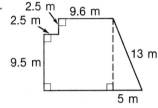
2.5 m, 2.5 m, 9.6 m, 9.5 m, 13 m, 5 m

7. a rectangle 8 cm by 9 cm   8. a square 9.4 km on a side   9. a rectangle 6.2 m by 10.4 m

The perimeter of each polygon is given. Find the missing sides.

★ **10.** a square with P = 100 m   ★ **11.** a rectangle with P = 55 cm, l = 15 cm

★ **12.** an equilateral triangle with P = 20.1 m   ★ **13.** a square with P = 26 m

Find the perimeter of each regular polygon.

14.
5 m

15.
4.6 cm

16.
50 cm

★ 17.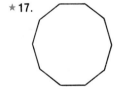
100 m

APPLICATION

18. One of the rectangular flower beds in the botanical garden on page 194 is 3.2 m long and 1.8 m wide. What is the perimeter of the flower bed?

19. One of the gardeners is edging the flower bed in **18** with bricks that are each 10 cm wide and 20 cm long. How many bricks will she need?

★ **20.** The sketch at the right shows how picket fencing will be used in another part of the garden. How many meters of fencing will be needed in all? If the fencing costs $6 per meter, how much will it cost to fence this flower bed?

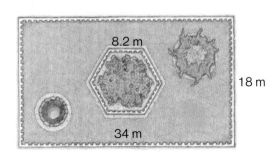
8.2 m, 18 m, 34 m

195

Area—Rectangles, Squares, Parallelograms

The **area** of a region is the number of square units needed to cover the region. **Square centimeter (cm²)**, **square meter (m²)**, and **square kilometer (km²)** are units of area.

People often grow herbs in rectangular or square beds. Herbs that grow well together in nature are grouped in sections of the garden. How much space is used for thyme in this garden?

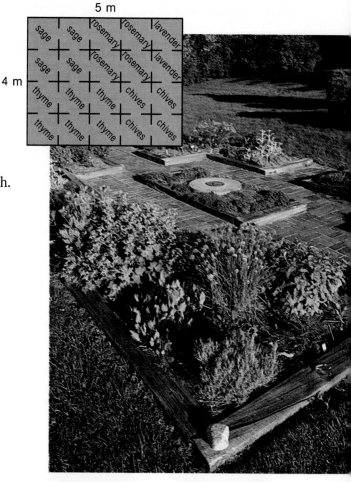

The area of a rectangle is its length times its width.

A = lw

Thyme grows in a rectangle 3 m by 2 m.

A = 3 m × 2 m = 6 m²

The space used for thyme is 6 m².

A square is a special rectangle where $l = w = s$.

A = s × s = s²

Sage grows in a square 2 m by 2 m. The area is

A = 2 m × 2 m = (2 m)² = 4 m².

The formula for the area of a rectangle can be used to find the area of a parallelogram with base b and height h. Rearrange the parallelogram as shown, and find the area of the new rectangle.

For the parallelogram at the right, if $b =$ 11 cm and $h = 7$ cm, then $A = bh =$ 11 cm × 7 cm = 77 cm².

A = base × height = bh

CLASSWORK

Find the area of each figure.

1.

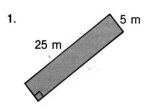

25 m · 5 m

2.

6 m, 6 m

3.

5.4 m · 10 m

4.

15.8 cm · 22.5 cm

5. square: $s = 2.3$ m

6. parallelogram: $b = 1.5$ km, $h = 0.8$ km

PRACTICE

Find the area of each figure.

1.
6 m

3 m

2.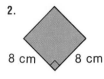
8 cm   8 cm

3.
18 cm

11 cm

4.
12.5 m   12.5 m

5.
10 cm
7 cm

Find the area of each rectangle or square.

6. $l = 12$ m, $w = 5$ m   **7.** $l = 8$ cm, $w = 1.7$ cm   **8.** $s = 12$ m

9. $l = 10.8$ cm, $w = 5.9$ cm   **10.** $s = 2.5$ m   **11.** $s = 7.8$ cm

Find the area of each parallelogram.

12. $b = 14$ cm, $h = 7$ cm   **13.** $b = 37$ m, $h = 5$ m   **14.** $b = 12.3$ cm, $h = 25.2$ cm

Find the area of each shaded region.

15.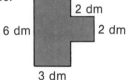
2 dm
6 dm   2 dm

3 dm

16.
3 m

5 m

17.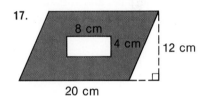
8 cm
4 cm   12 cm

20 cm

Solve.

★ **18.** Which is larger, a 10-meter square or 10 square meters? How much larger?

★ **19.** Which is larger, a 100-meter square or 100 square meters? How much larger?

APPLICATION

How much space is used for each herb in the garden on page 196?

20. rosemary   **21.** lavender   **22.** chives

SIDES OF A SQUARE

The area of this square is $A = s^2 = 100$ m². To find the length of a side of the square, find a number that when squared equals 100.

$$10^2 = 100, \text{ so } s = 10 \text{ m.}$$

s $A = 100$ m²

s

Find the length of a side of each square with the area as given below.

1. $A = 9$ m²   **2.** $A = 49$ cm²   **3.** $A = 25$ m²   **4.** $A = 36$ cm²   **5.** $A = 121$ m²

Area—Triangles, Trapezoids

1.5 km

1 km

Surveyors make topographical surveys by taking aerial photographs. Mr. Diaz photographed this triangular-shaped parcel of land. What is the area of the parcel?

The area of a triangle is one half the area of a parallelogram with the same base and the same height. In the figure at the right, the diagonal of the parallelogram divides it into two congruent triangles.

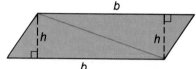

Area = $\frac{1}{2}$ × base × height   Another name for the height of a triangle is *altitude*.

$A = \frac{1}{2} bh$

The area of the parcel of land is $\frac{1}{2}$ × (1 km) × (1.5 km) = 0.75 km².

Divide a trapezoid into two triangles. The area of the trapezoid is the sum of the areas of the two triangles.

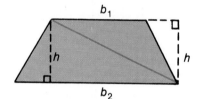

$A = \frac{1}{2} b_1 h + \frac{1}{2} b_2 h = \frac{1}{2} h (b_1 + b_2)$

For the trapezoid at the right, if $h = 5$ m, $b_1 = 8$ m, and $b_2 = 14$ m, then $A = \frac{1}{2}(5$ m)(8 m + 14 m) $= \frac{1}{2}(5$ m) (22 m) = 55 m².

CLASSWORK

Find the area of each figure.

1.

5 cm

9 cm

2.

4 cm

3 cm

3.

3 km

4 km

5 km

4.

7 cm

5 cm

4 cm

5. triangle: $b = 12.8$ cm, $h = 10.3$ cm   6. trapezoid: $h = 8.2$ m, $b_1 = 6$ m, $b_2 = 10.5$ m

Find the area of each figure.

1.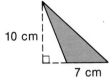
10 cm
7 cm

2.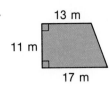
13 m
11 m
17 m

3.
3.5 km
5 km

4.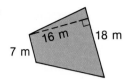
16 m
18 m
7 m

5. triangle: $b = 8$ m, $h = 2$ m

6. trapezoid: $h = 7$ cm, $b_1 = 10$ cm, $b_2 = 7$ cm

7. triangle: $b = 13$ cm, $h = 6.4$ cm

8. trapezoid: $h = 4.5$ m, $b_1 = 4$ m, $b_2 = 6$ m

9. triangle: $b = 3.5$ m, $h = 4.5$ m

10. trapezoid: $h = 30$ m, $b_1 = 65$ m, $b_2 = 48$ m

$\overline{AF} \parallel \overline{JG}$; $\overline{BI} \parallel \overline{CH} \parallel \overline{EG}$; $\overline{AJ} \parallel \overline{DH} \parallel \overline{FG}$; $\overline{AB} \cong \overline{BC} \cong$
$\overline{CD} \cong \overline{EF} \cong \overline{IH}$. **Find the area of each.**

11. *BIJ*
12. *ABJ*
13. *DFGH*
14. *BDHI*
15. *BCHJ*
16. *CEGH*
17. *BCHI*
★18. *BHI*
★19. *JCDG*

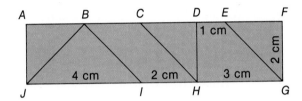

Find the area of each shaded region.

20.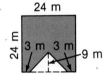
24 m
24 m
3 m 3 m
9 m

21.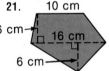
10 cm
6 cm
16 cm
6 cm

★22.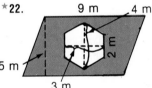
9 m   4 m
2 m
5 m
3 m

CALCULATOR

When substituting values in a formula, be careful of the key
sequence you use on a calculator. To find the area of this
trapezoid, press $\boxed{6}$ $\boxed{+}$ $\boxed{8}$ $\boxed{=}$ $\boxed{\times}$ $\boxed{7}$ $\boxed{\div}$ $\boxed{2}$ $\boxed{=}$ ▭ *49.*

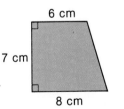
6 cm
7 cm
8 cm

The area is 49 cm^2.

If you press $\boxed{7}$ $\boxed{\times}$ $\boxed{6}$ $\boxed{+}$ $\boxed{8}$ $\boxed{\div}$ $\boxed{2}$ $\boxed{=}$, you might
get 25 or 46. Both answers are incorrect.

Show a correct key sequence to find the area of each figure.

1. 8 m
7 m 6 m
15 m

2. 11 m
7.5 m
8 m

3. 5.5 cm
7 cm
9 cm
5 cm

4.
2.6 m
1.5 m
3.0 m

199

Circles

This medicine wheel was built about 200 years ago by Native Americans in Wyoming. Its diameter is about 26 m. Find the perimeter and the area of the wheel.

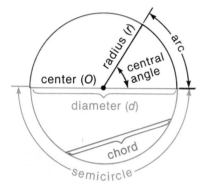

The perimeter of a circle is called its **circumference (C)**. In every circle the ratio $\frac{C}{d}$ is the same number, π (pi). Both 3.14 and $\frac{22}{7}$ are approximate values of π.

$$\frac{C}{d} = \pi, \text{ so } C = \pi d, \text{ or } C = 2\pi r.$$

The diameter is twice the radius. $d = 2r$

For the medicine wheel, $C = \pi d \approx 3.14 \times 26 \text{ m} = 81.64 \text{ m}.$

approximately equal to

Cut this circle apart to make a "parallelogram." Its height equals the radius of the circle. Its base is one half the circumference. The circle and the "parallelogram" have the same area.

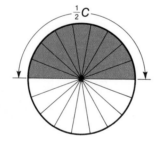

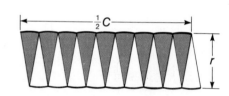

$$A = bh = \tfrac{1}{2}Cr = \tfrac{1}{2} \times 2\pi r \times r = \pi r \times r = \pi r^2$$

For the medicine wheel, $A = \pi r^2 \approx 3.14 \times (13 \text{ m})^2 = 3.14 \times 169 \text{ m}^2 = 530.66 \text{ m}^2$. To the nearest square meter, it covers 531 m².

$d = 26$, so $r = 13$.

CLASSWORK

Find the circumference and the area of each figure to the nearest one. Use 3.14 for π.

1.

2 cm
O

2.
8 m
O

3.
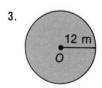
12 m
O

4. $d = 14$ mm

5. $d = 12$ m

6. $r = 2.5$ km

PRACTICE

Find the circumference and the area of each figure to the nearest one. Use 3.14 for π.

1.
7 cm
O

2.
24 m
O

3.
36 mm
O

4.
9 m
O

5. r = 5 m

6. r = 16 cm

7. d = 30 dm

8. d = 100 m

9. r = 10 m

10. d = 44 cm

11. r = 3.4 km

12. d = 12.7 cm

Find the area of the shaded portion to the nearest one.

13.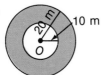
20 m
10 m
O

14.
5 m
O

15.
O
6 cm

16.
8 m
O

Write *true* or *false* for each statement.

17. The diameter of a circle is a chord.

18. The radius of a circle is twice its diameter.

19. A semicircle is an arc.

20. There are 360° around the center of a circle.

21. The vertex of a central angle of a circle is sometimes the center of the circle.

22. The ratio of the circumference to the diameter of all circles is the same.

★ 23. The length of a semicircle is one fourth the circumference of the circle.

★ 24. If a central angle of a circle measures 180°, it determines a semicircle.

APPLICATION

25. Stonehenge was built about 5,500 years ago in England. Find the circumference and the area of each circle marked in the picture. Round to the nearest one.

★ 26. How many times greater is the diameter of the larger circle? the circumference of the larger circle? the area?

30 m
45 m

═══ VISUAL THINKING ═══

These 2 chords divide the circle into 3 parts. Use 3 chords to divide the circle into the following.

1. 4 parts   2. 5 parts   3. 6 parts   4. 7 parts

Problem Solving

SKILLS AND STRATEGIES REVIEW

The Wichita County Park Commission is planting trees along the three sides of the park. The park is in the shape of an equilateral triangle. The three trees at the vertices have been planted. Three more trees were planted along one side, completing the planting on that side.

1. How many more trees must be planted?

2. How many trees will be planted in all along the sides of the park?

3. The table below shows the cost of the trees the Park Commission is purchasing. How much will the trees cost in all?

Total number of trees	1–4	5–8	9–13	14–17
Cost per tree	$25	$22	$20	$18

4. The table below shows the number of seeds in each row of a sunflower. How many seeds will there be in row 12?

Row	1	2	3	4	5	6	7	8
Number of seeds	1	1	2	3	5	8	13	21

5. Mona's dog Blue has a chain 5 m long. To the nearest square meter, what is the area of his "run"? Use $\pi \approx 3.14$.

6. The hour hand of the clock on Mercer City Hall is 40 cm long. To the nearest meter, how far does the tip of the hour hand travel in one day?

7. The earth is 150,000,000 km from the sun. To the nearest million kilometers, how far does the earth travel around the sun in one year?

8. Mr. Bray is paving his driveway. It is 5 m wide and 10 m long. The asphalt he has ordered costs $28.50 a square meter. How much will it cost to pave the driveway?

9. Below is a drawing of the cross-section of a nautilus shell. $AF = FB$ and $AM = MF$. What is the length of $\overline{AB}$?

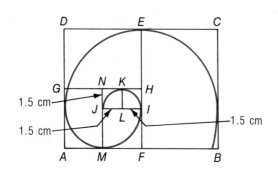

Problem Solving

WHAT IF . . . ?

Mr. Marcell has 36 pieces of slate. Each piece is a square 1 foot on a side. He wants to make a rectangular patio with the pieces of slate.

1. Make a table to show the length and width of each of the possible rectangular patios Mr. Marcell can make.

2. How many different patios are possible?

3. Mr. Marcell wants his patio to have a perimeter of 30 ft. What will the dimensions be?

What if Mr. Marcell cuts each slate in half to form rectangles 1 ft by $\frac{1}{2}$ ft?

4. Make a table to show the length and width of each of the possible rectangular patios.

5. How many different patios are possible?

6. Mr. Marcell wants his patio to have a perimeter of 40 ft. What will the dimensions be?

7. Make a drawing of the patio.

What if Mr. Marcell cuts each of the original square slates in half along the diagonal?

8. What shape will each resulting piece be?

9. How many different rectangular patios are possible?

10. Mr. Marcell wants his patio to have a perimeter of 24 ft. What will the dimensions be?

★ 11. The 1-foot pieces of slate cost Mr. Marcell $9.50 each. How much will this patio cost?

What if Mr. Marcell can buy rectangular pieces 1 ft by $\frac{1}{2}$ ft for $62 per dozen?

★ 12. Is it less expensive to buy pre-cut pieces or to cut his own?

★ 13. What is the difference in price?

203

Measure each angle. Then classify it as acute, right, or obtuse. pages 178–179

1.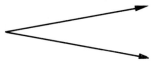

2.

Are the polygons in each pair congruent? If so, name the congruent sides and angles. Then state the congruence for the polygons. pages 180–181

3.

4.

Use the figure at the right to find each. m∠FGH = 130°. pages 182–185

5. perpendicular lines

6. parallel lines

7. ∠FGJ and ∠____ are alternate interior angles.

8. measure of the complement of ∠EFG

9. m∠KGJ

10. m∠FGJ

11. m∠EFG

12. m∠EFM

13. m∠NEF

Name each polygon. Then give the sum of the angle measures. pages 186–187

14.

15.

16.

For each polygon, find the missing measures. pages 188–191

17. equilateral triangle

18. rhombus

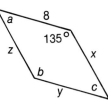

19. right isosceles triangle

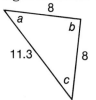

Find the perimeter or the circumference and the area of each figure to the nearest one. Use 3.14 for π. pages 194–201

20.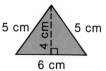

21.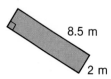

22.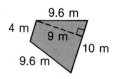

23.

24.

Solve. pages 192–193, 202–203

25. Sixty chairs are arranged in rows. The same number of chairs are in each row. What are the possible numbers of rows?

Use the figure at the right to answer 1–12.

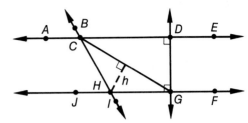

1. Name the perpendicular lines.

2. Name the parallel lines.

3. ∠ACB and ∠____ are vertical angles.

4. ∠ACB and ∠____ are corresponding angles.

5. Measure each angle of △CHG and classify it as acute, right, or obtuse.

6. Name the congruent sides and angles of △CHG.

7. If m∠CHG = 120°, then m∠DCH = ____.

8. Find m(the complement of ∠HCG).

9. Classify △CHG as scalene, isosceles, or equilateral; acute, right, or obtuse. Give the sum of its angle measures.

10. Classify CDGH as trapezoid, parallelogram, rhombus, rectangle, or square. Give the sum of its angle measures.

11. CG = 17.5 cm, CH = 10 cm, and h = 5 cm. Find the perimeter and area of △CHG.

12. CD = 9 m, DG = 4 m, GH = 5 m, and HC = 5 m. Find the perimeter and area of CDGH.

For each polygon, find the missing measures.

13. parallelogram

14. square

15. regular pentagon

16. scalene triangle
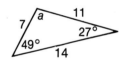

Find the perimeter or the circumference and the area of each figure. Use 3.14 for π. Round to the nearest one.

17. square with side 12 cm

18. circle with radius 4 m

Solve.

19. How much will it cost to fence in this field at Oneonta Zoo? Fencing costs $7.50 a meter.

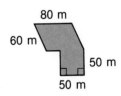

20. Bobbi, Maria, Sadie, and Alisha like to play tennis together. However, they are not all able to play on the same days.
   • Bobbi cannot play on Tuesdays, Wednesdays, and Saturdays.
   • Maria can play on Mondays, Wednesdays, and Thursdays.
   • Sadie cannot play on Mondays and Thursdays.
   • Alisha can play on Mondays, Tuesdays, and Fridays.
   • None of them can play on Sunday.
   a. Can each pair find a day on which to play?
   b. Are there any days when no games can be played?

Find the area of the shaded region. Use π ≈ 3.14. Round to the nearest one.

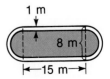

EXPLORE

GEOMETRIC PUZZLES

1. Make a copy of these equally spaced coins. Place your pencil on a coin. Without lifting your pencil from the paper, connect the coins, using only 4 line segments.

2. Arrange 10 coins in 5 rows of 4 coins each.

3. One spring, 3 straight cracks appeared in the surface of a sidewalk. The cracks separated each stone from every other stone. Place 7 stones on a piece of paper in the pattern shown at the right. Draw straight lines to show where the cracks were.

4. Which two shapes at the right will complete each rectangle?

a.

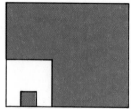

1   2   3   4   5

b.

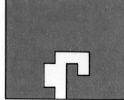

1   2   3   4   5   6

ANGLES AND CIRCLES

An **inscribed angle** is an angle with vertex on a circle and with sides that contain chords of a circle. An inscribed angle intercepts an arc of a circle.

inscribed angle *ABC*

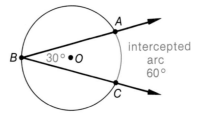

$\angle ABC$ intercepts $\overset{\frown}{AC}$. ⟵means *arc*.

▶The measure of an inscribed angle is one half the measure of its intercepted arc.

$$m\overset{\frown}{AC} = 60°$$
$$m\angle ABC = \tfrac{1}{2}(60°) = 30°$$

▶The measure of a central angle equals the measure of its intercepted arc.

$$m\overset{\frown}{DF} = m\angle DEF = 60°$$

central angle *DEF*

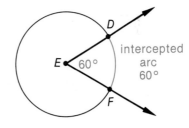

The length of an arc equals

$$\frac{\textbf{measure of arc}}{360°} \times \textbf{circumference.}$$
↑_____ measure of circle

For circle *E* with radius 6 cm, the length of $\overset{\frown}{DF}$ is as follows.

$$\frac{60°}{360°} \times 2\pi (6 \text{ cm}) = \tfrac{1}{6} \times 12\pi \text{ cm} = 2\pi \text{ cm} \approx 6.28 \text{ cm}$$

Rounded to the nearest one, the length of $\overset{\frown}{DF}$ is 6 cm.

Find the measure and the length of each arc. The radius of each circle is 12 m.

1.

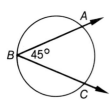

2.

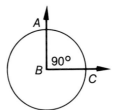

3.

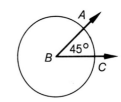

4.

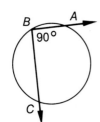

5.

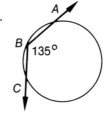

6.

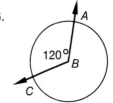

WORD PROCESSING

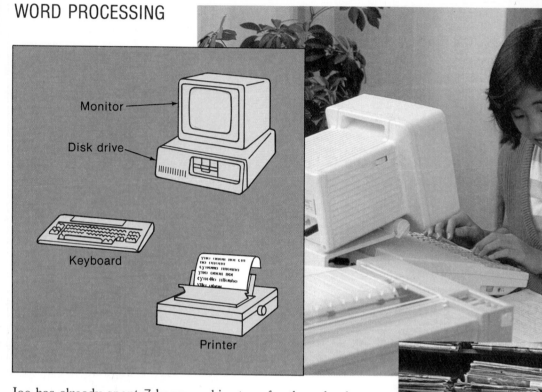

Monitor

Disk drive

Keyboard

Printer

Joe has already spent 7 hours on his story for the school newspaper. He still is not finished because of spelling and punctuation mistakes. Sally has spent 3 hours on her story. She is already finished because she used a word processor.

What does a word processor do?

It can change sentences or paragraphs around. It can correct spelling and punctuation. It can store part or all of a story until it is needed. It can even print an entire book!

How does a word processor work?

A word processing system usually has a keyboard, a monitor, a processing unit, and a printer. Some systems have a software program that is used with a computer. In both cases, words are typed on a keyboard, just as on a typewriter. The words appear on the monitor or screen as they are typed. To make changes, certain commands are used. The computer can be instructed to correct spelling, add or delete words, or move sentences. As a command is typed, the change appears on the screen. When the story is finished, another command orders the printer to print the story. Yet another command can then save the entire story to be used again later.

Authors use word processing systems to help them edit their books. It is easy to make corrections without having to retype an entire page.

Newspaper reporters use word processors also. They are able to generate their stories quickly and easily. Valuable time is saved because whole stories are never rewritten or retyped by the reporter.

Lawyers use word processors in preparing their notes for court.

Secretaries find word processors valuable. They are faster and more accurate in preparing letters, documents, and reports.

PROJECTS

1. Find 3 other occupations that use word processors. Write a paragraph for each, describing how the word processor is used.

2. Collect articles from newspapers and magazines that show the uses of word processing. Use the articles to create a bulletin board display.

3. Research the history of word processing. Find out how it got started.

★4. Visit a computer store. Ask for a demonstration of a word processing program. Write a report on your findings.

CUMULATIVE REVIEW

Choose the correct answers. Write A, B, C, or D.

1. What is the standard form?
   five million, thirty thousand, six

   A 5,306,000   **C** 5,030,600
   B 5,030,006   **D** not given

2. Round 3,965,000 to the nearest thousand.

   A 3,970,000   **C** 3,965,000
   B 4,000,000   **D** not given

3. Estimate. $4{,}862 \times 29$

   A 80,000   **C** 120,000
   B 150,000   **D** not given

4. $54{,}033 \div 67$

   A 860 R31   **C** 806 R31
   B 851 R14   **D** not given

5. What is the value of 6 in 32.065?

   A 0.6   **C** 600
   B 0.006   **D** not given

6. $4.6 + 0.15 + 13.094$

   A 17.844   **C** 13.155
   B 17.744   **D** not given

7. $\begin{array}{r} 0.024 \\ \times \ \ 0.08 \\ \hline \end{array}$

   A 0.0162   **C** 0.00192
   B 0.162   **D** not given

8. 3.015×10^5

   A 150.75   **C** 30,150
   B 301,500   **D** not given

9. $\begin{array}{r} 3 \text{ wk } 5 \text{ d} \\ \times \ \ \ \ \ 3 \\ \hline \end{array}$

   A 9 wk 5 d   **C** 11 wk 1 d
   B 9 wk 1 d   **D** not given

10. Estimate the height of a closet door.

    A 20 cm   **C** 200 mm
    B 2 m   **D** not given

11. Complete. 12.06 dag = ___ g

    A 120.6   **C** 1.206
    B 0.1206   **D** not given

12. What time is 6 h 32 min before 2:45 P.M.?

    A 9:17 P.M.   **C** 8:13 A.M.
    B 9:17 A.M.   **D** not given

13. What property is used?
    $(6 \times 2) + (6 \times 5) = 6(2 + 5)$

    A identity   **C** associative
    B commutative   **D** not given

14. $12 \div (2^3 + 4) \times 6$

    A 24   **C** 8
    B 6   **D** not given

15. Evaluate $2a + b^2$ for $a = 4$ and $b = 3$.

    A 17   **C** 22
    B 14   **D** not given

16. Solve this equation. $31 = \frac{n}{20}$

    A $n = 1.55$ **C** $n = 620$
    B $n = 51$ **D** not given

CUMULATIVE REVIEW

Choose the correct answers. Write A, B, C, or D.

17. Solve this equation. $b \times 2.4 = 12$

    A $b = 28.8$ **C** $b = 9.6$

    B $b = 5$ **D** not given

18. What is the prime factorization of 168?

    A $2^3 \times 3 \times 7$ **C** 6×21

    B $2^4 \times 3 \times 7$ **D** not given

19. What is the LCM of 8 and 12?

    A 48   **C** 4

    B 96   **D** not given

20. What is $\frac{27}{4}$ as a mixed number?

    A $4\frac{3}{4}$ **C** $6\frac{1}{4}$

    B $6\frac{3}{4}$ **D** not given

21. What is $7\frac{2}{3}$ as a decimal?

    A 0.66   **C** $7.\overline{6}$

    B $0.7\overline{3}$ **D** not given

22. $12\frac{2}{5}$

    $+\ 18\frac{3}{4}$

    A $30\frac{3}{20}$ **C** $30\frac{4}{5}$

    B $31\frac{1}{20}$ **D** not given

23. $5\frac{2}{9}$

    $-\ 2\frac{7}{9}$

    A $7\frac{8}{9}$ **C** $3\frac{4}{9}$

    B $2\frac{4}{9}$ **D** not given

24. $\frac{7}{8} \times 6$

    A $5\frac{1}{4}$ **C** $1\frac{1}{5}$

    B 7   **D** not given

25. $10\frac{4}{5} \div \frac{9}{25}$

    A $\frac{1}{30}$ **C** 30

    B $10\frac{9}{25}$ **D** not given

26. Complete. 6 lb 4 oz = ___ oz

    A 76   **C** 96

    B 100   **D** not given

27. What is the complement of a 35° angle?

    A 55°   **C** 45°

    B 145°   **D** not given

28. What is a triangle with 3 equal angles?

    A isosceles   **C** right

    B equilateral   **D** not given

29. What is the perimeter?

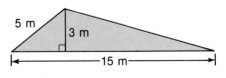

3.5 m   4.28 m   4.2 m   6.05 m

    A 18.03 m   **C** 11.1 m

    B 17.83 m   **D** not given

30. What is the area?

5 m   3 m   15 m

    A 28 m²   **C** 22.5 m²

    B 37.5 m²   **D** not given

CUMULATIVE REVIEW

Choose the correct answers. Write A, B, C, or D.

Solve.

31. Adams Junior High School is trying to raise money for student activities. Students will sell oranges at $.50 each. The cost to the school is $7.20 for a box of 24. What profit is made on each box?

    A $12.00   **C** $5.20
    B $4.80   **D** not given

32. How many boxes must be sold to raise $120.00?

    A 25   **C** 240
    B 40   **D** not given

33. If another company offers to sell the school oranges for $.25 each, what is the difference in the profit for each box?

    A $6.00   **C** $2.80
    B $1.20   **D** not given

Find the pattern. What are the next two numbers?

34. 5, 6, 8, 11, ___, ___

    A 15, 20   **C** 15, 19
    B 14, 18   **D** not given

35. 12.5, 12.41, 12.32, ___, ___

    A 11.5, 11.14   **C** 12.23, 12.14
    B 11.42, 10.52   **D** not given

36. 6, 12, 11, 22, ___, ___

    A 44, 43   **C** 21, 42
    B 28, 27   **D** not given

Solve.

37. Travel expenses are $.15 per mile. Mr. Adkins travels 42 miles on Wednesday and 157 miles on Friday. How much are his total travel expenses for Wednesday and Friday?

    A $28.85   **C** $39.85
    B $19.85   **D** not given

Use the graph below for 38–40.

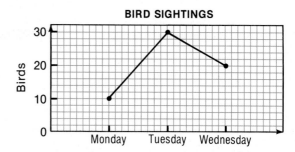

BIRD SIGHTINGS

38. The ornithology club went to the wildlife preserve to see how many kinds of birds they could observe. How many birds in all were seen on Monday, Tuesday, and Wednesday?

    A 65   **C** 45
    B 60   **D** not given

39. What was the average number of birds seen on each of these days?

    A 20   **C** 13
    B 21   **D** not given

40. If the goal of the club is to observe 100 different birds for the week, what total will be needed for Thursday and Friday?

    A 35   **C** 0
    B 18   **D** not given

Ratio · Proportion 8

Theme: Comparisons

Ratios

When the penny was first minted in 1796, it had strong purchasing power. A person could buy a dozen apples for 11¢. Today a dozen apples costs about $2.00.

▶A **ratio** is a pair of numbers that describes a rate or compares two quantities.

rate	Write	Read
12 apples for 11¢	$\frac{12}{11}$ or 12:11	12 to 11

comparison	Write	Read
13 states in 1776 50 states in 1986	$\frac{13}{50}$ or 13:50	13 to 50

$.01

$.10

Equal ratios describe the same rate or make the same comparison. You can find equal ratios by multiplying or by dividing.

$$\frac{12}{11} = \frac{12 \times 3}{11 \times 3} = \frac{36}{33} \leftarrow \text{first term} \atop \leftarrow \text{second term}$$

$$\frac{48}{44} = \frac{48 \div 4}{44 \div 4} = \frac{12}{11}$$

To test whether two ratios are equal, you can either multiply or divide, or you can use cross products.

▶If the cross products of two ratios are equal, then the ratios are equal.

a.
$$\overset{6 \times 2?}{\underset{9 \times 2?}{\frac{6}{9} \quad \frac{12}{18}}}$$

$$\frac{6}{9} = \frac{12}{18}$$

b.
$$\overset{24 \div 4?}{\underset{16 \div 4?}{\frac{24}{16} \quad \frac{6}{5}}}$$

$$\frac{24}{16} \neq \frac{6}{5}$$
is not equal to

c.
$$\frac{10}{12} \quad \frac{25}{30}$$

$10 \times 30 = 12 \times 25$,

so $\frac{10}{12} = \frac{25}{30}$.

d.
$$\frac{8}{10} \quad \frac{52}{55}$$

$8 \times 55 \neq 10 \times 52$,

so $\frac{8}{10} \neq \frac{52}{55}$.

CLASSWORK

Write a ratio in fraction form for each.

1. 12 apples for $2.00

2. 2 cans for 59¢

3. 5 telephones for every 2 houses

Write three more equal ratios for each.

4. $\frac{8}{3}, \frac{16}{6}, \frac{24}{9}$

5. $\frac{72}{120}, \frac{36}{60}, \frac{24}{40}$

6. $\frac{1.5}{5}, \frac{3}{10}, \frac{4.5}{15}$

Replace each ⬤ with = or ≠.

7. $\frac{3}{2} \ \bullet \ \frac{21}{14}$

8. $\frac{7}{8} \ \bullet \ \frac{28}{32}$

9. $\frac{5}{9} \ \bullet \ \frac{7}{13}$

10. $\frac{8}{6} \ \bullet \ \frac{9}{7}$

11. $\frac{3.2}{7} \ \bullet \ \frac{16}{35}$

Write a ratio in fraction form for each rate or comparison.

1. 2 cans for 89¢

2. 3 radios per family

3. 50 bottles per minute

4. 3 grapefruit for $2.00

5. 1.5 kg for $1.00

6. 6 computers for 25 students

7. 4 shoes to 12 socks

8. $195 per month

9. 15 km per L

10. 5 pairs for $2.99

11. 1 cm to 250 cm

12. 5 blouses to 3 skirts

Write three more equal ratios for each.

13. $\frac{1}{5}, \frac{2}{10}, \frac{3}{15}$

14. $\frac{3}{2}, \frac{6}{4}, \frac{9}{6}$

15. $\frac{2.5}{4}, \frac{5}{8}, \frac{7.5}{12}$

16. $\frac{36}{72}, \frac{18}{36}, \frac{12}{24}$

17. $\frac{120}{80}, \frac{60}{40}, \frac{30}{20}$

18. $\frac{75}{100}, \frac{37.5}{50}, \frac{25}{33\frac{1}{3}}$

Replace each ⬤ with = or ≠.

19. $\frac{2}{3}$ ⬤ $\frac{14}{21}$

20. $\frac{9}{32}$ ⬤ $\frac{2}{8}$

21. $\frac{16}{6}$ ⬤ $\frac{40}{15}$

22. $\frac{14}{15}$ ⬤ $\frac{52}{45}$

23. $\frac{21}{7}$ ⬤ $\frac{56}{15}$

24. $\frac{5}{7}$ ⬤ $\frac{20}{28}$

25. $\frac{14}{6}$ ⬤ $\frac{35}{15}$

26. $\frac{23}{8}$ ⬤ $\frac{54}{19}$

27. $\frac{3}{4}$ ⬤ $\frac{19}{25}$

28. $\frac{9}{10}$ ⬤ $\frac{8}{9}$

29. $\frac{7}{10}$ ⬤ $\frac{3.4}{5}$

30. $\frac{1.5}{2.5}$ ⬤ $\frac{150}{250}$

31. $\frac{\frac{2}{3}}{8}$ ⬤ $\frac{5}{60}$

32. $\frac{0.25}{4}$ ⬤ $\frac{1}{15}$

33. $\frac{3\frac{1}{5}}{7}$ ⬤ $\frac{8}{17\frac{1}{2}}$

In each case the four ratios are equal. Find the missing numbers.

★ 34. $\frac{a}{16}, \frac{6}{b}, \frac{4}{8}, \frac{c}{4}$

★ 35. $\frac{x}{8}, \frac{15}{y}, \frac{20}{32}, \frac{z+9}{16}$

★ 36. $\frac{6}{m+5}, \frac{n}{10}, \frac{18}{15}, \frac{24}{p+5}$

APPLICATION

Write a ratio for each.

37. In 1776 the population of the United States was about 3 million. Today the population is about 237 million.

38. In the Old West, stagecoaches traveled at about 15 km/h. Today the highway speed is 90 km/h.

═══ LOGICAL THINKING ═══

A commuter bus seats 96 passengers. On a trip to Dallas, there was one empty seat for every two occupied seats. How many passengers were on board?

Proportions

In the movie *King Kong*, the mighty ape appeared to be 50 ft tall. Actually, a model only 18 in. tall was used. How tall would a model tree have been that appeared to be 25 ft tall next to King Kong?

$$\frac{18}{50} = \frac{n}{25}$$

inches / feet

Solve this proportion to find the height of the model tree.

▶A **proportion** is a sentence stating that two ratios are equal.

You can *solve a proportion* by multiplying or dividing or by using cross products.

product of means = product of extremes

a.
$$18 \div 2$$
$$\frac{18}{50} = \frac{n}{25}$$
$$50 \div 2$$

$$n = 18 \div 2 = 9$$

b.
$$\frac{18}{50} = \frac{n}{25}$$
means / extremes

$$18 \times 25 = 50 \times n$$
$$450 = 50n$$
$$9 = n$$

Check
$$18 \times 25 = 50 \times 9$$
$$450 = 450$$

The model tree would have been 9 in. tall.

More Examples

c.
$$\frac{15}{n} = \frac{8}{5}$$
$$15 \times 5 = n \times 8$$
$$75 = 8n$$
$$9\frac{3}{8} = n$$

Estimate to check.
15 is about 8 × 2, so
n should be about 5 × 2, or 10.

The answer $9\frac{3}{8}$ makes sense, since it is about 10.

d.
$$\frac{1.7}{3.5} = \frac{5.1}{n}$$
$$1.7 \times 3 = 5.1$$
$$n = 3.5 \times 3 = 10.5$$

CLASSWORK

Solve. Check each answer.

1. $\frac{n}{15} = \frac{17}{3}$
2. $\frac{7}{n} = \frac{28}{12}$
3. $\frac{9}{6} = \frac{15}{n}$
4. $\frac{n}{5.1} = \frac{9}{27}$
5. $\frac{23}{5} = \frac{n}{\frac{1}{2}}$

Write a proportion for each. Then solve to find the answer.

6. 2 for 39¢
How many for $1.17?

7. 9 in 15
12 in how many?

8. 20 for 35
How many for 7?

Solve. Check each answer.

1. $\frac{4}{3} = \frac{n}{9}$

2. $\frac{n}{6} = \frac{8}{3}$

3. $\frac{10}{x} = \frac{15}{6}$

4. $\frac{42}{24} = \frac{7}{x}$

5. $\frac{9}{7} = \frac{n}{49}$

6. $\frac{8}{20} = \frac{30}{y}$

7. $\frac{n}{18} = \frac{10}{15}$

8. $\frac{35}{21} = \frac{x}{9}$

9. $\frac{n}{19} = \frac{10}{5}$

10. $\frac{28}{n} = \frac{36}{27}$

11. $\frac{32}{48} = \frac{38}{y}$

12. $\frac{24}{n} = \frac{27}{63}$

13. $\frac{30}{24} = \frac{x}{16}$

14. $\frac{x}{33} = \frac{4}{11}$

15. $\frac{32}{y} = \frac{5.6}{4.9}$

16. $\frac{n}{15} = \frac{3.2}{5}$

17. $\frac{10.5}{x} = \frac{5}{10}$

18. $\frac{32}{7.2} = \frac{n}{9}$

19. $\frac{n}{10} = \frac{4}{3}$

20. $\frac{600}{n} = \frac{3}{\frac{1}{2}}$

21. $\frac{9}{6.5} = \frac{4}{n}$

22. $\frac{2\frac{1}{3}}{5} = \frac{x}{12}$

23. $\frac{\frac{1}{2}}{5} = \frac{n}{20}$

24. $\frac{n}{7} = \frac{12}{24}$

Write a proportion for each. Then solve to find the answer.

25. 5 for 78¢
    25 for how much?

26. 5 for 59¢
    10 for how much?

27. 6 in 60
    How many in 10?

28. 4 in 20
    10 in how many?

29. 3 for 5
    9 for how many?

30. 1.5 for 6
    How many for 16?

★ 31. 8 in 30
    How many in 49?

★ 32. 2 for 89¢
    7 for how much?

★ 33. 6 for $1.97
    5 for how much?

APPLICATION

34. Models of the Sphinx and the Great Pyramid have to be made for a movie about Egypt. The Sphinx is actually 66 ft tall. The model is 11 in. tall. The Great Pyramid is 480 ft tall. How tall should the model be?

★ 35. The base of the Great Pyramid is 756 ft square. What should the base of the model be?

MENTAL ARITHMETIC

Try to solve each proportion mentally.

1. $\frac{1}{3} = \frac{4}{n}$

2. $\frac{1}{2} = \frac{x}{8}$

3. $\frac{x}{5} = \frac{40}{50}$

4. $\frac{3}{10} = \frac{n}{100}$

5. $\frac{2}{7} = \frac{14}{x}$

6. $\frac{n}{80} = \frac{6}{8}$

7. $\frac{75}{100} = \frac{7.5}{n}$

8. $\frac{3}{x} = \frac{18}{24}$

Unit Price

Be a comparison shopper. Which is the better buy?

To find the better buy, compare the unit prices.

▶ The **unit price** of an item is a ratio:
price per *unit of measure*.

$$\frac{p}{1} = \frac{25}{2} \;\longrightarrow\; p = \frac{25}{2} = 12.5$$

The unit price is $12.50.

$$\frac{p}{1} = \frac{35}{3} \;\longrightarrow\; p = \frac{35}{3} = 11\frac{2}{3}$$

The unit price is $11.67, rounded to the nearest cent.

The shirts selling at 3 for $35.00 are the better buy because their unit price is less.

Another Example

Find the unit price.

> 3 cans
> for $1.00

$$\frac{p}{1} = \frac{1}{3} \;\longrightarrow\; p = \frac{1}{3}$$

The unit price is $.33, rounded to the nearest cent. But if you bought only 1 can, you would pay $.34. Stores always round up to the next cent unless the remainder is 0.

CLASSWORK

Find the unit price. Round to the nearest cent.

1. 12 pencils for 84¢

2. 1.5 L for 72¢

3. 4 cans for $1.25

4. 5 pads for $1.60

5. 2.5 kg for $5.89

6. a dozen lemons for $1.00

PRACTICE

Find the unit price. Round to the nearest cent.

Item	Quantity or size	Price	Unit Price
1. jeans	3 pairs	$38.97	____ per pair
2. sport shorts	4 pairs	$ 9.28	____ per pair
3. soap	5 bars	$ 1.79	____ per bar
4. juice	6 cans	$ .99	____ per can
5. milk	4 L	$ 2.39	____ per L
6. greeting cards	box of 25	$ 8.75	____ per card
7. socks	12 pairs	$ 9.99	____ per pair
8. tissues	6 boxes	$ 2.00	____ per box
9. fruit bars	1 dozen	$ 2.98	____ per bar
10. Ping-Pong balls	$\frac{1}{2}$ dozen	$ 1.59	____ per ball
11. pet food	3 cans	$ .67	____ per can
12. chicken	2 kg	$ 1.58	____ per kg
13. peanut butter	250 g	$ 1.89	____ per kg
★ **14.** napkins	100	$ .89	____ per napkin
★ **15.** paper towels	250-sheet roll	$ 1.05	____ per 100 sheets

APPLICATION

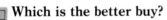

Which is the better buy?

16. pet food
  a. 3 cans for $.67
  b. 5 cans for $1.05

17. soap
  a. 5 bars for $1.79
  b. 4 bars for $1.49

18. greeting cards
  a. box of 25 for $8.75
  b. box of 30 for $11.25

19. baseball shirts
  a. 4 for $15.96
  b. 3 for $11.37

20. shampoo
  a. 375 mL for $2.95
  b. 425 mL for $3.25

★ **21.** juice
  a. 350 mL for $.23
  b. 1 L for $.67

ESTIMATION

Estimate the unit price.

1. 2 kg for $1.99

2. 3 pairs for $14.97

3. 4 boxes for $1.97

4. 3 shirts for $23.98

5. 5 pads for $1.07

6. 4 L for $2.19

7. box of 20 for $5.25

8. 1 dozen for $1.29

9. 110 sheets for $.93

Scale Drawing

A scale drawing can be a reduction or an enlargement of an actual object. The scale for the drawing is a ratio.

size of drawing:size of actual object

The scale for this scale drawing of a car is 1 cm:25 cm.

What is the actual length of the car?

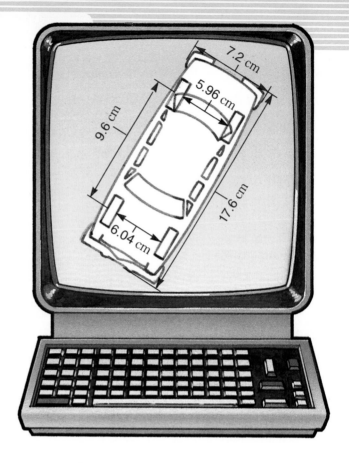

$$\frac{1}{25} = \frac{17.6}{n}$$

scale drawing ⟶ ⟵ actual

$$1 \times n = 25 \times 17.6$$
$$n = 440$$

The car is 440 cm long.

More Examples

a. scale   1 cm:5 mm
   length on scale drawing   5 mm
   actual length   ___

$$5 \text{ mm} = 0.5 \text{ cm}$$
$$\frac{1}{5} = \frac{0.5}{n}$$
$$1 \times n = 5 \times 0.5$$
$$n = 2.5$$

The actual length is 2.5 mm.

b. scale   1 cm to 2 m
   length on scale drawing   ___
   actual length   15.6 m

$$\frac{1}{2} = \frac{n}{15.6}$$
$$1 \times 15.6 = 2 \times n$$
$$7.8 = n$$

The length on the scale drawing is 7.8 cm.

CLASSWORK

Complete.

1. scale   1 mm:20 cm
   drawing   12 mm
   actual   ___

2. scale   1 cm:1 mm
   drawing   ___
   actual   7 mm

3. scale   1 cm to 2.5 km
   drawing   4.8 cm
   actual   ___

4. scale   1 cm:40 km
   drawing   3.2 cm
   actual   ___

5. scale   1 mm:1 cm
   drawing   10 cm
   actual   ___

6. scale   1 cm to 0.5 m
   drawing   ___
   actual   6.5 m

PRACTICE

Complete.

1. **scale**   1 cm:15 cm
   drawing   9 cm
   actual   ___

2. **scale**   1 mm to 5 mm
   drawing   ___
   actual   75 mm

3. **scale**   1 cm:1 mm
   drawing   7.8 cm
   actual   ___

4. **scale**   1 cm to 2.5 m
   drawing   ___
   actual   25 m

5. **scale**   1 cm:10 km
   drawing   12.5 cm
   actual   ___

6. **scale**   1 cm:2.5 mm
   drawing   ___
   actual   17.5 mm

7. **scale**   1 cm:5 mm
   drawing   ___
   actual   37.5 mm

8. **scale**   1 cm:50 cm
   drawing   ___
   actual   9.7 m

9. **scale**   1 mm to 10 km
   drawing   1.5 cm
   actual   ___

The scale on a map is 1 cm to 50 km. Find the actual
distance represented by each measurement on the map.

10. 3 cm   11. 10 cm   12. 4.2 cm   13. 5.5 cm   14. 5 mm

Which actual distance is longer, **a** or **b**?

★15.a. **scale**   1 cm:20 km
     drawing   16.25 cm
     actual   ___

   b. **scale**   1 cm:25 km
     drawing   15 cm
     actual   ___

★16.a. **scale**   1 mm:10 km
     drawing   1 cm
     actual   ___

   b. **scale**   1 cm:50 km
     drawing   2.5 cm
     actual   ___

APPLICATION

17. Make a table showing the length on the scale drawing and the
    actual length for all the dimensions of the car on page 220.

VISUAL THINKING

**Find six pairs of cars that are the same shape but *not* the
same size.**

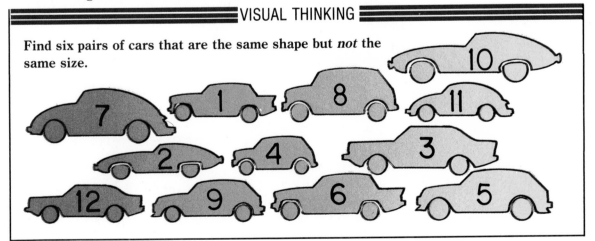

Distance, Rate, Time

A spacecraft can travel more than 400 times faster than an automobile. Traveling at 40,000 km per hour, a spacecraft can go from the earth to the moon in 10 hours. How far is the earth from the moon?

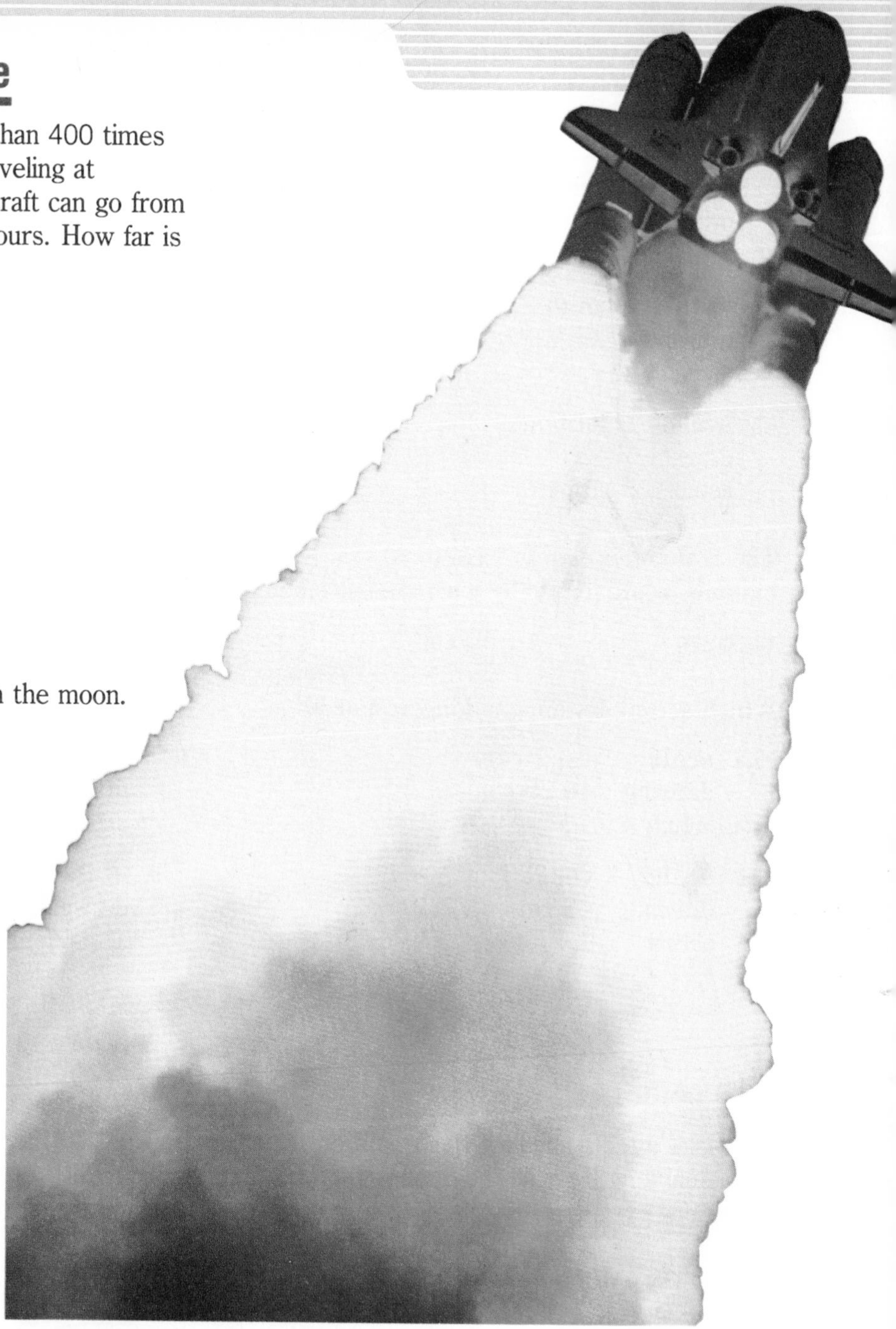

$$\frac{\text{distance } (d)}{\text{time } (t)} = \text{rate } (r)$$

$$\frac{40,000}{1} = \frac{d}{10}$$

$1d = 40,000 \times 10$

$d = 400,000$

The earth is 400,000 km from the moon.

More Examples

a. 450 km in 5 h
360 km in t h

$$\frac{450}{5} = \frac{360}{t}$$

$450 t = 5 \times 360$

$t = 4$

b. 300 km in 4 h
d km in 1 h

$$\frac{300}{4} = \frac{d}{1}$$

$300 \times 1 = 4d$

$75 = d$

CLASSWORK

Complete.

1. 40,000 km in 1 h
160,000 km in t h

2. 700 km in 2 h
d km in 8 h

3. 234 km in 3 h
d km in 1 h

4. 8 m in 12 min
1 m in t min

5. 2,400 km in 3 h
d km in 4.5 h

6. 360 m in 1 s
540 m in t s

Complete.

1. 240 km in 3 h
   d km in 5 h

2. 2,880 km in 4 h
   d km in 1 h

3. 663 km in 8.5 h
   78 km in t h

4. 80 km in 1 h
   100 km in t h

5. 5 km in 45 min
   1 km in t min

6. 7 m in 2 min
   d m in 9 min

7. 10,000 km in 4 h
   25,000 km in t h

8. 180 m in 4 min
   d m in 2.5 min

★ 9. 900 km in 1 h
   d km in 15 min

★ 10. 600 m in 1 min
   d m in 1 s

APPLICATION

11. It is about 640 km from Petersburg, Virginia, to New York City. It took Rosa 8 h to make the trip. On the average, how fast did she travel?

★ 12. Kyoko rode her bike 24 km in 1 hour. On the average, how far did she ride in 1 minute?

LOGICAL THINKING

Jeff and J.C. are 30 km apart, riding their bikes toward each other. They are each traveling at a speed of 15 km per hour. A fly starts from Jeff and flies to J.C., then back to Jeff, and so on. The fly continues back and forth at 60 km per hour until Jeff and J.C. collide, crushing the fly. How far did the fly travel?

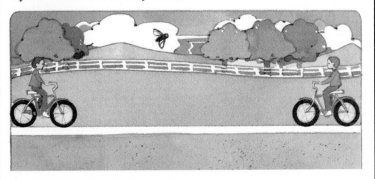

Mixed Practice

1. 143.62
    9.08
    + 74.57

2. $30.607 - 1.9467$

3. $3\frac{2}{3} + 4\frac{1}{2} + \frac{5}{6}$

4. $25\frac{3}{4}$
    $- 18\frac{7}{8}$

5. 0.308
    × 7.96

6. $\frac{1}{2} + \frac{1}{3} + \frac{1}{4}$

7. $\frac{5}{8} \times 3\frac{1}{5}$

8. $4.9\overline{)\$29.89}$

9. $9\frac{1}{6} - 4\frac{5}{12}$

10. 2.64
     × 0.03

11. $3\frac{2}{3} \div 4\frac{2}{5}$

Solve.

12. $x + \frac{3}{4} = 2\frac{1}{2}$

13. $7.8 = n - 8.4$

14. $\frac{3}{8}n = 6$

15. $12\frac{2}{3} = x - 7\frac{1}{3}$

16. $3.2\,n = 16$

Problem Solving

LOGIC

When it is necessary to draw logical conclusions from data, it is often helpful to organize the data in a table.

THINK
PLAN
SOLVE
LOOK
BACK

Anita, Barbara, Carol, and Ruth are circus clowns. They each wear a red, blue, green, or white costume.

Clue 1: Ruth and Anita left the ring before the clowns in the white costume and the blue costume.

Clue 2: The clown in red danced with Anita.

Clue 3: Barbara saw Carol put on the white costume.

Which costume is each person wearing?

Use a table to organize the information given in the clues. An X means "not wearing this color."

	Red	Blue	Green	White
Anita	X	X		X
Barbara				
Carol	X	X	X	
Ruth		X	X	X

Clue 1 tells that Ruth and Anita are not wearing white or blue. Put an *X* in each of their white and blue spaces.

Clue 2 tells us that Anita is not wearing red. Put an *X* in her red space. Since Anita is *not* wearing red, Ruth must be wearing red. Put an *X* in her green space.

Clue 3 tells us that Carol is wearing white. (Put an *X* in her red, blue, and green spaces.)

Barbara must be wearing blue.

Review the clues. Do the answers match the clues?

Solve.

1. The carpenter, the plumber, and the pharmacist in Mt. Bethel are Lopez, Jackson, and Cooper.

   • Cooper lives next door to the plumber.
   • The carpenter is Cooper's son.
   • Lopez and Cooper were on the track team together in high school.

   Which job does each person have?

2. Marci, Patti, Charles, and Brenda each went to a different movie last night. They saw *Space Voyage, Return to Planet K, Night Creatures,* and *Western Adventure.*

   • Brenda saw Patti coming out of the theater showing *Space Voyage.*
   • Marci did not want to see *Night Creatures.*
   • Charles and Marci had already seen *Western Adventure* two weeks ago.

   Which movie did each person see?

3. There were four acts in a circus performance. The elephants were on for 9 minutes, the clowns were on for 18 minutes, the lion tamer was on for 15 minutes, and the trapeze artists were on for 12 minutes. There was a 2-minute break between acts.

   • The trapeze act was on between the elephants and the clowns.
   • The elephants started promptly at 2:00 P.M.
   • The lion tamer finished at exactly 3:00 P.M.

   Draw a time line showing when each act was on and when the breaks took place.

★ 4. Seven cars were entered in the Memphis 4,300-mile auto race.

   • The winning car had an even number on it.
   • Car 4 beat car 7 by one length.
   • Car 6 blew a tire and finished last.
   • The driver of car 1 was the only one wearing yellow.
   • The driver of car 2 saw yellow on the driver ahead of her.
   • Car 7 finished two lengths ahead of car 1.
   • Cars 2 and 3 finished in a tie.
   • Car 5 finished second.

   In what order did the cars finish?

CREATE YOUR OWN PROBLEM

Fill in the blanks with appropriate data from the list at the right. Then solve the problem.

There were ____ girls at a party.
• Beverly wore a ____ dress.
• Ellen wore a white dress.
• Marty did not wear yellow.
• Sandy and the girl in ____ beat Beverly and the girl in yellow in a 3-legged race.
• The girl in the ____ skirt had to leave early.

What color did ____ wear? Which girl had to leave early?

DATA		
4	red	Joann
5	green	Ellen
6	pink	yellow

Drawing Similar Polygons

Louise wanted to build two birdhouses that were the same shape but different sizes. She used different-sized grids to draw the parts of the two houses. The fronts were similar polygons.

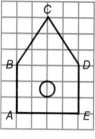

▶Two polygons are **similar** (~) if they have the same shape.

A figure can be made smaller or larger by drawing it on a smaller or larger grid.

It can also be drawn by using a ruler and a protractor. To make a polygon twice as large as *ABCDE*, draw each segment twice as long as the corresponding segment of *ABCDE*. Draw each angle the same size as the corresponding angle of *ABCDE*.

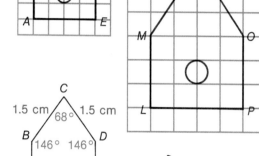

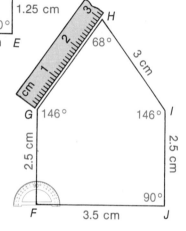

$$\angle A \cong \angle F \quad \angle B \cong \angle G \quad \angle C \cong \angle H$$
$$\angle D \cong \angle I \quad \angle E \cong \angle J$$

> Corresponding angles are congruent.

$$\frac{AB}{FG} = \frac{BC}{GH} = \frac{CD}{HI} = \frac{DE}{IJ} = \frac{EA}{JF}$$

> Corresponding sides are proportional.

$$ABCDE \sim FGHIJ$$

CLASSWORK

1. **a.** Which polygons are similar?
   b. Use a ruler and a protractor to draw a polygon three times as large as *MNOP*.

2. Use a larger or smaller grid to draw a similar figure.

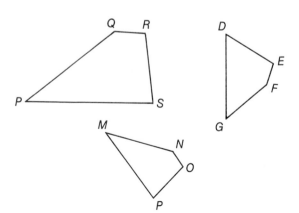

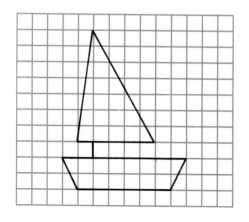

PRACTICE

Which polygons are similar?

1.

2.

3.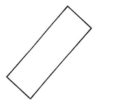

4.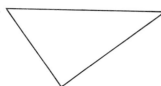

5.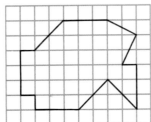

6.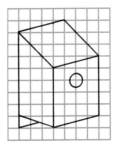

For each pair of similar polygons, complete the proportion.
Then name the congruent angles.

7. △ABC ~ △ADE

$$\frac{AB}{AD} = \frac{\square}{\square} = \frac{\square}{\square}$$

8. WALK ~ JUMP

$$\frac{WA}{JU} = \frac{\square}{\square} = \frac{\square}{\square} = \frac{\square}{\square}$$

9. SMILE ~ GRAND

$$\frac{SM}{GR} = \frac{\square}{\square} = \frac{\square}{\square} = \frac{\square}{\square} = \frac{\square}{\square}$$

Use a ruler and a protractor to draw each polygon as
described below.

10. twice as large as **1**

11. $\frac{3}{2}$ as large as **3**

12. half as large as **6**

Use a larger or smaller grid to draw a similar figure.

13.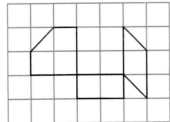

14.

15.

ABCD ~ EFGH. AB = 2 cm, BC = 1.5 cm, CD = 3.5 cm, EF = 5 cm,
FG = 3.75 cm, and EH = 7.5 cm. **Find each of the following.**

★16. $\frac{AB}{EF}$

★17. $\frac{BC}{FG}$

★18. $\frac{CD}{GH}$

★19. $\frac{DA}{HE}$

APPLICATION

20. Different kinds of birdhouses are designed to attract
different kinds of birds. The design at the right attracts
bluebirds. Use a larger grid to draw a similar birdhouse.

★21. Use a ruler and a protractor to draw a similar birdhouse
five times as large.

227

Similar Triangles

Dinosaurs are the largest land animals that ever lived. How long a shadow would this tyrannosaurus have cast compared with that of the modern man shown here?

tyrannosaurus

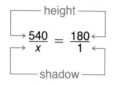

$$\frac{540}{x} = \frac{180}{1}$$

height — shadow

$$540 = 180x$$
$$3 = x$$

540 cm

average man

180 cm

x

1 m

The tyrannosaurus would have cast a 3-m shadow.

▶ If two triangles are similar, their corresponding angles are congruent and their corresponding sides are proportional. That is, the ratios of the measures of the corresponding sides are equal.

Another Example

$\triangle TAP \sim \triangle RUN$. Find x.

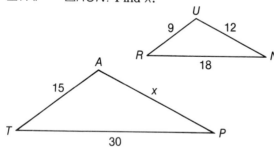

$$\frac{TA}{RU} = \frac{AP}{UN} = \frac{PT}{NR}$$

$$\frac{15}{9} = \frac{x}{12} = \frac{30}{18}$$

$$180 = 9x$$
$$20 = x$$

CLASSWORK

For each pair of similar triangles, find the unknown measures.

1.

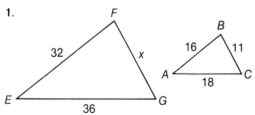

2.

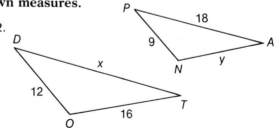

$\triangle ABC \sim \triangle DEF$. **Complete the chart.**

1.	$\dfrac{BC}{AC} = \dfrac{4}{3}$	$\dfrac{EF}{DF} = \dfrac{8}{\square} = \dfrac{4}{\square}$
2.	$\dfrac{AC}{AB} = \dfrac{\square}{\square}$	$\dfrac{DF}{DE} = \dfrac{\square}{10} = \dfrac{\square}{\square}$
3.	$\dfrac{AB}{BC} = \dfrac{\square}{\square}$	$\dfrac{DE}{EF} = \dfrac{\square}{\square} = \dfrac{\square}{\square}$

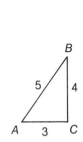

For each pair of similar triangles, find the unknown measures.

4.

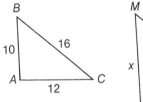

5.

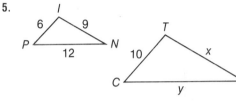

6.

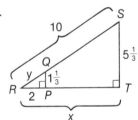

★7.

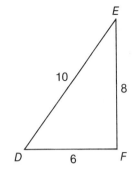

APPLICATION

Find each unknown measure.

8. Today the tallest land animal is the giraffe. It stands about 576 cm tall. How long a shadow would it cast compared with that of the tyrannosaurus on page 228?

9.

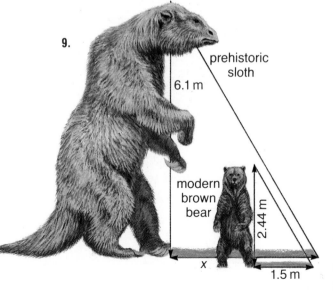

prehistoric sloth

6.1 m

modern brown bear

2.44 m

x

1.5 m

★10.

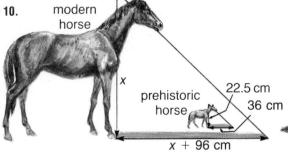

modern horse

prehistoric horse

x

22.5 cm

36 cm

x + 96 cm

Tangent Ratio

Ski jumps are built to resemble ski slopes. Snow Valley Ski Resort is building this ski jump. How high will the jump be?

▶In a right triangle, the **tangent (tan)** of an acute angle is the ratio of the length of the opposite leg to the length of the adjacent leg.

In $\triangle ABC$, $\overline{AB}$ is **opposite** $\angle C$ and $\overline{BC}$ is **adjacent** to $\angle C$. The side opposite the right angle, $\angle B$, is the **hypotenuse.**

$$\textbf{tan } 40° = \frac{x}{70}$$

To find tan 40°, use the table of values on page 497. Find 40 in the *Degree* column and then move to the right to the *Tan* column.

$$\textbf{tan } 40° = 0.8391 = \frac{x}{70}$$
$$70\,(0.8391) = x$$
$$58.737 = x$$

The jump will be about 58.7 m high.

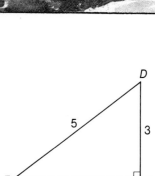
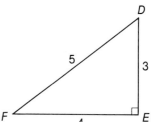

Another Example

Find the tangent of $\angle D$ to the nearest thousandth.

$$\text{tan } m\angle D = \frac{4}{3} = 1.333$$

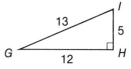

CLASSWORK

Use the table on page 497 to find each.

1. tan 30°   **2.** tan 10°   **3.** tan 45°   **4.** tan 70°

Find the tangent of each to the nearest thousandth.

5. $m\angle G$ **6.** $m\angle I$

Find x to the nearest tenth.

7.

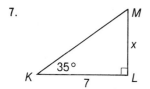

8.

PRACTICE

Use the table on page 497 to find the tangent or the measure of ∠A.

1. tan 9°   **2.** tan 20°   **3.** tan 42°   **4.** tan 50°   **5.** tan 67°

6. tan 74°   **7.** tan 80°   **8.** tan 88°   **9.** tan 89°   **10.** tan 90°

11. tan m∠A = 0.2126   **12.** tan m∠A = 0.4245   **13.** tan m∠A = 1.7321

14. tan m∠A = 1.0000   **15.** tan m∠A = 0.0875   **16.** tan m∠A = 11.4301

Find the tangent of each to the nearest thousandth.

17.

a. m∠A   **b.** m∠C

18.

a. m∠D   **b.** m∠F

19.

a. m∠K   **b.** m∠M

Find x to the nearest tenth.

20.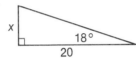

21.

★22.

★23.

APPLICATION

24. Find the height of this mountain slope to the nearest tenth.

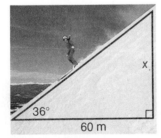

25. Andy, Beth, Cory, and Dave went skiing. They went to the ski slopes by car, bus, and train. Andy rode with Cory. Beth did not go by train. Only one person went by car. Only one person went by train. How did each person go to the ski slopes?

=== CALCULATOR ===

A table of tangent-ratio values of acute angles shows 4 or 5 decimal places. A calculator may display 7, 8, or 9 places. To find tan 10°, do the following.

Enter	Press	Display
10	tan	0.176327

Use a calculator to complete the chart at the right.

Degrees	Display
7	
20	
37	
45	
60	
75	
89	
90	

Problem Solving

SKILLS AND STRATEGIES REVIEW Transportation

How many passengers can each vehicle carry?

1. bus

2. Concorde

3. hovercraft

4. *QE 2*

VEHICLE CAPACITIES	
Bus	🧍
Concorde	🧍🧍
Boeing 747	🧍🧍🧍🧍🧍
Hovercraft	🧍🧍🧍🧍🧍
Queen Elizabeth 2 (QE 2)	🧍🧍🧍🧍🧍🧍🧍🧍🧍🧍 🧍🧍🧍🧍🧍🧍🧍🧍🧍🧍 🧍🧍🧍🧍🧍🧍🧍🧍🧍🧍

🧍 represents 100 passengers
(data rounded to nearest 50)

Use the pictograph to solve.

5. A Conover bus carries 43 passengers. How many buses would be needed to transport the passengers of a full Boeing 747 from the airport to town?

6. The *Mayflower* could carry about 130 people. How many times would it have had to cross from Europe to North America to carry as many passengers as the *QE 2* can carry in one trip?

7. The world's longest bus can carry 2.5 times as many passengers as a double-decker bus. A double-decker bus can carry 1.44 times as many passengers as a standard 50-passenger bus. How many passengers can the longest bus carry?

The proportions below are true for the capacities of each vehicle. Use the proportions to answer 8–11.

a. $\dfrac{\text{taxi}}{\text{bus}} = \dfrac{\text{Beechcraft}}{\text{Concorde}}$

b. $\dfrac{\text{Boeing 707}}{\text{Boeing 747}} = \dfrac{11}{25}$

8. A taxi holds 4 people. How many people does a Beechcraft airplane hold?

9. How many taxis would be needed to transport the passengers from a full *QE 2* from the dock to town?

10. How many passengers can a Boeing 707 carry?

11. Iroquois Airlines estimates that only 4 out of 5 people who reserve seats on a flight actually use their tickets. Flight 753 is scheduled to depart at noon and arrive in Cleveland at 2:00 P.M. The flight is sold out. Jim Chen is holding standby ticket #28. The plane used for Flight 753 is a Boeing 707. Is Jim likely to get on Flight 753?

The Tall and the Short of It

Coccus Bacillus Spirillus

0 0.001 mm
Scale

Use the picture above to answer 1–4.

1. To the nearest thousandth of a millimeter, what is the diameter of a coccus?

2. To the nearest thousandth of a millimeter, how long is a bacillus?

3. In the drawing, 1 cm represents 0.001 mm. What would 1 mm represent?

★ 4. How many times have the bacteria been magnified in the drawing above?

Usually orchids, sunflowers, dahlias, and hollyhocks are much smaller than the record breakers shown at the right. Use the picture to answer 5–10.

5. The world's tallest orchid was grown in Malaysia. How tall was it?

6. A sunflower grown in the United Kingdom broke all records. How tall was it?

7. Which plant pictured at the right has grown the tallest?

8. Which plant grew to be nearly twice as tall as the dahlia?

9. About how many times taller than the dahlia is the orchid?

10. Plants can grow much taller than the Malaysian orchid. The California redwood is the tallest living thing. The longest recorded strand of seaweed is shorter than a redwood but nearly 8 times the height of the orchid. A saguaro cactus can grow to twice the height of the orchid. The record for bamboo is 120 ft. List the redwood, seaweed, orchid, cactus, and bamboo from shortest to tallest.

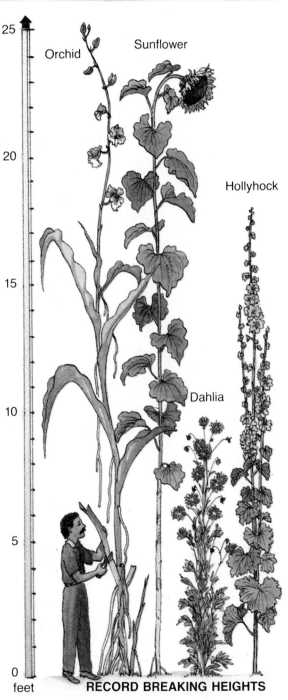

RECORD BREAKING HEIGHTS

233

Write three equal ratios for each. pages 214–215

1. $\frac{2}{3}$ 　　　 2. $\frac{4}{5}$ 　　　 3. $\frac{72}{24}$ 　　　 4. $\frac{5}{6}$ 　　　 5. $\frac{180}{150}$

Replace each ⬤ with = or ≠. pages 214–215

6. $\frac{5}{12}$ ⬤ $\frac{20}{46}$ 　　 7. $\frac{12}{18}$ ⬤ $\frac{28}{42}$ 　　 8. $\frac{11}{8}$ ⬤ $\frac{33}{24}$ 　　 9. $\frac{2.7}{3.9}$ ⬤ $\frac{3.5}{5}$ 　　 10. $\frac{3}{2\frac{1}{4}}$ ⬤ $\frac{32}{24}$

Solve. pages 216–217

11. $\frac{6}{8} = \frac{n}{12}$ 　　 12. $\frac{7}{y} = \frac{2}{9}$ 　　 13. $\frac{12}{15} = \frac{4}{x}$ 　　 14. $\frac{n}{10} = \frac{3.5}{7}$ 　　 15. $\frac{\frac{5}{12}}{15} = \frac{x}{9}$

Write a proportion for each. Then solve. pages 216–223

16. 3 for $1.17
18 for how much?

17. 12 m in 16 min
How far in 24 min?

18. 5 cans for $1.25
— per can

19. 70 km in 1 h
175 km in how long?

20. scale 　1 cm:25 km
drawing 　3.6 cm
actual 　—

21. 0.25 kg for 59¢
— per kg

Which polygons are similar? pages 226–227

22. 　　 23. 　　 24. 　　 25.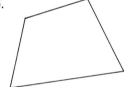

For the triangles at the right, △ABC ~ △DEF. pages 228–229

26. Name the congruent angles.

27. Name the proportional sides.

28. Find the unknown measures.

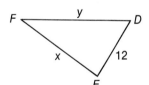

Find x to the nearest tenth. pages 230–231

29. 　　 30. 　　 31.

Solve. pages 224–225, 232–233

32. The Space Shuttle *Columbia* can fly as fast as 16,600 mph. How far can it go in $3\frac{1}{2}$ hours?

33. At Wells Market the manager, cashier, and stockboy are Brill, Kim, and Rios. The stockboy, an only child, earns the least. Rios, who married Brill's brother, earns more than the cashier. Who has each job?

Replace each ⬭ with = or ≠.

1. $\frac{8}{9}$ ⬭ $\frac{96}{108}$

2. $\frac{7}{10}$ ⬭ $\frac{34}{50}$

3. $\frac{3.2}{7}$ ⬭ $\frac{16}{3.5}$

4. $\frac{12}{15}$ ⬭ $\frac{16}{20}$

Solve.

5. $\frac{10}{n} = \frac{15}{9}$

6. $\frac{n}{15} = \frac{3.2}{5}$

7. $\frac{2\frac{1}{3}}{5} = \frac{n}{12}$

8. $\frac{21}{57} = \frac{7}{n}$

Write a proportion for each. Then solve.

9. 1.5 to 75
6 to how many?

10. 3 kg for $2.59
— per kg

11. 80 km in 1 h
200 km in how long?

12. 900 km in 2 h
How far in 3 h?

13. scale 1 cm:50 km
drawing —
actual 225 km

14. scale 1 cm:2 mm
drawing 8.5 cm
actual —

Which polygons are similar?

15. a.   **b.**    **c.**

The triangles in each pair are similar. Find the unknown measures.

16.

17.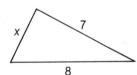

Solve.

18. For right triangle ABC, find x to the nearest tenth.
Tan 35° = 0.7002.

19. A spacecraft traveling from Earth at 40,000 km per h can reach Venus in 1,050 h. How far from Earth is Venus?

20. Fran planted yellow, white, red, and pink roses. The pink roses were not next to the yellow roses. The yellow roses were between the white roses and the red roses. The pink roses were to the right of the white roses. In what order did Fran plant the roses?

$\triangle ABC \sim \triangle DEF$. Find h and then give the measures of $\overline{AB}$ and $\overline{BC}$.

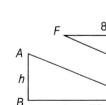

THE HUMAN BODY

Many ratios of dimensions of the human body illustrate a special ratio called the **golden ratio.**

The rectangle below is an example of this ratio. Its length and width satisfy the proportion $\frac{w + l}{l} = \frac{l}{w}$. The ratio of its length to its width is about 1.618 to 1. This is the golden ratio. To the ancient Greeks a rectangle in this ratio had the best proportion and balance.

1. Measure the distance from your waist to the floor. Find the ratio of your height to this distance. Is it a golden ratio?

2. Measure the distance from your waist to your knees. Find the ratio of the distance from your waist to the floor to this distance. Is it a golden ratio?

3. What other ratios of dimensions of your body are examples of the golden ratio?

ENRICHMENT

SINE AND COSINE RATIOS

▶ In a right triangle the **sine (sin)** of an acute angle is the ratio of the length of the opposite leg to the length of the hypotenuse.

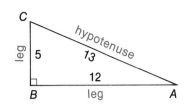

$$\sin m\angle A = \frac{\text{opposite leg}}{\text{hypotenuse}} = \frac{5}{13} \approx 0.3846$$

▶ In a right triangle the **cosine (cos)** of an acute angle is the ratio of the length of the adjacent leg to the length of the hypotenuse.

$$\cos m\angle A = \frac{\text{adjacent leg}}{\text{hypotenuse}} = \frac{12}{13} \approx 0.9231$$

Find the sine and cosine of each to the nearest thousandth.

1.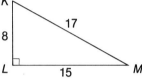

   a. $m\angle D$ **b.** $m\angle F$

2.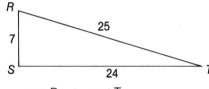

   a. $m\angle K$ **b.** $m\angle M$

3.

   a. $m\angle R$ **b.** $m\angle T$

Use the table on page 497 to find the sine or cosine of each angle measure or the measure of each angle.

4. $\sin 20°$	**5.** $\cos 45°$	**6.** $\sin 87°$	**7.** $\cos 10°$	**8.** $\sin 45°$
9. $\cos 70°$	**10.** $\sin 80°$	**11.** $\cos 65°$	**12.** $\sin 25°$	**13.** $\cos 1°$

14. $\sin m\angle A = 0.5000$ **15.** $\cos m\angle A = 0.5000$ **16.** $\sin m\angle A = 0.9511$

17. $\cos m\angle A = 0.0000$ **18.** $\sin m\angle A = 1.0000$ **19.** $\cos m\angle A = 0.1219$

Use the sine or the cosine ratio to find x to the nearest tenth.

20.

21.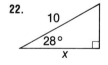

22.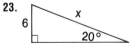

23.

Find each to the nearest ten-thousandth.

24. a. $\dfrac{\sin 30°}{\cos 30°}$

   b. $\tan 30°$

25. a. $\dfrac{\sin 35°}{\cos 35°}$

   b. $\tan 35°$

26. a. $\dfrac{\sin 45°}{\cos 45°}$

   b. $\tan 45°$

27. What is the relationship between the sine, the cosine, and the tangent of an angle?

MAINTAINING SKILLS

Choose the correct answers. Write **A, B, C,** or **D.**

1.   13.05
   $\times$ 0.39

   A 5,089.5   **C** 0.5365
   B 5.0895   **D** not given

8. What is the area?

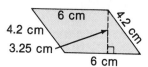

   6 cm
   4.2 cm
   3.25 cm
   4.2 cm
   6 cm

   A 19.5 cm^2 **C** 20.4 cm^2
   B 25.2 cm^2 **D** not given

2. What is the LCM of 21 and 14?

   A 7   **C** 14
   B 42   **D** not given

9. Complete. $\frac{3.5}{5} = \frac{\square}{10}$

   A 7   **C** 17.5
   B 6.5   **D** not given

3. $16\frac{1}{5} - 9\frac{2}{15}$

   A $6\frac{4}{5}$ **C** $7\frac{14}{15}$
   B $7\frac{1}{15}$ **D** not given

10. What is the unit price if 4 oranges cost $.95? Round to the nearest cent.

   A $.25   **C** $.24
   B $.23   **D** not given

4. $3\frac{5}{6} \div 5\frac{3}{4}$

   A $\frac{2}{3}$ **C** $\frac{12}{23}$
   B $1\frac{1}{3}$ **D** not given

11. Complete. 200 km in ___ h if 40 km in 1 h

   A 8,000   **C** 50
   B 5   **D** not given

5. What is 0.15 as a fraction in lowest terms?

   A $\frac{15}{100}$ **C** $\frac{3}{20}$
   B $\frac{3}{25}$ **D** not given

Use the table for 12–13.

	1st Hour	2nd Hour	3rd Hour
Cars	300	650	1,000
Trucks	120	195	270

6. What is a 102° angle called?

   A obtuse   **C** acute
   B right   **D** not given

12. The total number of cars and trucks entering the city for each of 3 hours is shown on the table. If traffic increases at the same rate, how many trucks can be expected the 4th hour?

   A 345   **C** 1,350
   B 930   **D** not given

7. What is the measure of the missing angle?

   n
   90°
   54°
   90°

   A 136°   **C** 126°
   B 36°   **D** not given

13. What will be the total number of cars for the first 4 hours?

   A 660   **C** 1,950
   B 3,300   **D** not given

Theme: City Life

Ratios and Percents

About 1 out of every 2 people who live in Los Angeles have moved there from other parts of the United States. What percent is this?

▶A **percent** is a ratio whose second term is 100. The symbol % is used for percent.

Here are two ways to write a ratio as a percent.

Use an equal ratio.

$\frac{1}{2} \times \frac{50}{50} = \frac{50}{100}$

So $\frac{1}{2} = \frac{50}{100}$, or 50%.

Use a proportion.

$\frac{1}{2} = \frac{n}{100}$

$100 = 2n$

$50 = n$

So $\frac{1}{2} = \frac{50}{100}$, or 50%.

About 50% of the people have moved to Los Angeles.

To write a percent as a ratio, divide by 100 and simplify if possible.

Write 5% as a ratio. $5\% = \frac{5}{100} = \frac{1}{20}$

More Examples

a Write $\frac{19}{20}$ as a percent.

$\frac{19}{20} \times \frac{5}{5} = \frac{95}{100}$

So $\frac{19}{20} = \frac{95}{100}$, or 95%.

b. Write $\frac{7}{12}$ as a percent.

$\frac{7}{12} = \frac{n}{100}$

$700 = 12n$

$58.\overline{3} = n$

So $\frac{7}{12} = \frac{58.\overline{3}}{100}$

$= 58.\overline{3}\%$, or $58\frac{1}{3}\%$.

c. Write 3.25% as a ratio.

$3.25\% = \frac{3.25}{100}$

$= \frac{325}{10,000}$

$= \frac{13}{400}$

CLASSWORK

Write each ratio as a percent and each percent as a ratio. Write all ratios in simplest form.

1. $\frac{47}{100}$ 2. $\frac{3}{5}$ 3. $\frac{3}{4}$ 4. 23%   5. 16%   6. 2%

7. 25%   8. $\frac{1}{10}$ 9. 1%   10. $\frac{16.7}{100}$ 11. 87.5%   12. $\frac{7}{20}$

PRACTICE

Write each percent as a ratio and each ratio as a percent.
Write all ratios in simplest form.

1. 39%
2. $\frac{3}{100}$
3. $\frac{9}{100}$
4. 20%
5. 51%
6. $\frac{5}{12}$

7. $\frac{3}{4}$
8. $33\frac{1}{3}\%$
9. 4.5%
10. $\frac{13}{25}$
11. $\frac{1}{20}$
12. $5\frac{1}{4}\%$

13. $\frac{3}{200}$
14. 47.5%
15. 12%
16. $\frac{3}{20}$
17. $\frac{2}{3}$
18. 12.5%

These are frequently used ratios whose percents you should
learn. Write each ratio as a percent.

19. $\frac{1}{2}$
20. $\frac{1}{4}$
21. $\frac{3}{4}$
22. $\frac{1}{8}$
23. $\frac{3}{8}$
24. $\frac{5}{8}$

25. $\frac{7}{8}$
26. $\frac{1}{5}$
27. $\frac{2}{5}$
28. $\frac{3}{5}$
29. $\frac{4}{5}$
30. $\frac{1}{10}$

31. $\frac{3}{10}$
32. $\frac{7}{10}$
33. $\frac{9}{10}$
34. $\frac{1}{3}$
35. $\frac{2}{3}$
36. $\frac{1}{6}$

37. $\frac{5}{6}$
38. $\frac{1}{20}$
39. $\frac{1}{50}$
★ 40. $\frac{1}{12}$
★ 41. $\frac{1}{9}$
★ 42. $\frac{1}{11}$

APPLICATION

43. The city of Los Angeles has about 3 million people.
California has about 24 million. What percent of the people
in the state live in Los Angeles?

44. Los Angeles has the largest population of any city in
California. The population of San Francisco is about
23% of that of Los Angeles. The population of San
Diego is about 30% of that of Los Angeles.
Sacramento is the capital of California. Of all these
cities, its population is the smallest. List these four
cities in order of population from smallest to largest.

=== LOGICAL THINKING ===

There are 3 balls in each
can and 20 cans in each
box. What percent of the
balls in a box are in
each can?

Decimals and Percents

Several large cities sponsor marathon races. In the 1984 New York Marathon, 0.79 of the entrants completed the race. What percent completed the race?

To write a decimal as a percent, move the decimal point two places to the right and write the percent symbol.

$$0.79 = \frac{79}{100} = 79\%$$

79% completed the race.

To write a percent as a decimal, move the decimal point two places to the left. Do not write the percent symbol.

$$79\% = \frac{79}{100} = 0.79$$

FINISH NEW YORK CITY FINISH MARATH
THE RUNNER · INNERCITY BROADCASTING · RUDIN FAMILY · PERRIER · KAPPA · HERTZ · MA

More Examples

a. Write 0.3 as a percent.

$$0.3 = \frac{3}{10} = \frac{30}{100} = 30\%$$

b. Write 0.375 as a percent.

$$0.375 = \frac{375}{1,000} = \frac{37.5}{100} = 37.5\%, \text{ or } 37\frac{1}{2}\%$$

c. Write 0.66 as a percent.

$$0.66 = \frac{66}{100} = 66\%$$

d. Write 0.05 as a percent.

$$0.05 = \frac{5}{100} = 5\%$$

e. Write 30% as a decimal.

$$30\% = \frac{30}{100} = 0.30 = 0.3$$

f. Write 37.5% as a decimal.

$$37.5\% = \frac{37.5}{100} = \frac{375}{1,000} = 0.375$$

g. Write $66\frac{2}{3}\%$ as a decimal.

$$66\frac{2}{3}\% = \frac{66\frac{2}{3}}{100} = 0.666\ldots = 0.\overline{6}$$

h. Write 5% as a decimal.

$$5\% = \frac{5}{100} = 0.05$$

CLASSWORK

Write each decimal as a percent and each percent as a decimal.

1. 0.21
2. 0.9
3. 15%
4. 69%
5. 4%
6. 0.62

7. 0.33
8. 12.5%
9. 0.99
10. 60%
11. 0.01
12. $86\frac{1}{2}\%$

PRACTICE

Write each percent as a decimal and each decimal as a percent.

1. 25%	**2.** 0.68	**3.** 0.05	**4.** 1%	**5.** 0.625	**6.** 0.875
7. 20%	**8.** 42%	**9.** 0.075	**10.** 75%	**11.** 10%	**12.** 0.0825
13. 0.33	**14.** 70%	**15.** 0.125	**16.** 0.015	**17.** 59%	**18.** 0.71
19. 0.065	**20.** $33\frac{1}{3}$%	**21.** 2%	**22.** 48.6%	**23.** 0.375	**24.** 0.055
25. $1\frac{1}{4}$%	**26.** 3.5%	**27.** $16\frac{2}{3}$%	**28.** 0.4	**29.** 0.08	**30.** $83\frac{1}{3}$%

APPLICATION

31. In the 1984 New York Marathon, 84% of the entrants were men. Change this percent to a decimal.

32. Not everyone who registers for a marathon runs the race. In the 1984 New York Marathon, 0.89 of the entrants ran the race. What percent ran the race?

★ **33.** One of the runners lost 5% of his body weight during the race. What decimal part of his original weight did he weigh after the race?

★ **34.** While training for the race, Janet ran for 2 hours out of every 24. How much of her time was spent training? Write the answer as a decimal and as a percent.

VISUAL THINKING

What will be the color pattern in the next row on the bottom?

1.

2.

243

Percents Less Than 1 or Greater Than 100

A city block association raised $10,000 to renovate a nearby park. The eighth-grade class at a local school donated $\frac{1}{2}$% of the money the association collected. Express the class donation as a ratio.

In working with percents less than 1 or greater than 100, follow the rules used for percents between 1 and 100.

$$\frac{1}{2}\% = \frac{\frac{1}{2}}{100} = \frac{1}{2} \times \frac{1}{100} = \frac{1}{200}$$ To write a percent as a ratio, divide by 100 and simplify if possible.

The class donated $\frac{1}{200}$ of the money.

More Examples

a. Write 275% as a ratio. $\quad 275\% = \frac{275}{100} = \frac{11}{4}$

b. Write $\frac{1}{400}$ as a percent.
$$\frac{1}{400} = \frac{n}{100}$$
$$100 = 400n$$
$$\frac{1}{4} = n \quad \text{So } \frac{1}{400} = \frac{1}{4}\%, \text{ or } 0.25\%.$$

c. Write $\frac{137}{100}$ as a percent. $\quad \frac{137}{100} = 137\%$

d. Write $\frac{3}{5}$% as a decimal. $\quad \frac{3}{5}\% = 0.6\%$ ⟵ Write as a decimal percent.
$$= 0.006 \quad \text{⟵ Move the decimal point 2 places to the left.}$$

e. Write 367% as a decimal. $\quad 367\% = 3.67$ ⟵ Move the decimal point 2 places to the left.

f. Write 3.07 as a percent. $\quad 3.07 = 307\%$ ⟵ Move the decimal point 2 places to the right.

CLASSWORK

Write each percent as a ratio and as a decimal.

1. $\frac{1}{4}$%
2. 159%
3. $\frac{1}{5}$%
4. 0.1%
5. 350%
6. 0.07%

Write each ratio as a percent and as a decimal.

7. $\frac{3}{2}$
8. $\frac{1}{200}$
9. $\frac{106}{100}$
10. $\frac{8}{1,000}$
11. $\frac{2}{500}$
12. $\frac{5}{4}$

Write each decimal as a percent and as a ratio.

13. 4.5
14. 0.004
15. 4.85
16. 0.002
17. 41
18. 25.4

PRACTICE

Write each as a decimal or as a percent.

1. 407% 2. 0.1% 3. 2.00 4. 0.002

5. 0.0025 6. 1.05 7. 0.5% 8. 0.008

9. $\frac{3}{4}$% 10. 1.35 11. 105% 12. 0.35%

Write each as a ratio or as a percent.

13. $\frac{3}{2}$ 14. 315% 15. $\frac{3}{500}$ 16. $\frac{407}{100}$

17. $\frac{1}{500}$ 18. 200% 19. $\frac{1}{125}$ 20. $\frac{3}{4}$%

21. $\frac{1}{1,000}$ 22. $\frac{1}{400}$ ★23. $\frac{17}{8}$ ★24. 1,000%

Copy and complete each chart. Write all ratios in simplest form.

	Ratio	Percent	Decimal
25.			1.75
26.		700%	
27.	$\frac{7}{6}$		

	Ratio	Percent	Decimal
28.			0.003
29.			0.006
30.	$\frac{1}{800}$		

APPLICATION

31. This circle graph shows the amount of money that various groups donated to the city park. Express as a ratio the percent each group donated.

32. Expressed as a decimal, how much did each group give?

DONATIONS FOR CITY PARK
100% = $10,000

Parks Dept. $12\frac{1}{2}$%

Local Merchants $36\frac{1}{4}$%

Eighth Grade $\frac{1}{2}$%

Members of the Association 50%

Private Contributions $\frac{3}{4}$%

═══ LOGICAL THINKING ═══

Every cube is the same weight. Every pyramid is the same weight. The weight of each cube is what percent of the weight of each pyramid?

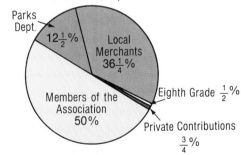

Finding a Percent of a Number

Brad bought a $15 shirt. The sales tax was 5%. What was the amount of tax he paid on his shirt?

Here are two ways to solve a percent problem.

- Use a proportion.

$$\frac{n}{15} = \frac{5}{100}$$

$$n \times 100 = 15 \times 5$$

$$100n = 75$$

$$n = 0.75$$

- Use a decimal.
Find 5% of $15.

$$0.05 \times 15 = n$$

$$0.75 = n$$

Brad paid $.75 tax.

Sometimes a ratio is easier to use than a decimal.

Find 25% of 160.

$$\frac{1}{4} \times 160 = 40$$

More Examples

a. Find 35% of 40.

$$\frac{35}{100} = \frac{n}{40}$$

$$35 \times 40 = 100 \times n$$

$$\frac{1,400}{100} = n$$

$$14 = n$$

b. Find $\frac{1}{10}$% of 98.

Think $\dfrac{\frac{1}{10}}{100} = \dfrac{1}{1,000} = 0.001$

$$0.001 \times 98 = n$$

$$0.098 = n$$

c. Find 125% of 80.

Think $\dfrac{125}{100} = \dfrac{5}{4}$

$$\frac{5}{4} \times 80 = n$$

$$100 = n$$

CLASSWORK

Find the percent of each number.

1. 60% of 40

2. 25% of 24

3. 2.2% of 65

4. 10% of 98

5. $33\frac{1}{3}$% of 126

6. 130% of 90

7. 0.5% of 15

8. $\frac{1}{4}$% of 100

PRACTICE

Write each as an equation, using a proportion; using a decimal.

1. 5% of 26 is *n*.

2. 12% of 3,200 is *n*.

3. 35% of 240 is *n*.

4. 150% of 46 is *n*.

5. 75% of 36 is *n*.

6. 62.5% of 3.6 is *n*.

7. $12\frac{1}{2}$% of $2\frac{2}{3}$ is *n*.

8. 80% of 64.5 is *n*.

9. 0.6% of 280 is *n*.

Find the percent of each number.

10. 40% of 200

11. 30% of 20

12. 125% of 80

13. 60% of 1,570

14. 45% of 460

15. $16\frac{2}{3}$% of 42

16. 12.5% of 96

17. 28.4% of 350

18. $5\frac{1}{4}$% of 2,500

19. 1,340% of 25

★ **20.** $36\frac{1}{2}$% of 78

★ **21.** $33\frac{1}{3}$% of $13\frac{1}{2}$

Choose the appropriate equation.

22. For the Spring Sale days, a store reduced the price of some shirts by 20%. If the shirts originally cost $17.50, by how much was the price reduced?

a. $0.8 \times \$17.50 = x$

b. $\frac{\$17.50}{20} = x$

c. $\frac{1}{5} \times \$17.50 = x$

d. $\$17.50 - (0.2 \times \$17.50) = x$

APPLICATION

23. Brad bought a $65 quilted jacket-vest on a layaway plan. He put a 15% deposit on the jacket-vest. How much did he put down?

24. Nora has saved 75% of the cost of her winter coat. If the coat costs $75, how much has she saved?

★ **25.** Brad had to pay 5% sales tax on his $65 jacket-vest. How much did he pay for the jacket-vest in all?

★ **26.** Cheryl saved 70% of her weekly salary of $120. She spent the rest on a pair of shoes. How much did the shoes cost?

=== MENTAL ARITHMETIC ===

Use a ratio to find the percent of each number.

1. 50% of 64

2. 10% of 160

3. $33\frac{1}{3}$% of 90

4. 25% of 200

5. 75% of 80

6. $66\frac{2}{3}$% of 150

7. 60% of 35

8. 20% of 45

9. 80% of 55

10. 2% of 50

11. 200% of 22

12. 5% of 80

Finding the Percent

Jason follows a weekly budget. He often saves his recreation money until he has enough to buy a ticket to see his hometown team, the Philadelphia 76ers, play basketball. What percent of his money does Jason use for recreation?

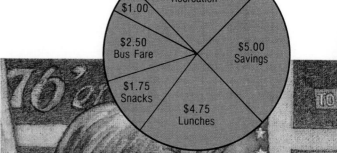

JASON'S WEEKLY BUDGET
TOTAL $20.00

What percent of 20 is 5?

To find the percent, use a proportion or a decimal.

a. $\frac{n}{100} = \frac{5}{20}$

$n \times 20 = 100 \times 5$

$20n = 500$

$n = 25$

$\frac{25}{100} = 25\%$

b. $n \times 20 = 5$

$n = \frac{5}{20}$

$n = 0.25$

$0.25 = 25\%$

Jason uses 25% of his money for recreation.

More Examples

c. What percent of 48 is 80?

$\frac{n}{100} = \frac{80}{48}$

$48n = 8{,}000$

$n = 166\frac{2}{3}$

$\frac{166\frac{2}{3}}{100} = 166\frac{2}{3}\%$

d. 4.75 is what percent of 20?

$4.75 = n \times 20$

$\frac{4.75}{20} = n$

$0.2375 = n$

$0.2375 = 23.75\%$

CLASSWORK

Find each percent.

1. What percent of 25 is 11?

2. 28 is what percent of 35?

Find each missing factor and write it as a percent.

3. $n \times 16 = 6$

4. $n \times 15 = 20$

5. $n \times 28 = 35$

6. $n \times 125 = 5$

PRACTICE

Write an equation to find each percent, using a proportion; using a decimal.

1. What percent of 26 is 13?
2. What percent of 15 is 25?
3. What percent of 8 is 7?
4. What percent of 300 is 7?
5. What percent of 15 is 45?
6. 27 is what percent of 9?
7. What percent of 36 is 2.4?
8. What percent of 6.4 is 0.32?
9. What percent of 250 is 25?

Find each percent.

10. What percent of 20 is 13?
11. What percent of 28 is 14?
12. What percent of 20 is 6?
13. What percent of 30 is 27?
14. 10 is what percent of 5?
15. What percent of 32 is 4?
16. What percent of 72 is 54?
17. 31 is what percent of 20?
18. What percent of 75 is 15?
19. What percent of 15 is 75?
20. 3 is what percent of 150?
21. What percent of 18 is 4.5?

Find each missing factor and write it as a percent.

22. $n \times 200 = 65.2$
23. $n \times 15 = 7\frac{1}{2}$
24. $n \times 245 = 73.5$
25. $n \times 150 = 1.2$
26. $n \times 225 = 0.9$
27. $n \times 1.8 = 0.6$
28. $n \times 124 = 161.2$
★29. $n \times 8 = 15$
★30. $n \times 2 = 9\frac{1}{2}$

APPLICATION

Use the circle graph on page 248 for 31–34.

31. Jason takes a bus to school, but rides home with a friend. What percent of his weekly spending money is used for bus fare?

32. Jason bought a $15 ticket to see the 76ers play basketball. What percent of his weekly recreation savings is the cost of the ticket?

33. What percent of the money in Jason's weekly budget does he reserve for each item other than recreation and bus fare?

★34. On the average, what percent of Jason's weekly spending money does he use for lunch each day?

Finding the Number When a Percent of It Is Known

Students in one city school system get a 25% discount on admission to an aquarium. Sara, an eighth grader, gets $.50 off the price of her ticket. What is the regular admission price?

25% of what number is $.50?

Write an equation using a decimal to solve.

25% of n is 0.50.

$0.25 \times n = 0.50$

$n = \frac{0.50}{0.25} = 2$

The regular admission price is $2.

Sometimes using a ratio is easier than using a decimal.

$33\frac{1}{3}$% of what number is 42?

$\frac{1}{3} \times n = 42$

$n = 42 \times 3 = 126$

More Examples

a. 75% of n is 9.

$\frac{3}{4} \times n = 9$

$n = 9 \times \frac{4}{3} = 12$

b. 20% of n is 2.5.

$0.2 \times n = 2.5$

$n = \frac{2.5}{0.2} = 12.5$

CLASSWORK

Write each as an equation, using decimals.

1. 5% of n is 56.5.
2. 66% of n is 37.
3. 0.5% of n is 10.
4. 120% of n is 1.

Find n.

5. 10% of n is 4.
6. 15% of n is 9.
7. $12\frac{1}{2}$% of n is 6.
8. 150% of n is 19.5.

Write each as an equation, using decimals.

1. 16% of n is 8. 2. 25% of n is 14.

3. 33% of n is 22. 4. 37% of n is 37.

5. $37\frac{1}{2}$% of n is 12. 6. 250% of n is 6.5.

7. 0.8% of n is 20. 8. 16% of n is 6.

Find n.

9. 30% of n is 21. 10. 5% of n is 10.

11. 25% of n is 10. 12. 50% of n is 27.

13. 56% of n is 112. 14. 72% of n is 108.

15. 184% of n is 414. 16. 95% of n is 285.

17. $33\frac{1}{3}$% of n is 30. 18. 2% of n is 6.82.

19. 7.5% of n is 24. 20. 225% of n is 81.

21. $66\frac{2}{3}$% of n is 28. 22. 75% of n is 159.

23. 40% of n is 32.2. 24. 30% of n is 7.5.

25. 80% of n is 20. 26. 12.8% of n is 32.

★ 27. $83\frac{1}{3}$% of n is $22\frac{1}{2}$. ★ 28. $\frac{1}{2}$% of n is 8.

★ 29. $62\frac{1}{2}$% of n is 22.5. ★ 30. 0.3% of n is 3.

APPLICATION

31. Students get a 50% discount on the city bus and subway. Sara uses the subway to go to the aquarium. She gets $.45 off. What is the regular subway fare?

32. Senior citizens get a 20% discount at the movies. Sara's grandmother, a senior citizen, gets $1 off. What is the regular price of admission?

★ 33. Posters at the aquarium are sold with a 10% discount for purchases of 3 or more. Judith buys 3 and saves $.90. How much was each one?

★ 34. The neighborhood bookstore gives a $33\frac{1}{3}$% discount to senior citizens and a 15% discount to students. Sara gets $.75 off her purchase and her grandmother gets $3.60 off. How much did each of them spend?

Problem Solving

MAKING A LIST

Sometimes making an organized list of all possibilities is the best way to solve a problem. The correct entry can be selected by using the conditions of the problem. Or the answer to the problem may be the entire list.

1. A piece of property was divided into smaller lots for a new development of houses. The lots were numbered as shown at the right, using the digits 1, 2, 3, and 7. A sign with the number of the lot was put on each lot. Three of the signs blew away. Which numbers were on them?

7231	2317	1273	1723
2731	7321	3721	3271
1372	3127		1237
2713	1732	7123	3217
7213			2173
1327	7312	2371	7132

Make an organized list of all the possible 4-digit arrangements of 1, 2, 3, and 7. Then compare your list with the lot numbers above to find the missing numbers.

1237	2137	3127	7123
1273	2173	3172	7132
1327	2317	3217	7213
1372	2371	3271	7231
1723	2713	3712	7312
1732	2731	3721	7321

The list shows that the missing numbers are 2137, 3172, and 3712.

2. The fence around a rectangular garden will be 20 m long. What should the dimensions be so that the garden has the greatest area?

List some of the possibilities to see if a pattern develops.

Dimensions (20-m perimeter)	Area
1 m by 9 m	9 m^2
2 m by 8 m	16 m^2
3 m by 7 m	21 m^2
4 m by 6 m	24 m^2
5 m by 5 m	25 m^2

As the figure gets closer to a square, the area becomes greater.

A garden 5 m by 5 m would have the greatest area.

PRACTICE

Solve.

1. Earl needs a quarter for a parking meter. He asks Sue for change for a 50¢ piece. List the ways Sue could give Earl change without using pennies.

2. The toll for the Watertown bridge is 50¢. Pennies cannot be used in the exact-change booth. In how many ways can the exact change be paid?

3. The custodian at City Hall has a day off from work every fourth day of a month, beginning with day 4. The elevator operator has a day off every sixth day of a month, beginning with day 6. On which days of the month can they go fishing together?

4. Four students are cleaning up their town park. So far they have picked up 10 bottles. Each person picked up an odd number of bottles. List the possible ways the bottles could have been divided among the students.

5. There were 15 tricycles and bicycles in the park. There were 36 wheels. How many tricycles and how many bicycles were there?

6. The perimeter of a park is 100 m. The park covers the greatest area possible. What are the dimensions of the park?

7. List the 3-digit numbers that can be written using the digits 3, 4, and 5.

★8. Use each of the digits 1 to 8 only once. Make two 4-digit numbers whose sum is 5,895.

★9. Guilford and Stirling are 99 km apart. There are 98 signposts between the two towns, one every kilometer. How many of these signposts use only two different digits? The one at the right uses only the two digits 1 and 8.

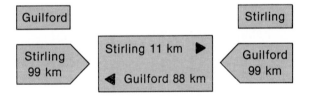

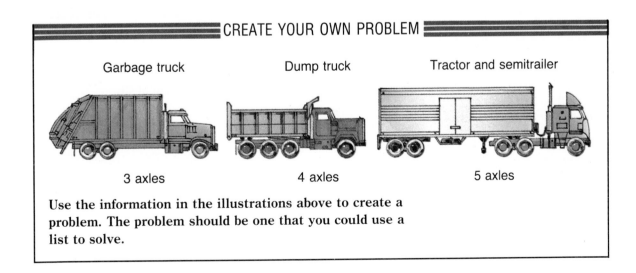

Use the information in the illustrations above to create a problem. The problem should be one that you could use a list to solve.

253

Estimating Percent

Jamie and Edward ate lunch at The Prospector. This is a copy of their bill. How much money should they leave as a tip?

Waiters and waitresses are usually tipped about 15%. But the tip is not computed exactly. Estimate to find the amount.

Think $9.65 is about $10.   What is 15% of $10?

$$\frac{15}{100} \times 10 = 1.50$$

Jamie and Edward should leave $1.50 as a tip.

More Examples

Estimate.

a. 65.7% of 24 is what number?

Think   65.7% is about $66\frac{2}{3}\%$, and $66\frac{2}{3}\% = \frac{2}{3}$.

Estimate, using $\frac{2}{3}$. $\frac{2}{3} \times 24 = 16$

65.7% of 24 is about 16.

b. What percent of 40 is 19?

Think   19 is about 20.

Estimate, using 20. $n \times 40 = 20$

$$n = \frac{1}{2} = 0.50$$

0.50 = 50%   19 is about 50% of 40.

c. 62% of what number is 29?

Think   29 is about 30. 62% is about $62\frac{1}{2}\%$, and $62\frac{1}{2}\% = \frac{5}{8}$.

Estimate, using 30 and $\frac{5}{8}$. $\frac{5}{8} \times n = 30$

$$n = 30 \times \frac{8}{5} = 48 \qquad 29 \text{ is } 62\% \text{ of about } 48.$$

CLASSWORK

Find an estimate for n.

1. 18% of 25 is n.

2. 34% of 33 is n.

3. 12% of 48 is n.

4. 52% of n is 12.

5. 75% of n is $31.40.

6. 59% of n is 16.

Estimate each percent.

7. What percent of 91 is 30?

8. What percent of $28 is $13?

9. What percent of 51 is 29?

---

the PROSPECTOR
Denver, Colorado

2 tomato soup	$1.50
1 turkey club	2.75
1 cheeseburger	2.00
1 milk	.15
1 lemonade	.15
1 apple pie	.95
1 cherry pie	.95
Subtotal	$9.65
Tax	
Total	

Find an estimate for *n* or for the percent.

1. 24% of 80 is *n*.

2. 49% of 244 is *n*.

3. 34% of $123 is *n*.

4. 63% of *n* is 10.

5. 147% of *n* is 20.

6. $66\frac{2}{3}$% of *n* is 17.7.

7. $37\frac{1}{2}$% of 156 is *n*.

8. 15% of $19.35 is *n*.

9. 88% of *n* is 35.

10. 71% of *n* is 42.

11. 90% of *n* is $82.30.

12. 12.8% of *n* is 39.

13. 67.1% of 36 is *n*.

14. 307% of 79 is *n*.

15. 5% of $29.50 is *n*.

16. What percent of 59 is 20?

17. What percent of 92 is 60?

18. What percent of 20 is 78?

19. What percent of 197 is 80?

20. What percent of 39 is 31?

21. What percent of 81 is 7.7?

Choose the best estimate for *n*.

22. 36.8% of 394 is *n*.
  a. 50
  b. 100
  c. 150

23. 19.2% of 3,196 is *n*.
  a. 400
  b. 600
  c. 800

24. 26.4% of *n* is 398.
  a. 1,600
  b. 1,800
  c. 2,000

★ **25.** $\frac{58}{179} = n$
  a. 25%
  b. $33\frac{1}{3}$%
  c. 40%

★ **26.** $\frac{917}{456} = n$
  a. 100%
  b. 150%
  c. 200%

★ **27.** $256\frac{1}{2}$% of 78 is *n*.
  a. 100
  b. 150
  c. 200

APPLICATION

28. The sales tax in Colorado is 3%. Estimate the amount of sales tax Jamie and Edward had to pay on their lunch.

29. Jamie and Edward took a taxi to the theater. The fare was $4.85. How much should they have given as a tip? (Use 15%.)

30. Jamie and Edward bought tickets to the theater. They each had a special discount coupon for 30% off. Each saved $1.43. Estimate the total cost of both tickets without the discount.

Percent of Increase or Decrease

Sue earns money by walking dogs for people who live on her block. She recently raised her daily fee from $.50 to $.60. What percent of increase was that?

The fee increased from $.50 to $.60.

increase = $.60 − $.50 = $.10

▶ percent of increase = $\dfrac{\text{increase}}{\text{original amount}}$

$$= \frac{\$.10}{\$.50} = 0.20 = 20\%$$

Her fee increased 20%.

Sue also babysits. On Thursday nights she reduces her hourly fee from $2.50 to $2.25. What percent of decrease is that?

The fee decreases from $2.50 to $2.25.

decrease = $2.50 − $2.25 = $.25

▶ percent of decrease = $\dfrac{\text{decrease}}{\text{original amount}}$

$$= \frac{\$.25}{\$2.50} = 0.10 = 10\%$$

Her fee decreases 10%.

CLASSWORK

Write *increase* or *decrease* for each, and find the percent.

	Original	New
1.	800	880
2.	60	30

	Original	New
3.	30	60
4.	120	200

	Original	New
5.	200	120
6.	40	38

Find the percent of increase or decrease.

7. cars sold last month = 100
   cars sold this month = 120

8. books read last week = 2
   books read this week = 3

9. packages sent today = 5
   packages sent yesterday = 6

10. miles traveled Sunday = 200
    miles traveled Monday = 250

PRACTICE

Write _increase_ or _decrease_ for each, and find the percent.

	Original	New
1.	40	36
2.	28	35
3.	200	100
4.	36	24
5.	72	18
6.	40	58
7.	2,400	300
8.	50	175

	Original	New
9.	90	108
10.	160	320
11.	45	81
12.	150	375
13.	120	138
14.	250	255
15.	5,400	2,025
16.	420	140

Find the percent of increase or decrease.

17. games this week = 10; games last week = 16

18. tickets sold Tuesday = 500; tickets sold Wednesday = 615

19. meals served yesterday = 400; meals served today = 450

20. hits first inning = 3; hits last inning = 4

21. birds banded Monday = 12; birds banded Friday = 14

22. bulbs planted Friday = 30; bulbs planted Sunday = 25

APPLICATION

23. A newspaper had a circulation of 300,000. A promotion increased circulation 4%. What is the new circulation?

24. Jerry, Sue's brother, earns money by delivering the Sunday paper in his building. Last year he delivered 70 papers per week. Now he delivers 60. What is the percent of decrease?

25. Jerry also earns money by delivering packages for the neighborhood grocery store. In his first month his average tip increased from $.25 per bag to $.40. What was the percent of increase?

★26. Last week, Jerry earned $20. During the next two weeks, his earnings will decrease by 4% and then increase by 3%. To the nearest cent, what will he be earning weekly at the end of the two weeks?

Mixed Practice

1. 4,765
8,901
+ 7,784

2. 15.543 + 7.4

3. 475.1 + 1.12

4. 6.54
− 4.09

5. 0.7 × 6.501

6. 14.1 × 0.5

7. $46.19 ÷ 6.2

8. $154.3\overline{)\$35.489}$

9. $4\frac{2}{5}$
$+ 7\frac{3}{8}$

10. $7\frac{6}{9} - 5\frac{1}{3}$

11. $5\frac{1}{3} \times 4\frac{1}{8}$

12. $6\frac{3}{7} \times 9\frac{4}{5}$

13. $5\frac{7}{9} \div 7\frac{1}{5}$

Complete.

14. ___ m = 4 km

15. ___ cm = 1 m

16. 4 L = ___ kL

17. ___ g = 0.075 kg

257

Discount and Sale Price

Ramón bought 10 clay pots to use for growing plants on his apartment balcony. How much did he pay altogether?

$5 each

25% off marked price

The **discount** is the amount that the regular price is reduced.

The **rate of discount** is the percent that the regular price is reduced.

▶**discount = regular price × rate of discount**

$$= \quad \$5 \quad \times \quad 0.25$$
$$= \quad \$1.25$$

▶**sale price = regular price − discount**

$$= \quad \$5 \quad - \quad \$1.25$$
$$= \quad \$3.75$$

$\$3.75 \times 10 = \$37.50 \leftarrow$ cost of 10 pots

Ramón paid $37.50 altogether.

Another Example

Find the sale price.

regular price = $10   rate of discount = 20%

discount = regular price × rate of discount

$$= \quad \$10 \quad \times \quad \frac{1}{5}$$
$$= \quad \$2$$

sale price = regular price − discount

$$= \quad \$10 \quad - \quad \$2$$
$$= \quad \$8$$

CLASSWORK

Copy and complete the chart.

	Regular Price	Rate of Discount	Discount	Sale Price
1.	$270	30%		
2.	$150	40%		
3.	$78	10%		
4.	$120	25%		

258

PRACTICE

Find the discount and the sale price for each.

1. regular price = $90
   rate of discount = 10%

2. regular price = $150
   rate of discount = 20%

3. regular price = $80
   rate of discount = 25%

4. regular price = $250
   rate of discount = 30%

5. regular price = $75
   rate of discount = 50%

6. regular price = $265
   rate of discount = 25%

7. regular price = $234.36
   rate of discount = $33\frac{1}{3}$%

8. regular price = $14.50
   rate of discount = 15%

9. regular price = $8.95
   rate of discount = 5%

Copy and complete the chart.

	Regular Price	Rate of Discount	Discount	Sale Price
★ 10.	$160			$128
★ 11.	$21			$15.75
★ 12.		50%		$35
★ 13.		30%		$83.93

APPLICATION

14. Ramón bought 10 plants, regularly priced at $.25 each, on sale for 10% off. How much did he pay altogether?

15. Ramón needed potting soil. It was on sale for $33\frac{1}{3}$% off. It regularly cost $1.59 per bag. What was the sale price?

★ 16. Jenny grew cherry tomato seedlings indoors. She sold each flat for $1.60 and offered a discount of $\frac{1}{4}$ off for 4 flats. Judy bought 4 flats. How much did she pay?

★ 17. Chives are sold in pots in the supermarkets in early spring. Cindy bought some at $\frac{1}{3}$ off. The sale price was $.90. What did the chives cost originally?

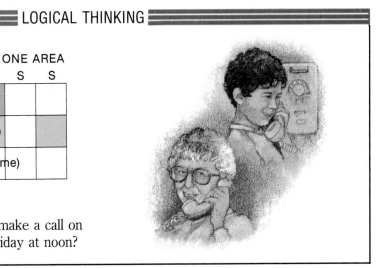

LOGICAL THINKING

TELEPHONE RATES FOR ONE AREA

	M	T	W	T	F	S	S
8 AM to 5 PM	daytime						
5 PM to 11 PM	evening (65% of daytime)						
11 PM to 8 AM	night (35% of daytime)						

How much will you save if you make a call on Saturday at noon rather than Friday at noon?

259

Markup and Selling Price

A buyer for a large department store pays $20 for each pair of jeans that the store is to sell. The store sells the jeans at a 50% markup. What is the amount of markup? What is the selling price for each pair of jeans?

The **cost** is the original amount paid.

The **amount of markup** is the increase.

The **markup,** written as a percent, is the percent of increase.

The **selling price** is the cost plus the amount of markup.

▶ amount of markup = cost × markup

$$= \$20 \times 0.50$$

$$= \$10$$

The amount of the markup is $10.

▶ selling price = cost + amount of markup

$$= \$20 + \$10 = \$30$$

The selling price is $30.

Another Example

Find the selling price.

cost = $32   markup = 25%

amount of markup = cost × markup

$$\$32 \times \tfrac{1}{4} = \$8$$

selling price = cost + amount of markup

$$= \$32 + \$8 = \$40$$

CLASSWORK

Find each selling price.

1. cost of boots = $36
   amount of markup = $18

2. cost of a book = $2
   markup = 75%

3. cost of furniture = $570
   markup = 60%

4. cost of flowers = $8.25
   amount of markup = $2.75

5. cost of jogging suit = $25
   markup = 50%

6. cost of stopwatch = $20
   amount of markup = $15

Find the amount of markup and the selling price for each.

1. cost = $90
   markup = 50%

2. cost = $120
   markup = 40%

3. cost = $30
   markup = 30%

4. cost = $150
   markup = $66\frac{2}{3}$%

5. cost = $4.50
   markup = $33\frac{1}{3}$%

6. cost = $58
   markup = 60%

7. cost = $72
   markup = 75%

8. cost = $10.50
   markup = 40%

9. cost = $36
   markup = 50%

10. cost = $75
    markup = 17%

11. cost = $70
    markup = 35%

12. cost = $5
    markup = 100%

Copy and complete the chart.

	Cost	Markup	Amount of Markup	Selling Price
★ 13.	$8.95			$13.43
★ 14.		$33\frac{1}{3}$%	$23.33	
★ 15.	$21			$35
★ 16.		250%		$419.65

APPLICATION

17. Lori bought a $50 jacket from a factory outlet. The same jacket is sold at a 40% markup in a department store. How much did she save?

18. Joshua ordered a take-out dinner from a Chinese restaurant. The food cost the restaurant $6. The markup on the price of the dinner was 30%. What did Joshua pay?

19. Terry had to raise the price of his corn by 5% this year. He now charges $2.00 per dozen. If he raises his price 5% each year, what will the corn cost in 5 years? Round to the nearest cent.

★ 20. A city department store pays $30 for designer sweaters. The store sells the sweaters at a 45% markup. During the month of September, the store puts the sweaters on sale at 30% off. What is the sale price?

CALCULATOR

Use the % key on the calculator to find each selling price.

$90 marked up 140%   **Press** 9 0 + 1 4 0 %   **Display** 216.

1. $40 marked down 20%

2. $10.50 marked down 40%

3. $4.99 marked up 65%

4. $7.50 marked up 175%

Simple Interest

The Kramers bought an exercise center for $425. They are paying for it in monthly installments over a 1-year period. The interest rate on the installment plan is 18%. How much interest will the Kramers pay? How much will the exercise center cost in all?

Paying on an **installment plan** usually requires paying more than the purchase price. The extra charge, the **interest,** is paid for borrowing the money. Money can also earn interest when placed in a bank.

The **principal** is money borrowed or placed in a bank. The **rate of interest** is the percent charged or earned. The rate of interest is usually based on 1 year (12 months).

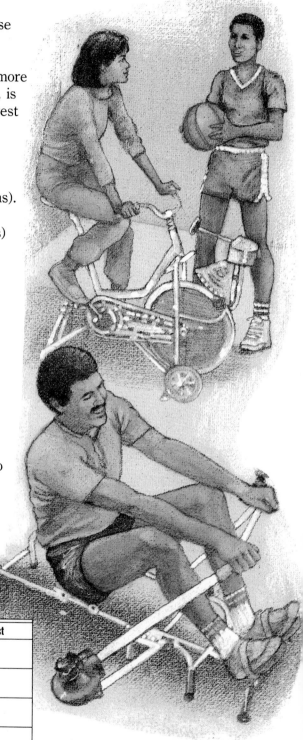

▶Interest = principal × rate of interest × time (in years)

$$I = p \times r \times t$$
$$= \$425 \times 0.18 \times 1$$
$$= \$76.50$$

The Kramers will pay $76.50 in interest.

$$\$425 + \$76.50 = \$501.50$$

In all, they will pay $501.50 for the exercise center.

Another Example

Find the interest.

principal = $480   rate of interest = 8%   time = 6 mo

$$I = p \times r \times t$$
$$= \$480 \times 0.08 \times \tfrac{1}{2} \quad \textbf{Think} \quad 6\ mo = \tfrac{1}{2}\ yr$$
$$= \$19.20$$

CLASSWORK

Copy and complete the chart.

	Principal	Rate of Interest	Time	Interest
1.	$1,500	6%	1 yr	
2.	$2,000	7%	3 yr	
3.	$300	$4\tfrac{1}{2}$%	2 yr	
4.	$500	8%	3 mo	

Find the interest for each.

1. $1,600 borrowed for a car
   rate of interest = 6%
   time = 1 yr

2. $580 paid for a couch
   rate of interest = 15%
   time = 1 yr

3. $680 borrowed for tuition
   rate of interest = $6\frac{1}{2}$%
   time = 1 yr

4. $420 deposited in a bank
   rate of interest = 8%
   time = 2 yr

5. principal = $900
   rate of interest = 12%
   time = 2 yr

6. principal = $750
   rate of interest = 9%
   time = 3 yr

7. principal = $1,200
   rate of interest = 5.5%
   time = 4 yr

8. principal = $1,450
   rate of interest = 5%
   time = $1\frac{1}{2}$ yr

9. principal = $775
   rate of interest = 6%
   time = $3\frac{1}{2}$ yr

10. principal = $2,400
    rate of interest = $8\frac{1}{2}$%
    time = $2\frac{1}{2}$ yr

11. principal = $2,640
    rate of interest = 10%
    time = 6 mo

12. principal = $1,800
    rate of interest = $7\frac{1}{2}$%
    time = 6 mo

Copy and complete the chart.

	Principal	Rate of Interest	Time	Interest
★13.	$750		9 mo	$67.50
★14.	$1,140	$4\frac{1}{4}$%		$60.56
★15.		11%	15 mo	$192.50

APPLICATION

16. On the installment plan the Kramers paid for their exercise center in 12 equal monthly payments. How much did they pay per month?

17. Eric borrowed $3,000 for his college tuition. The interest was 7%. Eric paid back the loan after 4 years. How much did he pay altogether?

18. The Willis family bought a $2,500 swimming pool on an installment plan for a 2-year period. The interest rate on the plan is $17\frac{1}{2}$% per year. How much will they pay for the pool, including interest?

19. Julie put $700 into a savings account. The annual interest is $5\frac{1}{2}$%. How much interest does she receive the first quarter?

★20. Jack bought a $450 stereo for his apartment on the installment plan. He put $100 down and paid 18% interest on the remainder. The remainder plus interest was paid in 12 monthly installments. How much was each installment?

Problem Solving

SKILLS AND STRATEGIES REVIEW

Solve.

1. The 12 koalas at the Wilson Zoo eat 36 lb of eucalyptus leaves each day. Next week the zoo will receive 3 more koalas. Then how many pounds of eucalyptus leaves will the zoo need daily?

2. ABC Contractors are building the new brick Mandigo City Hall. The mortar to hold the bricks is prepared by mixing 1 part lime, 2 parts cement, and 7 parts sand with water. One day 140 pounds of cement were used to make the mortar. How much sand and lime were used?

3. Nancy walks 22 blocks to school at an average rate of 1 block every 2 minutes. One morning she left her house at 8:00 A.M. She had walked halfway to school when she realized she had forgotten her lunch. She returned home to pick up her lunch and started out again. What is the earliest she could have arrived at school?

The table below shows the monthly rates for local telephone service in Boonton.

4. The Evans family made 68 calls in May. What was their total bill?

5. Their bill for June was $9.70. How many calls did they make?

6. A new telephone company is offering unlimited local calls for $10 a month (basic service included). How many calls must be made each month for the new service to be more economical than the present service?

Charges for Telephone Use

Basic service	$8.50
First 50 calls	free
Over 50 calls	$.12 each

The table below shows the cost and the selling price for several items at John's Sportswear Store. The store uses the same percent markup for all five items.

Article	Cost	Selling Price
Shirt	$ 8.00	$14.00
Tie	$ 4.80	$ 8.40
Socks	$ 1.60	$ 2.80
Jacket	$32.00	
Slacks	$20.00	

7. How much does a jacket sell for?

8. How much does a pair of slacks sell for?

9. Mr. Morrison purchased a shirt, a tie, and a pair of slacks. How much profit did the store make on the sale?

10. Mr. Lawrence purchased three different items. His bill was $67.20. Which items did he buy?

The members of the Altoona Chamber of Commerce are planting a garden of tulips—red, white, yellow, and black—on the town square.

11. They are making a rectangular garden. They have 40 feet of fencing. What should the dimensions be so that the garden has the greatest area?

12. They will plant the tulips in 4 rows, one color to a row. The red tulips will be at the left as you face north. The yellow tulips will be between the white and the black. The white will not be next to the red. Which color will be at the right?

Solve.

13. Suppose a fly was at the edge of a wheel as it turned around. How much farther would the fly travel in one revolution on a wheel with a 14-inch diameter than on a wheel with a 12-inch diameter?

★ 14. Here is a plan of the streets between Betty's house and Bill's house. Betty travels only in the direction of the arrows. How many different routes can she take to get to Bill's house?

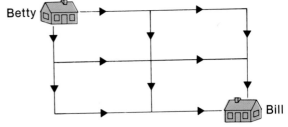

★ 15. It costs 75¢ each way to cross the Cimarron bridge. Commuters can buy a 30-day sticker for $10. They then pay only 25¢ each way. How many times must a commuter cross the bridge to make it economical to buy a sticker?

Write each ratio or decimal as a percent. pages 240–245

1. $\frac{3}{4}$ 2. 0.3 3. 0.875 4. $\frac{145}{100}$ 5. $\frac{1}{5}$

Write each percent as a decimal and as a ratio. pages 240–245

6. 25% 7. $\frac{1}{2}$% 8. 280% 9. 0.4% 10. $66\frac{2}{3}$%

Find *n* or the missing percent. pages 246–251

11. 60% of 75 is *n*. 12. $33\frac{1}{3}$% of 48 is *n*. 13. What percent of 50 is 12?

14. What percent of 76 is 57? 15. What percent of 48 is 72? 16. $62\frac{1}{2}$% of *n* is 25.

17. $66\frac{2}{3}$% of *n* is 30. 18. 250% of *n* is 36. 19. 400% of 3.6 is *n*.

20. 15% of $2.00 is *n*. 21. What percent of 44 is 16.5? 22. $33\frac{1}{3}$% of *n* is 17.

23. What percent of 2 is 20? 24. 500% of 30 is *n*. 25. What percent of 42 is 35?

26. What percent of 4.5 is 4.5? 27. $5\frac{1}{2}$% of $350 is *n*. 28. 80% of *n* is 64.

Find an estimate for *n* or for the percent. pages 254–255

29. 23% of 84 is *n*. 30. 86% of 320 is *n*. 31. 75% of 395 is *n*.

32. What percent of 88 is 30? 33. What percent of 45 is 10? 34. $66\frac{2}{3}$% of *n* is 19.

35. 48% of *n* is 22. 36. 195% of 61 is *n*. 37. What percent of 148 is 73?

Find each missing number. pages 256–263

38. regular price = $64
rate of discount = 15%
sale price = ____

39. regular price = $75
rate of discount = 25%
sale price = ____

40. original = 115
new = 138
percent of increase = ____

41. principal = $1,200
rate of interest = $10\frac{1}{2}$%
time = 6 mo
interest = ____

42. principal = $700
rate of interest = 8%
time = 2 yr
interest = ____

43. original = 120
new = 105
percent of decrease = ____

44. cost = $414
markup = $16\frac{2}{3}$%
amount of markup = ____
selling price = ____

45. cost = $570
markup = 60%
amount of markup = ____
selling price = ____

46. cost = $7.50
markup = $33\frac{1}{3}$%
amount of markup = ____
selling price = ____

Solve. pages 252–253, 264–265

47. Taro's discount store sells a $25 sweater at a 10% discount. What is the sale price?

48. A $50 skirt was discounted 10% each month for 4 months. What was the price after 4 months? Make a list to solve. Round to the nearest cent.

CHAPTER TEST

Write each percent as a decimal and as a ratio.

1. 75% **2.** 150% **3.** 0.5% **4.** $87\frac{1}{2}\%$

Write each ratio or decimal as a percent.

5. $\frac{2}{5}$ **6.** 0.047 **7.** 2.275 **8.** $\frac{5}{8}$

Find *n* or the missing percent.

9. 15% of 300 is *n*.

10. What percent of 15 is 12?

11. 40% of *n* is 6.

12. 225% of 32 is *n*.

Estimate.

13. 42% of 61

14. What percent of 49 is 12?

Find each missing number.

15. original = $75
new = $90
percent of increase = ___

16. regular price = $45.00
rate of discount = 25%
discount = ___
sale price = ___

17. cost = $72
markup = 40%
amount of markup = ___
selling price = ___

18. principal = $2,500
rate of interest = 7.5%
time = 2 yr
interest = ___

Solve.

19. Marsha borrowed $165 from her parents to buy a new bike. She is paying them 8% interest. She hopes to pay back the loan in 6 months. How much will she have paid in all for the bike?

20. How many times does the digit 4 appear in the page numbers from 1 to 99? Make a list.

The second time the price of this sweater was reduced, it was reduced 20%. What was the rate of discount the first time?

EXPLORE

PERCENT RUMMY

Commonly used percents and their equivalent ratios become the basis for a new version of a favorite old game for 2 players.

First write the equivalent ratio for each percent below.

2%	$33\frac{1}{3}$%	10%
25%	$66\frac{2}{3}$%	30%
50%	$16\frac{2}{3}$%	70%
75%	$83\frac{1}{3}$%	90%
20%	12.5%	$11\frac{1}{9}$%
40%	37.5%	$9\frac{1}{11}$%
60%	62.5%	$8\frac{1}{3}$%
80%	87.5%	5%

Make a deck of 49 cards: one card for each percent, one for each equivalent ratio, and one for the percent symbol.

Deal the entire deck to both players. Players place their matching percent and ratio cards face up, as pairs, on the table. Remaining cards are held by the players and play begins. One player chooses a single unknown card from the other player's cards. If this card can be paired with a card the player already holds, both cards are placed on the table. If no match can be made, the card is added to the player's hand. Players take turns choosing cards until all pairs have been made. The loser is the player left holding the percent-symbol card.

COMPOUND INTEREST

In a savings account at a bank, compound interest is received on the money in the account. **Compound interest** is added to the principal at the end of each interest period, so the principal becomes larger and larger. The interest is compounded at regular intervals, such as daily, monthly, or quarterly (every 3 mo).

Suppose $100 was put in a savings account that earned 6% interest compounded annually. This table shows how much money the account would have in it at the end of 3 years.

Year	Principal	Interest Earned	Balance at End of Year
1	$100	$100 × 0.06 = $6.00	$100 + $6 = $106
2	$106	$106 × 0.06 = $6.36	$106 + $6.36 = $112.36
3	$112.36	$112.36 × 0.06 = $6.74	$112.36 + $6.74 = $119.10

At the end of 3 years, there would be $119.10 in the account.
$119.10 − $100 = $19.10
The interest earned would be $19.10. How much would be earned if the rate was 6% simple interest?

This table shows how much money there would be in an account after 1 year if $100 was put in, earning 6% compounded quarterly.

Quarter	Principal	Interest Earned	Balance at End of Quarter
1st	$100.00	$100 × 0.06 × $\frac{1}{4}$ = $1.50	$100 + $1.50 = $101.50
2nd	$101.50	$101.50 × 0.06 × $\frac{1}{4}$ = $1.52	$101.50 + $1.52 = $103.02
3rd	$103.02	$103.02 × 0.06 × $\frac{1}{4}$ = $1.55	$103.02 + $1.55 = $104.57
4th	$104.57	$104.57 × 0.06 × $\frac{1}{4}$ = $1.57	$104.57 + $1.57 = $106.14

1. Would there be more or less at the end of a year if the money was compounded quarterly rather than annually? how much?

2. How much would be in the account after 3 years at 6% compounded quarterly?

Use a calculator to find the amount in each account.

3. $500 at 8% compounded annually for 5 years

4. $500 at 8% compounded semiannually for 5 years

5. $100 at $5\frac{1}{2}$% compounded quarterly for 2 years

6. $100 at $5\frac{1}{2}$% compounded monthly for 1 year

COMPUTING INTEREST

Interest is **compounded** by adding to the principal the interest earned for the current interest period *before* computing the interest for the next period.

The program below uses FOR and NEXT statements to repeat the process of computing and adding interest many times.

FOR and **NEXT** statements are always used together to create a loop, or sequence of commands that are repeated.

Example

```
10 FOR X = 1 TO 10 STEP 2
20 PRINT X , X * X
30 NEXT X
```

X is assigned the value 1.
X is increased by 2 and the loop is repeated until the value of X becomes *greater* than 10.

Output

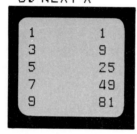

The comma in line 20 causes the output to be printed in columns.

This program finds the interest on $1,000 at 8% compounded quarterly for 3 years.

PROGRAM

```
                              10 REM COMPOUND INTEREST
```

Principal: $1,000	⟶ `20 LET P = 1000`
Interest rate: 8%	⟶ `30 LET R = 0.08`
Number of years: 3	⟶ `40 LET Y = 3`
Compound 4 times a year.	⟶ `50 LET N = 4`
Compound interest every $\frac{1}{4}$ year.	⟶ `60 FOR T = 1/N TO Y STEP 1/N`
Yearly interest is divided by 4.	⟶ `70 LET I = P * R/N`
Add interest to principal.	⟶ `80 LET P = P + I`
Display results.	⟶ `90 PRINT "YEARS: ";T , "PRINCIPAL: $"; P`
Repeat loop.	⟶ `100 NEXT T`
	`110 END`

Write the output for each program.

1.
```
10 FOR A = 1 TO 15 STEP 2
20 PRINT A
30 NEXT A
40 END
```

2.
```
10 FOR B = 1 TO 20 STEP 4
20 PRINT B
30 NEXT B
40 END
```

3.
```
10 FOR C = 17 TO 30 STEP 3
20 PRINT C
30 NEXT C
40 END
```

4.
```
10 FOR D = 1 TO 10 STEP 1
20 PRINT 11 - D
30 NEXT D
40 END
```

★5.
```
10 FOR I = 0 TO 5 STEP 0.5
20 PRINT I
30 IF I > 3 THEN GOTO 60
40 NEXT I
50 PRINT "THE END"
60 END
```

★6.
```
10 LET S = 0
20 FOR I = 1 TO 10 STEP 1
30 LET S = S + I
40 NEXT I
50 PRINT "SUM = " ;S
60 END
```

Write a program using FOR and NEXT statements to print each of the following.

7. your name 100 times

8. the even numbers from 6 to 28

9. the odd numbers from 49 to 85

10. every fourth number from 5 to 85

★11. the multiples of 3 from 3 to 99

★12. the whole numbers from 1 to 100 that are *not* multiples of 3

AT THE COMPUTER

Run the compound interest program on page 270, compounding the interest N times a year. Compare the principal at the end of 3 years for each.

1. N = 4   2. N = 2   3. N = 1   4. N = 12   5. N = 360   ★6. N = 6

To round a number N to the nearest hundredth, use the BASIC statement `LET R = INT(N * 100 + 0.5)/100`.

7. Write a program that will allow the user to input a decimal number and will print that number rounded to the nearest hundredth.

★8. Rewrite the compound interest program on page 270 so that all output is rounded to the nearest hundredth.

MAINTAINING SKILLS

Choose the correct answers. Write **A**, **B**, **C**, or **D**.

1. What is the LCM of 18 and 24?

   A 3   **C** 48

   B 72   **D** not given

2. $8\frac{3}{4} + 6\frac{2}{3}$

   A $14\frac{5}{12}$ **C** $15\frac{5}{12}$

   B $14\frac{1}{12}$ **D** not given

3. $3\frac{3}{4} \div 3\frac{3}{8}$

   A $\frac{9}{10}$ **C** $1\frac{1}{9}$

   B $22\frac{1}{2}$ **D** not given

4. What is the name of a 13° angle?

   A acute   **C** straight

   B obtuse   **D** not given

5. What kind of angles are $\angle AEB$ and $\angle CED$?

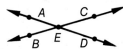

   A adjacent   **C** supplementary

   B vertical   **D** not given

6. What is the area of the parallelogram?

   14.9 cm   4.8 cm   5.3 cm

   A 25.44 cm²   **C** 78.97 cm²

   B 40.4 cm²   **D** not given

7. $\frac{3}{14} = \frac{n}{32.2}$

   A $n = 96.6$ **C** $n = 6.9$

   B $n = 450$ **D** not given

8. What is the unit price if 7 cans cost $2.31?

   A $.33   **C** $2.31

   B $16.17   **D** not given

9. What is the tangent ratio of $\angle B$?

   A $\frac{n}{9}$ **C** $\frac{n}{7}$

   B $\frac{9}{n}$ **D** not given

10. What is the percent of decrease? new amount = 60; original amount = 96

   A 37.5%   **C** 30%

   B 62.5%   **D** not given

11. What percent is $\frac{1}{6}$?

   A 16%   **C** 6%

   B 60%   **D** not given

12. What decimal is 0.04%?

   A 0.40   **C** 0.4

   B 0.0004   **D** not given

13. What is $33\frac{1}{3}\%$ of 171?

   A 57   **C** 513

   B 114   **D** not given

Solve.

14. There were three boys standing in a row.

   • The boy with the gray hat was behind Mark.

   • Dane was directly in front of Leon.

   • Dane's hat was not blue.

   • The boy with the brown hat was last.

In what order were the boys standing?

   A Leon, Dane, Mark   **C** Mark, Dane, Leon

   B Dane, Mark, Leon   **D** not given

Theme: Mountains

Writing and Comparing Integers

Integers can be used to express measurements above and below sea level. The base of Mauna Kea is about 6 km below sea level. Mt. Everest rises to about 9 km above sea level. Write these measurements as integers.

6 km below sea level can be represented by ⁻6 (negative 6).

9 km above sea level can be represented by ⁺9 (positive 9).

▶The numbers . . ., ⁻2, ⁻1, 0, ⁺1, ⁺2, . . . are **integers**. They can be shown on the number line.

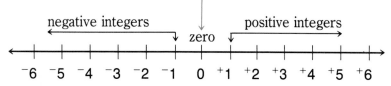

Zero is neither positive nor negative.

negative integers   positive integers

zero

▶The **absolute value** of an integer tells the distance the integer is from 0 on the number line.

$|^+2| = 2$ The absolute value of positive 2 equals 2.

$|^-2| = 2$ The absolute value of negative 2 equals 2.

The number line can be used to compare integers. Given two integers, the one farther to the right on the number line is the greater integer.

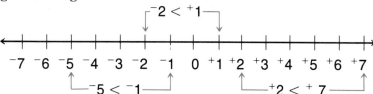

⁻2 < ⁺1

⁻5 < ⁻1   ⁺2 < ⁺7

MOUNTAINS OF THE WORLD

10 km

8

6

4

2

sea level — 0

⁻2

⁻4

⁻6

MAUNA KEA   MT. EVEREST   MT. McKINLEY   MT. BLANC   MT. FUJI

CLASSWORK

Write the integer for each.

1. positive sixteen   **2.** 20°F below zero   **3.** 7 units to the left of 0

Write the absolute value of each.

4. $|^-15|$ **5.** $|^+20|$ **6.** $|^+1|$ **7.** $|^-16|$ **8.** $|0|$

Compare. Use < or > for each ⬤.

9. ⁻3 ⬤ ⁺5   **10.** ⁺9 ⬤ ⁺12   **11.** 0 ⬤ ⁻7   **12.** ⁻14 ⬤ ⁻8

Write the integer for each.

1. 14°C above zero
2. a loss of 12 points
3. 30 m below sea level
4. positive nineteen
5. negative eight
6. positive fifty-one
7. 6 units to the right of 0
8. 10 units to the left of 0
9. 26 units to the left of 0
10. 17 units to the right of 0
★ 11. 5 units to the right of ⁻2
★ 12. 6 units to the left of ⁺3

Write the absolute value of each integer.

13. $|{}^+2|$
14. $|{}^+10|$
15. $|{}^-36|$
16. $|{}^-1|$
17. $|{}^-41|$
18. $|{}^+19|$
19. $|{}^+25|$
20. $|{}^+20|$
21. $|{}^-52|$
22. $|{}^+64|$
23. $|{}^-108|$
24. $|{}^+112|$

Compare. Use <, >, or = for each ⬤.

25. $^+6$ ⬤ $^+4$
26. $^-6$ ⬤ 0
27. $^+9$ ⬤ $^-10$
28. $^-7$ ⬤ $^-11$
29. $^-15$ ⬤ $^+1$
30. $^+15$ ⬤ $^-1$
31. $^-10$ ⬤ $^+10$
32. $^+8$ ⬤ $^-8$
33. $^-27$ ⬤ $^-35$
34. $^-19$ ⬤ $^-12$
35. $^-38$ ⬤ $^-45$
36. $^-54$ ⬤ $^-55$
37. $^-36$ ⬤ $^+49$
38. $^+78$ ⬤ $^+86$
39. $^+104$ ⬤ $^-104$
40. $|{}^+98|$ ⬤ $|{}^-98|$

Write the integers in order from least to greatest.

41. $^-8, {}^-10, {}^+4, 0$
42. $^+2, {}^-3, {}^-14, {}^+16$
43. $^+4, {}^-7, {}^+7, 0, {}^-1$
★ 44. $^-28, {}^-14, {}^+15, {}^-63, {}^+219, {}^-217, {}^+21$
★ 45. $^-42, 0, {}^+26, {}^+42, {}^-200, {}^-20, {}^+12, {}^+3, {}^-2$

APPLICATION

Use the graph on page 274 to find each to the nearest kilometer.

46. the height of the highest mountain above sea level
47. the height of Mount Blanc

48. the name of the lowest mountain above sea level

★ 49. the height of each mountain measured from its base in order from lowest to highest

Mt. Fuji, Japan

Adding Integers

In early February the snow base at the Pine Mountain ski area measured 55 inches. During a warm spell 7 inches of snow melted the first day and 4 inches the next. How much did the base change in the two days?

Find $^-7 + {}^-4$.

Use the number line. Start at 0. Move 7 units to the left ($^-7$), and then move 4 units to the left ($^-4$).

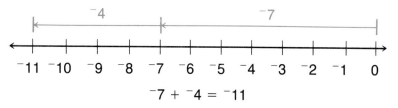

$$^-7 + {}^-4 = {}^-11$$

▶The sum of two negative integers is negative.

The snow base decreased 11 inches.

Find $^+6 + {}^+3$.

Start at 0 on the number line. Move 6 units to the right ($^+6$), and then move 3 units to the right ($^+3$).

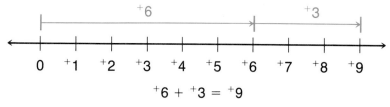

$$^+6 + {}^+3 = {}^+9$$

▶The sum of two positive integers is positive.

More Examples

a. $^-12 + {}^-15 = {}^-27$ b. $^-6 + {}^-3 = {}^-9$ c. $^+8 + {}^+14 = {}^+22$

CLASSWORK

Add.

1. $^+7 + {}^+4$ 2. $^-8 + {}^-3$ 3. $^-15 + {}^-2$ 4. $^+13 + {}^+7$

5. $^-21 + {}^-9$ 6. $^-18 + {}^-7$ 7. $^+35 + {}^+21$ 8. $^-32 + {}^-10$

9. $^+4 + {}^+5$ 10. $^-6 + {}^-4$ 11. $^-10 + {}^-30$ 12. $^+35 + {}^+3$

PRACTICE

Use a number line to complete this chart.

	Start at	Move Direction	Move Total Units	Stop at
1. $^+6 + {}^+7$	0	right	13	
2. $^-9 + {}^-10$				
3. $^+13 + {}^+25$				
4. $^-26 + {}^-11$				
5. $^-42 + {}^-15$				

Add.

6. $^+10 + {}^+8$ **7.** $^+8 + {}^+4$ **8.** $^-7 + {}^-5$ **9.** $^-6 + {}^-8$

10. $^+17 + {}^+8$ **11.** $^+4 + {}^+21$ **12.** $^-11 + {}^-15$ **13.** $^-34 + {}^-7$

14. $^+9 + {}^+25$ **15.** $^+27 + {}^+18$ **16.** $^-17 + {}^-35$ **17.** $^-47 + {}^-18$

18. $^+32 + {}^+78$ **19.** $^+55 + {}^+48$ **20.** $^-34 + {}^-43$ **21.** $^-74 + {}^-29$

22. $^-8 + {}^-6 + {}^-9$ **23.** $^+24 + {}^+59 + {}^+84$ **24.** $^-209 + {}^-18 + {}^-84$

25. $^+6 + {}^+1 + {}^+12$ **26.** $^-10 + {}^-14 + {}^-12$ **27.** $^-43 + {}^-4 + {}^-13$

28. $|^+4 + {}^+5|$ **29.** $|^-4 + {}^-5|$ **30.** $|^-5 + {}^-3 + {}^-2|$ **31.** $|^-2 + {}^-5|$

Compare. Use >, <, or = for each ⬤.

32. $^+4 + {}^+4$ ⬤ $^-4 + {}^-4$ **33.** $^+6 + {}^+2$ ⬤ $^+4 + {}^+4$ **34.** $^-5 + {}^-4$ ⬤ $^-4 + {}^-5$

Solve.

★**35.** Copy the figure at the right. Write $^-1$, $^-2$, $^-3$, $^-4$, $^-5$, $^-6$, $^-7$, $^-8$, or $^-9$ in each circle so the sum along each side of the triangle is $^-20$. Use each number once.

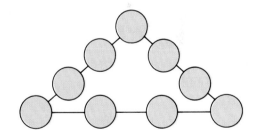

APPLICATION

36. On Monday the snow base measured 41 inches. Seven inches of snow fell overnight and 5 inches fell on Tuesday. What is the change in the snow base?

37. Doris, Eddie, Fran, Gary, and Hilda all want to ride in a 3-person chair on the chair lift. What are the possible combinations of 3 people riding in the chair?

★**38.** The temperature at the base of Pine Mountain was 15°F. During a storm the temperature fell each hour from 3 P.M. to 8 P.M. Use the table to find how many degrees the temperature changed in all from 3 P.M. to 8 P.M.

Time	Degrees Fallen
3 P.M. to 4 P.M.	1
4 P.M. to 5 P.M.	2
5 P.M. to 6 P.M.	2
6 P.M. to 7 P.M.	3
7 P.M. to 8 P.M.	2

Adding Positive and Negative Integers

Scouts from a wagon train were trying to find a mountain pass. One scout left the wagon train and rode 3 miles east and then 2 miles west. How many miles was he from the wagon train?

Find $^+3 + {}^-2$.

The addition can be shown on the number line. Start at 0. Move 3 units to the right ($^+3$), and then move 2 units to the left ($^-2$).

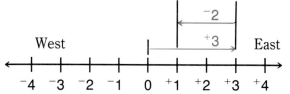

To add a positive and a negative integer, find the absolute value of each. Then *subtract* the lesser from the greater. The sign of the integer with the greater absolute value is the sign of the answer.

$$|^+3| - |^-2| = 3 - 2 = 1 \qquad {}^+3 + {}^-2 = {}^+1$$

$^+3$ has the greater absolute value, so the answer is positive.

The scout was 1 mile east of the wagon train.

Find $^+3 + {}^-3$.

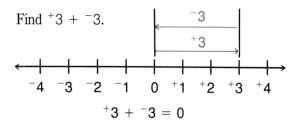

$$^+3 + {}^-3 = 0$$

$^+3$ is the opposite, or **additive inverse,** of $^-3$.

The Rocky Mountains—Emigrants Crossing the Plains by Currier and Ives

▶ The sum of an integer and its opposite, or additive inverse, is 0.

The Inverse Property of Addition

More Examples

a. $^-9 + {}^+3$
   $9 - 3 = 6$ $|^-9| = 9$
                 $|^+3| = 3$
   $^-9 + {}^+3 = {}^-6$

b. $^+12 + {}^-12$ $^+12$ is the additive inverse of $^-12$.
   $^+12 + {}^-12 = 0$

c. $^-15 + {}^+18$
   $18 - 15 = 3$ $|^-15| = 15$
                   $|^+18| = 18$
   $^-15 + {}^+18 = {}^+3$

CLASSWORK

Write the additive inverse of each integer.

1. $^-9$
2. $^+8$
3. $^-1$
4. 0
5. $^-25$

Add.

6. $^-4 + {}^+4$
7. $^-17 + {}^+8$
8. $^-10 + {}^+15$
9. $^-18 + {}^+7$
10. $^+26 + {}^-39$
11. $^+35 + {}^-12$
12. $^+24 + {}^-24$
13. $^+87 + {}^-13$

PRACTICE

Use a number line to complete this chart.

		Start at	Move Direction	Move Units	Move Direction	Move Units	Stop at
1.	$^-7 + {}^+9$	0	left	7	right	9	
2.	$^+8 + {}^-4$						
3.	$^+12 + {}^-12$						
4.	$^-10 + {}^+7$						
5.	$^+9 + {}^-19$						

Add.

6. $^+3 + {}^-6$ 7. $^+9 + {}^-5$ 8. $^-9 + {}^+9$ 9. $^+5 + {}^-7$

10. $^-10 + {}^+10$ 11. $^-8 + {}^+19$ 12. $^-12 + {}^+9$ 13. $^+11 + {}^-10$

14. $^+11 + {}^-12$ 15. $^+8 + {}^-15$ 16. $^+17 + {}^-17$ 17. $^-16 + {}^+32$

18. $^+75 + {}^-19$ 19. $^-87 + {}^+85$ 20. $^-124 + {}^+96$ 21. $^-147 + {}^+191$

Add. Complete the steps.

22. START $^+9$ $+ {}^-6$ $+ {}^-7$ STOP

★ 23. START $^-42$ $+ {}^+26$ $+ {}^-35$ $+ {}^-10$ $+ {}^+61$ STOP

APPLICATION

24. Two scouts left the wagon train to look for a place to camp. One scout rode 1 mile east and 3 miles west. The other scout traveled 3 miles west and 1 mile east. Where did the scouts meet?

25. A scout traveled 19 miles west from the wagon train the first day. The second day he traveled another 16 miles west before he started back. He traveled 8 miles east and made camp. How far is the scout from the wagon train?

MENTAL ARITHMETIC

Use the Inverse Property of Addition to find each.

1. $^-5 + {}^-6 + {}^+5 + {}^+7 + {}^+6$

2. $^-8 + {}^-10 + {}^+8 + {}^-9 + {}^+10$

3. $^-3 + {}^-2 + {}^-6 + {}^+5$

4. $^-4 + {}^-3 + {}^+20 + {}^-7 + {}^-6$

5. $^-9 + {}^-8 + {}^+1 + {}^+17$

6. $^+18 + {}^+10 + {}^-10 + {}^-19 + {}^-18$

7. $^+5 + {}^+11 + {}^-8 + {}^-16 + {}^+8$

8. $^+101 + {}^+20 + {}^-90 + {}^-11$

9. $^-1,000 + {}^+80 + {}^-1 + {}^+1 + {}^-80 + {}^+1,001$

10. $^-89 + {}^-101 + {}^+10 + {}^+100 + {}^+79$

279

Subtracting Integers

On December 5 the Martinez family went skiing in the Green Mountains of Vermont. What was the difference between the actual temperature and the windchill temperature on that day? (Windchill is an estimate of how cold the wind makes a person feel.)

TIME 10 AM
TEMPERATURE 15°F
WINDCHILL -3°F

Find $^+15 - {}^-3$.

To subtract an integer, *add* its opposite, or additive inverse.

The opposite of $^-3$ is $^+3$.

$$^+15 - {}^-3 = {}^+15 + {}^+3 = {}^+18$$

Check $^+18 + {}^-3 = {}^+15$

The difference was 18 degrees.

More Examples

a. $^+8 - {}^+12 = {}^+8 + {}^-12 = {}^-4$
The opposite of $^+12$ is $^-12$.

b. $^+9 - {}^-6 = {}^+9 + {}^+6 = {}^+15$
The opposite of $^-6$ is $^+6$.

c. $^-10 - {}^-14 = {}^-10 + {}^+14 = {}^+4$

d. $^-15 - {}^-15 = {}^-15 + {}^+15 = 0$

e. $^-16 - {}^+10 = {}^-16 + {}^-10 = {}^-26$

f. $^-20 - {}^-12 = {}^-20 + {}^+12 = {}^-8$

CLASSWORK

Subtract.

1. $^+9 - {}^-4$

2. $^-9 - {}^+4$

3. $^-9 - {}^-4$

4. $^+9 - {}^+4$

5. $^+15 - {}^+8$

6. $^+13 - {}^-13$

7. $^-6 - {}^-27$

8. $^+12 - {}^+20$

9. $^-10 - {}^+6$

10. $^+12 - {}^+12$

11. $^-42 - {}^-42$

12. $^+59 - {}^+49$

Write an equivalent expression using the additive inverse.

1. $^+10 - {}^-6$ **2.** $^-8 - {}^+9$ **3.** $^-16 - {}^-20$ **4.** $^+13 - {}^+21$

5. $^+25 - {}^+14$ **6.** $^-17 - {}^-11$ **7.** $^-20 - {}^+9$ **8.** $^+25 - {}^-10$

Find each difference.

9. $^+10 - {}^+6$ **10.** $^-8 - {}^+6$ **11.** $^-16 - {}^+12$ **12.** $^-10 - {}^-10$

13. $^-8 - {}^+16$ **14.** $^+14 - {}^+18$ **15.** $^-21 - {}^-17$ **16.** $^-13 - {}^-18$

17. $^+8 - {}^+18$ **18.** $^+8 - {}^-18$ **19.** $^+7 - {}^+19$ **20.** $^+16 - {}^-8$

21. $^-15 - {}^-35$ **22.** $^-20 - {}^+17$ **23.** $^-21 - {}^+11$ **24.** $^+21 - {}^+11$

Solve.

★**25.** Fill in the missing numbers to make the sentences true across and down.

$^-2$	$+$	$^+5$	$-$		$=$	$^+9$
$-$		$+$		$-$		$+$
$^-4$	$-$		$-$	$^-7$	$=$	$^+8$
$+$		$-$		$+$		$+$
$^-3$	$+$	$^-7$	$+$		$=$	
$=$		$=$		$=$		$=$
	$+$		$+$	$^+4$	$=$	

APPLICATION

What is the windchill temperature? What is the difference between the actual temperature and the windchill temperature?

26. $^+10°F$ with a 10-mph wind

27. $^-10°F$ with a 15-mph wind

28. $^+5°F$ with a 20-mph wind

29. $^-15°F$ with a 25-mph wind

WINDCHILL TEMPERATURES (°F)							
Wind Speed (mph)	Actual Temperature (°F)						
Calm	$^+15$	$^+10$	$^+5$	0	$^-5$	$^-10$	$^-15$
5	$^+12$	$^+7$	0	$^-5$	$^-10$	$^-15$	$^-21$
10	$^-3$	$^-9$	$^-15$	$^-22$	$^-27$	$^-34$	$^-40$
15	$^-11$	$^-18$	$^-25$	$^-31$	$^-38$	$^-45$	$^-51$
20	$^-17$	$^-24$	$^-31$	$^-39$	$^-46$	$^-53$	$^-60$
25	$^-22$	$^-29$	$^-36$	$^-44$	$^-51$	$^-59$	$^-66$

CALCULATOR

Some calculators have a change-of-sign key $\boxed{+/-}$. Use it to add or subtract integers.

Find $^-7 - {}^+5$. Press $\boxed{7}$ $\boxed{+/-}$ $\boxed{-}$ $\boxed{5}$ $\boxed{=}$ Display   On some calculators the negative sign appears to the right of the number.

Calculate.

1. $^-6 + {}^+4$ **2.** $^+5 - {}^-4$ **3.** $^-4 + {}^+7$ **4.** $^-2 - {}^-1$

5. $^-7 + {}^-6$ **6.** $^+4 + {}^-3$ **7.** $^-16 + {}^-15$ **8.** $^-4 - 0$

Problem Solving

WORKING BACKWARDS

Sometimes you are given the result of an action. Then you are asked to find information about the beginning of the action. For these problems, you should work backwards from the answer that is given.

THINK
PLAN
SOLVE
LOOK
BACK

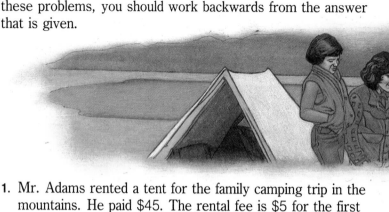

1. Mr. Adams rented a tent for the family camping trip in the mountains. He paid $45. The rental fee is $5 for the first day, $7 for the second day, and so on. Each day's cost is $2 more than the previous day. For how many days did Mr. Adams rent the tent?

For how many days did he rent the tent?

rate—$5 for the first day
The rate increases by $2 for each additional day.
total cost—$45

Work backwards to find the number of days.

first day	second day	third day	fourth day	fifth day
$45	$40	$33	$24	$13
− 5	− 7	− 9	− 11	− 13
$40	$33	$24	$13	$ 0

Mr. Adams rented the tent for 5 days.

Check by adding the 5 days' total.

$13 + $11 + $9 + $7 + $5 = $45

2. Wanda Evans hosts a local television show. She must plan exactly 1 full hour of time. Commercials will take 21.5 minutes. An interview with her special guest, a famous mountain climber, will take 17.5 minutes. The rest of the time will be spent taking questions from the studio audience. If she allows 3 minutes for each question, how many questions can she take?

Work backwards. Start with 60 minutes. Complete the solution.

PRACTICE

Solve by working backwards.

1. Luther works at a supply post near the campsite. During the morning he takes in $3.50, $7.50, $2.85, $4.15, and $6.05. He gives out 50¢, 80¢, 15¢, and 85¢ in change. At 12:00 noon his cash drawer has $53.75 in it. How much was in the cash drawer at the start of the day?

2. The owner of the supply post added $18 to the cost of a two-way radio for a carrying case. He increased the total 150% for the markup. Then he added sales tax of $7. The resulting selling price was $112. What was the original cost of the radio for the owner?

3. Erin bought 50 m of mountain-climbing rope. She also bought a backpack for $29.95 and a water flask for $11. Her total bill was $113.45. How much did the rope cost per meter?

4. Susan had a rock collection. She gave 9 to the school museum and shared the remainder equally with 7 of her friends. She had 5 rocks left. How many rocks were in her original collection?

5. Ellen wants to meet Ron at the campsite at 3:00 P.M. It is now 10:00 A.M., and she is at the lake. The lake is 5 km from the campsite. It takes Ellen 15 minutes to walk 1 km. She plans to spend 20 minutes locating wildlife for 6 photographs she will take on the way. She estimates she will spend 5 minutes for each photograph. What is the latest she can leave the lake to meet Ron on time?

6. An airplane was searching for some people who were lost in the mountains. The plane used 1,800 L of fuel in 4 hours. By the end of the third hour, it had used 1,400 L. During the third hour, it used $\frac{3}{4}$ as much fuel as it used during the fourth hour. It used the same amount of fuel during each of the first two hours. How much fuel did the plane use during the first hour?

7. Pete Standi is inspecting lookout stations on the mountain. He climbs 100 m up the mountain to Station 1. He then goes down 50 m to Station 2. Then he climbs 250 m to Station 3, which is 280 m above Station 4. How high is each station?

★ 8. The ranger station is giving first-aid kits to visiting schools. They give $\frac{1}{4}$ of them to the Woods School. They then give $\frac{1}{3}$ of what is left to the Barker School. Then they give $\frac{1}{2}$ of the remaining kits to the Logan School and the last 16 kits to the Rogers School. How many first-aid kits do they give away?

CREATE YOUR OWN PROBLEM

Scientists measuring the movement of a glacier used electrodes frozen at different levels on the ice. They drilled down 52 m to reach the bottom of the glacier. A string of electrodes spaced 4 m apart was lowered into the hole. Create a problem that can be solved working backwards.

Multiplying Integers

The temperature on a mountain drops 3 degrees for each increase of 1,000 feet of altitude. How much lower is the temperature at the point the lead climber has reached than the temperature at the base of the mountain?

Find $^-3 \cdot {}^+3$.

↑
means *times*

▶ The product of a positive and a negative integer is negative.

$$^-3 \cdot 3 = {}^-9 \longleftarrow (-) \cdot (+) = (-)$$

↑
Positive integers are commonly written without the $^+$

The temperature is 9 degrees lower.

▶ The product of two positive or two negative integers is positive.

$$(+) \cdot (+) = (+) \qquad (-) \cdot (-) = (+)$$
$$5 \cdot 5 \;\; = 25 \qquad {}^-3 \cdot {}^-5 = 15$$

More Examples

a. $7 \cdot {}^-7 = {}^-49$

b. $6 \cdot 3 = 18$

c. $^-8 \cdot {}^-3 = 24$

3,000 feet

sea level

Classwork

Multiply.

1. $^-7 \cdot 4$
2. $^-7 \cdot {}^-3$
3. $6 \cdot {}^-4$
4. $6 \cdot 4$

5. $^-6 \cdot {}^-4$
6. $5 \cdot {}^-15$
7. $^-3 \cdot {}^-6$
8. $^-12 \cdot 7$

9. $^-10 \cdot {}^-10$
10. $8 \cdot {}^-12$
11. $^-15 \cdot {}^-3$
12. $10 \cdot {}^-4$

Multiply.

1. $6 \cdot 9$
2. $6 \cdot {}^-9$
3. ${}^-6 \cdot 9$
4. ${}^-6 \cdot {}^-9$
5. ${}^-8 \cdot 4$
6. $8 \cdot 4$
7. ${}^-7 \cdot {}^-5$
8. $7 \cdot {}^-5$
9. $3 \cdot {}^-10$
10. ${}^-4 \cdot {}^-9$
11. $7 \cdot 8$
12. ${}^-8 \cdot 8$
13. ${}^-11 \cdot {}^-8$
14. $15 \cdot 0$
15. $4 \cdot {}^-15$
16. ${}^-10 \cdot 7$
17. ${}^-13 \cdot 5$
18. $5 \cdot 13$
19. ${}^-5 \cdot {}^-12$
20. $20 \cdot {}^-6$
21. ${}^-12 \cdot {}^-9$
22. $4 \cdot 1 \cdot {}^-2$
23. ${}^-7 \cdot 2 \cdot 4$
24. ${}^-4 \cdot {}^-6 \cdot 3$
25. ${}^-3 \cdot {}^-7 \cdot {}^-7$
26. $6 \cdot 3 \cdot {}^-10$
27. $8 \cdot {}^-1 \cdot {}^-5$
28. ${}^-6 \cdot {}^-8 \cdot 10$
29. ${}^-5 \cdot {}^-2 \cdot 4$
30. ${}^-15 \cdot {}^-2 \cdot 5$
★ 31. $({}^-8 + {}^-4) \cdot 7$
★ 32. $({}^-3 + 4) \cdot ({}^-5 - 7)$
★ 33. $({}^-2 + {}^-3) \cdot ({}^-5^3)$
★ 34. $({}^-3 - 7) \cdot (16 - {}^-6)$

APPLICATION

35. Mountains in Norway and Sweden are rising about 2 feet a century. How much lower would a climber on the summit have been 500 years ago?

36. Sir Edmund Hillary's autobiography, *Nothing Venture, Nothing Win*, describes his mountaineering expeditions. Climbers crossing glaciers find that glacial ice moves at different rates along mountain slopes. On steep slopes it may move 100 ft a day. How far might it move in a week?

MATH HISTORY

When the mathematician Carl Friedrich Gauss was a young student, his teacher asked the class to add all the numbers from 1 to 100. This is the way Gauss did it.

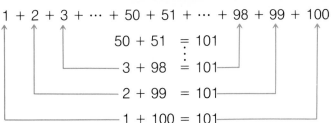

$$1 + 2 + 3 + \cdots + 50 + 51 + \cdots + 98 + 99 + 100$$

$$50 + 51 = 101$$
$$\vdots$$
$$3 + 98 = 101$$
$$2 + 99 = 101$$
$$1 + 100 = 101$$

There are 50 pairs of numbers, each with a sum of 101. So the sum of the numbers is 50×101, or 5,050.

Use Gauss's method to find each sum of integers.

1. 1 to 50
2. ${}^-50$ to ${}^-1$
3. ${}^-20$ to 20
★ 4. ${}^-35$ to 10

Dividing Integers

A team of climbers was able to descend only 78 meters in 3 hours. What was the average number of meters they descended per hour?

Find $^-78 \div 3$.

▶ The quotient of a positive and a negative integer is negative.

$$(-) \div (+) = (-) \qquad (+) \div (-) = (-)$$

$$^-78 \div 3 \ = \ ^-26$$

They descended 26 meters per hour.

▶ The quotient of two positive or two negative integers is positive.

$$(-) \div (-) = (+) \qquad (+) \div (+) = (+)$$

$$^-20 \div ^-5 = 4 \qquad 30 \div 6 \ = \ 5$$

More Examples

a. $18 \div ^-3 = ^-6$

b. $^-8 \div ^-2 = 4$

c. $25 \div 5 = 5$

CLASSWORK

Divide.

1. $36 \div ^-9$

2. $^-36 \div ^-9$

3. $81 \div 9$

4. $^-81 \div ^-9$

5. $^-72 \div 8$

6. $^-75 \div ^-25$

7. $64 \div ^-4$

8. $108 \div 12$

9. $^-8 \div ^-4$

10. $^-60 \div 5$

11. $^-14 \div 7$

12. $^-9 \div 3$

13. $54 \div ^-6$

14. $77 \div ^-1$

15. $121 \div 11$

16. $^-100 \div 4$

PRACTICE

Divide.

1. 36 ÷ 4
2. 36 ÷ ⁻4
3. ⁻36 ÷ ⁻4
4. ⁻36 ÷ 4

5. ⁻56 ÷ ⁻7
6. 56 ÷ ⁻7
7. ⁻42 ÷ 7
8. ⁻63 ÷ 9

9. 35 ÷ ⁻5
10. 36 ÷ 12
11. ⁻64 ÷ 8
12. ⁻49 ÷ ⁻7

13. 54 ÷ ⁻9
14. ⁻48 ÷ 8
15. ⁻42 ÷ ⁻6
16. ⁻24 ÷ 3

17. 34 ÷ ⁻2
18. ⁻34 ÷ ⁻17
19. ⁻72 ÷ ⁻9
20. 90 ÷ ⁻5

21. 0 ÷ ⁻16
22. 80 ÷ ⁻5
23. ⁻80 ÷ ⁻4
24. 144 ÷ 12

25. ⁻75 ÷ ⁻5
26. 115 ÷ ⁻5
27. ⁻63 ÷ ⁻9
28. ⁻132 ÷ 11

Follow the rules for the order of operations.

29. ⁻32 ÷ ⁻8 ÷ ⁻2
30. 6 · ⁻5 ÷ 10
31. 63 ÷ 7 ÷ ⁻3

32. 16 ÷ 4 ÷ ⁻4
33. ⁻12 ÷ 4 ÷ ⁻1
34. 72 ÷ ⁻8 ÷ 3

★ 35. (⁻1 + ⁻5) ÷ 2
★ 36. (⁻2 − 6) ÷ ⁻4
★ 37. (⁻9 − ⁻1) ÷ (⁻2 + 4)

Complete.

★ 38. Write ⁻36, ⁻15, ⁻8, ⁻2, 4, 18, or 72 in each circle so the product of the three numbers along each line is 2,160. Use each number once.

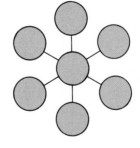

APPLICATION

39. An expedition descends 49 m in 2 hours and 17 m in the next hour. On the average, how far did they descend each hour?

40. On Tuesday 10 cm of snow fell on a mountain. The next day 5 cm of snow fell. That brought the snow base up to 90 cm. What was the base on Tuesday before the snowfall?

=== LOGICAL THINKING ===

Three women shared a hotel room during the Sweet Adelines singing competition. They paid $90 when they checked in. The clerk should have charged them only $85, so she sent the bellhop up with a $5 refund. Since the $5 could not be divided evenly among the three women, they took $3 and gave the bellhop $2 as a tip. Therefore, each person paid $29, for a total of $87. The bellhop received $2, for a total of $89. What happened to the extra $1?

287

The Coordinate Plane

The Martin family made a list of places they wanted to visit in Mount Rainier National Park. One of the places was Unicorn Park. To locate the park, they used a coordinate plane drawn on the map.

Points on a **coordinate plane** can be located by using two perpendicular number lines. The horizontal line is called the **x-axis**. The vertical line is called the **y-axis**.

The location of any point on a coordinate plane is given by the **ordered pair (x, y)**.

Unicorn Park can be located by the ordered pair (3, ⁻5).

The ordered pair (0, 0) locates the **origin**, the intersection of the axes.

The x-axis and the y-axis separate the plane into four **quadrants**.

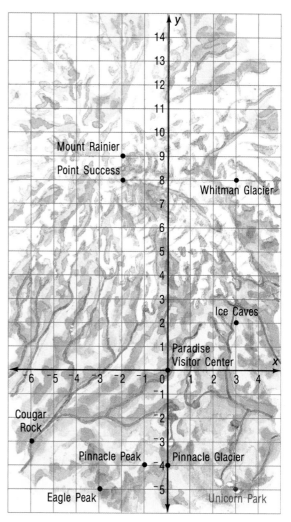

Point	Ordered Pair	Quadrant
A	(1, 2)	I
B	(⁻1, 2)	II
C	(⁻1, ⁻2)	III
D	(1, ⁻2)	IV

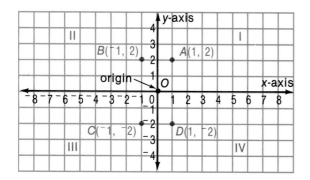

CLASSWORK

Write the ordered pair that locates each point.

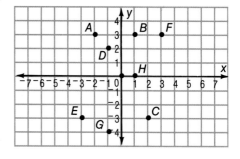

1. A   **2.** B   **3.** C

4. D   **5.** E   **6.** F

7. G   **8.** H   **9.** origin

10. Name the quadrant for each point in **1–7.**

PRACTICE

Write the ordered pair that locates each point.

1. A
2. B
3. C
4. D
5. E
6. F
7. G
8. H
9. I
10. J
11. K
12. L

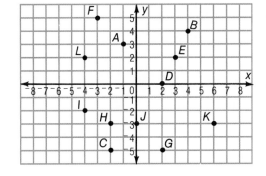

Copy the chart. Name the point located by each ordered pair. Give the quadrant for each point.

	Point	Ordered Pair	Quadrant
13.		(5, 4)	
14.		($^{-}$4, $^{-}$4)	
15.		(4, $^{-}$2)	
16.		(3, 1)	
17.		($^{-}$3, 3)	
18.		($^{-}$2, $^{-}$1)	
★ 19.		($^{-}$4, 0)	
★ 20.		(0, 5)	

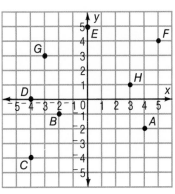

Solve.

★ 21. What is the ordered pair for any point located on the x-axis?

★ 22. What is the ordered pair for any point located on the y-axis?

APPLICATION

The map on page 288 shows the places that the Martin family plans to visit. Give the ordered pair for each.

23. Mount Rainier
24. Point Success
25. Eagle Peak
26. Ice Caves
27. Cougar Rock
28. Pinnacle Peak
29. Whitman Glacier
30. Pinnacle Glacier

Mixed Practice

1. $\begin{array}{r} 137.5 \\ -2.05 \\ \hline \end{array}$

2. $\begin{array}{r} 4,368 \\ \times\,0.47 \\ \hline \end{array}$

3. $34.4 \div 4.3$

4. $0.004 \div 0.02$

5. $\begin{array}{r} 76.32 \\ \times\,2.7 \\ \hline \end{array}$

6. $\frac{1}{2} + \frac{3}{8}$

7. $\frac{3}{4} - \frac{2}{5}$

8. $7\frac{1}{2} + 6\frac{3}{8}$

9. $74 + 12\frac{1}{8} - 51\frac{1}{2}$

10. $15 \div \frac{3}{5}$

Solve.

11. $\frac{5}{10} = \frac{n}{5}$

12. $\frac{3}{8} = \frac{n}{12}$

13. $\frac{10}{5} = \frac{n}{3}$

14. $\frac{n}{14} = \frac{28}{7}$

15. $\frac{n}{12} = \frac{15}{2}$

289

Graphing Ordered Pairs

Parts of the lunar surface are rough and mountainous. Scientists studied the surface to determine where lunar landings should be made. Apollo 15 landed near the Apennines, a mountain range.

On a coordinate plane each point is assigned an ordered pair. Each ordered pair locates a point.

In an ordered pair (x, y), the first coordinate, x, tells how many units to move left or right of the origin. The second coordinate, y, tells how many units to move up or down from the origin.

To graph point $A(1, 6)$, where Apollo 15 landed, move right from the origin to 1, and then move up to 6.

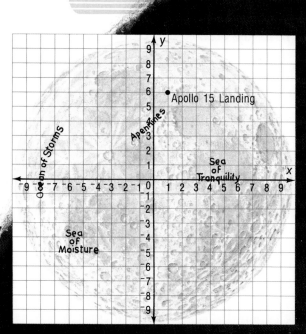

More Examples

a. To graph the point $B(^-2, 3)$, move left from the origin to $^-2$, and then move up to 3.

b. To graph the point $C(^-4, ^-1)$, move left from the origin to $^-4$, and then move down to $^-1$.

c. To graph the point $D(3, ^-4)$, move right from the origin to 3, and then move down to $^-4$.

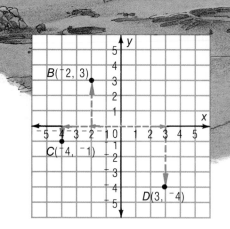

CLASSWORK

Draw the x-axis and the y-axis on graph paper and graph these points.

1. $A(^-5, 2)$
2. $B(^-3, ^-1)$
3. $C(4, ^-4)$
4. $D(0, ^-3)$
5. $E(3, 2)$
6. $F(4, ^-3)$
7. $G(4, 0)$
8. $H(^-3, 4)$
9. $I(5, ^-2)$
10. $J(^-2, 0)$
11. $K(^-6, ^-4)$
12. $L(0, 4)$

PRACTICE

Draw the *x*-axis and the *y*-axis on graph paper and graph these points.

1. $A(2, 1)$
2. $B(^-2, ^-3)$
3. $C(^-4, ^-3)$
4. $D(^-4, 3)$
5. $E(3, ^-4)$
6. $F(1, ^-6)$
7. $G(^-3, 2)$
8. $H(^-5, ^-5)$
9. $I(^-1, 3)$
10. $J(^-2, ^-2)$
11. $K(5, 0)$
12. $L(0, ^-1)$
13. $M(^-2, 0)$
14. $N(0, 4)$
15. $O(0, 0)$
16. $P(1, ^-2)$

Draw the *x*-axis and the *y*-axis on graph paper. Graph each group of ordered pairs.

17. $(^-3, 3)$, $(3, 3)$, $(3, ^-3)$, $(^-3, ^-3)$, $(^-3, 3)$
Connect the points in order.
What figure is formed?

18. $(^-3, ^-4)$, $(^-1, ^-2)$, $(3, 2)$
Connect the points. Give the coordinates of another point on the same line.

On which axis does each point lie?

19. $A(5, 0)$
20. $B(0, 2)$
21. $C(^-7, 0)$
22. $D(0, ^-8)$

In which quadrant is each point (x, y)?

★ 23. $x > 0$ and $y > 0$

★ 24. $x < 0$ and $y < 0$

★ 25. $x < 0$ and $y > 0$

★ 26. $x > 0$ and $y < 0$

APPLICATION

You can create a piece of string art by connecting nails (points on these axes) with colored string in this way. Connect the nail farthest from the origin on one axis with the nail closest to the origin on the other axis. Connect the nail second farthest from the origin on one axis with the nail second closest to the origin on the other axis. Continue in this way until each nail is connected to its corresponding nail on the other axis. How many segments of string are there? How many intersections are there?

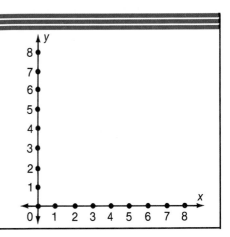

291

Problem Solving

SKILLS AND STRATEGIES REVIEW

Solve. Use the table for 1–2.

This table shows the four highest mountains on the continent of Africa.

1. What is the average height of the four mountains?

2. List the mountains in order from highest to lowest.

Highest Mountains in Africa	
Margherita, Zaire	5,127 m
Kenya, Kenya	5,194 m
Toubkal, Morocco	4,164 m
Kilimanjaro, Tanzania	5,895 m

3. A goat descends nearly vertical slopes by a series of running jumps. How many jumps does it take to travel 24 m downhill?

4. Corn growing in some mountain regions takes about 10 months to mature. It takes a week to prepare the soil for planting. If a harvest occurs the first week in September, when was the soil prepared?

A geological survey team is scaling Mt. McKinley in Alaska. When they left the base of the mountain, the temperature was 11°C. The temperature fell 0.75 degree for every 100 m they climbed.

5. After climbing 1,000 m, what was the temperature?

6. How high had they climbed when the temperature reached 5°C?

7. How high had they climbed when the temperature fell below freezing?

8. The windchill factor at 2,000 m made it feel 25 degrees colder than the actual temperature. How cold would it feel?

9. One morning Mike, Susan, and Barbara tried to guess how low the temperature had gone during the night. Barbara's guess was 6 degrees too low. Mike's guess was 8 degrees below Susan's and 2 degrees above Barbara's. Susan guessed ⁻10°C. What was the actual low temperature?

Problem Solving

WHAT WOULD YOU DO . . . ?

You are planning a 7-day vacation in one of three mountain resorts in the Northeast. You have received a brochure from each resort.

	Berkshires	**Catskills**	**Poconos**
Daily rates	$58	$45	$52
Meals included	3	breakfast only	breakfast and dinner
Facilities	Health Club - $5 a day	Indoor pool, tennis courts - free	outdoor pool, tennis courts, riding stable - free

You need to evaluate this information to make a choice. Answer each question.

1. Would you be primarily concerned with the facilities available?

2. Would you take into consideration the distance you had to travel to get to the resort?

3. Would the cost of the resort be a major factor in making your decision?

4. Are there other factors you would take into account?

You can estimate the cost of each resort as follows.

Berkshires:
$58 × 7 days = $406 (weekly rate)
No cost for meals
Use health club 5 days → $5 × 5 = $25
} $406 + $25 = $431

Catskills:
$45 × 7 days = $315 (weekly rate)
Approximate weekly cost of 2 meals
    per day → $30 × 7 days = $210
} $315 + $210 = $525

Poconos:
$52 × 7 days = $364 (weekly rate)
Approximate weekly cost of lunch
    each day → $10 × 7 days = $70
} $364 + $70 = $434

What would you do? Which resort would you choose? Why?

5. Do you live within 250 miles of one of these resorts? If you did not, would your choice be different?

CHAPTER REVIEW

Write an integer for each. pages 274–275

1. a gain of 20 lb
2. 4 ft below sea level
3. 11 degrees below zero
4. positive fifty
5. negative thirty-one
6. positive forty-six

Find each absolute value. pages 274–275

7. $|^-6|$
8. $|8|$
9. $|^-18|$
10. $|^-12|$
11. $|6|$
12. $|18|$

Compare. Use > or < for each . pages 274–275

13. $^-11$ ⬤ 14
14. 10 ⬤ $^-4$
15. $^-8$ ⬤ $^-10$
16. 0 ⬤ $^-5$

Write the opposite of each integer. pages 278–279

17. 10
18. $^-15$
19. 37
20. $^-6$
21. $^-80$
22. 125

Add, subtract, multiply, or divide. pages 276–281, 284–287

23. $18 + {^-9}$
24. $^-4 - {^-7}$
25. $19 - {^-3}$
26. $^-20 + 20$
27. $9 + {^-15}$
28. $12 - {^-12}$
29. $15 - {^-6}$
30. $^-15 + {^-6}$
31. $^-8 \cdot {^-6}$
32. $11 \cdot {^-9}$
33. $72 \div {^-8}$
34. $^-18 \div {^-3}$

Write the ordered pair that locates each point. pages 288–289

35. A
36. B
37. C
38. D
39. E
40. F

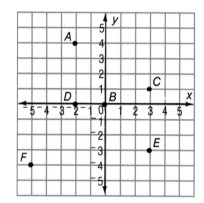

On graph paper, draw the x- and y-axes and graph these points. Give the quadrant or axis location for each point. pages 290–291

41. A(1, 1)
42. B($^-2$, 3)
43. C(0, $^-3$)
44. D($^-4$, $^-2$)

Solve. pages 282–283, 292–293

45. From 6 P.M. to 11 P.M., the temperature change on the mountain was $^-15$ degrees. What was the average change in temperature per hour?

46. Before the weekend, 12 inches of snow fell on the ski area. Five inches fell on Saturday and 6 inches fell on Sunday, bringing the snow base up to 48 inches. What was the base on Saturday before the snowfall?

CHAPTER TEST

Write an integer for each.

1. a gain of 10 yards

2. negative forty

3. the opposite of ⁻6

Replace each ⬤ with > or <.

4. ⁻91 ⬤ ⁻9

5. 26 ⬤ ⁻32

6. ⁻48 ⬤ ⁻27

Find each absolute value.

7. |21|

8. |⁻17|

9. |0|

Add, subtract, multiply, or divide.

10. ⁻15 + ⁻8

11. ⁻20 − 14

12. ⁻11 + 11

13. 6 · ⁻9

14. ⁻7 · ⁻9

15. ⁻45 ÷ 5

16. ⁻9 − ⁻3

17. ⁻32 ÷ ⁻4

Write the ordered pair that locates each point.

18. A

19. B

20. C

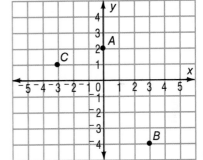

Give the quadrant or axis location for each point.

21. Q(⁻6, 0)

22. R(⁻1, ⁻4)

23. S(3, 1)

Solve.

24. For five days in January, the temperature at the Pine Mountain ski area changed as follows: up 3 degrees, down 1 degree, down 1 degree, up 2 degrees, up 2 degrees. What was the total change?

25. On February 1 the temperature at the ski area dropped 8 degrees between noon and midnight. By noon on February 2 it had risen 6 degrees. At noon on February 3 it had gone up 4 degrees to 3°C. What had been the noon temperature on February 1?

Solve.

⁻7(3 + ⁻6 − ⁻9) − ⁻50 ÷ ⁻5 + 13 · 4

TREASURE HUNT

You have probably been on a treasure hunt before. Here is a different version of a game that 2 players play using graph paper.

Make 2 grids like the ones shown below for each player.

Game Rules

1. Each player has 3 treasures: a chest of coins, a crystal ball, and a magic cloak. Each player marks a secret location on the first grid for each treasure. The chest covers a row of 3 points on the grid, the ball covers a row of 2, and the cloak covers a row of 5. Treasures may only be placed horizontally or vertically.

2. An ordered pair, such as (3, 5), names each point. Each player in turn calls out a point on the grid to try to find a treasure.

3. The second grid is used to record points as they are called. *F* marks a point found and *N* marks a point where nothing is found.

4. If a player calls a point that is part of a treasure location, the other player must name that treasure. Every point of a treasure location must have been called before the treasure can be found.

5. Players continue taking turns. The winner is the first player to find all the opponent's treasures.

LOCATION OF TREASURES

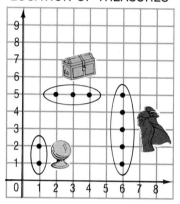

RECORD OF CALLS

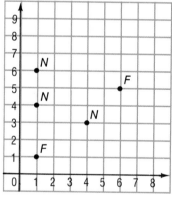

LIFE IN TWO DIMENSIONS

Can you imagine life in a 2-dimensional world? Everything would be flat! Even the planet would be flat.

What would the inhabitants look like? Perhaps they would look like Ard. With no third dimension their arms and legs could never cross. Because they could not turn around to go in the opposite direction, their knees would have to bend both ways.

How would they see?

How would they eat?

What would happen if Ard met someone going in the opposite direction? They could not go around each other. How would they pass?

Homes would probably be built underground. Why?

Rooms could be at different levels connected by stairs or elevators. The doors for rooms would have to swing open upward. Furniture would be in the way unless it was designed properly.

Design a two-bedroom house for a family of three. Include as many rooms as you wish (living room, dining room, kitchen, and so on). Show some furnishings for each room. Describe the way Ard would live in this house.

An underground house on Astria: Collapsible furniture, lightweight gadgets and partitions to hold up the roof

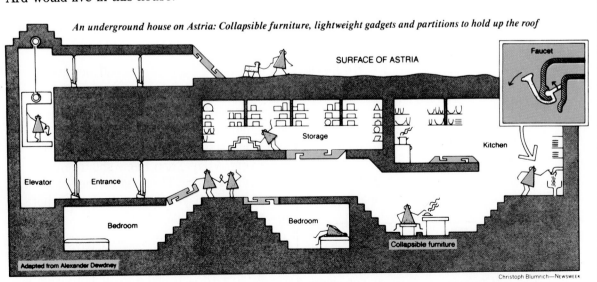

Christoph Blumrich—NEWSWEEK

NEWSWEEK/JANUARY 18, 1982

MAINTAINING SKILLS

Choose the correct answers. Write A, B, C, or D.

1. $24\frac{1}{6} - 9\frac{3}{8}$

    A $14\frac{19}{24}$ **C** $15\frac{5}{24}$

    B $15\frac{19}{24}$ **D** not given

2. Complete. $6\frac{2}{3}$ ft = ___ in.

    A 20   **C** 60

    B 80   **D** not given

3. What is the area?

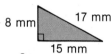

8 mm   17 mm   15 mm

    A 135.72 mm²   **C** 41 mm²

    B 60 mm²   **D** not given

4. What is the circumference to the nearest tenth? Let $\pi = 3.14$.

3.25 m

    A 10.2 m   **C** 20.4 m

    B 33.2 m   **D** not given

5. Solve. $\frac{3}{15} = \frac{n}{36}$

    A $n = 180$ **C** $n = 1.25$

    B $n = 7.2$ **D** not given

6. What is the unit price if 7 cost $8.05?

    A $1.15   **C** $1.34

    B $56.35   **D** not given

7. Complete.

    scale   1 cm to 3 m
    drawing   15.8 cm
    actual   ___

    A 18.8 m   **C** 47.4 m

    B 5.26 m   **D** not given

8. What percent is $\frac{105}{100}$?

    A 105%   **C** 1.05%

    B 1.5%   **D** not given

9. What is the sale price if the regular price is $348 and the rate of discount is $33\frac{1}{3}$% off?

    A $1,044   **C** $232

    B $116   **D** not given

10. What percent of 710 is 305.3?

    A 21%   **C** 43%

    B 50%   **D** not given

11. $15 + {}^-24$

    A $^-9$ **C** 9

    B $^-39$ **D** not given

12. $^-30 - 14$

    A $^-16$ **C** 44

    B $^-44$ **D** not given

Make a list to help solve 13 and 14.

13. Mrs. Blake needed change for a coin-operated telephone. She gave the clerk 1 dollar. How many ways could she get her change without pennies or nickels?

    A 6   **C** 10

    B 8   **D** not given

14. Phil and Peg are crew members on 2 different ships that sail out of San Francisco. Phil's ship returns to port every 5 days, and Peg's ship returns every 7 days. They sail on the same day. On which days will they both be in port in the next 100 days?

    A days 25, 50, 75 and 100   **C** days 35 and 70

    B days 12, 24, and 48   **D** not given

Theme: Countries of the World

Frequency Tables and Histograms

▶**Statistics** is the science of collecting, organizing, and analyzing **data.**

Shown below are the years in which the nations of the United Nations (U.N.) became members and the numbers of nations that joined in those years. The data are organized in a **frequency table** and in a **histogram**. In each the data are grouped into equal intervals of 10 years and the frequency of the data is found for each interval. The histogram displays the same data as the frequency table but in graph form.

frequency table

NATIONS JOINING THE U.N.	
Years	Frequency
1945–1954	60
1955–1964	55
1965–1974	23
1975–1984	21

histogram

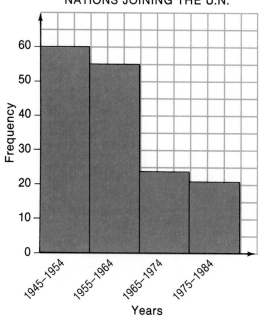

NATIONS JOINING THE U.N.

The range of a set of data can be found easily from a frequency table.

▶The **range** is the difference between the greatest and the least items of data.

The range of the years the nations joined the U.N. is 1984–1945, or 39.

CLASSWORK

Use the frequency table and the histogram above to answer 1–6.

1. In which ten-year interval did the most nations join the U.N.?

2. In which ten-year interval did a total of 23 members join?

3. How many nations joined from 1955 to 1964?

4. How many nations joined in 1945?

5. When did the first nation join the U.N.?

6. How many members of the U.N. are there?

Use the data in the table below to answer 7–8.

AGES OF U.S. PRESIDENTS WHEN FIRST INAUGURATED																			
57	61	57	57	58	57	61	54	68	51	49	64	50	48	65	52	56	46	54	49
50	47	55	55	54	42	51	56	55	51	54	51	60	62	43	55	56	61	52	69

7. Make a frequency table and a histogram for the data. Use the intervals 40–44, 45–49, 50–54, 55–59, 60–64, 65–69.

8. What is the range of the ages?

PRACTICE

Use these two histograms to answer 1–7.

1. The smallest football stadium seats 40,605. The largest seats 106,721. What is the range of the seating capacities?

2. Which size stadium is most common?

3. How many football stadiums are there?

4. What was the most popular time to shop at Shopbest? the least popular time?

5. To the nearest hundred, how many customers shopped during the opening 2 hours?

6. Explain why there might be so few shoppers between 5 P.M. and 7 P.M.

★7. Which 2-hour time period would be best for Shopbest to have special sales?

Use the data below to answer 8–10.

RECORDED SPEEDS OF VEHICLES IN A 35-MPH ZONE									
25	27	30	30	31	23	45	33	38	36
37	35	47	35	32	33	35	37	37	40
25	30	35	40	34	42	38	37	36	29
30	27	30	45	40	37	35	40	37	32

8. Make a frequency table and a histogram. Use the intervals 21–25, 26–30, 31–35, 36–40, 41–45, 46–50.

9. What is the range of the speeds?

10. How many vehicles exceeded the speed limit?

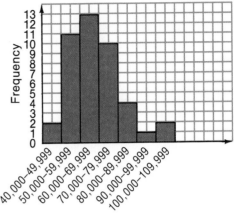

SEATING CAPACITIES OF U.S. FOOTBALL STADIUMS

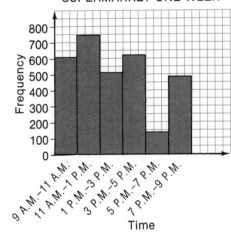

CUSTOMERS AT SHOPBEST SUPERMARKET ONE WEEK

APPLICATION

=== RELATIVE FREQUENCY ===

One way to compare frequencies is to find the relative frequency of an item of data.

$$\text{relative frequency} = \frac{\text{frequency of item}}{\text{total of frequencies}}$$

Look at the table on page 300. The relative frequency of nations joining the U.N. between 1945 and 1954 is $\frac{60}{159} \approx 38\%$. About 38% of the nations joined between 1945 and 1954.

Find the relative frequency of each. Round to the nearest percent.

1. 1955–1964

2. 1965–1974

3. 1975–1984

Measures of Central Tendency

What is the average population of the largest cities in the world?

Each of the three measures of central tendency—mean, median, and mode—is a type of average.

▶ The **mean** is the sum of all the data divided by the number of data.

▶ The **median** is the middle number or the mean of the two middle numbers when the data are arranged in order.

▶ The **mode** is the number that occurs most often. There may be more than one mode.

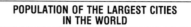

POPULATION OF THE LARGEST CITIES IN THE WORLD	
City	Population (in millions)
Shanghai, China	11
Beijing, China	9
Tianjin, China	7
Seoul, S. Korea	8
Tokyo, Japan	8
Calcutta, India	9
Bombay, India	8
Moscow, U.S.S.R.	8
New York, U.S.A.	7
Mexico City, Mexico	9

The mean for the population is

$$\frac{11 + 9 + 7 + 8 + 8 + 9 + 8 + 8 + 7 + 9}{10} = 8.4.$$

The median and the mode for the populations are as follows.

mode

11 9 9 9 8 8 8 8 7 7

median ⟶ 8

CLASSWORK

Find the mean, the median, and the mode of each.

1. 4, 3, 5, 0, 4, 3, 4, 4, 1, 2

2. 35, 30, 16, 23, 16, 24, 14, 24, 16

3. 189, 80, 83, 133, 83, 133, 94, 89

4. 560, 900, 900, 840, 775

Find the mean, the median, and the mode of each.

1. 5, 7, 6, 10, 6, 9, 8, 9, 10, 6
2. 27, 69, 60, 32, 61, 69, 41, 69, 58, 54
3. 23, 23, 8, 11, 23, 10, 19, 11
4. 26, 37, 38, 14, 37, 26, 26, 37, 38
5. 600, 240, 860, 600, 200, 500
6. 320, 340, 334, 340, 350, 344
7. 91, 100, 90, 95, 92, 95, 102
8. 108, 106, 112, 94, 88, 94, 112
9. 405, 407, 397, 375, 393, 405
10. 613, 704, 454, 809, 908, 454

The mean of each group of three numbers is 29. What is the third number?

11. 28, 29, ☐
12. 16, 35, ☐
13. 21, 29, ☐
14. 15, 16, ☐

Find the mean, the median, the mode, and the range of these data: 1, 3, 5, 4, 2, 4, 3, 2. If 5 was changed to 10, would each of these measures change?

15. mean
16. median
17. mode
18. range

Make up a set of data for which each is true.

★ 19. There is one mode.

★ 20. There is more than one mode.

★ 21. The mean, the median, and the mode are all equal.

APPLICATION

Find each for the data at the right.

22. mean
23. median
24. mode
25. range

Compare the measures above with those for the data on page 302.

26. Is the mean for the world greater than that for the Americas?

27. Is the median for the world greater than that for the Americas?

★ 28. What conclusion can you draw about the population of the Americas in relation to that of the world?

POPULATION OF THE LARGEST CITIES IN THE AMERICAS	
City	Population (in millions)
Chicago, U.S.	3
New York, U.S.	7
Los Angeles, U.S.	3
Mexico City, Mexico	9
Rio de Janeiro, Brazil	5
São Paulo, Brazil	7
Lima, Peru	3
Bogotá, Colombia	4
Santiago, Chile	4
Buenos Aires, Argentina	3

Using Measures of Data

Data can be analyzed in many ways, depending on whether the mean, the median, the mode, or the range is used.

NATIONALITY OF THE GREAT COMPOSERS OF THE WESTERN WORLD	
Country	Number of Composers
Austria	7
Belgium	1
Brazil	1
Czechoslovakia	2
Denmark	1
Finland	1
France	17
Germany	17
Great Britain	6
Hungary	3
Italy	17
Norway	1
Poland	2
Soviet Union	12
Spain	1
Switzerland	2
United States	15

Using the mean The average number of composers from any one country is about 6.

Using the median Half the countries have contributed 3 or more composers each.

Using the mode Most countries have contributed 1 composer.

Using the range Sixteen more composers have come from France than have come from Spain.

CLASSWORK

Tell whether the mean, the median, the mode, or the range was used to analyze the data.

1. The average age of a United States president when first inaugurated is about 55 years.

2. In a survey, more people like baseball than any other sport.

3. Half the students in Ms. Dupree's class are no taller than 160 cm.

4. In one year 17.7 million more viewers watched the first-ranked TV series than watched the last-ranked series.

5. Half the countries listed in the table above contributed more than 90% of the great composers of the western world.

PRACTICE

Tell whether the mean, the median, the mode, or the range was used to analyze the data.

1. The average July temperature in Bombay, India, is 80°F.

2. The lowest score on the test was 40 points below the highest score.

3. More students selected class rings with red stones than with any other color.

4. Half the continents of the world have an area less than that of South America.

5. Between 1901 and 1914 more Nobel peace prizes were awarded to citizens of Switzerland than were awarded to those of any other country.

6. Half the hit Broadway shows had more performances than the 1,775 performances of the play *Harvey*.

7. The average time in the 400-m freestyle event was 4 min 17 s.

8. The average age of those who attended the concert was 19.

9. In Mr. Harrison's class the favorite hobby was coin collecting.

10. In tests by The New York Zoological Society, the fastest animal, the cheetah, traveled 70 mph faster than the slowest animal, the garden snail.

APPLICATION

Make a statement about the data in this table, using each measure in 11–14.

GREAT AUSTRIAN COMPOSERS	
Composer	**Number of Major Works**
Alban Berg	28
Anton Bruckner	37
Joseph Haydn	829
Gustav Mahler	61
Wolfgang Mozart	723
Arnold Schoenberg	179
Franz Schubert	1,147

11. mean

12. median

13. mode

14. range

Take a survey of 20 classmates to find how many of the great Austrian composers each person recognizes. Then analyze your data, using each measure.

★ 15. mean

★ 16. median

★ 17. mode

★ 18. range

Graphing Data

Graphs are often used to organize and present data. They provide a picture that shows at a glance the relationships between items of data. Different kinds of graphs are used for different purposes.

▶A **bar graph** is used to show comparisons.

This double-bar graph compares the populations of Sweden, in Europe, and Upper Volta, in Africa.

To make a bar graph, do the following.

- Use graph paper. Choose a scale for each axis. Draw the axes and label them.

- Draw a bar for each item of data. The length of each bar corresponds to the item of data. Sometimes it helps to round the data.

- Title the graph.

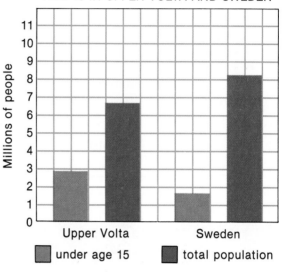

TOTAL POPULATION AND PEOPLE UNDER AGE 15 IN UPPER VOLTA AND SWEDEN

▶A **line graph** is used to show trends or changes over time.

This line graph shows the change in temperature over the year in Moscow and in Copenhagen.

To make a line graph, do the following.

- Use graph paper. Choose a scale for each axis. Draw the axes and label them.

- Locate the point on the graph for each pair of data. Then connect the points.

- Title the graph.

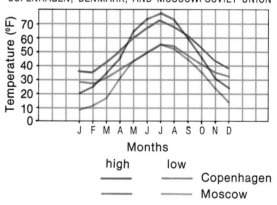

NORMAL HIGH AND LOW TEMPERATURES, IN TWO CITIES: COPENHAGEN, DENMARK; AND MOSCOW, SOVIET UNION

CLASSWORK

Decide whether a bar graph or a line graph would be better to present each set of data. Then construct the graph.

1.

U.S. PETROLEUM IMPORTS (in thousands of barrels per day)				
	Iran	Saudi Arabia	Mexico	Canada
1973	223	486	16	1,325
1983	48	337	826	547

2.

AUTOMOBILES REGISTERED IN U.S. (in millions)					
Year	1940	1950	1960	1970	1980
Number	27	40	62	89	122

PRACTICE

Choose a bar graph or a line graph to present each set of data. Then construct the graph.

1.

LEADING VEGETABLE-GROWING COUNTRIES	
Country	Production (in millions of tons)
China	266
Soviet Union	117
United States	107
India	76
Brazil	55

2.

DOGS REGISTERED WITH AMERICAN KENNEL CLUB		
	Number Registered	
Type of Dog	1975	1980
Cocker spaniel	39,064	76,113
Doberman pinscher	57,336	79,908
German shepherd	76,235	58,865
Irish setter	58,622	14,938
Poodle	139,750	95,250

3.

U.S. NATIONAL DEBT	
Year	Dollars (in billions)
1930	16
1940	43
1950	256
1960	284
1970	370
1980	907

4.

U.S. POPULATION DISTRIBUTION						
		Census Year				
		1790	1800	1810	1820	1830
Percent of Population	Urban	5	6	7	7	9
	Rural	95	94	93	93	91
		Census Year				
		1840	1850	1860	1870	1880
Percent of Population	Urban	11	15	20	26	28
	Rural	89	85	80	74	72

Use the data from the graphs to answer 5–12.

5. Rank the dogs registered in 1975 in order.

6. Rank the dogs registered in 1980 in order.

7. From 1790 to 1880, did the percent of urban population increase or decrease? Did the percent of rural population increase or decrease?

8. What was the trend of the population in the United States from 1790 to 1880?

9. How much did the United States national debt increase from 1960 to 1980?

10. During which decade did the United States national debt increase the most?

11. Which country produces more vegetables than any other country in the world?

12. How many more tons of vegetables does China produce than does India?

APPLICATION

Line graphs are often used to make predictions about the future. Based on the trend of this graph, estimate each of the following.

13. population under age 15 in 1990

14. population over age 15 in 1990

15. How many more people over age 15 than under 15 will there be in 2000?

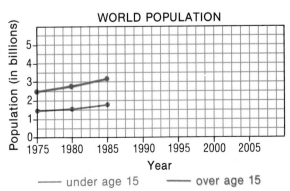

307

Circle Graphs

Circle graphs are best used to compare parts of a whole. This graph shows the population of the world by continent.

To make a circle graph, do the following.

- If it is not given, find the percent of the circle each item of data represents.

- Find the number of degrees each percent represents.

Asia
↓
58.3% of 360° = 0.583 × 360° ≈ 210°
↑
number of degrees around
the center of a circle

- Use a compass to draw a circle. Then draw the central angle representing each percent. Label each part of the circle.

- Title the graph.

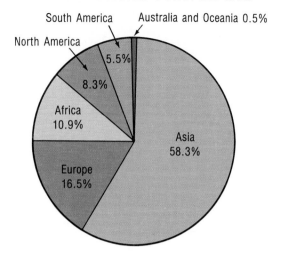

WHERE THE WORLD'S PEOPLES LIVE

South America • Australia and Oceania 0.5%
North America
5.5%
8.3%
Africa 10.9%
Asia 58.3%
Europe 16.5%

CLASSWORK

Find the measure of each central angle in the graph above. Round to the nearest degree.

1. Europe   2. North America

3. Africa   4. South America

5. Australia and Oceania

Use the data below to answer 6–9.

ALANO'S WEEKLY BUDGET					
Expense	Food	School supplies	Transportation	Savings	Recreation
Amount	$6	$1	$3	$5	$5

6. Make a circle graph.

7. What percent of his weekly budget does Alano spend on recreation?

8. On which item does Alano spend the most? the least?

9. On which item does he spend as much as on school supplies and savings combined?

308

PRACTICE

Find the measure of the central angle represented by each percent of a circle graph. Round to the nearest degree.

1. 50%	**2.** 75%	**3.** 40%	**4.** 55%	**5.** 25%
6. 36%	**7.** 37.5%	**8.** 88%	**9.** 94%	**10.** 12%

Construct a circle graph for each set of data. Round to the nearest percent.

11.

GASES IN THE AIR	
Gas	Percent
Nitrogen	78
Oxygen	21
Other gases	1

12.

AUTOMOBILES MANUFACTURED IN ONE YEAR IN U.S.	
Maker	Number of Automobiles (to the nearest 50,000)
American Motors	200,000
Chrysler	900,000
Ford	1,550,000
General Motors	4,000,000
Other	150,000

★ **13.**

MEDALS WON IN 1984 WINTER OLYMPIC GAMES	
Country	Number of Medals
Canada	4
Czechoslovakia	6
East Germany	24
Finland	13
Norway	9
Soviet Union	25
Sweden	8
Switzerland	5
United States	8
West Germany	4

Use the data from the graphs to answer 14–19.

14. What percent of the air is nitrogen and oxygen combined?

15. What percent of the air is hydrogen?

16. What percent of the automobiles manufactured in the United States were made by Ford?

17. What percent of the automobiles were made by Ford and General Motors combined?

★ **18.** To the nearest 10, what percent of the medals won in the 1984 Winter Games did the Soviet Union and East Germany win?

★ **19.** On which continent are the countries that won over 80% of the medals in the 1984 Winter Olympic Games?

APPLICATION

ESTIMATION

Estimate the percent of the world's population that lived on each continent in 1900.

1. Europe
2. South America
3. Africa
4. North America
5. Asia
6. Australia and Oceania

WHERE THE WORLD'S PEOPLES LIVED IN 1900

Exploring Scattergrams

Is your height related to the length of your shoe?

Is your height related to the number of letters in your name?

Tom Thumb   Larry Bird   Kareem Abdul-Jabar

WORKING TOGETHER

Work in a group of four.

1. Survey 20 students in your class to find their heights, the lengths of their shoes, and the total number of letters in their first and last names.

    Make a table to record your data.

Student	Height (centimeters)	Shoe Length (centimeters)	Number of Letters in Name
Marcia Fairfax	160	24	13
Josh Martin	177		

2. Make two graphs. Use the data in the columns for height and shoe length first. Plot the pairs of numbers as shown.

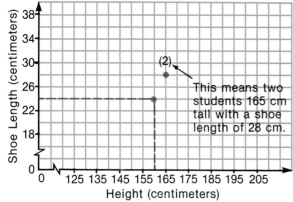

SHOE LENGTH VS. HEIGHT

(2) This means two students 165 cm tall with a shoe length of 28 cm.

Make a second graph for the data in the columns for height and number of letters. Decide what scale you will use for each axis.

310

The graphs you have made are called **scattergrams.**

Share your graphs with another group. Study the table of data and the scattergrams you drew.

1. Does the table of data seem to indicate that shoe length is related to height?

2. Does the table show a relationship between height and the number of letters in a person's name? Explain.

3. Do the scattergrams help to show whether a relationship exists? How?

4. Did both groups survey the same students? Does this affect the scattergrams? If so, how?

======= THINKING IT THROUGH =======

1. For each scattergram, use the edge of your ruler to find a line that is as close to as many points as possible. Then draw the line on your graph. This line is called a *line of best fit.* Look at the graphs at the right. Does your line have a positive or a negative slope?

2. Compare your graph with that of another group. Compare the way the points spread out around the line. In which graph are most of the points close to the line?

3. Compare your lines of best fit with the lines of best fit found by other groups. What do you notice? Discuss with the other groups the ways the lines of best fit are different or alike.

4. If the slope of a line of best fit is positive, what do you think that tells about the relationship between two sets of data?

5. If the slope of the line is negative, what does that tell you?

6. Write a summary of your findings.

positive slope

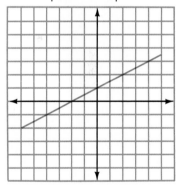

negative slope

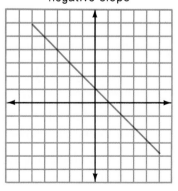

Making Scattergrams

For a school social studies project, Patty decided to collect data about her classmates and to look for relationships in the data. She surveyed 12 girls. Here is her data table.

Student	Height (inches)	Shoe Size	TV Watched (hours in a day)
Amy	62	6	3
Barbara	66	8	1
Charlene	60	5	2
Denise	68	9	3
Erin	69	9	6
Evie	57	5	7
Lauren	58	6	0
Marla	70	10	2
Nora	61	5	1
Terry	66	8	3
Willie	64	7	4
Yuma	63	6	0

Student	Grade on Last Mathematics Exam	Number of Brothers and Sisters	Number of Pets
Amy	80	0	3
Barbara	95	3	1
Charlene	100	0	0
Denise	68	3	3
Erin	60	4	0
Evie	56	4	4
Lauren	80	1	1
Marla	76	1	3
Nora	88	0	5
Terry	90	7	1
Willie	82	2	4
Yuma	100	2	0

WORKING TOGETHER

Work in a group.

1. Draw three scattergrams.

   - One scattergram should compare height and shoe size.

   - The second should compare TV watching and mathematics exam grade.

   - The third should compare the number of brothers and sisters and the number of pets.

2. For each scattergram, draw the line you think fits the data best.

1. Look at the three scattergrams you drew. In which of the three are most of the points near your line of best fit? In which are most of them not? What do you think it means if most of the points are near your line?

2. For each of the three scattergrams, discuss whether there is a relationship between the sets of data being studied. Describe any relationships you find. What seems to happen to shoe size as height increases? What happens to test scores as the amount of TV viewing increases?

3. Can you think of other data that would be related in the same way as height and shoe size? test scores and hours of TV watched?

4. Are there two other columns of Patty's data that you think might show an interesting relationship? Tell why or why not.

1. Do you think that when two events are related, one always *causes* the other? Explain.

2. Suppose a scattergram showed this relationship between locker numbers and test scores. Does the relationship mean that the test scores are affected by the locker assignments? Why or why not? Explain.

3. Discuss whether the price of a used car is related to the age of the car. What sources of data could you use to support your opinion? Tell how you would organize the data. Would it be important to consider different makes of cars separately? What are some other things you would have to consider?

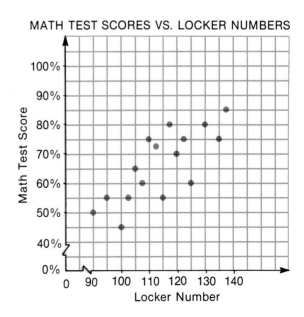

MATH TEST SCORES VS. LOCKER NUMBERS

313

Problem Solving

LOGIC

The ability to think logically is an important problem-solving skill. It may involve drawing correct conclusions from given facts or deciding whether two or more statements can be true at the same time.

1. Can the following statements all be true at the same time?

   A man left home at 10:00 A.M.
   He arrived at his destination 100 miles away at 12:00 noon.
   He never drove faster than 55 mph.

Examine each statement. Decide what the information in each statement means.

The first two statements say that the man traveled for 2 hours and covered 100 miles. His average rate was 50 mph.

The third statement is consistent with this result. Therefore, it follows that all three statements could be true at the same time.

Check to be sure that you used the information in each statement correctly.

2. What conclusion can be drawn from the following statements?

   Babe Ruth held the record of 714 home runs in a major league career.
   Hank Aaron hit his 715th home run on April 8, 1974.

The first statement establishes that 714 home runs was a major league record.

The second statement establishes that Hank Aaron hit 715 home runs.

What conclusion can be drawn?

Dallas, Texas

314

Can the statements be true at the same time?

1. The temperature outside is 82°F.
   It is snowing.

2. A 7-ounce tube of toothpaste cost $1.69.
   The unit price is 26¢ per ounce.

3. It is raining very hard outside.
   Mike was wet when he arrived at the office.

4. Dallas is southwest of Memphis.
   Memphis is southwest of Louisville.
   Louisville is northeast of Dallas.

5. Red kangaroos can leap as far as 42 feet per jump.
   A red kangaroo leaped 307 feet in 5 jumps.

6. The distance from Polk to Lehigh is 250 mi.
   Lewis traveled at an average of 55 mph.
   Lewis completed the trip from Polk to Lehigh in 3 hours.

Determine whether the conclusion follows from the given statements.

7. All cats are animals.
   All dogs are animals.
   Conclusion: All cats are dogs.

8. Walton is between Rose City and Ashley.
   Milville is between Walton and Ashley.
   Conclusion: Milville is between Rose City and Ashley.

9. The perimeter of a square is $4s$.
   The area of a square is s^2.
   Conclusion: The area of a square is always greater than its perimeter.

10. The world's tallest building is in Chicago.
    The World Trade Center is in New York.
    Conclusion: The World Trade Center is not the world's tallest building.

Draw a conclusion from the two statements.

11. The highest league score for three consecutive games in bowling is 886.
    Mike bowled 250, 280, and 266 in three consecutive games.

12. It normally takes 2 hours to fly the 985 miles from Canton to Elton.
    Ms. Velardi's plane averaged 400 mph on the flight.

13. All squares are rectangles.
    $ABCD$ is a square.

14. Lions are in the cat family.
    Cats are mammals.

CREATE YOUR OWN PROBLEM

Use two statements from A to create a problem. Do the same from B. Then draw a conclusion from each pair of statements.

A $ABCD$ is a parallelogram.
  $PQRS$ is a rhombus.
  $WXYZ$ is not a rhombus.
  All rhombuses are parallelograms.

B Lake Superior, a natural lake, is 31,820 square miles in area.
  Lake Victoria is about one fifth the size of the Caspian Sea.
  The Caspian Sea is larger than any other natural lake in the world.
  Greenland is the largest island in the world.

Exploring Combinations

Each year schools throughout the state may send a team of their top mathematics students to a statewide competition.

WORKING TOGETHER

Work in a group of 5. Imagine that the members of your group are the top mathematics students in your school. Explore how many different teams you could send to the All-State Mathematics Competition. Fill out a roster for each team you could send.

1. Select 2 people from your group as eligible to go to the competition. Use their names to make rosters for each 1-member team you could send. Make rosters for each 2-member team. How many 1-member teams are possible? How many 2-member teams?

2. Now select 3 people from your group as eligible to compete. Use their names to make a roster for each possible team. How many 1-member teams are possible? How many 2-member teams? How many 3-member teams?

3. Make a roster for each possible team if 4 people from your group are eligible to compete.

4. If all members of your group are eligible, how many 1-member teams are possible? How many 5-member teams? Make a roster for each possible team.

5. What if no members of your group were eligible for the finals of the competition? How would your roster sheet look? For any number of eligible students, there is only *one* way to have a roster for a team with no members.

Work as a class. Record each group's results in the appropriate row of an array like the one shown below.

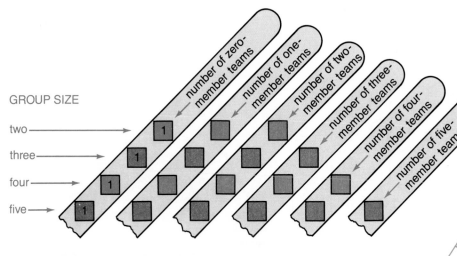

GROUP SIZE

1. For different-sized groups, what do you notice about the number of teams that include all members of the group?

2. What relationship do you see between the number of members in a group and the number of 1-member teams that can be formed?

3. What relationship do you see between the number in a group and the number of teams that have 1 member fewer than the number in the group? For example, how many 3-member teams are possible from a group of 4?

4. What other patterns can you find in the array? Make a list.

======= THINKING IT THROUGH =======

Work in a small group.

1. The 6 members of the Math League at Lincoln High are eligible to go to their state competition. A 2-member team is being sent. How many 2-member teams are possible?

2. From the 6 eligible members, how many 5-member teams would be possible?

3. Make up a problem using the information from the array. Challenge other groups to solve it.

All-State Mathematics Competition
1 Dolores Cabrera
2 Mark Okada

All-State Mathematics Competition
1 Janet Chen
2 Mark Okada

All-State Mathematics Competition
1 Dolores Cabrera
2 Janet Chen
3 Chad Felter

All-State Mathematics Competition
1 Mark Okada
2 Janet Chen
3 Chad Felter
4 Ann Schmitt

Patterns in Pascal's Triangle

Pascal's triangle is an array of numbers formed by following a simple set of rules. Despite its simplicity, the triangle is used to help solve many complicated problems in mathematics. The first few rows of the triangle are shown below.

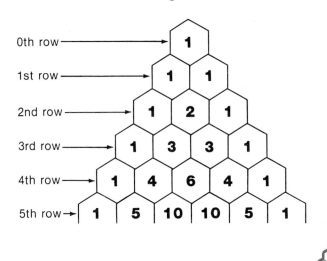

0th row — 1

1st row — 1 1

2nd row — 1 2 1

3rd row — 1 3 3 1

4th row — 1 4 6 4 1

5th row → 1 5 10 10 5 1

WORKING TOGETHER

Work in a small group.

1. Make a copy of Pascal's triangle, as shown, for each member of your group. Be sure to leave space for at least eight more rows on your page.

2. Describe a pattern that will help you find the numbers in the next row.

3. Complete the next six rows of Pascal's triangle.

1. Find the sum of each of the first five rows. What is the pattern?

2. Use the pattern you found in **1**. What is the sum of the numbers in the 10th row? in the 100th row? in the nth row?

3. In the 5th row, 5 divides evenly into all the entries other than 1. This is not true of 6 in the 6th row. For which rows in your triangle are the entries other than 1 divisible by the row number? Make a conjecture about the rows for which this is true. Test your conjecture by completing some more rows of your triangle.

4. Study the patterns between the second and third numbers in each row. Predict the second and third numbers of the next row, based on the pattern you see. Check your prediction by completing the next row.

5. Where do prime numbers appear in Pascal's triangle? Circle the primes you find on your triangle. do you see?

6. What other number patterns can you find? Discuss.

(2) ⟶ (1)

(3) ⟶ (3)

(4) ⟶ (6)

(5) ⟶ (10)

1. Relate Pascal's triangle to the teams in the previous lesson. To what does the third entry of the 5th row of Pascal's triangle correspond? Explain.

2. How can you use Pascal's triangle to find the number of four-member teams that could be formed from a group of seven people? to find the number of seven-member teams that could be formed from a group of ten people?

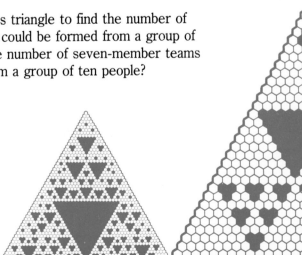

Possible Paths and Pascal's Triangle

An ant, who lives at point A on a 5 × 5 grid, works at point B. The ant does not waste time in getting to work, so it always follows a downward path. "I have been walking to work every morning for two months now," the ant said, "and I still have not followed the same route twice."

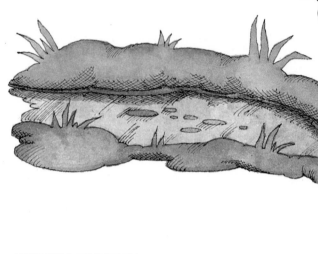

WORKING TOGETHER

Work with a small group. Find how many different ways the ant can walk to work.

1. Copy the diagram shown above. Draw each point as a circle large enough to write in.

2. Discuss how you could find the number of ways the ant can walk to work. Try one of these ways.

3. One method is to work downward from A. First find the number of ways to get from A to each point in the row beneath it. Look at the diagram at the right.

   • What numbers should you write in the third row?

   • Try this method.

   • How do your results compare with your results in **2**?

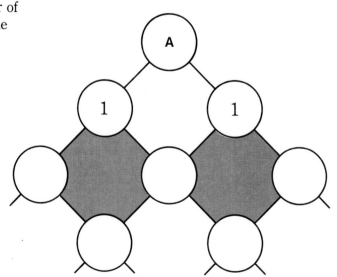

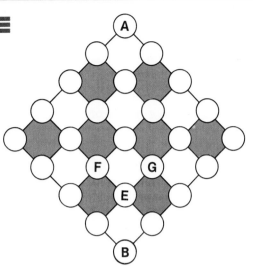

Discuss with your classmates.

1. Explain how the ant problem relates to Pascal's triangle.

2. In order for the ant to reach point *E*, it must travel through point *F* or *G*. What connection do you see between this observation and the rule by which Pascal's triangle is formed?

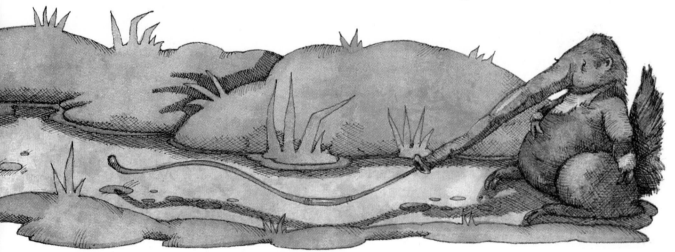

====== THINKING IT THROUGH ======

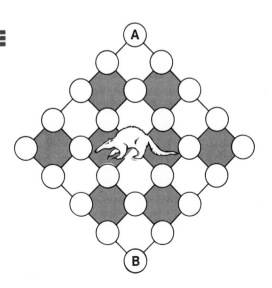

1. The ant's aunt lives on an 8 × 8 grid. How many days could she go to work without taking the same route twice?

2. One day, an anteater moved in at the center square of the 5 × 5 grid. Unperturbed, the ant said, "There are still plenty of ways for me to get to work."

   • Discuss how to find the number of safe paths remaining, without making a list.

   • How many are there?

Sample Spaces

Probability theory had its beginnings in Italy and France. The Italian mathematician Girolamo Cardano (1501–1576) wrote *The Book on Games of Chance,* one of the first books on probability. But the French mathematicians Pierre de Fermat (1601–1665) and Blaise Pascal (1623–1662) are the acknowledged founders of the theory of probability.

▶ A **sample space** for an experiment is all the possible results, or **outcomes**. An **event** is any part of the sample space. An event may consist of no outcomes, one outcome, or more than one outcome. The outcomes of an event are called the *favorable outcomes.*

If a number cube is tossed, there are six possible ways for it to land—with 1, 2, 3, 4, 5, or 6 up. All the outcomes are *equally likely.*

Blaise Pascal

▶ The **probability** that an event will occur is the ratio of the number of favorable outcomes to the number of possible outcomes in the sample space.

$$P(E) = \frac{\text{number of favorable outcomes}}{\text{number of possible outcomes}}$$

probability of event E

▶ The probability of an event that is certain to happen is 1. The probability of an event that is impossible is 0. The sum of the probabilities of all the outcomes in a sample space is always 1.

Experiment: Roll a number cube.   Number of Outcomes in Sample Space: 6

Event	Favorable Outcomes	Number of Favorable Outcomes	Probability
Roll a 2.	2	1	$\frac{1}{6}$
Roll an even number.	2, 4, 6	3	$\frac{3}{6}$, or $\frac{1}{2}$
Roll an 8.	impossible	0	$\frac{0}{6}$, or 0
Roll a number less than 7.	1, 2, 3, 4, 5, 6	6	$\frac{6}{6}$, or 1

CLASSWORK

List the possible outcomes for each experiment.

1. Draw one cube from a bag containing a red, a blue, a yellow, and a white cube.

2. Spin the spinner.

Give the favorable outcomes and the probability of each event. Use the bag of cubes in 1, and the spinner in 2.

3. Draw a red cube.   4. Draw a green cube.   5. Spin a number < 6.   6. Spin an odd number.

PRACTICE

List the possible outcomes for each experiment.

1. Toss a cube lettered A to F.

2. Spin the spinner.

3. Pick a number from 1 to 10.

★ 4. Pick a letter from your name.

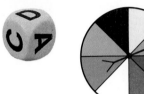

Give the favorable outcomes and the probability of each event.

5. Roll an A on the cube in **1**.

6. Roll a consonant on the cube in **1**.

7. Pick an even number in **3**.

8. Pick a number less than 4 in **3**.

9. Pick a prime number in **3**.

10. Spin yellow on the spinner in **2**.

★ 11. Spin purple on the spinner in **2**.

★ 12. Spin a primary color on the spinner in **2**.

Andrei Kolmogorov (1903–   )

APPLICATION

==== MATH HISTORY ====

German, Swiss, and other French mathematicians of the eighteenth and nineteenth centuries—such as Bernoulli, Laplace, DeMoivre, and Gauss—contributed to the study of probability theory. Laplace was one of the first to apply probability to topics other than games of chance. In the twentieth century the major contributions in the development of probability as mathematical theory have come from Russian mathematicians, such as Markov and Kolmogorov. Today the uses of probability have expanded far beyond the study of games of chance. Probability is used in medicine, biology, meteorology, and industry, among other fields. Can you name some ways it is used in these fields?

Mixed Practice

1. $^-17 + {}^-8$

2. $^-9 \cdot 12$

3. $^-13 + 25$

4. $^-9 + 24 + {}^-6$

5. $^-81 \div 9$

6. $^-36 - {}^-42$

7. $^-324 \div {}^-9$

8. $^-7 \cdot {}^-5$

9. $20 \cdot {}^-7$

10. $36 - 54$

11. $^-57 - 44 + 97$

12. $^-25 \cdot 8$

13. $125 \div {}^-5$

14. $^-11 \cdot {}^-11$

15. $^-24 - 18$

Solve.

16. $8n = 56$

17. $x + 27 = 38$

18. $y - 51 = 14$

19. $\frac{n}{5} = 16$

20. $n - 38 = 104$

Mutually Exclusive Events

The science of genetics began in Austria with the experiments of the botanist Gregor Mendel. His experiments led to the discovery that the second generation of pink four-o'clocks, a type of flower, produced flowers in this ratio: 1 red, 2 pink, 1 white. What is the probability a flower would be red or white?

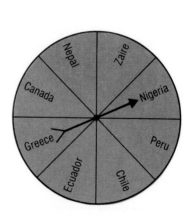

A flower cannot both be red and be white. These two events are **mutually exclusive**.

▶If A and B are mutually exclusive events, then

$$P(A \text{ or } B) = P(A) + P(B)$$

Since there are four choices, 1 red, 2 pink, and 1 white,

$$P(\text{red or white}) = P(\text{red}) + P(\text{white}) = \frac{1}{4} + \frac{1}{4} = \frac{1}{2}.$$

The probability that a flower would be red or white is $\frac{1}{2}$.

Another Example

Experiment: Spin the spinner.

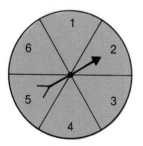

Event	Favorable Outcomes	Probability
A: Spin a prime number.	2, 3, 5	$\frac{3}{6}$, or $\frac{1}{2}$
B: Spin a number > 5.	6	$\frac{1}{6}$
A or B	2, 3, 5, 6	$\frac{1}{2} + \frac{1}{6} = \frac{4}{6}$, or $\frac{2}{3}$

CLASSWORK

Find the probability of spinning each.

1. $P(\text{CANADA or PERU})$

2. $P(\text{a country in Asia or in Africa})$

3. $P(\text{a country in North America or in South America})$

4. $P(\text{a country in the Americas or in Europe})$

5. $P(\text{a country in Europe or in Asia})$

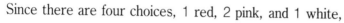

PRACTICE

A card is drawn from a deck of 26 cards, each printed with a different letter of the alphabet. Find each probability.

1. P(A or B)

2. P(A or E or I)

3. P(M or A or T or H)

4. P(consonant or A)

5. P(consonant or vowel)

6. P(Z or any letter A–L)

7. P(any letter in *COMPUTER* or any letter in *DISK*)

A marble is selected from this jar. Find each probability.

8. P(red or white)

9. P(green or red or white)

10. P(red or purple)

11. P(black or purple)

A number cube is tossed. Find each probability.

12. P(1 or 2)

13. P(1 or 2 or 3)

14. P(3 or 7)

15. P(even or 5)

16. P(odd or even)

17. P(1 or prime)

18. P(number $\leq$ 2 or number $\geq$ 5)

19. P(number $\leq$ 1 or number $\geq$ 7)

The spinner is spun. Find each probability.

20. P(TIGER or LIZARD)

21. P(SNAKE or ANT or COW)

22. P(mammal)

★ **23.** P(mammal or insect)

★ **24.** P(reptile or insect)

★ **25.** P(insect or bird)

★ **26.** P(bird or amphibian)

★ **27.** P(reptile or mammal or insect)

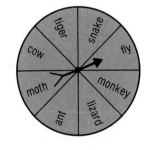

APPLICATION

People inherit one of four blood types: A, B, AB, or O. Characteristics like blood type are passed from one generation to another in genes. Every person carries two genes for blood type. This table shows the equally likely blood types that are possible for a child whose mother carries genes for types A and O and whose father carries genes for types B and O. A and B are both *dominant* over O. So the child could have type AB, type B (BO), type A (AO), or type O (OO).

		mother	
		A	O
father	B	AB	BO
	O	AO	OO

Use the table to find each.

28. P(type A or B)

29. P(type AB or O)

30. P(type A or B or O)

325

Making Predictions

A deck of 25 cards to be used in a test for extrasensory perception (ESP) was developed at Duke University in the United States. The deck contains 5 of each card shown below.

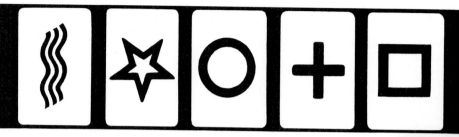

A person must guess the symbol on each card before it is turned faceup. Janet scored 7 correct out of her first 25 trials. How many can she predict that she will guess correctly out of 1,000 trials?

$$P(\text{correct}) = \frac{7}{25}$$

Out of 1,000 trials, Janet can predict she will guess

$\frac{7}{25} \times$ **1,000**, or **280**, cards correctly.

Two hundred eighty cards is an approximation. To get a closer estimate, Janet should take a larger sample. That is, she should make more trials.

CLASSWORK

1. Defects were found by quality control in 3 out of every 100 light bulbs. How many defective bulbs would quality control expect to find in 500 light bulbs?

2. A TV rating service reported that 375 out of the 500 viewers in their sample watched last Wednesday night's movie. For a city of 100,000 people, approximately how many people watched the movie?

3. Out of a bag of 100 blue marbles and red marbles, five students drew a total of 8 blue marbles and 17 red marbles. Predict the number of blue marbles and the number of red marbles in the bag.

4. Toss a tack 25 times and record the results (point up or point down) in a frequency table. Predict the number of times each event will occur in 1,000 tosses.

PRACTICE

The table at the right shows some batting statistics for the Cougars baseball team. Use the table to answer 1–3.

	Year to Date	
Player	Hits	At Bats
Jeff	5	20
Gayle	4	15
Wanda	9	25
Assad	6	16

1. How many hits would you expect Jeff to get during the next 12 times at bat?

2. How many hits would you expect each player to get in 1,000 times at bat?

3. A baseball player's batting average is found by dividing the number of hits by the number of times at bat. It is recorded to the nearest thousandth. Compute each player's average so far this year.

4. Harmon's batting average is 0.318. To the nearest one, how many hits would you expect him to get in 20 times at bat?

Predict the number for each.

5. In a bag of 20 apples, 3 were bruised. How many bruised apples would you expect to find in a case of 100?

6. Predict the number of apples that would be bruised in a bin of 1,500.

7. In two bins of 1,500 apples each, how many unbruised apples would you expect to find?

8. Out of a drawer of 40 socks, 5 people drew a total of 4 white and 6 blue ones. Predict the number of each color in the drawer.

9. Out of a jar of 500 marbles, ten people drew a total of 16 clay marbles, 25 agates, and 9 sulfides. Predict the number of each type in the jar.

★ 10. In a sample, an ornithologist counted 10 starlings, 8 wrens, 8 robins, 5 jays, 2 cardinals, 4 finches, and 3 orioles. In a population of 1,000 birds, how many of each kind could he expect to find?

APPLICATION

The probability that a person will correctly guess the symbol on a card in the deck described on page 320 is $\frac{1}{5}$. Scientists investigating ESP believe that if a test subject guesses better than $\frac{1}{5}$ of at least 100 cards correctly, that person may well have ESP.

Listed at the right are the correct guesses for six people. Predict the number of correct guesses in 500 trials for each. Which people may have ESP?

CORRECT GUESSES OUT OF 100 TRIALS	
Person	Number Correct
Tomaso	28
Greg	17
María	12
Gail	8
Dom	7
Sadie	32

11. Tomaso

12. Greg

13. María

14. Gail

15. Dom

16. Sadie

Independent and Dependent Events

These six cards are placed in a box. One card is drawn and replaced. A second card is then drawn. The second drawing is not affected by the first.

When two events have no effect on one another, they are **independent events**. A **compound event** consists of two or more independent events.

What is the probability of drawing a boy's name from the box, followed by a girl's name?

Use this rule to find the probability of two or more independent events.

$$P(A,B) = P(A) \cdot P(B)$$

$P(\text{boy's name, girl's name}) = \frac{2}{3} \cdot \frac{1}{3} = \frac{2}{9}$

Suppose the first card drawn was not replaced. The second drawing would be affected by the first drawing.

When a second event is affected by a first event, they are **dependent events**.

What is the probability of drawing a boy's name followed by a girl's name if the first card drawn is not replaced?

For the first draw, $P(\text{boy's name}) = \frac{2}{3}$. If a boy's name is drawn and not replaced, there are now 5 cards in all. Of these 5, 2 are girl's names. So $P(\text{girl's name}) = \frac{2}{5}$.

Multiply to find the probability that both will occur.

$P(\text{boy's name, girl's name}) = \frac{2}{3} \cdot \frac{2}{5} = \frac{4}{15}$

CLASSWORK

Toss two number cubes.

1. Are the tosses independent or dependent events? Explain.

2. What is $P(\text{even number}, 5)$?

Draw 2 of 5 cards, each with a letter from the word *event*. The first draw is not replaced.

3. Are the drawings independent or dependent? Explain.

4. What is $P(\text{vowel, consonant})$?

PRACTICE

First determine whether the events are independent or dependent. Then find *P(A,B)*.

A number cube is rolled and a coin is tossed.

1. *A:* Roll a 6.
   B: Toss a head.

2. *A:* Roll a 3.
   B: Toss a tail.

3. *A:* Roll a prime number.
   B: Toss a head.

4. *A:* Roll a number < 3.
   B: Toss a head.

5. *A:* Roll a 7.
   B: Toss a tail.

6. *A:* Roll a number < 7.
   B: Toss a head or a tail.

Two cards are drawn at random without replacement.

7. *A:* Draw a 5.
   B: Draw a 1.

8. *A:* Draw an even number.
   B: Draw a 3.

9. *A:* Draw a 5.
   B: Draw a 10.

10. *A:* Draw an odd number.
    B: Draw an even number.

Two marbles are picked without replacement.

11. *A:* Pick red.
    B: Pick blue.

12. *A:* Pick red or blue.
    B: Pick yellow.

13. *A:* Pick green.
    B: Pick black or white.

14. *A:* Pick purple.
    B: Pick black.

Draw a card at random from a 26-card deck with 13 red cards numbered 1 to 13 and 13 black cards numbered 1 to 13. Replace the card, shuffle the deck, and draw another card.

15. *A:* Draw an 8.
    B: Draw a 2.

16. *A:* Draw a red card.
    B: Draw a black card.

17. *A:* Draw a black card.
    B: Draw a 10.

★18. *A:* Draw a 2 or a 4.
     B: Draw a red card.

★19. *A:* Draw a number > 9.
     B: Draw a black 3.

★20. *A:* Draw a black 3.
     B: Draw a red 14.

APPLICATION

Tree diagrams are a useful tool for listing the outcomes of a compound event. At the right is a tree diagram that shows the outcomes for two consecutive births.

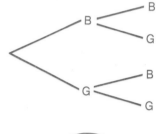

21. List the outcomes. What is the probability of having two consecutive girls?

22. Use a tree diagram to show the outcomes for rolling a number cube followed by spinning this spinner. What is *P*(prime number, vowel)?

Counting Principle

If 3 airlines fly from Auckland, New Zealand, to Sydney, Australia, and 4 airlines fly from Sydney to Manila, Philippines, how many ways would there be to fly from Auckland to Manila?

▶ **Counting Principle**   If there are m choices for a first decision and n choices for a second decision, then there are $m \times n$ choices for the first decision followed by the second.

So there would be 3×4, or 12, ways to fly from Auckland to Manila.

The counting principle can be used to find probabilities of compound events.

Compound Event (Events A and B)	Number of Outcomes		$P(A,B)$
	Event	Sample Space	
A: Toss a head. B: Toss a head.	A: 1 B: 1	A: 2 B: 2	$\frac{1 \times 1}{2 \times 2} = \frac{1}{4}$
A: Roll an odd number. B: Toss a tail.	A: 3 B: 1	A: 6 B: 2	$\frac{3 \times 1}{6 \times 2} = \frac{3}{12} = \frac{1}{4}$
A: Choose tens digit > 5. B: Choose ones digit < 3.	A: 4 B: 3	A: 9 B: 10	$\frac{4 \times 3}{9 \times 10} = \frac{12}{90} = \frac{2}{15}$

CLASSWORK

Use the counting principle to answer 1–2.

1. There are 5 roads from Wayne to Flint and 4 roads from Flint to Hope. How many ways can you go from Wayne to Hope?

2. Bess has 3 skirts, 4 blouses, and 2 vests that match. How many outfits can she make?

Find the probability of each compound event, $P(A,B)$.
Use spinner X at the right, a coin, and a number cube for 3–5.

3. A: Spin red or blue.
 B: Toss a head.

4. A: Spin red, orange, or yellow.
 B: Roll a prime number.

5. A: Choose a vowel in the word *SLICE*.
 B: Roll a multiple of 3.

6. A: Choose tens digit < 4.
 B: Choose ones digit > 6.

PRACTICE

Use the counting principle to answer each.

1. Willie has 6 shirts and 8 ties that match. How many different combinations of shirt and tie are possible?

2. Connie made up a code consisting of a letter followed by a 1-digit number. How many different combinations are possible?

3. If Connie also uses a 1-digit number followed by a letter, how many combinations are possible in all?

4. Godwin has 7 shirts, 5 pairs of slacks, 3 sport jackets, and 3 ties that match. How many outfits can he make?

At Sally's Deli the following items are available for a sandwich.

Breads	Meats or Fish	Cheeses	Vegetables	Condiments
rye	turkey	provolone	tomato	mustard
whole wheat	roast beef	Swiss	lettuce	oil & vinegar
oatmeal	tuna	muenster	onion	
pita			sprouts	

5. One selection is made from each column. How many different sandwiches can be made at Sally's Deli?

6. One selection is made from each column. How many meatless sandwiches can be made at Sally's Deli?

7. One selection is made from each column. How many different sandwiches can be made using rye bread?

★ 8. A Super Sandwich is made with one kind of cheese, one condiment, all the vegetables, and the two kinds of meat. How many different Super Sandwiches can be made?

Use spinner X on page 324, a deck of 10 cards, each printed with a different number from 0 to 9, and a coin. Find the probability of each compound event, P(A,B).

9. A: Spin red or white.
   B: Draw an even number.

10. A: Draw a prime number.
    B: Spin green or blue.

11. A: Draw a number < 2.
    B: Toss a tail.

12. A: Choose tens digit < 5.
    B: Choose ones digit ≤ 9.

★ 13. A: Draw a prime number.
    B: Toss a tail.
    C: Spin red or blue.

★ 14. A: Spin purple.
    B: Draw a number > 7.
    C: Spin white or green.

APPLICATION

=== CALCULATOR ===

A New Jersey license plate can have 3 letters followed by 3 digits or 3 digits followed by 3 letters. Zero can be used in any position in a number. Each symbol can be used more than once.

1. How many different license plates are possible?

2. How many different license plates beginning with A or B are possible?

331

CHAPTER REVIEW

Use the histogram at the right. pages 300–301

1. How many students received an *A*?

2. What was the most common grade?

3. Eight students all received the same grade. Which grade was it?

4. The highest grade was 98. The lowest was 62. What is the range of the data?

Use the data at the right. pages 302–307

5. Find the mean, the median, and the mode.

6. Make a line graph of this data.

7. For more than half the week the temperature was above 89°F. Was the mean, the median, the mode, or the range used to make this statement?

Use the graphs at the right. pages 308–313

8. How many inches of snow fell in the city with the lowest temperature?

9. Does there appear to be a correlation between the temperature and the amount of snowfall? If so, what kind?

10. From the circle graphs does it appear that there are more people in urban areas in Saudi Arabia or in Turkey?

11. The population of Saudi Arabia is 10,400,000. The population of Turkey is 49,200,000. In which country are there actually more people in urban areas?

Use the spinner and the deck of cards to find each. The probabilities in 13, 19, and 20 are without replacement. pages 324–325, 328–329

12. *P*(even)
13. *P*(vowel, T)
14. *P*(even or 11)
15. *P*(M or N)
16. *P*(even, vowel)
17. *P*(8, E)
18. *P*(vowel)
19. *P*(consonant, vowel)
20. *P*(M, N)

Solve. pages 314–315, 330–331

21. How many different outfits can be made from 3 skirts and 5 blouses that match?

22. What conclusion can you draw from these statements? The world's longest river is in Africa. The Amazon River is in South America.

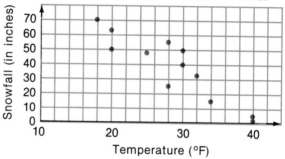

SCORES ON A MATH TEST

	DAILY HIGH TEMPERATURES FOR ONE WEEK (°F)						
	M	T	W	T	F	S	S
	82	90	87	87	89	93	95

SNOWFALL VS. TEMPERATURE IN 12 CITIES

WHERE PEOPLE LIVE

Saudi Arabia · Turkey

■ urban ■ nonurban

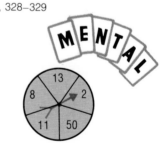

Use the bar graph and the circle graph to answer 1–9.

LEADING RICE-PRODUCING COUNTRIES

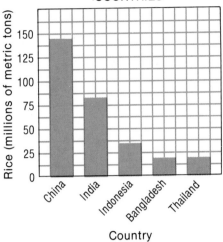

1. To the nearest 25 million tons, how much rice does China produce?

2. Which countries produce less than 25 million tons?

3. Which country produces more rice, India or Indonesia? To the nearest 25 million tons, how much more?

4. On which continent are the leading rice-producing nations?

5. The average amount of rice produced per country is about 60 million tons. Was the mean, the median, the mode, or the range used to make this statement?

6. Which item represents the largest percent of Japan's imports from the United States? Explain why this might be so.

7. Which item represents the smallest percent of Japan's imports from the United States?

8. What percent of Japanese imports are food and machinery?

9. To the nearest degree, how many degrees were allowed for *Food* in this circle graph?

JAPANESE IMPORTS FROM THE UNITED STATES

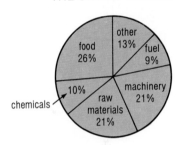

Find each for this set of data: 9, 12, 4, 8, 19, 9, 16.

10. mean   11. median   12. mode   13. range

Use the deck of cards and the spinner to find each. The probabilities in 21–22 are without replacement.

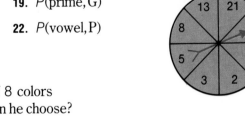

14. $P(G)$ 15. $P(\text{vowel, odd})$ 16. $P(6)$

17. $P(\text{odd or 2})$ 18. $P(\text{consonant or vowel})$ 19. $P(\text{prime, G})$

20. $P(\text{consonant})$ 21. $P(G, \text{vowel})$ 22. $P(\text{vowel, P})$

Solve.

23. Jack wants to buy a T-shirt. He has a choice of 8 colors and 7 designs. From how many different shirts can he choose?

24. What conclusion can you draw from these statements? All rectangles are parallelograms. *ABCD* is a rectangle.

25. How many outfits can Sylvia make with 3 skirts, 5 blouses, and 2 blazers that match?

What is the sum of the numbers in the 25th row of Pascal's triangle?

A SECRET CODE

Can you decode this secret message?

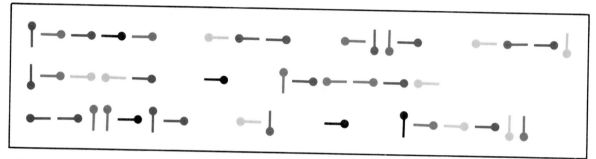

The bar graph below shows the average number of times you will see each letter of the alphabet in a group of 100 letters in ordinary English. Each symbol in the secret message stands for a letter of the alphabet.

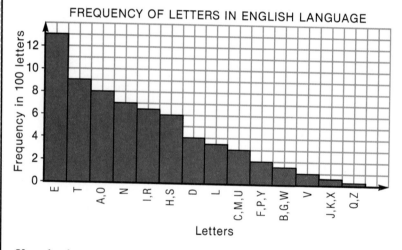

FREQUENCY OF LETTERS IN ENGLISH LANGUAGE

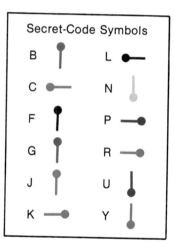

Secret-Code Symbols

Use the bar graph to answer the questions below.

1. What is the most frequently used letter in the English language? Write this letter beneath the symbol that appears most frequently in the message.

2. What is the second most frequently used letter? Write this letter beneath the symbol that appears second most frequently.

3. Now use the list of secret-code symbols to fill in more letters.

4. What is the third most frequently used letter? Can you guess which of these letters is used third most frequently in the message?

5. What is the message?

ODDS

The **odds** in favor of an event are the ratio of the number of ways the event can occur to the number of ways it cannot occur.

Select a marble.

The odds in favor of selecting a red marble are 3 to 2, or $\frac{3}{2}$.

The odds against selecting a red marble are 2 to 3, or $\frac{2}{3}$.

Spin the spinner.

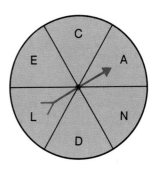

What are the odds

1. against spinning C?

2. in favor of spinning A, B, C, or D?

3. in favor of spinning a vowel?

4. in favor of spinning a consonant?

Draw a card.

What are the odds

5. against drawing yellow?

6. in favor of drawing a square?

7. against drawing a circle?

8. in favor of drawing a red triangle?

Draw a card.

What are the odds

9. in favor of drawing an odd number?

10. against drawing a prime number?

11. in favor of drawing a multiple of 3?

12. against drawing a number that is a perfect square?

COMPUTER

SIMULATIONS

A **random number generator** causes a computer to output a decimal number *between* 0 and 1. Each number has approximately the same probability of being selected.

The random number function **RND** outputs a random number strictly between 0 and 1. Some computers use the statement LET R = RND, while other computers use LET R = RND(1).

The RND function is often used with the INT function to generate integers within a given range.

Statement	Result
LET R = RND or LET R = RND(1)	R will be a decimal number between 0 and 1.
LET R = 8 * RND or LET R = 8 * RND(1)	R will be a decimal number between 0 and 8.
LET R = INT(8 * RND) or LET R = INT(8 * RND(1))	R will be an integer in the range 0 to 7.
LET R = INT(8 * RND) + 1 or LET R = INT(8 * RND(1)) + 1	R will be an integer in the range 1 to 8.

This program uses the RND and INT functions to *simulate* spinning a spinner that has 5 equally likely results.

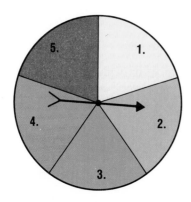

PROGRAM

```
10 LET S = INT(5 * RND(1)) + 1
20 PRINT "YOUR SPIN IS ";S
30 PRINT
40 PRINT "SPIN AGAIN?"
50 PRINT "1 = YES, 0 = NO"
60 INPUT A
70 PRINT
80 IF A = 1 THEN GOTO 10
90 END
```

Describe the range of numbers that will be generated by each program.

```
1. 10  FOR I = 1 TO 10
   20  PRINT INT(20 * RND(1))
   30  NEXT I
   40  END
```

```
2. 10  FOR J = 1 TO 10
   20  PRINT INT(50 * RND(1))
   30  NEXT J
   40  END
```

```
3. 10  FOR A = 1 TO 10
   20  PRINT INT(30 * RND(1)) + 1
   30  NEXT A
   40  END
```

```
4. 10  FOR B = 1 TO 10
   20  PRINT INT(34 * RND(1)) + 1
   30  NEXT B
   40  END
```

```
★5. 10  FOR X = 1 TO 10
    20  PRINT INT(9 * RND(1)) + 6
    30  NEXT X
    40  END
```

```
★6. 10  FOR Y = 1 TO 10
    20  PRINT INT(11 * RND(1)) - 5
    30  NEXT Y
    40  END
```

Write a statement to print a random integer in each range.

7. from 0 to 9

8. from 1 to 15

9. from 0 to 99

10. from 1 to 2

★11. from 8 to 16

★12. from $^-9$ to $^+9$

AT THE COMPUTER

Write a program to simulate each experiment. Run each program several times and record the results.

1. Toss the number cube at the right sixty times. Each side has one of the digits 1, 2, 3, 4, 5, or 6 on it. How many times was the number 2 tossed?

★2. Spin the spinner on page 336 one hundred times. Count the number of times an even number is spun.

★3. Make up an experiment and simulate the results.

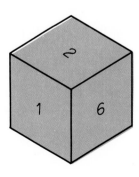

CUMULATIVE REVIEW

Choose the correct answers. Write A, B, C, or D.

1. Estimate. $3{,}207 - 742$

   A 3,000   **C** 8,000

   B 2,000   **D** not given

2. 0.03×5.06

   A 0.1518   **C** 8.06

   B 15.18   **D** not given

3. $2.2032 \div 0.72$

   A 3.06   **C** 0.36

   B 3.60   **D** not given

4. Complete. $5.08 \text{ cm} = \underline{\hspace{1cm}} \text{ mm}$

   A 0.508   **C** 50.8

   B 508   **D** not given

5. Which property is used?
   $(3 \times 2) + (6 \times 2) = (3 + 6)2$

   A identity   **C** associative

   B commutative   **D** not given

6. $24 \div (12 \div 2)$

   A 1   **C** 12

   B 4   **D** not given

7. What is the prime factorization of 48?

   A $2^4 \times 3$ **C** $2^3 \times 3^2$

   B $2^3 \times 6$ **D** not given

8. What is the LCM of 8 and 12?

   A 4   **C** 12

   B 96   **D** not given

9. $8\frac{1}{6} - 2\frac{2}{3}$

   A $5\frac{1}{2}$ **C** $10\frac{5}{6}$

   B $6\frac{1}{2}$ **D** not given

10. $\frac{8}{9} \times 8\frac{1}{4}$

    A 16   **C** $14\frac{2}{3}$

    B $8\frac{7}{36}$ **D** not given

11. What is the name of a $23°$ angle?

    A obtuse   **C** acute

    B scalene   **D** not given

12. What is a triangle with all sides equal?

    A equilateral   **C** pentagon

    B isosceles   **D** not given

13. Solve. $\frac{n}{8} = \frac{27}{36}$

    A $n = 6.75$ **C** $n = 8$

    B $n = 6$ **D** not given

14. What is the unit price if 8 cost $2.16?

    A $.27   **C** $.26

    B $.20   **D** not given

15. Which ratio is equal to $\frac{1.2}{3.2}$?

    A $\frac{2.4}{4.4}$ **C** $\frac{3.6}{9.6}$

    B $\frac{1}{3}$ **D** not given

16. Complete. 440 m in 8 h
    $\underline{\hspace{1cm}}$ m in 1 h

    A 55 m   **C** 45 m

    B 40 m   **D** not given

Choose the correct answers. Write A, B, C, or D.

17. What is the tan (m∠B)?

A $\frac{6}{8}$ **C** $\frac{10}{8}$

B $\frac{8}{10}$ **D** not given

18. What is the ratio for 37.5%?

A $\frac{32}{100}$ **C** $\frac{325}{100}$

B $\frac{3}{8}$ **D** not given

19. What is the decimal for 0.2%?

A 0.2   **C** 0.04

B 0.002   **D** not given

20. What is 15% of 230?

A 34.5   **C** 1,533.3

B 2,300   **D** not given

21. What percent of 33 is 22?

A 33%   **C** 66%

B $66\frac{2}{3}$%   **D** not given

22. 120% of what number is 54?

A 648   **C** 45

B 6.48   **D** not given

23. Compare. ⁻23 ⬤ ⁻6

A >   **C** =

B <   **D** not given

24. ⁻48 + ⁻19

A 67   **C** 29

B ⁻29   **D** not given

25. ⁻4 − 6

A ⁻4   **C** 10

B 2   **D** not given

26. ⁻10 · ⁻6

A 60   **C** ⁻16

B ⁻60   **D** not given

27. 54 ÷ ⁻6

A 9   **C** ⁻9

B ⁻8   **D** not given

28. What is the mode of 8, 16, 8, 5, 9, 10, and 19?

A 10.1   **C** 19

B 9   **D** not given

29. How many three-digit numbers can be formed from the digits 3, 4, and 5?

A 27   **C** 9

B 333   **D** not given

30. Which is not a measure of central tendency?

A mean   **C** median

B range   **D** not given

31. What is P(odd number on a number cube)?

A 1   **C** $\frac{1}{2}$

B $\frac{1}{6}$ **D** not given

32. What is the probability of spinning an even number?

A $\frac{1}{3}$ **C** $\frac{1}{2}$

B $\frac{2}{8}$ **D** not given

CUMULATIVE REVIEW

Choose the correct answers. Write A, B, C, or D.

Use simulation to solve.

33. Four people walk into a room. Each person shakes hands with every other person. How many handshakes are exchanged?

    A 12   C 2
    B 16   D not given

Find the pattern and complete.

34. 10, 15, 21, 28, 36, ___

    A 46   C 44
    B 45   D not given

35. 19.2, 9.6, ___, 2.4, 1.2

    A 6.4   C 4.8
    B 3.2   D not given

Solve.

36. Misako delivers flowers for a local florist. She charges $1.25 for orders delivered within 1 mile and $1.75 for orders delivered beyond 1 mile. In 1 week she delivered 17 orders within 1 mile and 21 beyond. How much did she earn?

    A $58.00   C $56.00
    B $40.00   D not given

37. If Willis had helped Misako by delivering just the orders that were delivered farther than a mile, for $.90 each, how much would Misako have earned?

    A $21.25   C $40.80
    B $41.95   D not given

Make a drawing to help solve.

38. Sara wants to stack blocks for scenery in the shape of a pyramid. If she has 28 blocks, how many levels high can her pyramid be?

    A 27   C 7
    B 17   D not given

Make a list to help solve 39 and 40.

39. A series of license plates is being printed, using 5 characters. The first 2 characters must be the letters *AD,* in that order. The next 3 characters can be any even digits. Each digit can be used more than once. How many different license plates can be made?

    A 12   C 4
    B 25   D not given

40. All the offices on one floor of an office building are numbered with 3 digits, using only 1, 2, and 3. Each digit can be used more than once. How many offices can have 2 ones in the number?

    A 18   C 7
    B 10   D not given

Solve.

41. On May 1 Leah opened a savings account. By the end of May she had doubled her savings. On June 5 she withdrew $58, but by the end of June she had tripled her balance. On July 10, when she withdrew $98, there was $106 in the account. How much had Leah deposited on May 1?

    A $45   C $162
    B $63   D not given

Theme: Architecture

Sketching Geometric Relationships

Nikola Tesla, a famous inventor, had an amazing ability to visualize things. Being able to visualize means seeing a clear picture of something in your mind. Tesla could picture his inventions in his mind in complete detail and could even visualize where the wear spots would be on some machines.

WORKING TOGETHER

Visualizing geometric relationships helps you understand and solve problems. Often it helps to draw or sketch geometric relationships. Work with a partner. Copy the geometric figures shown below and sketch each of the relationships described. Discuss the sketches with your partner as you proceed.

1. Sketch the shortest path from point A to point B.

- B

- A

2. Sketch the shortest path from point D to line BC.

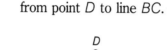

3. Sketch all points 1 cm from point E.

- E

4. Sketch all points 1 cm from the circle L.

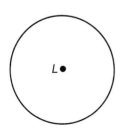

5. Sketch all points 1 cm from line segment LM.

6. Sketch all points that are both 2 cm from point N and 3 cm from point P.

1. Compare your sketches with those of the rest of your class. Did everyone sketch the same figures? If not, discuss and determine which are the correct sketches.

2. What do you think the sketch in the fourth figure would look like if the circle *L* had a radius of less than 1 cm? Sketch it and discuss.

3. What do you think the sketch in the sixth figure would look like if points *N* and *P* were less than 2 cm apart? Sketch it and discuss.

===== THINKING IT THROUGH =====

Your sketches were done on a plane. Now think in three dimensions.

1. Rethink the last four sketches you did earlier. Now try to picture each geometric relationship in space. Discuss with your partner what each new set of points would look like. Try to sketch the figure that describes each relationship.

2. Discuss and compare the methods you used with the methods the rest of the class used. Decide as a group which are the correct figures. Draw a class sketch for each relationship on the chalkboard.

3. Compare the results of the four sketches in space with the corresponding sketches in the plane. How are they different? How are they the same? Discuss.

Geometric Constructions

Large corporations often hire professional designers to create a logo for their company. They use this logo on their buildings, advertising, and products. Most logos are geometric designs, like those shown here.

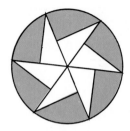

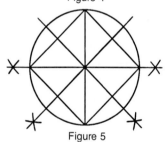

WORKING TOGETHER

A. Each member of your team needs a compass, a straightedge, and some paper. Create the designs shown below. You will need to experiment. Visualize where the centers of the arcs will be.

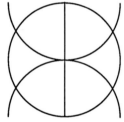

Figure 1

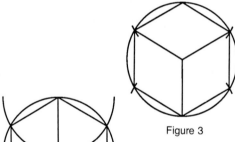

Figure 2

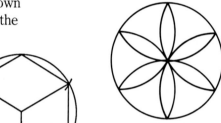

Figure 3

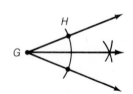

Figure 4

Figure 5

B. Here are three basic geometric constructions. Visualize where the centers of the arcs lie. Discuss with your team how each construction is performed.

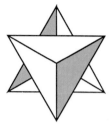

Copy of a
line segment

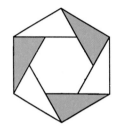

Perpendicular bisector
of a line segment

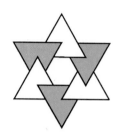

Bisector of an
angle

Use the constructions on page 344 to help you create two of the designs shown below. Check with team members to see if they used the same method to make the designs.

Figure 6

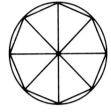
Figure 7

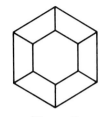
Figure 8

===SHARING YOUR THINKING===

1. In Figure 1, where did you place the compass point for each arc?

2. Why are the sides of the hexagon in Figures 2 and 3 all congruent?

3. In creating these designs, did you use a diameter of a circle each time? If so, how?

4. Explain to your team members how you would construct Figure 7. Does any team member have a different approach? If so, describe it.

5. What is a good way to begin the design in Figure 8?

6. Discuss any problems you had creating these designs.

More Geometric Constructions

WORKING TOGETHER

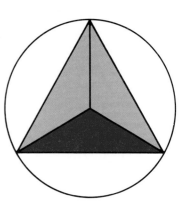

A. The logo design at the right shows a triangle whose three angles are bisected. The construction can be done in more than one way.

    1. Construct the design.

    2. Use a straightedge to draw a large triangle of any shape. Exchange triangles with your partner. Construct the angle bisector of each angle.

B. Shown below are two basic geometric constructions.

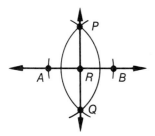
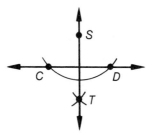

    Perpendicular to a
    line from a point on
    the line

    Perpendicular to a
    line from a point not
    on the line

Draw another triangle. Again exchange triangles with your partner. Construct the altitude to each side (or side extended) of the triangle.

C. The drawings below show relationships of lines, arcs, and bisectors that are hidden in each final design. Choose one of them. Study each stage carefully. See if you can visualize a construction plan. Try to construct the final design with a compass and straightedge.

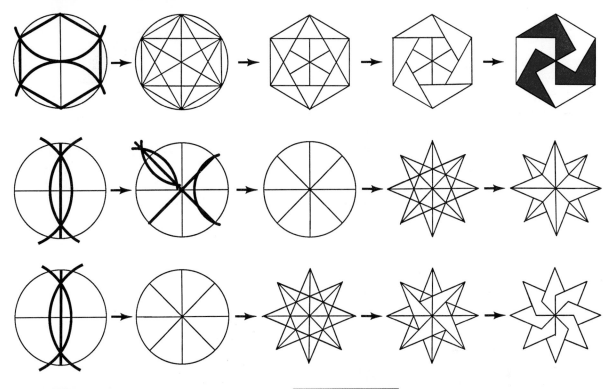

1. Compare the methods used by students in your group to construct angle bisectors. Which method was easiest?

2. What conclusion, if any, did your group reach about the results of bisecting the three angles of a triangle?

3. What seems to be true about the three altitudes of a triangle?

1. How can visualizing hidden lines and circles help you understand and create geometric shapes?

2. Where might you expect to see geometric designs outside your school?

3. Create a logo of your own.

Congruent Triangles

The two gables of this house form a pair of congruent triangles.

Two triangles are **congruent** if their corresponding sides and angles are congruent.

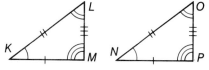

$\overline{KM} \cong \overline{NP}$ $\angle K \cong \angle N$
$\overline{KL} \cong \overline{NO}$ $\angle L \cong \angle O$
$\overline{LM} \cong \overline{OP}$ $\angle M \cong \angle P$

To show that two triangles are congruent, it is not necessary to show that all corresponding parts are congruent.

▶**Side-Side-Side rule (SSS)**

Two triangles are congruent if their corresponding sides are congruent.

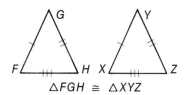

$\triangle FGH \cong \triangle XYZ$

▶**Side-Angle-Side rule (SAS)**

Two triangles are congruent if two corresponding sides and the included angle are congruent.

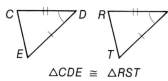

$\triangle CDE \cong \triangle RST$

▶**Angle-Side-Angle rule (ASA)**

Two triangles are congruent if two corresponding angles and the included side are congruent.

$\triangle MNO \cong \triangle ABC$

These rules can be used to construct congruent triangles.

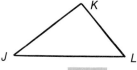

Construct a triangle congruent to $\triangle JKL$, using ASA.

Step 1

Draw $\overrightarrow{DP}$. Construct $\angle D$ congruent to $\angle J$.

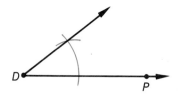

Step 2

On $\overrightarrow{DP}$ construct $\overline{DF}$ congruent to $\overline{JL}$.

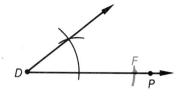

Step 3

Construct $\angle F$ congruent to $\angle L$. Label E. $\triangle JKL \cong \triangle DEF$

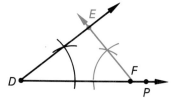

CLASSWORK

Which triangles are congruent to $\triangle ABC$? Tell which rule applies.

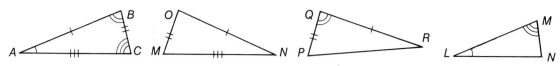

Which triangles are congruent to △XYZ? Tell which rule applies.

1.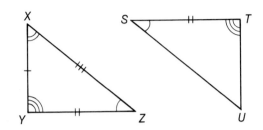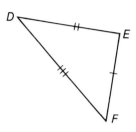

2.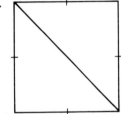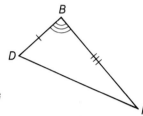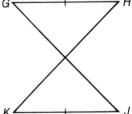

Each pair of triangles is congruent. Tell why. $\overline{GH} \parallel \overline{KJ}$.

3. 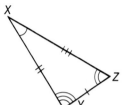 4. 5. G, H, K, J

Construct.

6. Write the steps used to construct △MOT congruent to △JSL by the SAS rule. Construct the triangle.

APPLICATION

LOGICAL THINKING

Two people buy a piece of land shaped as shown at the right. They wish to divide the land into two parts of equal area by drawing a straight line through the property. How can they do it?

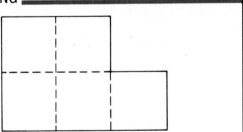

Problem Solving

GUESS AND TEST

Guessing the answer to a problem is a good way to try to
solve the problem. However, a guess must be tested to see if
it satisfies the conditions of the problem. If it does not,
another guess must be made and tested. As the guesses are
refined by testing, the correct answer is eventually found.

There are a total of 500 offices in the three towers of a
building complex. Building B has 20 more offices than Building
A. Building C has 32 fewer offices than Building B. How many
offices are there in each building?

NUMBER OF OFFICES IN THREE BUILDINGS					
Guess	Building A	Building B	Building C	Total	
1	100	120	88	308	← too few
2	200	220	188	608	← too many
3	180	200	168	548	← too many
4	160	180	148	488	← too few
5	164	184	152	500	← correct

There are 164 offices in Building A, 184 offices in Building B,
and 152 offices in Building C.

Check your answer against the given facts in the problem.

Does Building B have 20 more offices than Building A? Does
Building C have 32 fewer offices than Building B? Does the
number of offices in all three buildings total 500?

PRACTICE

Solve.

1. The parking lot for the building complex has 210 parking spaces. There are twice as many spaces for compact cars as there are for full-size cars. How many spaces of each size are there?

2. The 500 offices are being repainted, some beige, some blue, and the rest yellow. There will be twice as many beige ones as blue ones and 20 more yellow ones than blue ones. How many of each color will there be?

3. The area of a rectangular patio is 760 ft². The perimeter is 116 ft. What are the dimensions of the patio?

4. A textbook is opened at random. To which pages is it opened if the product of the facing page numbers is 2,970?

5. Shown below are nine paths connecting four water fountains. Can you visit each fountain, walking along each path exactly once, and return to the fountain where you started? If so, how?

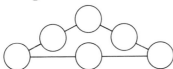

6. Copy the grid below. Color three squares red, three squares black, and three squares yellow. No two squares in the same row or column may be the same color.

7. Place the numbers 1, 2, 3, 4, 5, and 6 in the circles so that the sum along each side of the triangle is 10.

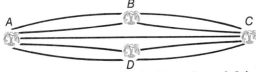

★ 8. The carton below holds 24 cans. Put 18 cans in the carton so that each row and each column has an even number of cans.

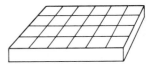

CREATE YOUR OWN PROBLEM

Buildings A, B, and C in the building complex are each a different height. Write a problem about the number of floors in each building. Have a classmate solve the problem using Guess and Test.

Surface Area of Prisms

The points of a **space figure** lie in more than one plane. A **polyhedron** is a space figure whose surfaces, or **faces**, are all flat.

A **prism** is a polyhedron with two parallel and congruent faces called **bases**. The other faces, called **lateral faces**, are parallelograms.

The shape of its bases is used to name a prism.

rectangular prism   **triangular prism**

A rectangular prism whose faces are all congruent squares is a **cube**.

pentagonal prism   **hexagonal prism**

   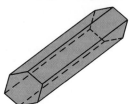

▶The **surface area** of a space figure is the sum of the areas of all its faces. The surface area of a cube with side s is $6s^2$.

To find the surface area of a prism, first make a pattern to show the faces. Then find the sum of the areas of all the faces.

Find the surface area of this rectangular prism.

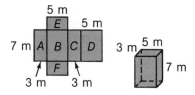

Area A = Area C = $3 \times 7 = 21$ **Think** Congruent faces
Area B = Area D = $5 \times 7 = 35$ have equal areas.
Area E = Area F = $3 \times 5 = 15$

The sum of all the areas = $2(21) + 2(35) + 2(15) = 142$ The surface area is 142 m².

Another Example

Find the surface area of this triangular prism.

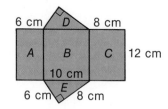

Area A = $6 \times 12 = 72$
Area B = $10 \times 12 = 120$
Area C = $8 \times 12 = 96$
Area D = Area E = $\frac{1}{2} \times 6 \times 8 = 24$

The sum of the areas = 336   The surface area is 336 cm².

CLASSWORK

Find the surface area of each prism.

1.   2.   3.

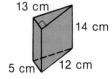

Find the surface area of each prism.

1.
5 m
3 m   2 m

2.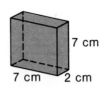
7 cm
7 cm   2 cm

3.
17 m
16 m
8 m   15 m

4.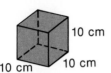
10 cm
10 cm   10 cm

5.
9 m
5 m   3 m

6.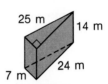
25 m   14 m
7 m   24 m

7.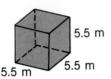
5.5 m
5.5 m   5.5 m

8.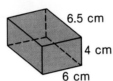
6.5 cm
4 cm
6 cm

9.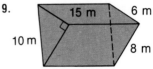
15 m   6 m
10 m   8 m

Solve.

10. The surface area of a cube is 96 m².
   a. What is the area of each face of the cube?
   b. What is the length of each side of the cube?

★ 11. The area of each base of a rectangular prism is 35 cm². Two of the lateral faces have an area of 15 cm². The remaining two faces have an area of 21 cm². Find the length, width, and height of the prism.

APPLICATION

In an A-frame building the two sides of the roof are congruent. Use the picture to solve 12–14.

12. What is its outside surface area? (Do not include the floor.)

13. Leon plans to paint the front of the building, and Anna will paint the back. Find the total area they will paint.

14. A 4-liter can of paint covers about 30 square meters. How many cans will Leon and Anna need?

15. A sign showing a house number uses 5 different digits. Installed upside down, it shows a number 63,783 more than the correct number. What is the correct number?

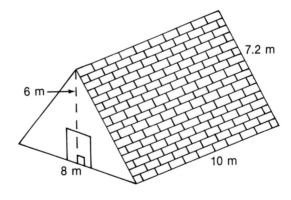
7.2 m
6 m
8 m
10 m

Volume of Prisms

The United Nations Secretariat Building in New York City is a rectangular prism. How much space does the building enclose?

The **volume** of a figure is the number of cubic units needed to fill the figure.

Cubic centimeters (cm³), cubic decimeters (dm³), and **cubic meters (m³)** are measures of volume.

▶The volume of a prism is the area of the base (B) multiplied by the height (h) of the prism.

$$V = Bh \qquad B = 88 \times 22 = 1,936$$
$$h = 154$$
$$V = 1,936 \times 154 = 298,144$$

Think The area of a rectangular base equals length times width.

The building encloses 298,144 m³ of space.

▶The volume of a cube with side s is s^3.

Another Example

Find the volume of this triangular prism.

$$V = Bh \qquad B = \tfrac{1}{2} \times 60 \times 80 = 2,400$$
$$h = 90$$
$$V = 2,400 \times 90 = 216,000$$

The volume is 216,000 cm³.

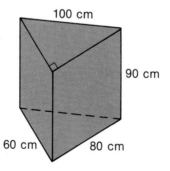

CLASSWORK

Find the volume of each prism.

1. 7 cm, 6 cm, 2 cm

2. 5 cm, 14 cm, 12 cm

3. 8 m, 8 m, 8 m

4. 10 cm, 10 cm, 10 cm

5. 5 m, 9 m, 3 m

6. 14 m, 3 m, 3 m

PRACTICE

Find the volume of each prism.

1.
5 m
3 m   2 m

2.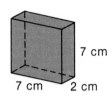
7 cm
7 cm   2 cm

3.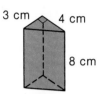
3 cm   4 cm
8 cm

4.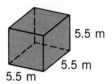
5.5 m
5.5 m
5.5 m

5.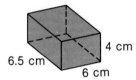
4 cm
6.5 cm   6 cm

*6.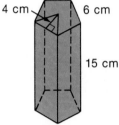
4 cm   6 cm
15 cm

Choose the appropriate equation.

7. A rectangular prism is 4 m wide and 7 m long. Its volume is 252 m^3. What is its height?

   a. $h = 252 \div (4 \times 7)$ **b.** $h = (4 + 7) \times 252$ **c.** $h = 252 \div \frac{1}{2}(4 \times 7)$

Solve.

8. The area of the base of a triangular prism is 15 cm^2. The volume of the prism is 180 cm^3. What is its height?

★ 9. The volume of a cube is 343 m^3. What are its dimensions?

APPLICATION

10. A cooling system recirculates air. What volume of air is recirculated in a building shaped like a triangular prism 350 m high with a base area of 4,000 m^2?

11. Each tower of the World Trade Center in New York City is a rectangular prism. The volume is 2,317,500 m^3. The height of a tower is about 412 m. Find the area of its base.

★ 12. A building with a volume of 5,625 m^3 has a height of 9 m. If the base is a square, how long is each side?

MENTAL ARITHMETIC

Four congruent pentagonal prisms are stacked one on top of another. Each prism has a height of 2.5 cm and a base area of 7.3 cm^2. Without using paper or a calculator, find the volume of the entire stacked figure. (Think about the height of the stacked figure.)

Surface Area of Cylinders

Daniel is making a cardboard model of a medieval castle. How much cardboard does he need to make one cylindrical tower that is 6 cm wide and 9 cm high?

A **cylinder** is a space figure with two parallel bases that are congruent circles. A cylinder also has a curved surface called the **lateral surface.**

To find the surface area of a cylinder, first make a pattern. The lateral surface is shown as a rectangle.

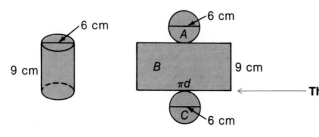

Think Length of lateral surface equals circumference of base, πd.

▶The surface area of a cylinder is the sum of the areas of both circles plus the area of the rectangle.

Area A = Area C = πr^2 Area B = πdh
$\approx 3.14 \times 3^2$ $\approx 3.14 \times 6 \times 9$
≈ 28.26 ≈ 169.56

The sum of the areas is about $2(28.26) + 169.56 = 226.08$.
Daniel needs about 226 cm^2 of cardboard to make a tower.

Another Example

Find the surface area of the cylinder. Round to the nearest one.

Surface area = $2\pi r^2 + \pi dh$
$\approx 2 \times 3.14 \times 2.25 + 3.14 \times 3 \times 1.5$
$\approx 14.13 + 14.13$
≈ 28.26

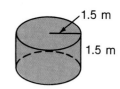

The surface area is 28 m^2.

CLASSWORK

Find the surface area. Use 3.14 for π. Round to the nearest one.

1.
2 m
6 m

2.
4 m
3 m

3.
8 cm
15 cm

PRACTICE

Find the surface area of each cylinder. Use 3.14 for π.
Round to the nearest one.

1. 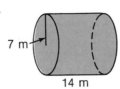 3 cm

9 cm

2. 7 m

14 m

3. 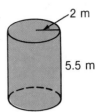 2 m

5.5 m

4. 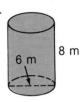 8 m

6 m

5. r = 3 m
   h = 17 m

6. r = 5 cm
   h = 5 cm

7. r = 2 dm
   h = 9 dm

8. r = 10 m
   h = 30 m

Use the figure below to answer 9–11. Use 3.14 for π.

9. Find the combined area of the two bases.

10. Find the area of the lateral surface.

11. What is true about the answers to **9** and **10**? Do you think this is always true about a cylinder with a height equal to its radius? Explain.

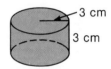 3 cm

3 cm

APPLICATION

The Renaissance Center is in Detroit, Michigan. The Westin Hotel, which is located there, is in the shape of a cylinder. It is about 35 m in diameter and about 230 m tall.

12. The hotel's lateral surface is glass. How much glass was used to make the lateral surface?

13. Suppose the glass used to make the lateral surface of the Westin Hotel came in plates with an area of 16 m². About how many plates would have been needed?

CALCULATOR

Use the formula and the calculator's memory to find surface area.

Surface area = $2\pi r^2 + \pi dh$

2 × 3 · 1 4 × 6 × 6 = M+

3 · 1 4 × 2 × 6 × 5 = M+

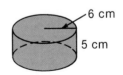 6 cm

5 cm

Now press RM. The screen shows 414.48. The surface area is about 414.48 m².

Find the surface area of each cylinder. Use 3.14 for π.

1. radius = 11.5 m; height = 19.2 m

2. diameter = 6.4 cm; height = 10.9 cm

Volume of Cylinders

Wheat is stored in cylindrical terminal grain elevators. Later it is sold to flour-milling companies. Most terminal elevators can hold over 40,000 m³ of wheat.

▶The volume of a cylinder is the area of the base (B) multiplied by the height (h) of the cylinder.

Find the volume of the cylinder to the nearest one.

$$V = Bh$$

Think The area of a circle is πr^2.

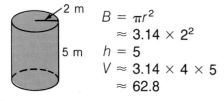

$B = \pi r^2$
$\approx 3.14 \times 2^2$
$h = 5$
$V \approx 3.14 \times 4 \times 5$
≈ 62.8

The volume is about 63 m³.

More Examples

Find the volume. Round to the nearest one.

a.
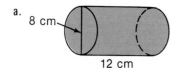

$V = Bh = \pi r^2 h$
$\approx 3.14 \times 4^2 \times 12$
$\approx 3.14 \times 16 \times 12$
≈ 602.88 cm³

The volume is 603 cm³.

b.

8 dm   10 dm

$V = Bh = \pi r^2 h$
$\approx 3.14 \times 10^2 \times 8$
$\approx 3.14 \times 100 \times 8$
$\approx 2{,}512$ dm³

The volume is 2,512 dm³.

CLASSWORK

Find the volume. Use 3.14 for π. Round to the nearest one.

1.
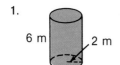
6 m   2 m

2.
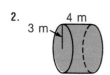
4 m
3 m

3.
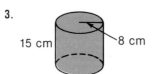
15 cm   8 cm

4.
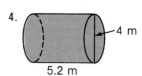
4 m
5.2 m

PRACTICE

Find the volume. Use 3.14 for π. Round to the nearest one.

1.
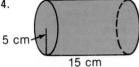
9 cm 3 cm

2.
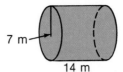
7 m 14 m

3.
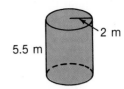
2 m 5.5 m

4.
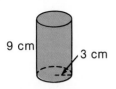
5 cm 15 cm

5.
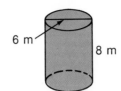
6 m 8 m

6.
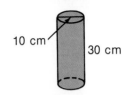
10 cm 30 cm

7.
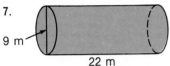
9 m 22 m

8.
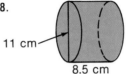
11 cm 8.5 cm

9.
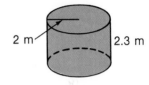
2 m 2.3 m

Solve. Use 3.14 for π.

10. The volume of a cylinder is 936 m³. The area of its base is 78 m². What is its height?

11. The volume of a cylinder is 165 cm³. The height of the cylinder is 15 cm. Find the area of its base.

★ 12. The volume of a cylinder is 2,512 cm³. The height of the cylinder is 8 cm. What is the radius of the base rounded to the nearest one?

★ 13. The volume of a cylinder is 25,120 m³. The radius of the base equals the height of the cylinder. Find the radius of the base rounded to the nearest one.

Find the volume of the shaded part of each figure. Use 3.14 for π. Round to the nearest one.

★14.
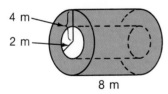
4 m
2 m
8 m

★15.
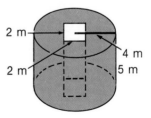
2 m
2 m
4 m
5 m

APPLICATION

16. Busch Memorial Stadium in St. Louis is in the shape of a cylinder. It is 40 m high and 240 m in diameter. How much space does it occupy?

★ 17. The Astrodome in Houston, Texas, occupies about 2,279,640 m³ of space. It is a cylinder 220 m in diameter. How high is it?

Volume of Pyramids and Cones

The largest pyramid in Egypt is the Great Pyramid built for the pharaoh Khufu. It is a rectangular pyramid.

A **pyramid** is a polyhedron with one base. All the lateral faces are triangles. The shape of the base is used to name the pyramid.

square pyramid   pentagonal pyramid

A **cone** is a space figure with a circular base and one vertex.

▶The volume of a pyramid is one third the volume of a prism with the same base and height.

$V = \frac{1}{3} Bh$

Find the volume of the pyramid.

4 m
5 m
3 m

$V = \frac{1}{3} Bh$ **Think** $B = lw$

$= \frac{1}{3} \times 3 \times 5 \times 4$

$= 20$

The volume is 20 m³.

▶The volume of a cone is one third the volume of a cylinder with the same base and height.

$V = \frac{1}{3} Bh$

Find the volume of the cone. Use 3.14 for π. Round to the nearest one.

6 cm
3 cm

$V = \frac{1}{3} Bh$ **Think** $B = \pi r^2$

$\approx \frac{1}{3} \times 3.14 \times 3^2 \times 6$

≈ 56.52

The volume is 57 cm³.

CLASSWORK

Find the volume. Use 3.14 for π. Round to the nearest one.

1.
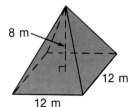
8 m
12 m
12 m

2.
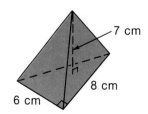
7 cm
8 cm
6 cm

3.
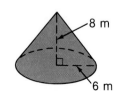
8 m
6 m

PRACTICE

Find the volume. Use 3.14 for π. Round to the nearest one.

1.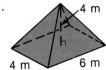
4 m, 4 m, h, 6 m

2.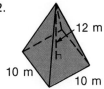
12 m, h, 10 m, 10 m

3.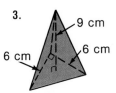
9 cm, 6 cm, 6 cm

4.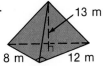
13 m, 8 m, h, 12 m

5.
5 cm, 3 cm

6.
15 m, 6 m

7.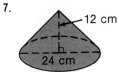
12 cm, 24 cm

8.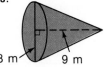
8 m, 9 m

9.
5 cm, 10 cm, 8 cm

10.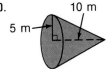
10 m, 5 m

11.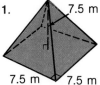
7.5 m, 7.5 m, 7.5 m

12.
5 cm, 13 cm

Solve. Use 3.14 for π. Round to the nearest one.

★ **13.** Find the volume of this figure.

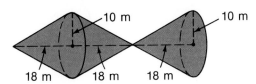
10 m, 10 m, 18 m, 18 m, 18 m

APPLICATION

14. The base of the Great Pyramid of Khufu is a square with sides about 230 m long. Its height is about 150 m. What is its volume?

★ **15.** The area of the base of a pyramid is 111 m². The volume of the pyramid is 555 m³. What is its height?

1. $\frac{3}{5} + \frac{5}{8}$

2. $\frac{1}{3} + \frac{17}{18}$

3. $1\frac{1}{4} + 2\frac{3}{8}$

4. $7\frac{5}{4} - 6\frac{1}{4}$

5. $\frac{16}{11} - \frac{7}{11}$

6. $\frac{1}{2} \times 3\frac{1}{3}$

7. $2 \div 4\frac{1}{8}$

8. $\frac{7}{3} \times \frac{1}{3}$

9. $7\frac{1}{2} \div 5$

10. $\frac{5}{2\frac{1}{2}}$

11. $\frac{7\frac{1}{3}}{6}$

12. $12 \times \frac{3}{4} \times 6$

13. $4\frac{3}{4} \times 7\frac{1}{2} \div 19$

Write as a decimal.

14. 10%

15. $3\frac{1}{2}$%

16. 4%

17. 225%

18. $66\frac{2}{3}$%

361

Relating Length, Mass, and Capacity

The bottle holds 1 L of water. It will fill
1 cubic decimeter. The water weighs 1 kg.

The cube has a volume of
1 cubic centimeter. It holds
1 mL of water. 1 mL of
water weighs 1 gram.

Volume	Mass	Capacity
1 cm³	1 g	1 mL
1 dm³	1 kg	1 L

Find the weight of the water the tank holds.

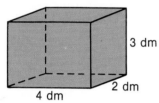

First find the volume of the tank.

$V = Bh$
$= 4 \times 2 \times 3$
$= 24 \text{ dm}^3$

1 dm³ weighs 1 kg, so 24 dm³ weighs 24 kg.

The tank can hold 24 kg of water.

Another Example

Find the capacity of this cup. Round to the nearest one. Use
3.14 for π.

$V = \frac{1}{3} Bh$
$= \frac{1}{3} \pi r^2 h = \frac{1}{3} \times 3.14 \times (2.4)^2 \times 5 \approx 30.144$

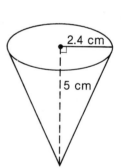

The volume of the cup is about 30 cm³.
The capacity of the cup is 30 mL.

CLASSWORK

Complete.

1. 5 L = ____ dm³

2. 8 dm³ of water weighs ____ kg.

3. ____ mL = 7 cm³

Find the capacity of each. Use 3.14 for π. Round to the nearest one.

4.
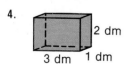

5.
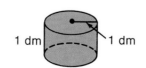

6.
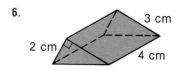

PRACTICE

Complete.

1. 36 mL = ___ cm^3

2. 15 L = ___ dm^3

3. 3.9 dm^3 = ___ L

4. ___ mL = 16 cm^3

5. ___ dm^3 = 5.4 L

6. ___ mL = 4 cm^3

7. 5 L of water weighs ___ kg.

8. 16 mL of water weighs ___ g.

9. 25 cm^3 of water weighs ___ g.

10. 36.2 dm^3 of water weighs ___ kg.

★ 11. 3,500 mm^3 of water weighs ___ g.

★ 12. 1 m^3 of water weighs ___ t.

Complete the chart for each amount of water.

	Volume	Mass	Capacity
13.			5 mL
14.	3 dm^3		
15.	7 cm^3		

	Volume	Mass	Capacity
16.			43 L
17.	1.5 cm^3		
18.			10 L

Find the capacity of each container and the weight of the water it holds. Use 3.14 for π. Round to the nearest one.

19.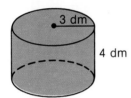
3 dm
4 dm

20.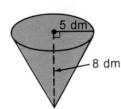
5 dm
8 dm

21.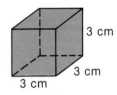
3 cm
3 cm
3 cm

Give the volume and capacity of each.

22. a cube that measures 4 cm on a side

23. a cube that measures 15 dm on a side

Find the measure of a side.

★ 24. a cube with a capacity of 1,728 L

APPLICATION

This swimming pool holds about 1,000,000 L of water.

25. How many cubic meters of water does the pool hold?

★ 26. How many metric tons does the water weigh?

Problem Solving

SKILLS AND STRATEGIES REVIEW   Amazing Structures

In medieval Ireland, pencil-shaped towers were built as a refuge from invading Vikings. The townspeople would take as much as they could carry and run to the local tower when warnings of approaching Vikings were sounded. The ladder to the entrance would be pulled in by the last person to enter.

Use the diagram of the tower to answer 1–6.

1. How many stories high was the tower?

2. How high off the ground was the entrance?

3. How thick were the walls at the entrance?

4. How tall was the tower?

5. What was the circumference of the tower at the entrance? Round to the nearest tenth.

★ 6. How many cubic feet of space were there in the tower?

In the first century B.C., the Chinese Emperor Wu Ti had a castle built to float on water. More than 2,000 people were housed on it.

7. The square float the castle was on measured 600 ft on a side. How many square feet did the float occupy?

8. A Manhattan brownstone may measure 25 ft wide by 30 ft long. How many feet would a brownstone with these dimensions occupy?

9. How many brownstones, each 25 ft wide by 30 ft long, would have fit on Emperor Wu Ti's floating fortress?

10. Draw a diagram showing how the brownstones would fit side by side on the floating fortress.

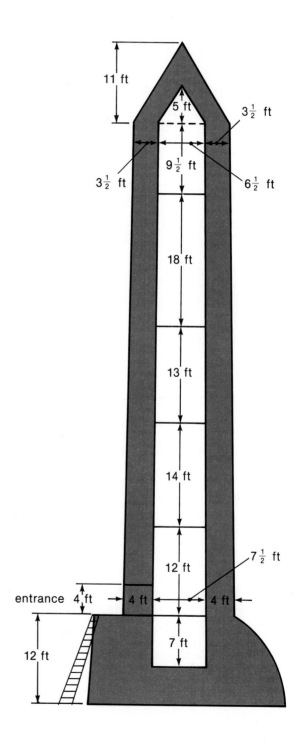

364

The Great Wall of China was built about 200 B.C. by Emperor Ch'in Shih Huang Ti. It is estimated that 1,500,000 workers constructed it. When completed, this stone wall stretched 2,500 miles. It was about 20 ft wide and 20 ft high.

11. How many square feet of stone lined the top surface of the Great Wall?

12. To the nearest tenth, how many square miles of stone lined the top surface of the Great Wall? (1 mile = 5,280 feet)

13. How many cubic feet of stone were used to build the Great Wall?

14. On the average there was a tower every 250 yd along the wall. On the average how many towers were there every mile?

15. About how many towers were there in all along the Great Wall?

SOMETHING EXTRA

STRATEGY GAME

Here is a game for two people—Circular Tic-tac-toe. To play, make a copy of the game board at the right. Follow the rules below.

1. The first player puts an *X* in any space.

2. The second player puts an *O* in any empty space.

3. Players continue alternating turns until one player gets four marks in a winning path. Winning paths are shown below. A winning path may *not* cross the center of the board.

straight path

curved path

spiral path

4. If no one gets four marks in a winning path, the game is a draw.

Construct congruent figures. pages 344–345

1. Use a ruler to draw a segment with length 4.5 cm. Then use a straightedge and compass to construct a congruent segment.

2. Use a protractor to draw an angle with measure 85°. Then use a straightedge and compass to construct a congruent angle.

Trace each figure. Use a straightedge and compass to bisect it. pages 344–345

3.

4.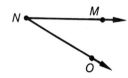

5.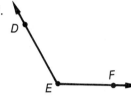

Construct the following. pages 346–347

6. Trace the figure at the right. Construct a line perpendicular to $\overleftrightarrow{JK}$ through K. Then construct a line parallel to $\overleftrightarrow{JK}$ through B.

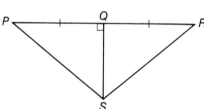

Tell why the triangles in each pair are congruent. Write *side-side-side*, *side-angle-side*, or *angle-side-angle*. pages 348–349

7.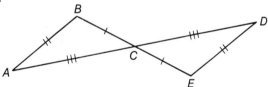

8.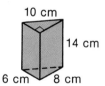

Find the surface area and the volume. Use 3.14 for π. Round to the nearest one. pages 352–361

9.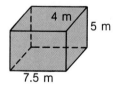
4 m 5 m 7.5 m

10.
10 cm 14 cm 6 cm 8 cm

11.
7 cm 11 cm

Complete. pages 362–363

12. $143 \text{ cm}^3 = \_\_\_ \text{ mL}$

13. $6.42 \text{ L} = \_\_\_ \text{ dm}^3$

14. $59 \text{ mL} = \_\_\_ \text{ cm}^3$

Solve. pages 350–351, 364–365

15. Travel costs per mile are 7¢ by car, 3¢ by bus, and 40¢ by plane. The same distance is traveled on each vehicle for a total cost of $25. How much is spent for each kind of transportation? Guess and test to solve.

CHAPTER TEST

Construct congruent figures.

1. Use a ruler to draw a segment with length 60 mm. Then use a straightedge and compass to construct a congruent segment.

2. Use a protractor to draw an angle with measure 110°. Then use a straightedge and compass to construct a congruent angle.

Trace each figure. Use a straightedge and compass to bisect it.

3.

4.

5.

Construct the following.

6. Trace the figure at the right. Construct a line perpendicular to $\overleftrightarrow{DE}$ through F. Then construct a line parallel to $\overleftrightarrow{DE}$ through G.

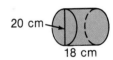

Tell why the triangles in each pair are congruent. Write *side-side-side, side-angle-side,* **or** *angle-side-angle.*

7.

8.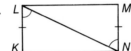

Find the surface area for 9–11 and the volume for 12–14. Use 3.14 for π. Round to the nearest one.

9.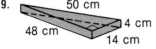

50 cm, 4 cm, 48 cm, 14 cm

10.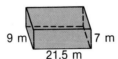

9 m, 7 m, 21.5 m

11.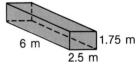

20 cm, 18 cm

12.

10 cm, 12 cm

13.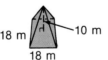

18 m, 10 m, 18 m

14.

6 m, 1.75 m, 2.5 m

Complete.

15. $11.2 \text{ mL} = \underline{\quad} \text{ cm}^3$

16. $700 \text{ dm}^3 = \underline{\quad} \text{ L}$

17. $400 \text{ cm}^3 = \underline{\quad} \text{ mL}$

18. 12 L of water weighs _____ kg.

19. 6 cm^3 of water weighs _____ g.

Solve.

20. A gardener has 10 boards of equal size to use. How can he enclose 5 colonial herb gardens of equal size?

A bucket has a diameter of 10 cm and a height of 15 cm. Can it hold 12 liters of water?

PATTERN FOLDING

Copy each pattern below. Cut out your copy. Fold along the
dashed lines and tape to form a 3-dimensional space figure.

1.

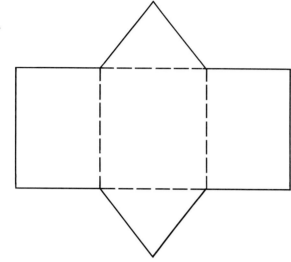

2.

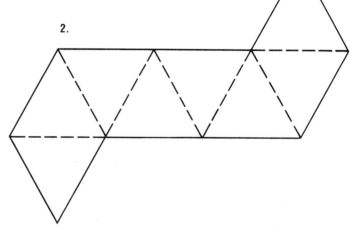

3. Draw a pattern for this figure. Cut it out,
fold it, and tape it.

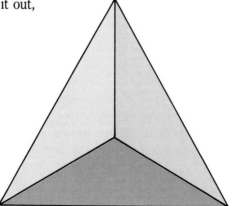

SPHERES

A **sphere** is a space figure with all points the same distance from a point called the **center**. The distance from the center to a point on the sphere is the **radius**.

▶The surface area of a sphere with radius r is $4\pi r^2$.

▶The volume of a sphere with radius r is $\frac{4}{3}\pi r^3$.

Think of a plane passing through the center of a sphere. The intersection of the sphere and the plane is a **great circle** of the sphere. The radius of a great circle is the same as the radius of the sphere.

1. The Unisphere symbolized the theme of the New York World's Fair (1964–1965), "Peace Through Understanding." The Unisphere is 40 m in diameter. How much space does it occupy? Round to the nearest cubic meter.

2. Find the circumference of a great circle of the Unisphere. Round to the nearest meter.

3. The Atomium symbolized the theme of the Brussels World's Fair (1958), "Nuclear Energy for Peace." Its nine aluminum spheres are each about 18 m in diameter. Find the total surface area of all nine spheres. Round to the nearest square meter.

Atomium

Unisphere

MAINTAINING SKILLS

Choose the correct answers. Write A, B, C, or D.

1. Which ratio is equal to $\frac{7}{10}$?

   A $\frac{14}{15}$ C $\frac{35}{40}$

   B $\frac{21}{30}$ D not given

2. Solve. $\frac{14}{21} = \frac{24}{n}$

   A $n = 36$ C $n = 16$
   B $n = 3$ D not given

3. What is 125% of 56?

   A 14   C 70
   B 67.2   D not given

4. $66\frac{2}{3}$% of what number is 42?

   A 28   C 126
   B 63   D not given

5. $^-17 + {}^-21$

   A $^-4$ C 38
   B 4   D not given

6. $^-48 - 12$

   A $^-60$ C $^-7$
   B $^-36$ D not given

7. $^-49 \div 7$

   A $^-343$ C 36
   B 7   D not given

8. Jill has a batting average of 0.295. To the nearest one, how many hits would you expect her to get in 25 times at bat?

   A 20   C 10
   B 7   D not given

9. What is the range of the data: 7; 3.04; 16.4; and 5.2?

   A 7.91   C 13.36
   B 6.1   D not given

10. How many choices of a hat and a scarf are there with 5 hats and 3 scarves?

    A 8   C 30
    B 15   D not given

11. What is the surface area of a cube 2.2 m on a side?

    A 19.36 m²   C 14.52 m²
    B 29.04 m²   D not given

12. Complete. 7 cm³ = ___ mL

    A 70,000   C 700
    B 7   D not given

13. What rule of congruence applies?

    A ASA   C SAS
    B SSS   D not given

Solve.

14. Which statement cannot be true?

    Trudy drives to work.
    Trudy attends classes part-time.
    Trudy likes tennis.
    Trudy is ___.

    A in school at night   C 13 years old
    B on the swimming team   D not given

15. *ABCD* is a quadrilateral. m∠ *ABC* is 90°. $\overline{AB}$ is not parallel to $\overline{CD}$. What is the only statement that could be true? *ABCD* is ___.

    A a rectangle   C a trapezoid
    B a parallelogram   D not given

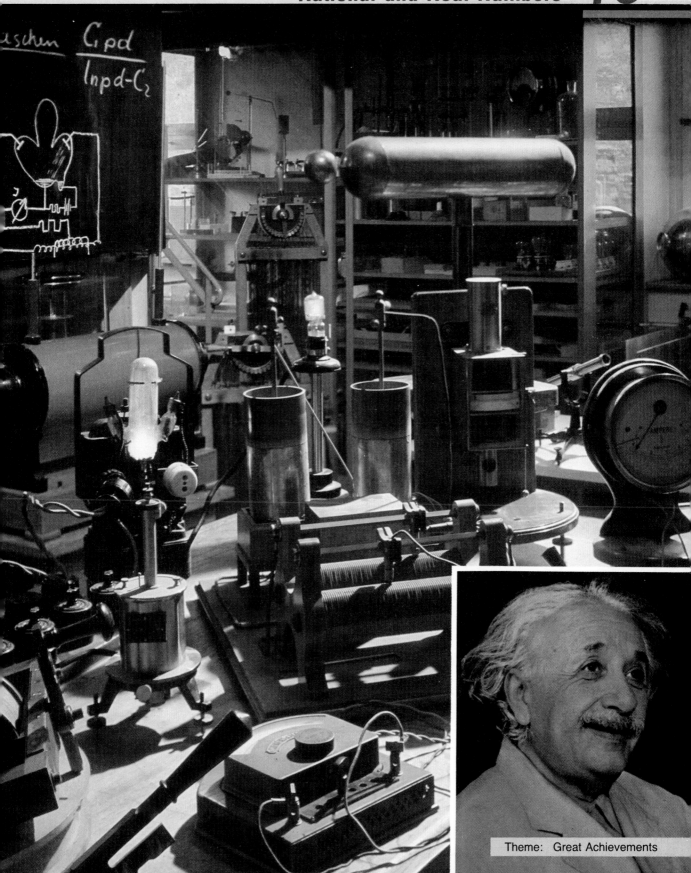

Theme: Great Achievements

Writing and Comparing Rational Numbers

Chuck Yaeger was the first person to fly faster than the speed of sound (Mach 1). In 1947, Yaeger flew a Bell XS-1 rocket plane at a speed of Mach 1.02. In an earlier flight he had reached the speed of Mach 0.94.

1.02 and 0.94 are rational numbers.

▶A **rational number** is any number that can be expressed as the quotient of two integers where the divisor is not 0.

$$1.02 = \frac{102}{100} \qquad 0.94 = \frac{94}{100}$$

Another way to think of rational numbers is as all the positive fractions, their opposites, and zero.

Rational numbers can be shown on a number line.

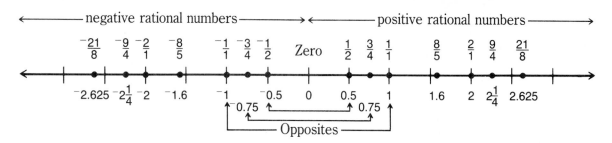

Rational numbers on a number line increase in value from left to right.

$$\frac{^-9}{4} < \frac{^-3}{4} \qquad \frac{^-3}{4} < \frac{3}{4} \qquad \frac{3}{4} < \frac{9}{4} \qquad ^-1.6 < 0 \qquad 0 < 1.6 \qquad 1.6 < 2$$

CLASSWORK

Write each as the quotient of two integers in lowest terms.

1. 7 **2.** $^-1.2$ **3.** $2\frac{3}{5}$ **4.** $^-1\frac{1}{3}$ **5.** 6.25 **6.** $^-0.12$

Write the opposite of each.

7. $\frac{^-1}{4}$ **8.** 0.875 **9.** $\frac{^-6}{5}$ **10.** $3\frac{1}{4}$ **11.** $^-8.7$ **12.** 17.32

Compare. Use <, >, or = for each ⬤.

13. $\frac{1}{4}$ ⬤ $\frac{^-5}{4}$ **14.** $\frac{^-4}{10}$ ⬤ $\frac{^-2}{5}$ **15.** $^-1.2$ ⬤ 2.7 **16.** $^-0.5$ ⬤ $^-0.2$

PRACTICE

Write each as the quotient of two integers in lowest terms.

1. 3   **2.** ⁻5   **3.** ⁻1   **4.** $1\frac{1}{4}$ **5.** $^-2\frac{1}{2}$

6. ⁻0.3   **7.** 1.5   **8.** $^-5\frac{3}{8}$ **9.** ⁻0.27   **10.** ⁻0.6

Write the opposite of each.

11. $\frac{1}{5}$ **12.** $\frac{^-1}{3}$ **13.** $\frac{^-7}{3}$ **14.** 0.25   **15.** ⁻5.8

Compare. Use <, >, or = for each ⬤.

16. $\frac{^-3}{8}$ ⬤ $\frac{^-5}{8}$ **17.** $\frac{^-1}{4}$ ⬤ $\frac{3}{4}$ **18.** $^-1\frac{1}{5}$ ⬤ $^-1\frac{2}{5}$ **19.** $3\frac{1}{8}$ ⬤ $4\frac{1}{2}$

20. ⁻0.4 ⬤ ⁻0.1   **21.** ⁻0.3 ⬤ ⁻0.7   **22.** ⁻7.2 ⬤ 6.5   **23.** 0.5 ⬤ 0.50

24. $^-6\frac{3}{8}$ ⬤ $^-6\frac{6}{16}$ **25.** ⁻0.25 ⬤ ⁻0.6   **26.** ⁻5.75 ⬤ ⁻5.4   **27.** $\frac{^-1}{2}$ ⬤ ⁻0.5

Write each in lowest terms. Write *positive*, *negative*, or *neither*.

28. $\frac{^-3}{15}$ **29.** $-\frac{100}{24}$ **30.** $\frac{^-4}{8}$ **31.** $\frac{0}{^-5}$ **32.** $\frac{^-64}{^-16}$

Write in order from least to greatest.

★ **33.** $\frac{1}{2}$, $^-1\frac{3}{5}$, $^-1\frac{1}{2}$, $\frac{3}{5}$ ★ **34.** 0.5; ⁻0.55; 0.55; ⁻0.05

APPLICATION

35. The official air-speed record is 1.5 times as fast as the cruising speed of the Concorde. Write 1.5 as the quotient of two integers in lowest terms.

36. The official air-speed record is 2,193.17 mph. Write the air-speed record as an improper fraction.

═══ VISUAL THINKING ═══

Match each fraction-coded shape with its identical decimal-coded shape.

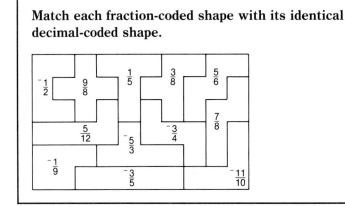

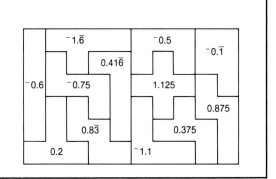

373

Adding and Subtracting Rational Numbers

When a great achievement is announced in a field, such as aerospace, the stocks of companies in that field show a gain. A share of General Aerospace dropped $\frac{1}{2}$ in the morning but rose $\frac{7}{8}$ in the afternoon. What was the total change for the day?

Add to find the total. $\quad \frac{-1}{2} + \frac{7}{8}$

To add or subtract rational numbers, follow the rules for adding and subtracting integers.

First write equivalent fractions using the LCD.

$$\frac{-1}{2} + \frac{7}{8} = \frac{-4}{8} + \frac{7}{8}$$

Think To add a positive and a negative rational number, subtract the smaller absolute value from the larger. Use the sign of the number with the larger absolute value.

$$\left|\frac{7}{8}\right| - \left|\frac{-4}{8}\right| = \frac{3}{8}$$

$$\frac{-4}{8} + \frac{7}{8} = \frac{3}{8}$$

The total change for the day was a gain of $\frac{3}{8}$.

More Examples

a. $\ ^-8.4 + \ ^-10.3 = \ ^-18.7$

b. $3 - \frac{-5}{8} = 3 + \frac{5}{8} = 3\frac{5}{8}$ ⟵ $(+) - (-) = (+) + (+)$

Think To subtract a rational number, add its opposite.

c. $\ ^-0.45 - 0.73 = \ ^-0.45 + \ ^-0.73 = \ ^-1.18$ ⟵ $(-) - (+) = (-) + (-)$

CLASSWORK

Add or subtract.

1. $\frac{4}{5} + \frac{-2}{5}$

2. $\frac{-2}{3} + \frac{-2}{3}$

3. $^-1\frac{3}{4} - \frac{1}{4}$

4. $\frac{3}{2} - \frac{-3}{4}$

5. $\ ^-1.2 + 1.2$

6. $\ ^-3.7 + \ ^-5.4$

7. $\ ^-3.7 - 8.2$

8. $8.9 - 10.1$

PRACTICE

Add or subtract.

1. $1\frac{3}{5} + \frac{4}{5}$

2. $\frac{^-5}{6} + \frac{^-1}{6}$

3. $\frac{7}{4} - \frac{9}{4}$

4. $\frac{5}{8} - \frac{^-9}{8}$

5. $\frac{^-1}{3} + \frac{2}{3}$

6. $\frac{5}{8} + \frac{^-7}{8}$

7. $^-1\frac{1}{3} - \frac{2}{3}$

8. $\frac{^-3}{4} + \frac{3}{4}$

9. $\frac{3}{8} - \frac{^-1}{2}$

10. $\frac{^-1}{2} - \frac{^-1}{4}$

11. $^-1\frac{1}{2} + \frac{^-1}{4}$

12. $2 - 2\frac{1}{4}$

13. $^-0.6 + ^-3.1$

14. $^-1.7 + 1.9$

15. $^-0.1 - 2.4$

16. $^-1.8 - ^-3.9$

17. $6.4 + ^-6.4$

18. $4.5 + ^-2.9$

19. $0 - 1.8$

20. $^-2.7 + 1.6$

21. $^-0.9 + ^-0.8$

22. $^-6.7 + ^-2.5$

23. $^-3.4 - ^-0.7$

24. $22.8 - 36.1$

25. $^-5.23 + 5.23$

26. $\frac{1}{4} + \frac{^-4}{16}$

27. $^-0.3 + ^-0.5$

28. $^-0.8 + ^-2.4$

★ 29. $^-2\frac{1}{3} + \left(1\frac{2}{3} - \frac{^-2}{3}\right)$

★ 30. $\frac{^-3}{4} - \left(\frac{^-5}{4} - \frac{^-7}{2}\right)$

★ 31. $3.4 - ^-2.3 + ^-7.8$

★ 32. $8.19 - ^-3.07 + ^-6.41$

★ 33. START $+ \frac{^-7}{8}$ $+ 2\frac{3}{4}$ $+ \frac{^-5}{8}$ STOP

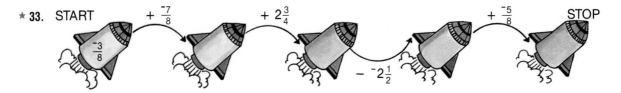

$\frac{^-3}{8}$ $- ^-2\frac{1}{2}$

APPLICATION

34. Unitech stock opened at $37\frac{3}{8}$. At the end of the day, the stock was down $2\frac{3}{4}$. What was the final selling price?

★ **35.** Space Industries stock opened at $43\frac{1}{2}$ on Wednesday morning. It closed down $7\frac{1}{8}$. On Thursday the stock gained $2\frac{3}{4}$, and on Friday it gained $1\frac{3}{8}$. What was the final price?

CALCULATOR

If your calculator has a change-of-sign key, $\boxed{^+/_-}$, use it to enter negative rational numbers.

Press $\boxed{0}\boxed{\cdot}\boxed{7}\boxed{^+/_-}$

Display $\boxed{-\quad\quad 0.7}$

Add. $^-0.7 + 1.5$ **Press** $\boxed{0}\boxed{\cdot}\boxed{7}\boxed{^+/_-}\boxed{+}\boxed{1}\boxed{\cdot}\boxed{5}\boxed{=}$ Display $\boxed{\quad\quad 0.8}$

Subtract. $^-2.1 - ^-4.3$ **Press** $\boxed{2}\boxed{\cdot}\boxed{1}\boxed{^+/_-}\boxed{-}\boxed{4}\boxed{\cdot}\boxed{3}\boxed{^+/_-}\boxed{=}$ Display $\boxed{\quad\quad 2.2}$

Calculate.

1. $^-1.6 + 4.2$

2. $3.1 + ^-2.8$

3. $^-3.9 + 2.6$

4. $7.3 + ^-10.6$

5. $^-5 - 1.3$

6. $7.8 - 3.9$

7. $^-1.2 - 6.6$

8. $^-68.3 - ^-31.92$

Multiplying and Dividing Rational Numbers

In 1953 the bathyscaphe *Trieste*, a ship used for deep-sea exploration, descended to a depth of about 10,240 feet. In 1960 the explorer Jacques Piccard and United States Navy Lieutenant Don Walsh dove the *Trieste* 3.5 times as deep in the Pacific Ocean. How deep did the *Trieste* go in 1960?

Multiply to find the depth.

$$^-10{,}240 \cdot 3.5$$

To multiply or divide rational numbers, follow the rules for multiplying and dividing integers.

$$^-10{,}240 \cdot 3.5 = {}^-35{,}840$$

$$(-) \cdot (+) = (-)$$

The *Trieste* descended to a depth of about 35,840 feet.

More Examples

a. $\dfrac{^-2}{5} \cdot \dfrac{^-3}{7} = \dfrac{6}{35}$ ← $(-) \cdot (-) = (+)$

b. $2.6 \cdot 6.7 = 17.42$ ← $(+) \cdot (+) = (+)$

c. $\dfrac{^-1}{2} \div {}^-1\dfrac{2}{3}$ ← $(-) \div (-) = (+)$

$$= \dfrac{^-1}{2} \div \dfrac{^-5}{3}$$

$$= \dfrac{^-1}{2} \cdot \dfrac{^-3}{5} = \dfrac{3}{10}$$

↑ —— **Think** Multiply by the reciprocal of $\dfrac{^-5}{3}$.

d.
$$\begin{array}{r} ^-9.4 \leftarrow (+) \div (-) = (-) \\ ^-2.3\overline{)21.6\,2} \\ \underline{20\ 7} \\ 9\ 2 \\ \underline{9\ 2} \\ 0 \end{array}$$

CLASSWORK

Multiply or divide.

1. $\dfrac{^-4}{5} \cdot \dfrac{1}{4}$

2. $^-2 \cdot \dfrac{^-3}{4}$

3. $9 \div \dfrac{^-3}{4}$

4. $\dfrac{^-1}{6} \div \dfrac{^-1}{4}$

5. $0.7 \cdot {}^-1.5$

6. $^-1.7 \cdot {}^-20$

7. $^-1.2 \div 1.2$

8. $^-7.2 \div {}^-1.5$

9. $0 \div \dfrac{^-3}{8}$

10. $^-4.8\overline{)\,^-0.6}$

11. $^-1\dfrac{3}{5} \div {}^-3\dfrac{1}{5}$

12. $^-6 \cdot 3\dfrac{1}{2}$

376

Multiply or divide.

1. $\dfrac{-1}{3} \cdot \dfrac{1}{5}$

2. $\dfrac{1}{4} \cdot \dfrac{-1}{2}$

3. $2\dfrac{2}{3} \cdot {}^-1\dfrac{1}{2}$

4. $\dfrac{-1}{5} \cdot {}^-5$

5. $\dfrac{4}{5} \div \dfrac{-4}{3}$

6. $\dfrac{3}{4} \div 9$

7. $\dfrac{-1}{2} \div {}^-2$

8. $0 \div \dfrac{-5}{8}$

9. $\dfrac{-7}{8} \cdot \dfrac{-8}{7}$

10. $4\dfrac{1}{2} \cdot {}^-2$

11. ${}^-5 \div 1\dfrac{2}{3}$

12. $\dfrac{-3}{5} \div {}^-1\dfrac{1}{2}$

13. ${}^-0.5 \cdot 1.2$

14. ${}^-0.8 \cdot {}^-0.9$

15. $7.6 \cdot {}^-0.7$

16. ${}^-3.4 \cdot 0$

17. ${}^-21.7 \div 7$

18. ${}^-18.9 \div {}^-9$

19. ${}^-225 \div 1.5$

20. ${}^-0.72 \div {}^-0.8$

21. $0.5 \cdot {}^-0.5$

22. ${}^-1.2 \div 0.6$

23. ${}^-200 \cdot 3.2$

24. ${}^-7.5 \cdot {}^-0.8$

★ 25. $\dfrac{1}{2} \cdot \left({}^-6 \div \dfrac{1}{3}\right)$

★ 26. ${}^-3.4 \cdot {}^-0.1 \cdot {}^-20$

★ 27. $\left(\dfrac{-1}{2} + \dfrac{-1}{2}\right) \cdot \left(\dfrac{3}{4} - \dfrac{-1}{4}\right)$

Follow the rule, if given, to find each missing number.

Rule: Multiply by $\dfrac{-1}{2}$.

	Input	Output
28.	$\dfrac{1}{2}$	
29.		0
30.	$\dfrac{-1}{2}$	
31.		${}^-2$

Rule: Divide by ${}^-0.2$.

	Input	Output
32.	0.2	
33.	0	
34.	${}^-1$	
35.		4

Find the rule.

	Input	Output
★ 36.	${}^-0.2$	0.1
	$\dfrac{1}{6}$	$\dfrac{1}{12}$
	2.6	1.3
	${}^-7$	$\dfrac{7}{2}$

APPLICATION

37. The deepest cave in the United States is the Neffs Canyon cave in Utah. Its deepest point is about 1,170 feet below the entrance. One of the deepest caves in the world is the Pierre Saint-Martin cave on the border of France and Spain. It is about 3.7 times as deep as the Neffs Canyon cave. How deep is the Pierre Saint-Martin cave?

38. A textbook is opened at random. To what pages is it opened if the product of the facing page numbers is 3,192?

ESTIMATION

Estimate each answer. Then use a calculator to find the exact answer. Use the estimate to check.

1. $25.638 + {}^-37.542$

2. $131.649 \div {}^-21$

3. ${}^-16.258 \cdot {}^-3.2$

4. ${}^-7.9 \cdot {}^-6.384 + 2.987$

5. $(10.981 - 16.3) \div {}^-4.5$

6. ${}^-12.1 \div 3.9 \cdot {}^-2.1$

Problem Solving

MAKING AND USING GRAPHS

Graphs can be used to organize facts in a problem. A graph provides a picture of what has taken place.

The United States Postal Service has been a great achievement in the field of communications. It is one of the world's largest organizations. The cost of first-class mail is directly related to its weight. In 1986 the cost of a letter that weighs up to and including one ounce is 22¢. Each additional ounce or less up to 12 ounces costs 17¢. Mrs. Russell has a letter that weighs $4\frac{1}{2}$ ounces. How much postage is required?

Postage is 22¢ for the first ounce and 17¢ for each additional ounce or less.

Make a graph of the postage for first-class letters.
Show weight on the horizontal axis and cost on the vertical axis.

The graph is a series of "steps" as shown. Note that you cannot have a letter that weighs 0 ounces. On the graph the circle is not part of the step. The solid dot is part of the step.

Find $4\frac{1}{2}$ ounces on the horizontal axis. Then find the step for $4\frac{1}{2}$ ounces on the graph. The vertical axis shows that the cost is 90¢. It will cost Mrs. Russell 90¢ to mail her letter.

Check and make sure that the graph was drawn and read correctly.

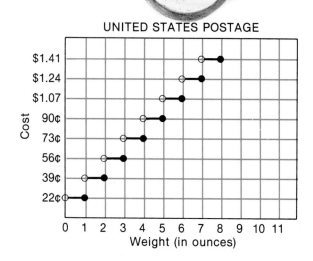

UNITED STATES POSTAGE

PRACTICE

Solve. Use the graph on page 378 for 1–4.

1. How much would it cost to mail a letter that weighs $3\frac{2}{3}$ ounces?

2. How much would it cost to mail a letter that weighs exactly 5 oz?

3. What is the weight of a letter that costs 56¢ to mail?

4. What is the weight of a letter that costs $1.58 to mail?

The invention of the paper cup was a great public health achievement. Previously, people shared a single metal cup at public drinking fountains. The graph shows the cost of a paper cup over the years.

5. With what year does the graph begin?

6. In what year did a paper cup cost 5¢?

7. How much did a paper cup cost in 1960?

8. During what 10-year period did the cost of a paper cup change the most?

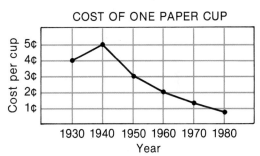

COST OF ONE PAPER CUP

The invention of the automobile was a great achievement in the field of transportation. Some automobiles are used as taxicabs. In Nova City, taxi fares are $1.20 for the first $\frac{1}{5}$ of a mile and 20¢ for each additional $\frac{1}{5}$ of a mile or less.

9. Make a graph like the one on page 378 to show fares for up to $2\frac{1}{5}$ mi.

10. Mr. Jones took a taxi for $\frac{4}{5}$ of a mile. How much did he pay?

11. Lisa took a taxi for $2\frac{1}{5}$ miles. How much did she pay?

12. Mike and his father paid $2.60 for taxi fare. How far did they travel?

CREATE YOUR OWN PROBLEM

Write two problems using the information shown on this graph.

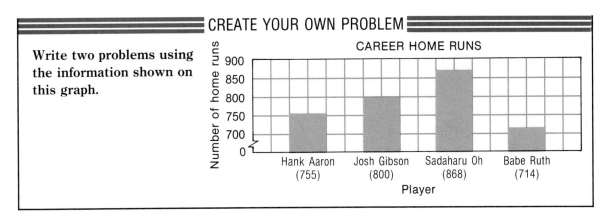

CAREER HOME RUNS

Powers of 10

Many scientists contributed to the development of the electron microscope. Electron microscopes enable scientists to see tiny specimens, such as viruses. Some viruses are only 0.000001, or 10^{-6}, centimeter in size.

▶Negative integer exponents express numbers less than 1 but greater than 0.

Study this pattern.

$10^2 = \frac{10^3}{10^1} = 100$
As the exponent decreases, the number is decreased by dividing by 10.

$10^1 = \frac{10^2}{10^1} = 10$

$10^0 = \frac{10^1}{10^1} = 1$
For any number n except 0, $n^0 = 1$.

$10^{-1} = \frac{10^0}{10^1} = \frac{1}{10^1} = 0.1$

$10^{-2} = \frac{10^{-1}}{10^1} = \frac{1}{10^2} = 0.01$

To write a negative power of 10 as a decimal, look at the exponent. The absolute value of the exponent tells how many decimal places there are.

$10^{-2} = 0.01$

▶For any integer n, $10^{-n} = \frac{1}{10^n}$. $\qquad 10^{-3} = \frac{1}{10^3} \qquad 10^{-8} = \frac{1}{10^8}$

To multiply powers of 10, add the exponents.

a. $10^1 \cdot 10^2 = 10^{1+2} = 10^3 = 1{,}000$ $\qquad$ **b.** $10^{-1} \cdot 10^3 = 10^{-1+3} = 10^2 = 100$

To divide powers of 10, subtract the exponents.

c. $10^5 \div 10^3 = 10^{5-3} = 10^2 = 100$ $\qquad$ **d.** $10^{-2} \div 10^3 = 10^{-2-3} = 10^{-5} = 0.00001$

CLASSWORK

Write each as a decimal.

1. 10^{-3} $\qquad$ **2.** 10^{-5} $\qquad$ **3.** $\frac{1}{10^2}$ $\qquad$ **4.** $\frac{1}{10^4}$

Write each as a single power of 10.

5. 0.0001 $\qquad$ **6.** 100,000,000 $\qquad$ **7.** 0.1 $\qquad$ **8.** 10,000

9. $10^4 \div 10^5$ $\qquad$ **10.** $10^4 \div 10^{-5}$ $\qquad$ **11.** $10^5 \cdot 10^1$ $\qquad$ **12.** $10^{-7} \div 10^{-1}$

Write each in standard form.

1. 10^{-2} 2. $\frac{1}{10}$ 3. 10^{-4} 4. $\frac{1}{10^3}$

5. $\frac{1}{10^6}$ 6. 10^{-1} 7. $\frac{1}{10^2}$ 8. 10^{-7}

9. 10^0 10. 10^4 11. $\frac{1}{10^4}$ 12. 10^{-8}

Write each as a single power of 10.

13. 1,000   14. 1,000,000,000   15. 100,000

16. 0.001   17. 0.00001   18. 0.01

19. $10^3 \div 10^{-4}$ 20. $10^{-7} \div 10^2$ 21. $10^5 \cdot 10^{-8}$

22. $10^7 \cdot 10^{-4}$ 23. $10^6 \cdot 10^{-6}$ 24. $10^{-6} \cdot 10^{-2}$

25. $\frac{10^{11}}{10^6}$ 26. $\frac{10^{-4}}{10^{-1}}$ 27. $\frac{10^{-2}}{10^{-3}}$

28. $\frac{10^{12}}{10^{-6}}$ 29. $\frac{10^{-4}}{10^4}$ 30. $1,000 \cdot 10$

31. $1,000,000 \div 10^{-1}$ 32. $10^{-4} \div 10,000$

★ 33. $\frac{10^4 \cdot 10^{-5}}{10^{-4}}$ ★ 34. $10^{-2} \cdot 10^3 \div 10^{-1}$

★ 35. $10^{-2} \div 10 \div 10^{-6}$ ★ 36. $10^0 \cdot 10^0 \div 10^0$

★ 37. $\frac{10^{12} \cdot 10^{-6} \cdot 10^2}{10^9}$ ★ 38. $\frac{10^7 \cdot 10^3 \cdot 10^{-6}}{10^9 \div 10^{-3}}$

APPLICATION

39. The diameter of an influenza virus is about 0.00001 mm. Write the diameter in centimeters, using a power of 10.

40. A certain cell has a diameter of 0.0025 centimeter. If 1,000 of these cells were lined up next to each other on a microscope slide, what would the total length be?

★ 41. What would the total length be if 600 cells, each 0.0025 cm wide, were lined up?

★ 42. A group of scientists bought $70,000 worth of equipment. When the bill came, it was for $70. By what power of 10 was the bill misstated?

Scientific Notation

A Scottish chemist, Sir William Ramsay, discovered the chemical element helium in 1895. For his work on gases, Ramsay received the 1904 Nobel Prize for chemistry. It is estimated that helium makes up only about 0.00000005, or 5×10^{-8}, of the earth's atmosphere.

A number between 0 and 1 can be written in **scientific notation** as a product of two factors. The first factor is a number from 1 to 10. The second factor is a negative power of 10 in exponent form.

Write 0.00000005 in scientific notation.

• Find the first factor by moving the decimal point to the right of the first nonzero digit.

0.00000005

8 places

• Write the second factor as a negative power of 10. Use the number of places the decimal point was moved as the exponent.

10^{-8}

• Write the number as the product of these two factors.

$0.00000005 = 5 \times 10^{-8}$

To change a number written in scientific notation to its standard form, multiply the factors.

$$7.3 \times 10^{-4} = 7.3 \times 0.0001$$
$$= 0.00073$$

Think The decimal point moves 4 places to the left.

More Examples

a. $0.0000017 = 1.7 \times 10^{-6}$ **b.** $3.6 \times 10^{-3} = 0.0036$ **c.** $1.02 \times 10^{-2} = 0.0102$

CLASSWORK

Write each in scientific notation.

1. 0.007   **2.** 0.0064   **3.** 0.000009   **4.** 0.00813

5. 0.000000202   **6.** 0.000000055   **7.** 0.0001   **8.** 0.00000101

Write in standard form.

9. 2×10^{-2} **10.** 4.7×10^{-5} **11.** 3.98×10^{-6} **12.** 1.05×10^{-5}

13. 1.1×10^{-6} **14.** 2.01×10^{-3} **15.** 6.66×10^{-5} **16.** 4.003×10^{-2}

PRACTICE

Find each missing exponent.

1. $0.05 = 5 \times 10^{\square}$
2. $0.00008 = 8 \times 10^{\square}$
3. $0.00061 = 6.1 \times 10^{\square}$
4. $0.0000077 = 7.7 \times 10^{\square}$
5. $0.00429 = 4.29 \times 10^{\square}$
6. $0.00000123 = 1.23 \times 10^{\square}$

Find each missing factor.

7. $0.02 = \square \times 10^{-2}$
8. $0.00009 = \square \times 10^{-5}$
9. $0.000753 = \square \times 10^{-4}$
10. $0.00404 = \square \times 10^{-3}$
11. $0.8642 = \square \times 10^{-1}$
12. $0.000000333 = \square \times 10^{-7}$

Write each in scientific notation.

13. 0.07
14. 0.0009
15. 0.0000004
16. 0.00063
17. 0.000051
18. 0.0000028
19. 0.00987
20. 0.000113
21. 0.00000006037
22. 5 ten-thousandths
23. 8 millionths
★24. 211 ten-millionths

Write in standard form.

25. 6×10^{-3}
26. 7×10^{-7}
27. 8.5×10^{-5}
28. 4.73×10^{-6}
29. 5.062×10^{-4}
30. 9.9909×10^{-8}

APPLICATION

31. An English chemist, Henry Cavendish, discovered hydrogen in 1766. The atomic mass of hydrogen is 0.00000000000000000000001675. Write the number in scientific notation.

32. The diameter of a hydrogen atom is 6.4×10^{-7} centimeter. Write the number in standard form.

33. The diameter of an oxygen atom is 1.4×10^{-7} centimeter. Write the number in standard form.

Mixed Practice

1. $^-6 + 8$
2. $^-6 + {}^-7$
3. $17 + {}^-12$
4. $41 - 13$
5. $79 - {}^-16$
6. $^-51 - 40$
7. $5 \cdot 5$
8. $^-7 \cdot {}^-15$
9. $^-3 \cdot 12$
10. $12 \div 3$
11. $^-12 \div 3$
12. $^-16 \div {}^-4$

Write as a percent or a decimal.

13. $\frac{1}{4}$
14. $\frac{3}{5}$
15. $\frac{5}{2}$
16. $\frac{1}{50}$
17. 35%
18. 135%
19. 54%
20. 4%

Real Numbers

One of civilization's greatest achievements was the Sumerians' invention of the wheel about 5,000 years ago. The circumference of any wheel is equal to the product of its diameter and the number π.

π is an irrational number. π = 3.14159.... In decimal form an **irrational number** is nonterminating and nonrepeating.

Rational Numbers
Decimal form ⟶ terminating or repeating
Examples ⟶ 1   5.3̄   7.6   3   0

Irrational Numbers
Decimal form ⟶ nonterminating, nonrepeating
Examples ⟶ 1.4142...   6.1123...

▶The rational numbers and the irrational numbers together form the **real numbers.**

Every number on the number line is either rational or irrational.

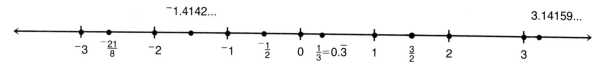

The real numbers completely fill the number line, that is, the real numbers are **complete.**

▶Between any two real numbers, there is always another real number. This is the **property of density.**

Find a real number between 1.2 and 1.3. $\frac{1.2 + 1.3}{2} = \frac{2.5}{2} = 1.25$

1.25 is a real number between 1.2 and 1.3.
Other real numbers between 1.2 and 1.3 are 1.2̄, 1.27, and 1.289.

CLASSWORK

Classify each. Write the terms that apply: *integer, rational, irrational,* **and** *real.*

1. ⁻1

2. $\frac{1}{4}$

3. 4

4. 1.14...

5. 1.21

Find a real number between each two numbers.

6. 2.5 and 2.6

7. 0.4 and 0.5

8. ⁻1.1 and ⁻1.2

9. ⁻0.65 and ⁻0.66

PRACTICE

Copy the charts. Classify each number.

		Integer	Rational	Irrational	Real
1.	-26				
2.	1.7320508...				
3.	2.2360679...				
4.	2,011				

		Integer	Rational	Irrational	Real
5.	$\frac{3}{4}$				
6.	$-1\frac{1}{2}$				
7.	0				
8.	$\frac{9}{2}$				

Write *true* or *false* for each.

9. All integers are rational numbers.

10. All rational numbers are integers.

11. No terminating decimals are rational numbers.

12. All repeating decimals are rational numbers.

13. All integers are real numbers.

14. All irrational numbers are real numbers.

15. All real numbers are rational numbers.

16. All rational numbers are real numbers.

Find a real number between each two numbers.

17. 3.8 and 3.9

18. 0.7 and 0.8

19. -2.3 and -2.4

20. -0.35 and -0.36

21. 10.1 and 10.2

22. -5.2 and -5.3

23. 0.456 and 0.457

24. -0.088 and -0.089

25. Can another integer be found between 3 and 4? between -7 and -8? between 155 and 156? Do the integers have the property of density?

⋆ 26. Use *real numbers, rational numbers,* and *integers* to label the diagram of the number systems correctly. Provide a definition for each term.

APPLICATION

=== LOGICAL THINKING ===

Digits in a nonrepeating, nonterminating decimal sometimes follow a pattern. For example, in 2.757755777555 ..., one more 7 and one more 5 are added each time.

Study the pattern in each of these irrational numbers. Write the next ten digits of each.

1. 0.101001000100001...

2. 0.12113111411115...

3. 2.05010015020025...

4. 1.248163264128...

5. 0.1121231234...

6. 10.109910981097...

Squares and Square Roots

Since the square of 8 is 64 ($8^2 = 64$), 8 is the **square root** of 64. For a square with area 64 m², a side of the square is 8 m.

How can you find the length of a side of the square piece of cloth shown? Its area is 887 cm².

Work in a small group. Use a calculator. Suppose the $\boxed{\sqrt{}}$ key on your calculator is not working. Devise a method to find the square root of a number.

1. Write the steps you would follow.

2. Use your method to find $\sqrt{887}$.

3. Test the method by multiplying the answer by itself.

4. On the chalkboard, record both the square root you found and the square of the square root. How close to 887 was the square?

5. Use your method to find the following square roots:

    a. $\sqrt{95}$ **b.** $\sqrt{350}$

Record your results on the chalkboard.

SHARING YOUR THINKING

1. Show the other groups your method for finding the square root of a number.

2. Choose one of the square roots above. Try using one of the other methods.

3. Compare and contrast each method with the others. Is one method faster? Is one more accurate?

4. Study the data on the chalkboard. Which method gave the best estimate?

5. Isaac Newton used a method called the divide-and-average method. Study the example below.

Find $\sqrt{44}$.

   a. Estimate: $\sqrt{44}$ is near 7.

   b. Divide: $\frac{44}{7} \approx 6.29$

   c. Average: $\frac{7 + 6.29}{2} = 6.645$

   d. New estimate: $\sqrt{44}$ is near 6.645.

   e. Divide: $\frac{44}{6.645} \approx 6.622$

   f. Average: $\frac{6.645 + 6.622}{2} = 6.6335$

How accurate an answer do you need? Decide how many times you need to repeat this process.

6. Draw a flowchart for Newton's method. Use the flowchart to find $\sqrt{207}$, correct to 5 decimal places. How will you know when to stop dividing and averaging?

7. Did your group develop a method similar to Newton's method? How does Newton's method compare to the methods you devised? Is it faster? Does it seem to give better estimates?

THINKING IT THROUGH

1. List some numbers that have integer square roots. Why are these numbers called perfect squares?

2. Explain why the operations $\sqrt{x}$ and x^2 are called inverse operations.

3. What is meant by the third and fourth roots of a number? Why do you think third roots are called cube roots? How could you use the $\boxed{\sqrt{}}$ key to find fourth roots? Discuss.

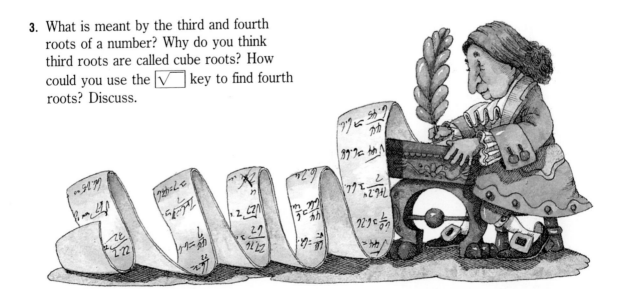

Using Calculators to Investigate Square Roots

WORKING TOGETHER

Work in a group to investigate each problem.

1. What is a square root of 9? Find two different numbers whose square is 9. Are there two square roots of 9? Discuss.

2. Use a calculator with a square root key. Find the square root of 20. Is the answer exact? Discuss.

3. Make a table. List several values of n in the first column. Use a calculator to find the square root of each value. List them in the second column. Use both whole numbers and decimals for n. Graph the data in your table.

4. Investigate using $\boxed{\sqrt{}}$ repeatedly.

   • Enter a number greater than 1 on your calculator. Press $\boxed{\sqrt{}}$ 15 times. Record the result.

   • Now enter a number greater than 10,000. Press $\boxed{\sqrt{}}$ 15 times, and record the result. Compare the two answers.

   • Enter a number between 0 and 1. Again, press $\boxed{\sqrt{}}$ 15 times. Compare the result with the other two answers. Discuss.

5. Press $\boxed{0}$ $\boxed{-}$ $\boxed{9}$ $\boxed{=}$ $\boxed{\sqrt{}}$. What is the display? Try to find a number that, when squared, gives −9. Discuss.

6. What result do you expect if you multiply $\sqrt{2} \times \sqrt{2}$? Now do the multiplication on your calculator. What keys did you press in order to do this? Did you get the result you expected? Compare your results with those of others. Did different calculators give different answers? require different key sequences?

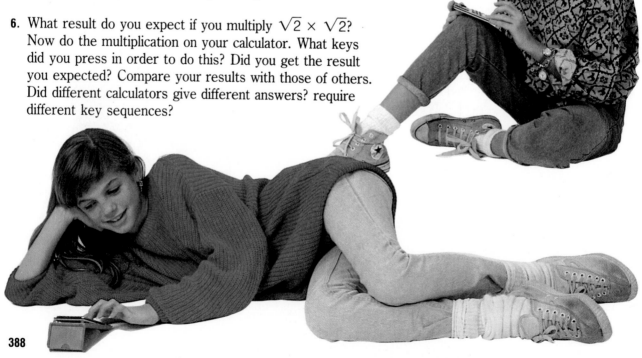

1. Compare the graphs you made for **3** on page 388 with those of your classmates. What do the graphs show about square roots?

2. Explain what happens when you enter a number and then press $\boxed{\sqrt{}}$ over and over.

3. Explain what happens when you enter a negative number and press $\boxed{\sqrt{}}$.

4. Did all the calculators in your group show square roots in exactly the same way?

===== **THINKING IT THROUGH** =====

1. Compare your answers for problems **1–6** with those of other groups. What conclusions can you draw about square roots?

2. Which is larger, n or $\sqrt{n}$? Discuss.

3. Find some numbers that have integer square roots. Find a number that has an integer cube (third) root. Find a number that has an integer sixth root, and one that has an integer seventh root. Challenge another group to find the roots of these numbers.

Pythagorean Rule

This 3,000-year-old mural shows some of the tools ancient Egyptians used. To mark off a piece of land, a surveyor could use a rope with 12 equidistant knots on it. The rope could be pulled into a right triangle with sides measuring 3, 4, and 5 units long.

Egyptian Expedition of the Metropolitan Museum of Art, Rogers Fund, 1930. (30.4.44)

In a right triangle the side opposite the right angle is called the hypotenuse. The other sides are called legs. The figure at the right shows the relationship between the hypotenuse and the legs of a right triangle.

$$(3 \text{ cm})^2 + (4 \text{ cm})^2 = (5 \text{ cm})^2$$

▶ For every right triangle the sum of the areas of the squares on the legs equals the area of the square on the hypotenuse. Let a and b be the lengths of the legs and c the length of the hypotenuse.

$$a^2 + b^2 = c^2$$

This is called the **Pythagorean Rule.**

▶ If the sides of a triangle satisfy the Pythagorean Rule, then the triangle is a right triangle.

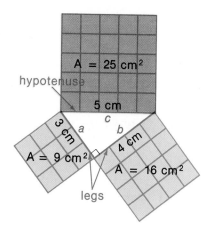

Use the Pythagorean Rule to find whether each triangle is a right triangle.

a.

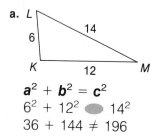

$$a^2 + b^2 = c^2$$
$$6^2 + 12^2 \ \bullet \ 14^2$$
$$36 + 144 \neq 196$$

△KLM is not a right triangle.

b.

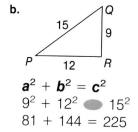

$$a^2 + b^2 = c^2$$
$$9^2 + 12^2 \ \bullet \ 15^2$$
$$81 + 144 = 225$$

△PQR is a right triangle.

CLASSWORK

Tell whether each is a right triangle.

1.

2.

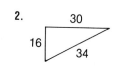

3.

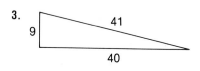

Name the hypotenuse and the legs of each right triangle.

1.

2.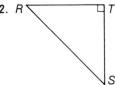

3.

Use the figure at the right to find the value of each.

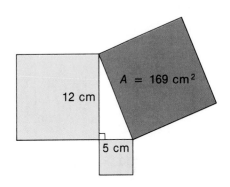

4. the length of the longer leg

5. the length of the shorter leg

6. the length of the hypotenuse

7. the area of the square on the shorter leg

8. the area of the square on the longer leg

9. the sum of the areas of the squares on the legs

Tell whether each is a right triangle.

10.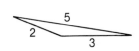

11.

12.

Tell whether a triangle having the given three side measures is a right triangle.

13. 6 m, 11 m, 12 m

14. 9 cm, 14 cm, 10 cm

15. 12 m, 16 m, 20 m

16. 4 km, 7 km, 8 km

17. 6 mm, 8 mm, 10 mm

18. 7 m, 13 m, 15 m

19. 8 cm, 14 cm, 12 cm

20. 7 km, 24 km, 25 km

21. 10 m, 24 m, 26 m

APPLICATION

PYTHAGOREAN TRIPLE

The three whole-number measures of a right triangle are called a **Pythagorean triple.** For any whole number m, the numbers $2m$, $m^2 - 1$, and $m^2 + 1$ are a Pythagorean triple.

The value $m = 7$ gives the triple 14, 48, 50. That is, $14^2 + 48^2 = 50^2$.

Find the Pythagorean triple for each value of m.

1. $m = 11$ 2. $m = 19$ 3. $m = 40$ 4. $m = 99$ 5. $m = 1,000$

Missing Sides of Right Triangles

The McMath solar telescope in Arizona, the largest solar telescope in the world, is used to study the sun. The building that houses the telescope forms the shape of a right triangle.

Use the Pythagorean Rule to find the length of one side of a right triangle when the lengths of the other two sides are known.

- Find the length of the hypotenuse.

$$a^2 + b^2 = c^2$$
$$5^2 + 12^2 = c^2$$
$$25 + 144 = c^2$$
$$169 = c^2$$
$$\sqrt{169} = c$$
$$13 = c$$

The length of the hypotenuse is 13 cm.

- Find the length of the leg, a.

$$a^2 + b^2 = c^2$$
$$a^2 + 8^2 = 10^2$$
$$a^2 + 64 = 100$$
$$a^2 = 36$$
$$a = \sqrt{36}$$
$$a = 6$$

The length of the leg is 6 cm.

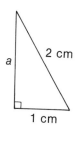

More Examples

a. Find c.

$$a^2 + b^2 = c^2$$
$$1^2 + 1^2 = c^2$$
$$1 + 1 = c^2$$
$$2 = c^2$$
$$\sqrt{2} = c$$
$$1.4 \text{ m} = c$$

b. Find a.

$$a^2 + b^2 = c^2$$
$$a^2 + 1^2 = 2^2$$
$$a^2 + 1 = 4$$
$$a^2 = 3$$
$$a = \sqrt{3}$$
$$a = 1.7 \text{ cm}$$

← to the nearest tenth →

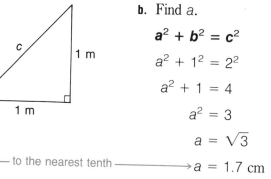

CLASSWORK

For each right triangle, find the missing measure to the nearest tenth.

1.
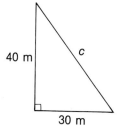
40 m, c, 30 m

2.
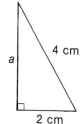
a, 4 cm, 2 cm

3.
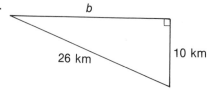
b, 26 km, 10 km

Find the length of each hypotenuse to the nearest tenth.

1.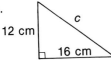

2.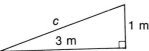

3.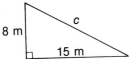

4.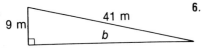

Find each missing measure to the nearest tenth.

5. 9 m, 41 m, b

6. 30 cm, 34 cm, a

7. $a = \_\_\_$
   $b = 24$ m
   $c = 25$ m

8. $a = 5$ km
   $b = \_\_\_$
   $c = 13$ km

9. $a = 2$ m
   $b = 5$ m
   $c = \_\_\_$

10. $a = 9$ m
    $b = \_\_\_$
    $c = 15$ m

11. $a = 2$ km
    $b = 2$ km
    $c = \_\_\_$

★ 12. $a = 2$ cm
     $b = \sqrt{5}$ cm
     $c = \_\_\_$

★ 13. $a = \_\_\_$
     $b = 3$ m
     $c = 3\sqrt{3}$ m

★ 14. $a = \frac{1}{4}$ m
     $b = \_\_\_$
     $c = \frac{\sqrt{5}}{4}$ m

Hubble Space Telescope
Astronaut Kathy Sullivan

APPLICATION

15. The telescope is supported by a tower that casts a shadow 40 m long. The distance from the top of the tower to the end of the shadow is 50 m. How high is the tower?

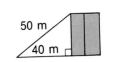

16. An access ramp to a building rises 1 meter high and is 3 meters long. To the nearest tenth, what is the distance from the bottom of the ramp to the base of the building?

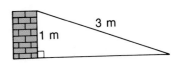

17. An astronomer walks across a field from the telescope (T) to a laboratory (L). To the nearest meter, what is the length of the shortest path he can take?

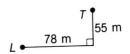

Graphing Ordered Pairs

The French mathematician René Descartes (1596–1650) developed the graphing system that bears his name. It is called the Cartesian coordinate system. Any ordered pair of real numbers can be graphed, using this system.

Real numbers can be located as points on a real number line. Pairs of real numbers can be located as points on a **real number plane.**

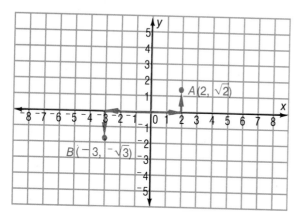

Graph the ordered pair $A(2, \sqrt{2})$. From the origin, move 2 units to the right, and then move up to $\sqrt{2}$.

Think $\sqrt{2} \approx 1.41$

Label the point A.

Another Example

Graph the ordered pair $B(^-3, \,^-\sqrt{3})$. From the origin, move 3 units to the left, and then move down to $^-\sqrt{3}$.

Think $^-\sqrt{3} \approx \,^-1.73$

Label the point B.

CLASSWORK

Use the real number plane below. Name the point located by each ordered pair.

1. $\left(^-2, \frac{1}{2}\right)$ 2. $(1, \sqrt{2})$ 3. $\left(\frac{1}{2}, \,^-1\right)$
4. $(2, \,^-\sqrt{3})$ 5. $(3.5, \sqrt{4})$ 6. $(\sqrt{3}, \,^-\sqrt{16})$

Write the ordered pair for each point.

7. G 8. H 9. J

10. K 11. L 12. M

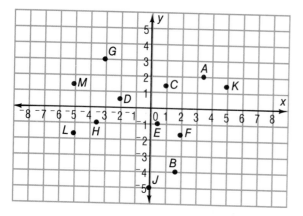

PRACTICE

Use the real number plane at the right.
Name the point located by each ordered pair.

1. $(^-2, 1)$ 2. $\left(1, \frac{1}{3}\right)$ 3. $(0, \sqrt{3})$

4. $(^-1.5, 3)$ 5. $\left(^-\frac{1}{2}, \frac{1}{4}\right)$ 6. $(\sqrt{2}, ^-2)$

7. $\left(^-2, ^-\frac{1}{2}\right)$ 8. $\left(3, ^-\frac{1}{2}\right)$ 9. $\left(^-\frac{3}{4}, 2\right)$

10. $(^-\sqrt{2}, 0)$ 11. $\left(^-2.5, ^-\frac{3}{4}\right)$ 12. $(\sqrt{5}, 1)$

Write the ordered pair for each point.

13. O 14. N 15. P

16. R 17. B 18. Q

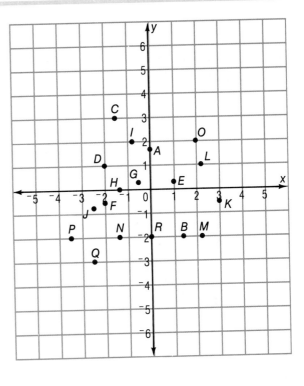

Draw the coordinate axes. Graph and label
these points.

19. $A(1, 3)$ 20. $B\left(^-2, \frac{1}{2}\right)$

21. $C(0, ^-\sqrt{3})$ 22. $D(^-0.5, ^-1)$

23. $E(\sqrt{2}, 0)$ 24. $G(2, \sqrt{3})$

★ 25. $F(\sqrt{5}, ^-1)$ ★ 26. $H(^-\sqrt{5}, ^-\sqrt{3})$

Use the diagram at the
right. Write the quadrant in
which each point is found.

27. $(1, 1)$ 28. $(^-1, ^-1)$

29. $(1, ^-1)$ 30. $(^-1, 1)$

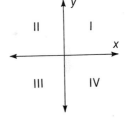

Write the sign for each coordinate of the ordered pairs in
each quadrant.

★ 31. III   ★ 32. I   ★ 33. IV   ★ 34. II

APPLICATION

★ 35. Find a state map that shows the city or town where you
live. Draw a coordinate system over the map, with the
origin at the point where you live. Using your coordinate
system, give the location of other places of interest, such
as cities, towns, parks, lakes, and mountains. Be sure to
include points in each quadrant.

Problem Solving
SKILLS AND STRATEGIES REVIEW

Many advances in air travel have been achieved since the first flight by the Wright brothers in 1903. Today a Boeing 747 is a common sight at any major airport.

1. The highest point of the fuselage of a Boeing 747 is 37 feet above the ground. How high is the cockpit of the plane if the cockpit is 7 feet lower than the highest point?

2. The main landing gear of the Boeing 747 has 4 separate legs with 4 wheels mounted on each. How much weight does each wheel carry?

3. A jet plane is cruising at a speed of 600 miles per hour. It leaves the airport and travels west for $\frac{1}{2}$ hour. It then travels north for 45 minutes. It turns west and travels for another $\frac{1}{2}$ hour. Finally, it travels north for 35 minutes. How far from the airport is the plane now?

4. The Concorde, designed for supersonic flight, can cross the Atlantic in 3 hours. When it is 8 P.M. in London, it is 3 P.M. in New York. If the Concorde leaves London for New York at 12 noon, what time is it in New York when it arrives?

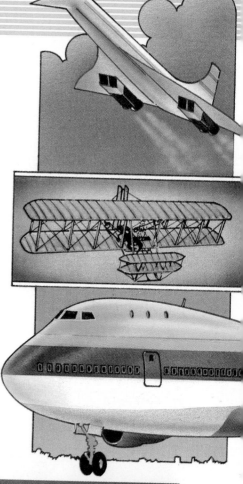

The field of aviation is one of many fields to take advantage of the recent achievements in computers.

5. Aircraft approaching London's Heathrow Airport are monitored by a computer system called Mediator. Fifteen planes are tracked in one hour, 14 planes the next, and 30 planes the third hour. What is the number of planes tracked in the fourth hour if the average of the 4 hours is 20 planes tracked?

★ 6. On Monday, 6,000 reservations were recorded by a computer; on Tuesday, 1,400 more than on Monday were recorded. On Wednesday, 500 less than on Monday were recorded; on Friday, 200 more than the total for Tuesday and Thursday were recorded. How many were recorded on Thursday if 10,000 were recorded on Friday?

Problem Solving

WHAT WOULD YOU DO . . . ?

Car-rental firms offer different plans to attract different types of customers. You need to rent a car for 2 days while your car is being repaired. You plan to drive it no more than 100 miles. You have found the three advertisements shown below.

RENT-THE-BEST	**RENT-AN-OLDIE**	**BEAUTIFUL RENTALS**
New car rentals	Used but usable cars	Rent a new car
$39.95 a day	$17 a day and	for only $22 a day,
First 100 miles free	13¢ a mile	22¢ a mile.
Each additional mile 12¢		

Evaluate this information to make a choice. Answer each question.

1. Would the location of the firm influence your decision?

2. Would you take into consideration the condition of the car—old or new?

3. Would the cost of renting the car be your primary concern?

4. Are there other factors you would take into account?

5. Estimate the cost of renting a car from each firm for 2 days. Use a distance of 100 miles.

What would you do? Which car would you rent? Why?

6. Suppose RENT-THE-BEST was 2 miles from your home and BEAUTIFUL RENTALS was 10 miles from your home. Would your choice be different?

7. You are planning to rent a car for a 3-day weekend vacation. You will be driving a total of about 300 miles. Which car would you rent? Why?

Write the opposite of each. pages 372–373

1. $\frac{1}{4}$ 2. $^-5$ 3. $^-1.7$ 4. $4\frac{1}{6}$ 5. $\frac{^-10}{7}$

Compare. Use <, >, or = for each ●. pages 372–373

6. $\frac{2}{3}$ ● $^-2\frac{1}{3}$ 7. $^-4$ ● $^-8$ 8. $\frac{^-1}{5}$ ● 0   9. $^-0.5$ ● $^-0.10$ 10. 2.1 ● $^-11.5$

Add, subtract, multiply, or divide. pages 374–377

11. $\frac{3}{8} + \frac{^-1}{4}$ 12. $3 - {}^-8$ 13. $81 \div 0.9$ 14. $^-0.4 \cdot 6.3$

Write as a single power of 10. pages 380–381

15. $10^4 \cdot 10^{-6}$ 16. $10^{-7} \div 10^2$ 17. $10^5 \div 10^{-3}$

Write in scientific notation. pages 382–383

18. 0.005 19. 0.00019 20. 0.00467

Find a real number between each pair. pages 384–385

21. 2.5 and 2.6 22. $^-0.137$ and $^-0.138$ 23. 74.001 and 74.002

Find each square root. pages 386–387

24. $\sqrt{100}$ 25. $^-\sqrt{36}$ 26. $\sqrt{225}$

Find the missing side. pages 390–393

27. hypotenuse = 35 ft   leg = 28 ft

pages 394–395

Name the point located by each ordered pair.

28. $\left(1, \frac{^-1}{2}\right)$ 29. $(^-\sqrt{2}, 2)$
30. $\left(\frac{1}{2}, ^-2\right)$ 31. $(1, \sqrt{2})$

pages 394–395

Write the ordered pair for each point.

32. A 33. D 34. F 35. I

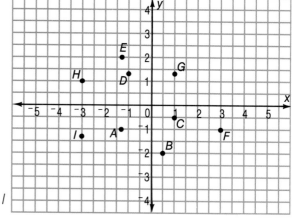

Use the graph at the right to solve. pages 378–379, 396–397

36. Mark borrows tapes from a library. The fee is $1.25 for each tape for 2 days. $.75 is charged for each overdue day.

   a. How much is owed for a tape borrowed for 3 days?

   b. How much is owed for a tape returned 3 days late?

LIBRARY BORROWING FEES

Write the opposite of each.

1. $\frac{1}{2}$

2. $^-3$

3. $^-2.8$

Compare. Use <, >, or = for each ⬤.

4. $\frac{3}{4}$ ⬤ $^-1\frac{1}{2}$

5. $^-3$ ⬤ $^-5$

6. 0 ⬤ $^-\frac{1}{10}$

Add, subtract, multiply, or divide.

7. $\frac{7}{8} + \frac{^-1}{2}$

8. $4 - {^-9}$

9. $64 \div 0.8$

10. $^-15 \div \frac{^-3}{5}$

11. $^-1.7 + {^-3.6}$

12. $^-10 \cdot \frac{^-1}{11}$

13. $10^{-3} \cdot 10^8$

14. $10^{-2} \div 10^{-5}$

Write in scientific notation.

15. 0.003

16. 0.00082

Find the hypotenuse for each.

17. $a = 18$ yd; $b = 24$ yd   18. $a = 12$ in.; $b = 16$ in.

Find each square root.

19. $\sqrt{81}$

20. $^-\sqrt{49}$

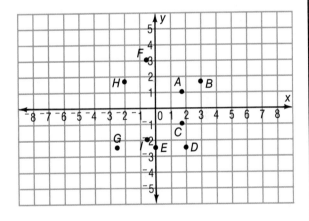

Name the point located by each ordered pair.

21. $\left(0, {^-2\frac{1}{2}}\right)$

22. $(\sqrt{3}, 1)$

Write the ordered pair for each point.

23. C

24. B

Use the graph at the right to solve.

25. Susan works after school as a cashier. The sales tax in her state is 6%. This graph shows the amount of tax due on sales less than $1.11.

   a. What is the tax on a purchase of $.74?

   b. Greg was charged $.03 tax. What was the least possible price of the item he purchased?

SALES TAX (6%)

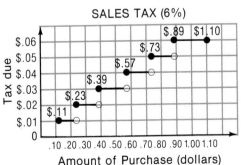

Evaluate.

$(3.5 \times {^-5.2}) + 6\frac{1}{2} - ({^-3.6} \div 1.8 \times 10^{-3})$

SPACE GRAPHICS

The microcomputer screen is displaying computer art of a spaceship. Use graph paper to draw your own figure. You can graph the ordered pairs listed below and follow the directions to connect the points. What have you drawn?

1. Connect the following points in the order given: $\left(-1\frac{1}{2}, 1\frac{1}{2}\right)$, $\left(0, 4\frac{1}{2}\right)$, $(5, 4)$, $(6, 5)$, $(6, 6)$, $\left(5\frac{1}{2}, 7\frac{1}{2}\right)$, $(-16, 8)$, $\left(-18, 7\frac{1}{2}\right)$.

2. Connect $(5, 4)$ to $(4, 5)$ to $(4, 6)$ to $\left(4\frac{1}{2}, 7\right)$ to $\left(5\frac{1}{2}, 7\frac{1}{2}\right)$. Connect $\left(-\frac{1}{2}, 5\right)$ to $\left(-2\frac{1}{2}, 1\frac{1}{2}\right)$.

3. Connect $(-13, 3)$ to $\left(-8\frac{1}{2}, -4\frac{1}{2}\right)$. Connect $(-10, 3)$ to $\left(-10\frac{1}{2}, 4\right)$ to $\left(-10\frac{1}{2}, 5\right)$ to $\left(-9, 6\frac{1}{2}\right)$.

4. Connect $(7, 2)$ to $(7, 1)$ to $\left(10, \frac{1}{2}\right)$ to $\left(13, \frac{1}{2}\right)$ to $(15, 2)$.

5. Connect $\left(3, -11\frac{1}{2}\right)$ to $(2, -10)$ to $(2, -8)$ to $(3, -6)$ to $\left(5, -5\frac{1}{2}\right)$.

6. Connect $(2, -3)$ to $\left(1\frac{1}{2}, -4\right)$. Connect $\left(-3\frac{1}{2}, -2\frac{1}{2}\right)$ to $\left(-4, -3\frac{1}{2}\right)$. Connect $(-4, -2)$ to $\left(-5, -3\frac{1}{2}\right)$. Connect $\left(-4\frac{1}{2}, -1\frac{1}{2}\right)$ to $\left(-5\frac{1}{2}, -3\frac{1}{2}\right)$. Connect $\left(-7\frac{1}{2}, 5\right)$ to $(-7, -3)$.

7. Connect the following points in the order given: $(-8, -3)$, $\left(1\frac{1}{2}, -4\right)$, $(6, -6)$, $(6, -9)$, $\left(5, -10\frac{1}{2}\right)$, $\left(3, -11\frac{1}{2}\right)$, $(-14, -6)$, $(-14, -3)$, $\left(-13, -2\frac{1}{2}\right)$, $\left(-10\frac{1}{2}, -2\frac{1}{2}\right)$.

8. Connect the following points in the order given: $\left(-10, -4\frac{1}{2}\right)$, $(-15, 3)$, $\left(-32\frac{1}{2}, 4\frac{1}{2}\right)$, $(-33, 6)$, $\left(-34\frac{1}{2}, 7\right)$, $(-32, 8)$, $\left(-9, 6\frac{1}{2}\right)$, $(-8, 6)$, $\left(-7\frac{1}{2}, 5\right)$, $\left(-7\frac{1}{2}, 4\right)$, $(-8, 3)$, $\left(-12\frac{1}{2}, 3\right)$, $(-8, -4)$.

9. Connect the following points in the order given: $\left(28, -\frac{1}{2}\right)$, $(28, -2)$, $\left(25, -3\frac{1}{2}\right)$, $(22, -4)$, $(9, -4)$, $(2, -3)$, $(-4, -2)$, $\left(-4\frac{1}{2}, \frac{1}{2}\right)$, $(0, 2)$, $(7, 2)$, $\left(10, 3\frac{1}{2}\right)$, $\left(11\frac{1}{2}, 4\right)$, $\left(13\frac{1}{2}, 3\right)$, $(15, 2)$, $(19, 2)$, $(24, 1)$, $\left(28, -\frac{1}{2}\right)$, $(25, -2)$, $\left(19, -2\frac{1}{2}\right)$, $\left(11, -2\frac{1}{2}\right)$, $(4, -2)$, $(-2, -1)$, $\left(-4\frac{1}{2}, \frac{1}{2}\right)$.

10. Use graph paper to draw your own figure. Identify several points that can be used to describe the graph. Make a list of these points and directions telling how to connect them. Give to a classmate to graph.

SERIES

▶A sequence written as a sum is a series.

Sequence: $\frac{1}{2}, \frac{1}{4}, \frac{1}{8}, \frac{1}{16}, \ldots, \frac{1}{1,024}$

Series: $\frac{1}{2} + \frac{1}{4} + \frac{1}{8} + \frac{1}{16} + \ldots + \frac{1}{1,024}$

Each number in the series is a term. To find the sum of the terms, try to find a pattern. Find the pattern for the series above.

$$\frac{1}{2} = 1 - \frac{1}{2} \qquad \frac{1}{2} + \frac{1}{4} = \frac{3}{4} = 1 - \frac{1}{4}$$

The sum equals 1 minus the last term.

Use this pattern to find each sum below. Then add to check the answer.

1. $\frac{1}{2} + \frac{1}{4} + \frac{1}{8}$

2. $\frac{1}{2} + \frac{1}{4} + \frac{1}{8} + \frac{1}{16}$

3. $\frac{1}{2} + \frac{1}{4} + \frac{1}{8} + \ldots + \frac{1}{128}$

4. $\frac{1}{2} + \frac{1}{4} + \frac{1}{8} + \ldots + \frac{1}{1,024}$

Find each sum or difference. What is the pattern relating a and b?

5. a. $\frac{1}{3} + \frac{1}{9}$

   b. $1 - \frac{1}{9}$

6. a. $\frac{1}{3} + \frac{1}{9} + \frac{1}{27}$

   b. $1 - \frac{1}{27}$

7. a. $\frac{1}{3} + \frac{1}{9} + \frac{1}{27} + \frac{1}{81}$

   b. $1 - \frac{1}{81}$

Use the pattern in 5–7 to find each sum.

8. $\frac{1}{3} + \frac{1}{9} + \frac{1}{27} + \frac{1}{81} + \frac{1}{243}$

9. $\frac{1}{3} + \frac{1}{9} + \frac{1}{27} + \ldots + \frac{1}{6,561}$

Find each sum. Then find a pattern for finding the sum of each series. (Write the denominator of each term as the product of two consecutive integers.)

10. $\frac{1}{2} + \frac{1}{6}$

11. $\frac{1}{2} + \frac{1}{6} + \frac{1}{12}$

12. $\frac{1}{2} + \frac{1}{6} + \frac{1}{12} + \frac{1}{20}$

Use the pattern you found in 10–12 to find the sum of each series.

13. $\frac{1}{2} + \frac{1}{6} + \frac{1}{12} + \ldots + \frac{1}{110}$

14. $\frac{1}{2} + \frac{1}{6} + \frac{1}{12} + \ldots + \frac{1}{9,900}$

PERIMETER

READ and DATA statements are another way
to assign values to variables.

The statement **READ A** assigns the next number
in the **DATA** statement to the variable **A**.

Example Together these statements assign the values
A = 1, B = 12, and C = 6.

```
10 READ A , B , C
20 DATA 1 , 12 , 6
```

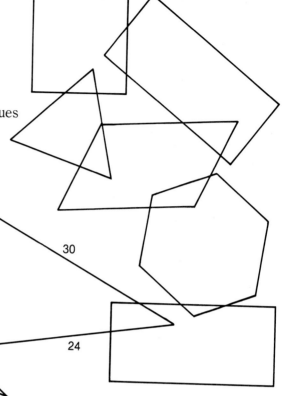

This program uses READ and DATA statements
to find the perimeter of a polygon.

PROGRAM

```
10 REM PERIMETER OF A POLYGON
```

Read the number of sides. ⟶
```
20 READ N
```

Begin with the perimeter = 0. ⟶
```
30 LET P = 0
```

```
40 FOR I = 1 TO N
```

Read the length of one side. ⟶
```
50 READ S
```

```
60 PRINT "SIDE ";I; " = ";S
```

Add that length to the perimeter. ⟶
```
70 LET P = P + S
```

Go back and read the next length. ⟶
```
80 NEXT I
```

```
90 PRINT "PERIMETER = ";P
```

This polygon has 3 sides. ⟶
```
100 DATA 3
```

The lengths of the sides are 24,
18, and 30. ⟶
```
110 DATA 24 , 18 , 30
```

```
120 END
```

Placing DATA statements near the end of a program makes
them easy to find and change.

Write the output for each program.

1. ```
10 FOR I = 1 TO 5
20 READ A
30 PRINT A
40 NEXT A
50 DATA 1 , 2 , 3 , 6 , 9
60 END
```

2. ```
10 READ B
20 IF B = 0 THEN GOTO 60
30 PRINT B * B
40 GOTO 10
50 DATA 4 , 7 , 5 , 8 , 0
60 END
```

3. ```
10 REM AREA OF A RECTANGLE
20 READ L , W
30 LET A = L * W
40 PRINT "AREA = " ;A;" SQUARE
   UNITS"
50 DATA 22 , 24
60 END
```

4. ```
10 REM AREA OF A TRIANGLE
20 READ B , H
30 LET A = 1/2 * B * H
40 PRINT "AREA = " ;A;" SQUARE
   UNITS"
50 DATA 17 , 19
60 END
```

Rewrite the program on page 402 to find the perimeter of each.

5. a quadrilateral with sides 12, 14, 18, and 21

6. a pentagon with sides 26, 28, 32, 33, and 13

★7. a rectangle with width 25 and length 34

Write a program using READ and DATA statements to find each.

8. the area of a trapezoid with bases 5 and 8 and height 7

9. the perimeter and area of a square with side 23

★10. the surface area and volume of a cube with side 8

=AT THE COMPUTER=

Run the program on page 402 with each group of changes to see what happens.

1. ```
110 DATA 24
111 DATA 18
112 DATA 30
```

2. `110 DATA 24 , 18 , 30 , 50`

★3. `110 DATA 24 , 18`

4. Run each program you wrote for **5–10** and write the results.
```

MAINTAINING SKILLS

Choose the correct answers. Write A, B, C, or D.

1. What percent of 48 is 24?

   A 25%   **C** 37%
   B 38%   **D** not given

2. $43 - {}^-21$

   A 64   **C** $^-22$
   B 22   **D** not given

3. $^-8 \cdot {}^-10$

   A $^-18$ **C** 80
   B $^-80$ **D** not given

4. How many choices are there with 3 colors and 6 shapes?

   A 18   **C** 3
   B 9   **D** not given

5. What is the mean of 12, 16, 3, and 2.4?

   A 8.35   **C** 7.5
   B 9.6   **D** not given

6. What is P(1 or even on a number cube)?

   A $\frac{1}{12}$ **C** $\frac{2}{3}$
   B $\frac{1}{2}$ **D** not given

7. What is the volume of the rectangular prism? $l = 12$ m, $w = 3.5$ m, $h = 4$ m

   A 42 m^3 **C** 168 m^3
   B 19.5 m^3 **D** not given

8. What is the surface area?

   3 cm   5 cm   2 cm

   A 62 cm^2 **C** 42 cm^2
   B 30 cm^3 **D** not given

9. Complete. ___ cm^3 = 6,000 mL

   A 60   **C** 0.6
   B 600   **D** not given

10. $\frac{2}{3} \cdot \frac{^-5}{6}$

    A $\frac{^-5}{9}$ **C** $^-1\frac{1}{5}$
    B $\frac{5}{9}$ **D** not given

11. Simplify. $10^4 \times 10^{-2}$

    A 10^{-8} **C** 10^{-2}
    B 10^2 **D** not given

12. $4.23 \cdot 10^{-3}$

    A 4,230   **C** 42.3
    B 0.00423   **D** not given

13. What is the square root of 196?

    A 98   **C** 14
    B 49   **D** not given

Guess and test to solve 14 and 15.

14. The area of a rectangular quilt is 2,976 ft^2. The perimeter is 240 ft. What are the dimensions of the quilt?

    A 48 ft by 62 ft   **C** 1,488 ft by 1,488 ft
    B 48 ft by 52 ft   **D** not given

15. What is the three-digit number? The tens digit is 3 times greater than the ones digit. The hundreds digit is prime, and the sum of the digits is 19.

    A 562   **C** 793
    B 731   **D** not given

Theme: The Sea

Inverses

The tide is the regular daily rising and falling of ocean waters. The tide in the Bay of Fundy in eastern Canada sometimes rises 50 feet and then falls 50 feet.

$$50 + {}^-50 = 0$$

ADDITION PROPERTIES

Inverse Property (for every number a)

$$a + {}^-a = 0 \qquad \frac{1}{4} + \frac{{}^-1}{4} = 0$$

The sum of a number and its additive inverse, or opposite, is 0.

MULTIPLICATION PROPERTIES

Inverse Property (for every number a except 0)

$$a \cdot \frac{1}{a} = 1 \qquad 3 \cdot \frac{1}{3} = 1$$

The product of a number and its multiplicative inverse, or reciprocal, is 1.

You can also use these familiar properties when adding or multiplying.

Commutative Property

$${}^-8 + 5 = 5 + {}^-8$$

$$6 \cdot {}^-9 = {}^-9 \cdot 6$$

Associative Property

$$2 + \left(\frac{{}^-2}{3} + \frac{1}{6}\right) = \left(2 + \frac{{}^-2}{3}\right) + \frac{1}{6}$$

$$\frac{{}^-4}{9}\left(3 \cdot \frac{{}^-3}{4}\right) = \left(\frac{{}^-4}{9} \cdot 3\right) \cdot \frac{{}^-3}{4}$$

Identity Property

$${}^-6 + 0 = {}^-6 \qquad 0 + {}^-6 = {}^-6$$

$$\frac{{}^-1}{2} \cdot 1 = \frac{{}^-1}{2} \qquad 1 \cdot \frac{{}^-1}{2} = \frac{{}^-1}{2}$$

Zero Property

$$\frac{1}{4} \cdot 0 = 0 \qquad 0 \cdot \frac{1}{4} = 0$$

Distributive Property

$${}^-2(6 + {}^-8) = {}^-2 \cdot 6 + {}^-2 \cdot {}^-8$$

CLASSWORK

Give the additive and multiplicative inverses of each.

1. ${}^-2$
2. $\frac{1}{6}$
3. $\frac{{}^-2}{5}$
4. 10
5. $\frac{6}{5}$
6. ${}^-2\frac{1}{3}$

Name the property illustrated.

7. $\frac{{}^-4}{3} \cdot \frac{{}^-3}{4} = 1$
8. $\frac{{}^-1}{3} + \frac{1}{3} = 0$
9. $1 \cdot {}^-20 = {}^-20$
10. $\frac{{}^-2}{3} \cdot 0 = 0$

11. ${}^-8 + ({}^-14 + 9) = ({}^-8 + {}^-14) + 9$
12. $3\left(\frac{{}^-2}{3} + \frac{1}{6}\right) = 3 \cdot \frac{{}^-2}{3} + 3 \cdot \frac{1}{6}$

PRACTICE

Give the additive and multiplicative inverses of each.

1. $\frac{3}{2}$ 2. $^-5$ 3. $\frac{1}{5}$ 4. $\frac{3}{4}$

5. 8 6. $\frac{^-4}{5}$ 7. 1 8. $1\frac{1}{3}$

9. $\frac{^-1}{2}$ 10. $\frac{^-2}{3}$ 11. $^-2\frac{3}{5}$ 12. $1\frac{2}{3}$

Name the property illustrated.

13. $\frac{1}{2} \cdot \frac{2}{3} = \frac{2}{3} \cdot \frac{1}{2}$ 14. $0 + {}^-52 = {}^-52$

15. $1 \cdot \frac{^-3}{4} = \frac{^-3}{4}$ 16. $4 + \frac{1}{3} = \frac{1}{3} + 4$

17. $\frac{3}{4} + \frac{^-3}{4} = 0$ 18. $^-4 \cdot \frac{^-1}{4} = 1$

19. $\frac{5}{8} \cdot \frac{8}{5} = 1$ 20. $^-8 + 8 = 0$

21. $\left(\frac{1}{2} + {}^-\frac{1}{4}\right) + \frac{3}{8} = \frac{1}{2} + \left({}^-\frac{1}{4} + \frac{3}{8}\right)$

22. $^-6\left(\frac{1}{3} + {}^-\frac{5}{6}\right) = {}^-6 \cdot \frac{1}{3} + {}^-6 \cdot {}^-\frac{5}{6}$

Write *true* or *false* for each statement.

23. The sum of a number and its additive inverse is 0.

24. The product of a number and its multiplicative inverse is $^-1$.

25. When a number is divided by 1, the quotient is 1.

26. The additive inverse of a number is the number itself.

27. The additive inverse of zero is zero.

28. Zero does not have a reciprocal.

★ 29. Every number has an additive inverse.

★ 30. Every number has a multiplicative inverse.

★ 31. The reciprocal of $-\frac{a}{b}$ is $\frac{b}{a}$.

★ 32. The opposite of $-\frac{1}{a}$ is a.

APPLICATION

MENTAL ARITHMETIC

Use the properties to help you mentally compute each answer.

1. $\left(3 + \frac{3}{8}\right) + \frac{5}{8}$ 2. $\left(2 \cdot \frac{1}{4}\right) + \left(2 \cdot \frac{3}{4}\right)$ 3. $^-\frac{5}{6} + \left(\frac{2}{3} + \frac{5}{6}\right)$

4. $\left(\frac{4}{9} \cdot \frac{^-4}{3}\right) \cdot \frac{^-3}{4}$ 5. $\frac{1}{2} + \left(\frac{1}{2} + \frac{1}{3}\right)$ 6. $^-\frac{1}{4} + \left(\frac{1}{4} + 1\right)$

7. $\left(2 \cdot \frac{1}{2}\right) + {}^-1$ 8. $\left(3 \cdot \frac{5}{6}\right) + \left(3 \cdot \frac{1}{6}\right)$ 9. $\left(3\frac{1}{2} + \frac{1}{3}\right) + {}^-\frac{1}{3}$

Adding to Solve Equations

In winter the ice in the middle of the Arctic Ocean may be 10 feet thick. That is 4 feet thicker than it is along the coast. How thick is the coastal ice?

Let x be the thickness of the coastal ice.

$$x + 4 = 10$$

You can use additive inverses to solve addition and subtraction equations.

$x + 4 = 10$	Use the additive inverse of 4 to solve.
$x + 4 + {}^-4 = 10 + {}^-4$	Add $^-4$ to both sides of the equation.
$x + 0 = 6$	Using the Inverse Property of Addition, $4 + {}^-4 = 0$.
$x = 6$	Solution
Check $6 + 4 = 10$	Replace x with 6 in the original equation.

The coastal ice is 6 feet thick.

More Examples

a.

$y - 3 = {}^-6$ Change subtracting 3 to adding the opposite of 3.

$y + {}^-3 = {}^-6$

$y + {}^-3 + 3 = {}^-6 + 3$ Add 3 to both sides of the equation.

$y + 0 = {}^-3$

$y = {}^-3$

Check ${}^-3 - 3 = {}^-6$

b.

${}^-5 = n - {}^-7$ Change subtracting $^-7$ to adding the opposite of $^-7$.

${}^-5 = n + 7$

${}^-5 + {}^-7 = n + 7 + {}^-7$ Add $^-7$ to both sides of the equation.

${}^-12 = n + 0$

${}^-12 = n$

Check ${}^-5 = {}^-12 - {}^-7$

CLASSWORK

First tell what must be done to both sides of the equation. Then solve. Check each solution.

1. $x + 7 = 14$ **2.** $y - {}^-9 = 14$ **3.** $y - 2 = {}^-9$ **4.** ${}^-15 + x = 11$

5. $4 = {}^-6 + n$ **6.** $0 = y - 21$ **7.** $n - 7 = {}^-8$ **8.** $12 + x = 0$

PRACTICE

Solve. Check each solution.

1. $x + 8 = 15$ **2.** $y - 17 = 9$ **3.** $n - 15 = 0$ **4.** $^-5 + n = 8$

5. $x + {}^-7 = 0$ **6.** $y + 8 = {}^-7$ **7.** $x - 6 = {}^-4$ **8.** $n - {}^-13 = 9$

9. $n - {}^-9 = {}^-11$ **10.** $12 + y = {}^-15$ **11.** $^-10 + w = 0$ **12.** $^-15 = 3 + n$

13. $y - 19 = {}^-17$ **14.** $^-9 = w - 18$ **15.** $^-23 + x = {}^-13$ **16.** $19 + y = {}^-26$

17. $36 = x - {}^-27$ **18.** $^-28 = 0 + n$ **19.** $^-27 = w - {}^-32$ **20.** $42 = {}^-37 + n$

21. $n - \frac{3}{8} = {}^-\frac{1}{2}$ **22.** $\frac{1}{2} = y + \frac{3}{5}$ **23.** $n - 3.7 = {}^-2.1$ **24.** $^-18.1 = x + 8.4$

★ **25.** $n - 8 \cdot 5 = {}^-32$ ★ **26.** $2({}^-6 + 4) = y + 1$ ★ **27.** $^-\frac{3}{2} \cdot \frac{1}{2} = n - 1\frac{1}{4}$ ★ **28.** $w + 6.1 = {}^-1.8 - 1.6$

Write an equation for each sentence. Then solve.

29. Six more than a number x is $^-7$.

30. Ten less than a number m is $^-5$.

31. A number n minus $^-8$ is 27.

32. The sum of $^-13$ and a number y is 20.

33. A number w added to $^-24$ equals $^-38$.

34. Fifty-seven equals a number p minus $^-49$.

★ **35.** The sum of a number n and $^-2.3$ equals the sum of $^-7.4$ and 8.2.

★ **36.** Seven and three fourths less than a number m equals the sum of $^-2\frac{1}{2}$ and 3.

APPLICATION

CALCULATOR

A calculator can be used to solve equations.

$n + {}^-5 = 10 \longrightarrow 10 - {}^-5 = n$ **Press** | 15. |

Use a calculator to solve each.

1. $n - 10 = {}^-4$ **2.** $^-24 = 0 + x$ **3.** $^-36 + n = 45$ **4.** $w - 38 = {}^-73$

5. $y + 54 = {}^-18$ **6.** $^-130 = w - {}^-61$ **7.** $n + {}^-58 = {}^-46$ **8.** $^-144 = x + {}^-68$

9. $153 = x - {}^-87$ **10.** $n + {}^-25.1 = {}^-22.7$ **11.** $50 = n - {}^-48.9$ **12.** $36.7 = x - 32.1$

Multiplying to Solve Equations

Many kinds of penguins live in the Antarctic Ocean. The biggest penguins, the emperors, weigh about 10 times as much as most other penguins. On the average an adult emperor penguin weighs 90 lb. On the average what do most other adult penguins weigh?

Let n be the weight of most other adult penguins.

$$10n = 90$$

You can use multiplicative inverses to solve multiplication and division equations.

$10n = 90$	Use the multiplicative inverse of 10 to solve.
$\frac{1}{10} \cdot 10n = \frac{1}{10} \cdot 90$	Multiply both sides of the equation by $\frac{1}{10}$.
$\left(\frac{1}{10} \cdot 10\right)n = \frac{1}{10} \cdot 90$	
$1n = 9$	Using the Inverse Property of Multiplication, $\frac{1}{10} \cdot 10 = 1$.
$n = 9$	Solution
Check $10 \cdot 9 = 90$	Replace n with 9 in the original equation.

On the average most other adult penguins weigh 9 lb.

Another Example

$\frac{x}{^-5} = 4$	
$^-\frac{1}{5}x = 4$	Change dividing by $^-5$ to multiplying by the reciprocal of $^-5$.
$^-5 \cdot {}^-\frac{1}{5}x = {}^-5 \cdot 4$	Multiply both sides by $^-5$.
$\left(^-5 \cdot {}^-\frac{1}{5}\right)x = {}^-5 \cdot 4$	
$x = {}^-20$	

Check $\dfrac{^-20}{^-5} = 4$

CLASSWORK

First tell what must be done to both sides of the equation.
Then solve. Check each solution.

1. $^-3x = 12$

2. $5y = {}^-35$

3. $\frac{x}{2} = {}^-8$

4. $\frac{n}{^-7} = {}^-1$

5. $^-8y = 1$

6. $\frac{x}{^-6} = 10$

7. $^-y = 2$

8. $\frac{n}{8} = {}^-3$

PRACTICE

Solve. Check each solution.

1. $5x = 30$
2. $3 = \frac{n}{9}$
3. $^-8y = 8$
4. $\frac{x}{2} = ^-9$

5. $9n = ^-36$
6. $^-7y = ^-49$
7. $^-17 = \frac{n}{3}$
8. $\frac{w}{^-5} = ^-8$

9. $^-15y = 45$
10. $^-9y = 3$
11. $^-19 = ^-19n$
12. $125 = ^-5x$

13. $^-13 = \frac{x}{9}$
14. $\frac{n}{^-4} = ^-12$
15. $5n = ^-2$
16. $^-10n = 1$

17. $\frac{x}{5} = ^-36$
18. $41 = \frac{w}{^-10}$
19. $\frac{2}{3}x = ^-18$
20. $^-\frac{4}{5}x = 16$

21. $^-6.8 = ^-1.7y$ ★22. $^-3n = 4(^-14 - 10)$ ★23. $\left(\frac{1}{2} + ^-\frac{2}{3}\right)n = ^-21$ ★24. $\frac{n}{^-6} = 1.25 \cdot 0.6$

Write an equation for each sentence. Then solve.

25. The product of $^-8$ and a number n is $^-56$.

26. A number x divided by 5 is $^-11$.

27. Three fourths times a number t is $^-18$.

28. The product of $^-12$ and a number q is $^-3$.

★29. A number w divided by $^-7$ equals the product of $^-10$ and $\frac{1}{2}$.

★30. A number y times the sum of $\frac{1}{3}$ and $^-\frac{3}{4}$ equals the product of $^-3$ and 5.

APPLICATION

31. It takes about 40 days for Adélie penguins to hatch their eggs. This is about $\frac{2}{3}$ the time needed for the emperors to hatch their eggs. In how many days will an emperor penguin's eggs hatch?

32. The tallest penguins are known to grow to about 48 inches. This is about 3 times the height of the shortest. What is the height of the shortest penguins?

LOGICAL THINKING

Find a 4-digit number such that the product of the first and the fourth digits is 40, the product of the middle two digits is 54, and the thousands digit is as much more than the units digit as the hundreds digit is more than the tens digit. If 3,267 is subtracted from the number, the result is the digits of the original number reversed.

411

Inequalities

The surface water of the Atlantic Ocean varies from about 27°C in the tropics to ⁻2°C near the Arctic and Antarctic oceans. What is the maximum that the surface temperature can vary between any two places?

Let n be the maximum number of degrees the surface temperature can vary.

$$^-2 + n \le 27 \longleftarrow \text{inequality}$$

▶ An **inequality** is a sentence that uses one of the symbols $<, >, \le, \ge,$ or $\ne$.

less than or equal to greater than or equal to

An inequality is solved in the same way that an equation is solved.

$$^-2 + n \le 27 \quad \text{Use the opposite of } ^-2 \text{ to solve.}$$

$$^-2 + 2 + n \le 27 + 2 \quad \text{Add 2 to both sides of the inequality.}$$

$$0 + n \le 29$$

$$n \le 29 \quad \text{Solution}$$

The maximum that the surface temperature can vary is 29 degrees.

More Examples

Solve each inequality *over the integers*. That is, find only the solutions that are integers.

a. $3n \ge ^-18$ Use the reciprocal of 3 to solve.

$\frac{1}{3} \cdot 3n \ge \frac{1}{3} \cdot ^-18$ Multiply both sides by $\frac{1}{3}$.

$1n \ge ^-6$

$n \ge ^-6$

Over the integers the solutions are ⁻6, ⁻5, ⁻4, ...

Check $3 \cdot ^-6 \ge ^-18, 3 \cdot ^-5 \ge ^-18,$
$3 \cdot ^-4 \ge ^-18, \ldots$

b. $\frac{x}{7} < ^-4$

$\frac{1}{7}x < ^-4$ Use the reciprocal of $\frac{1}{7}$ to solve.

$7 \cdot \frac{1}{7}x < 7 \cdot ^-4$ Multiply both sides by 7.

$1x < ^-28$

$x < ^-28$

Over the integers the solutions are . . ., ⁻31, ⁻30, ⁻29.

Check   . . ., $\frac{^-31}{7} < ^-4, \frac{^-30}{7} < ^-4, \frac{^-29}{7} < ^-4$

CLASSWORK

Solve over the integers. List the first three solutions. Check.

1. $y + 9 \ge 4$

2. $x - 5 \le 2$

3. $w + 7 < ^-3$

4. $n - ^-8 > 6$

5. $4x > 12$

6. $5y \le ^-20$

7. $\frac{n}{3} \ge ^-9$

8. $\frac{x}{5} < 2$

Solve over the integers. List the first three solutions. Check.

1. $x + 2 > 9$ **2.** $n - 1 < 11$ **3.** $y + 5 < 2$

4. $8n \geq 24$ **5.** $2w \leq 2$ **6.** $\frac{x}{2} \geq 4$

7. $y + {}^-5 \geq 3$ **8.** $x - 5 \geq {}^-5$ **9.** $d - {}^-2 > {}^-1$

10. $n + {}^-4 < {}^-17$ **11.** $x - 3 \leq {}^-4$ **12.** ${}^-6 + d > 0$

13. $4n > {}^-8$ **14.** $\frac{x}{3} < {}^-5$ **15.** $6y > 0$

16. $\frac{n}{7} < 9$ **17.** $3x \leq {}^-6$ **18.** $7x \geq 28$

19. $17 > 8 + x$ **20.** ${}^-12 \leq y - 5$ **21.** $y - 2.7 < 1.3$

★ **22.** $14n < 7$ ★ **23.** $8y \geq 20$ ★ **24.** ${}^-5\frac{3}{4} \geq w - \frac{1}{4}$

Write an inequality for each. Then solve over the integers.

25. The sum of a number m and ${}^-6$ is greater than 5.

26. A number x minus ${}^-5$ is less than ${}^-4$.

27. The product of 6 and a number q is less than or equal to ${}^-18$.

28. A number t divided by 2 is greater than or equal to ${}^-5$.

★ **29.** The product of a number n and 8 is greater than the sum of ${}^-6$ and ${}^-4$.

★ **30.** A number y plus ${}^-3.2$ is less than or equal to ${}^-1.6$.

APPLICATION

31. Adam lives along the Atlantic coast. He recorded the following average temperatures of ocean waters for April to September: 13°C, 14°C, 16°C, 19°C, 21°C, 22°C. Graph his results. From which month to the next was the change in temperature the greatest?

★ **32.** Sandi is an art dealer. She bought a carving of a seagull and sold it for $160. She saw it for sale a year later for $190. She bought it and later sold it for $250. She made at least $100 from the two sales of the carving. What is the most she could have paid for it the first time she bought it?

Mixed Practice

1. ${}^-\frac{2}{3} + \frac{5}{6}$

2. $2.7 + {}^-6.4$

3. $2\frac{1}{2} - {}^-3\frac{1}{4}$

4. ${}^-\frac{1}{3} \cdot 2 \cdot {}^-\frac{3}{8}$

5. $\begin{array}{r} {}^-2.45 \\ \times \quad 3.6 \\ \hline \end{array}$

6. ${}^-4.5\overline{)36.9}$

7. $13\frac{5}{8} - 18\frac{1}{2}$

8. $1\frac{1}{4} - 3\frac{2}{5} + 2\frac{1}{2}$

9. 25% of 68

10. 36% of 50

11. 24 is what percent of 96?

12. 12 is what percent of 96?

Find the area of each.

13. a square with side 6.5 m

14. a rectangle 3.4 m by 2.5 m

15. a parallelogram with base 7 cm and height 6 cm

16. a right triangle with one leg 18.4 cm and the other leg 9 cm

Problem Solving

SOLVING A SIMPLER PROBLEM

Sometimes solving a difficult or complicated problem can be made easier by solving a similar problem that is simpler.

The Sea Horse Boat Company has 15 boats to distribute to their 3 branches. In how many ways can the boats be distributed if each branch must get at least 1 boat?

To determine how to distribute 15 boats among the 3 branches requires a great deal of work. Solve a simpler problem and see if a pattern results.

Start with 3 boats, distributed among 3 branches. Then find the number of ways 4 boats can be distributed among 3 branches. Continue until a pattern develops. The table at the right shows the results for 3, 4, 5, and 6 boats.

Total boats	Branch A	Branch B	Branch C	
3	1	1	1	1 way
4	2	1	1	3 ways
	1	2	1	
	1	1	2	
5	3	1	1	6 ways
	2	2	1	
	2	1	2	
	1	3	1	
	1	2	2	
	1	1	3	
6	4	1	1	10 ways
	3	2	1	
	3	1	2	
	2	3	1	
	2	2	2	
	2	1	3	
	1	4	1	
	1	3	2	
	1	2	3	
	1	1	4	

DISTRIBUTION OF BOATS

The table below summarizes the results and extends them to include 15 boats.

Total number of boats	3	4	5	6	7	8	9	10	11	12	13	14	15
Number of ways to distribute	1	3	6	10	15	21	28	36	45	55	66	78	91
Difference		2	3	4	5	6	7	8	9	10	11	12	13

The 15 boats can be distributed in 91 ways.

Check to be sure all the possible cases were included in the original table. Be sure the summary table was interpreted correctly.

PRACTICE

Solve.

1. The six officers of the cruise ship Pacific Prince meet in the captain's stateroom. Each person shakes hands with each of the other people. How many handshakes are made altogether?

2. The cruise line is distributing 20 signal flares among the 3 storage cabinets on the ship. Each cabinet must have a minimum of 3 flares. In how many ways can they distribute the 20 flares?

3. Captain Martinez enters the marina at point *A*. He wants to moor his boat at dock *H*. He must follow the directions of the arrows. In how many different ways can he get to the dock?

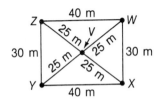

4. The drawing at the right shows the location of Barney's five lobster traps. He starts at trap *W* and visits each trap once. How many different paths can he take to empty every trap?

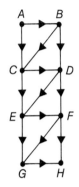

5. How long is the shortest path Barney can take?

6. If a polygon has 9 diagonals, how many sides will it have?

7. If a polygon has 10 diagonals, how many sides will it have?

★8. An underwater exploration team is mapping an area on the ocean floor 5 km by 5 km. The area is divided into 1-km squares as shown here. How many squares are there in all?

★9. A school has exactly 1,000 students and 1,000 lockers numbered from 1 to 1,000. On the first day of school the students agree to do the following: The first student will enter the building and open all the lockers. The second student will then enter and close every even-numbered locker. The third student will either open or close every third locker. The fourth student will either open or close every fourth locker, and so on, until all 1,000 students in turn have entered the building and either opened or closed the appropriate lockers. Which lockers will finally remain open?

CREATE YOUR OWN PROBLEM

Write a problem for which this drawing might be used to find the solution. The problem should be one that would be easier to solve by using a simpler problem.

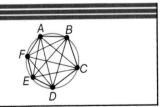

Two-Step Equations

This seascape was painted by Michele Sanok. In framing it, how much room was left on each side, between the picture and the edge of the frame?

Let n be the distance between the picture and the edge of the frame.

$$2n + 30 = 38$$

Sometimes both addition and multiplication are needed to solve an equation.

$2n + 30 + {}^-30 = 38 + {}^-30$ First add $^-30$ to both sides of the equation.

$$2n = 8$$

$\frac{1}{2} \cdot 2n = \frac{1}{2} \cdot 8$ Then multiply both sides of the equation by $\frac{1}{2}$.

$$n = 4$$

Check $2 \cdot 4 + 30 = 38$

There was 4 in. left on each side.

Another Example

$$\frac{n}{4} - 1 = {}^-2$$

$$\frac{n}{4} + {}^-1 = {}^-2$$

$\frac{n}{4} + {}^-1 + 1 = {}^-2 + 1$ First add 1 to both sides.

$$\frac{n}{4} = {}^-1$$

$$\frac{1}{4}n = {}^-1$$

$4 \cdot \frac{1}{4}n = 4 \cdot {}^-1$ Then multiply both sides by 4.

$$n = {}^-4$$

Check $\frac{{}^-4}{4} - 1 = {}^-2$

CLASSWORK

Tell what must be done to both sides of the equation. Then solve. Check each solution.

1. $4x + 1 = 5$

2. $2n - 5 = 1$

3. $\frac{n}{2} + 1 = 7$

4. $9 = {}^-3y + 6$

5. $\frac{x}{{}^-5} + 2 = {}^-4$

6. $3 - 2y = {}^-9$

Solve. Check each solution.

1. $3x + 7 = 10$

2. $4y - 5 = 3$

3. $2x - 3 = 3$

4. $\frac{n}{3} + 1 = {}^-4$

5. $^-7 = 2n + 1$

6. $\frac{x}{2} - 3 = 4$

7. $^-5x - 10 = 0$

8. $7x - {}^-2 = {}^-19$

9. $4 - 2y = 6$

10. $^-1 = \frac{w}{^-5} + 9$

11. $1 - 5n = 6$

12. $\frac{x}{^-3} + 1 = {}^-1$

13. $6x - {}^-1 = {}^-17$

14. $^-1 - w = {}^-1$

15. $^-1 = 8 - 3n$

16. $3w + 7 = 9$

17. $^-1 - \frac{w}{2} = 6$

18. $\frac{3}{2}n - 1 = 11$

19. $0.2w + 1 = 3$

20. $5 = 0.5x + 3$

21. $^-7 = 3 - 4y$

★ 22. $\frac{1}{3}(y + 1) = 3$

★ 23. $^-\frac{3}{4}n - \frac{1}{2} = {}^-5$

★ 24. $4(x - 1) = {}^-3$

Write an equation for each. Then solve.

25. The product of $^-2$ and a number n, minus 3 is 7.

26. Five minus the product of 3 and a number y is $^-7$.

27. Six plus the quotient of a number x and $^-4$ is 1.

28. When the product of 6 and a number y is subtracted from $^-6$, the result is 0.

29. When the quotient of a number n and 3 is subtracted from $^-8$, the result is 2.

★ 30. When the sum of a number y and $^-5$ is multiplied by $\frac{1}{2}$, the result is $^-1$.

★ 31. When $\frac{5}{6}$ is subtracted from the product of $^-\frac{5}{2}$ and y, the result is $1\frac{1}{4}$.

APPLICATION

32. The width of the frame for the seascape on page 416 is 1 in. wide. How much matting will show on each side of the picture?

33. When a picture is matted, the width of the mat at the top should match the width of the sides. Will the width of the mat at the bottom of the seascape be larger or smaller than that at the sides? How much?

Combining Terms

Two pearl divers brought oyster shells to the surface. One diver's shells contained 4 valuable pearls, while the other's shells had 9. The total value of the pearls was $455. All the pearls were of equal worth. What was the value of each pearl?

Let x be the value of each pearl.

$$4x + 9x = 455$$

$$(4 + 9)x = 455 \quad \text{Use the Distributive Property to add } 4x + 9x.$$

$$13x = 455$$

$$\tfrac{1}{13} \cdot 13x = \tfrac{1}{13} \cdot 455$$

$$x = 35$$

Check $4 \cdot 35 + 9 \cdot 35 = 455$

The value of each pearl was $35.

More Examples

a.
$$3y - 6y = 12$$
$$3y + {}^-6y = 12$$
$$(3 + {}^-6)y = 12 \quad \text{Use the Distributive Property to add } 3y \text{ and } {}^-6y.$$
$$^-3y = 12$$
$$y = {}^-4$$

Check $3 \cdot {}^-4 - 6 \cdot {}^-4 = 12$

b.
$$72 = {}^-7n + {}^-2n$$
$$72 = ({}^-7 + {}^-2)n \quad \text{Use the Distributive Property to add } {}^-7n \text{ and } {}^-2n.$$
$$72 = {}^-9n$$
$$^-8 = n$$

Check $72 = {}^-7 \cdot {}^-8 + {}^-2 \cdot {}^-8$

CLASSWORK

Solve and check.

1. $3x + 7x = 20$

2. $7n + n = 24$

3. $8n - 2n = 12$

4. $4y - 7y = 21$

5. $^-10 = {}^-6x + 8x$

6. $^-3x - 2x = 15$

PRACTICE

Solve and check.

1. $4y + 7y = 33$

2. $10x - 5x = 20$

3. $3n + 5n = {}^-16$

4. $2n + 7n = {}^-45$

5. $49 = 6x + x$

6. $^-y + 5y = 32$

7. $6x - 3x = 36$

8. $9n - n = {}^-72$

9. $3y - 9y = {}^-48$

10. $18 = {}^-8y - y$

11. $2a - 4a = {}^-6$

12. $5n - 9n = 24$

13. $^-7 = {}^-3x - 4x$

14. $^-5y - 3y = 32$

15. $^-5n + 7n = 0$

16. $^-2n + 5n = 2$

17. $1 = 6a - 2a$

18. $y + 4y = 3$

19. $\frac{1}{2}n + \frac{1}{2}n = 5$

20. $\frac{1}{2}x - \frac{2}{5}x = 1$

21. $8.2y + 3.8y = 24$

★ **22.** $3n - 7n + 8 = 12$

★ **23.** $4w - 6w + 3w = {}^-4$

★ **24.** $5z - z + 2z = {}^-12$

★ **25.** $13t - 9t + 6 = {}^-4$

★ **26.** $10 - 6n - 4n = 15$

Write each in words.

27. $3x - 4x = 5$

28. $2w + 7w = 10$

29. $6 - 5n = 10$

★ **30.** $8n - 14n = {}^-4 \cdot 3$

★ **31.** $8y - 15 = {}^-3 + 12$

★ **32.** $\frac{n}{4} - \frac{n}{3} = 1$

APPLICATION

MATH HISTORY

"Best of clocks, how much of the day is past?
There remains twice two thirds of what is gone."

The *Greek Anthology,* compiled in the Middle Ages, is a collection of Greek epigrams (short poems). Some of the epigrams were written as early as 700 B.C. A number of them are mathematical problems, like the one above. How many hours of the day have passed?

Inequalities

Mr. and Mrs. Johnson and their ten-year-old son will fly to the Pacific island of Oahu for a vacation. The airfare for all three people will not be more than $1,100. The son's airfare is $300. What is the maximum airfare for each parent?

Let x be the maximum airfare for each parent.

$$2x + 300 \leq 1{,}100$$

Sometimes both addition and multiplication are needed to solve an inequality. You can solve inequalities in the same way you solve equations.

$$2x + 300 \leq 1{,}100$$

$$2x + 300 + {}^-300 \leq 1{,}100 + {}^-300 \quad \text{First add } {}^-300 \text{ to both sides of the inequality.}$$

$$2x \leq 800$$

$$\tfrac{1}{2} \cdot 2x \leq \tfrac{1}{2} \cdot 800 \quad \text{Then multiply both sides by } \tfrac{1}{2}.$$

$$x \leq 400$$

The maximum airfare for each parent is $400.

Another Example

$$14y - 6y > {}^-16$$

$$14y + {}^-6y > {}^-16$$

$$(14 + {}^-6)y > {}^-16 \quad \text{Use the Distributive Property to add } 14y \text{ and } {}^-6y.$$

$$8y > {}^-16$$

$$\tfrac{1}{8} \cdot 8y > \tfrac{1}{8} \cdot {}^-16$$

$$y > {}^-2$$

CLASSWORK

Solve and check.

1. $7n - 4 \leq 10$

2. $\frac{x}{4} + 7 > 9$

3. $3x + 1 \leq 10$

4. $5y - 3y \leq {}^-4$

5. $9x - 3x \geq {}^-18$

6. $7t - 3t < 8$

Solve and check.

1. $3x + 1 < 7$
2. $4n - 1 \geq 11$
3. $2x + 3 > 9$
4. $\frac{n}{3} - 4 > {}^-2$
5. $9y + 2 \leq {}^-7$
6. $\frac{n}{4} + 5 < {}^-1$
7. $1 + 4x > 5$
8. $6n - 3 \geq {}^-15$
9. ${}^-17 + \frac{x}{2} \leq {}^-12$
10. $4t + 3 > 5$
11. $0 > \frac{w}{6} + 3$
12. $8y + 1 \leq {}^-1$
13. $5x - 2x \geq {}^-15$
14. $7n + n > 24$
15. ${}^-y + 5y < 32$
16. $8t - 6t \leq {}^-10$
17. $13y - 9y > {}^-4$
18. ${}^-3n + 9n < 18$
19. ${}^-2 > 6n - 4n$
20. $7x - x < {}^-3$
21. ${}^-6 > 8n - 5n$
★ 22. $\frac{n}{3} - \frac{5}{3} \geq \frac{7}{3}$
★ 23. $5n - 3n + 7n < 18$
★ 24. ${}^-25 > {}^-2x - x + 8x$
★ 25. $\frac{w}{2} - \frac{w}{4} > 3$
★ 26. $5.1t - 3.7t + 7.4t < 0$
★ 27. $\frac{3}{4}n + \frac{1}{2}n - \frac{2}{3}n \leq {}^-14$

APPLICATION

28. There are 5 major Hawaiian islands that tourists can visit. How many ways can the Johnsons choose two islands to visit?

29. The Johnsons are making a budget for expenses other than airfare on their trip. They have decided not to spend more than $1,000. The son's portion is $250. What is the maximum each parent can spend?

30. In their budget the Johnsons have allowed $30 a day per person for food. What is the maximum each person can spend on items other than food (entertainment, souvenirs, emergency items, and so on)?

Graphing on the Number Line

The solutions of an equation or an inequality can be graphed on the number line.

Solve the equation $3w = {}^-9$ and graph its solution.

$$3w = {}^-9$$

$$\frac{1}{3} \cdot 3w = \frac{1}{3} \cdot {}^-9$$

$$w = {}^-3$$

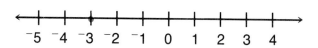

Solve the inequality $n + 8 \geq 3$ and graph its solution.

$$n + 8 \geq 3$$

$$n + 8 + {}^-8 \geq 3 + {}^-8$$

$$n \geq {}^-5$$

To show that $^-5$ is a solution, use a solid dot.

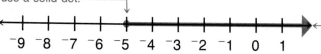

To show that all numbers greater than $^-5$ are solutions, shade all points to the right of $^-5$.

Solve the inequality $3n - 5 < 7$ and graph its solution.

$$3n - 5 < 7$$

$$3n + {}^-5 + 5 < 7 + 5$$

$$3n < 12$$

$$\frac{1}{3} \cdot 3n < \frac{1}{3} \cdot 12$$

$$n < 4$$

To show that 4 is not a solution, use a hollow dot.

To show that all numbers less than 4 are solutions, shade all points to the left of 4.

CLASSWORK

Solve each and graph its solution.

1. $x + 1 \leq 2$

2. $2w < {}^-4$

3. $4t + 5 = 17$

4. $n - 2 \geq 0$

5. $\frac{w}{2} = {}^-8$

6. $2y - 3 > {}^-7$

Solve each and graph its solution.

1. $2x = {}^-20$

2. $3b \geq 0$

3. $x + 6 > 7$

4. $n - 5 < {}^-8$

5. $t + 3 = {}^-4$

6. $x + {}^-2 = 0$

7. $4t > {}^-20$

8. $y + 5 \leq 2$

9. $\frac{w}{{}^-5} = 2$

10. $n - 7 < {}^-3$

11. $\frac{x}{3} < {}^-4$

12. $0 \geq n + 3$

13. ${}^-25 < 5y$

14. $1 + m < {}^-3$

15. ${}^-3 = \frac{n}{2}$

16. $3t + 2 = 2$

17. $2x - 1 < 9$

18. ${}^-10 = 3n - 4$

19. ${}^-2 < \frac{n}{4} - 6$

20. ${}^-7 \geq {}^-3 + 4x$

21. $7n + 4n = {}^-11$

★ 22. $2t - 4 \leq {}^-3$

★ 23. ${}^-8 < 4n - 5$

★ 24. ${}^-2x + 5x > {}^-2$

APPLICATION

=== VISUAL THINKING ===

step 1
crease

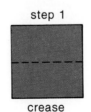
step 2
fold

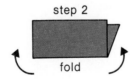
step 3
punch

Which shape will result when the paper is unfolded?

1

2

3

4

5

Problem Solving

SKILLS AND STRATEGIES REVIEW

Solve.

1. Stan is loading four boxes of provisions onto his boat. Together the boxes weigh 80 pounds. Each box is one third the weight of the next heavier box. What is the weight of each box?

2. A new marina is under construction. The berths will be numbered consecutively, beginning with 1. The numbering process will require 489 individual brass digits. How many berths will there be?

3. The fishing fleet left Manilow Bay when the water level reached 32 feet. At 5:00 A.M., the depth was 27 feet. The tide rose at the rate of $1\frac{1}{2}$ feet per hour for the next 6 hours. The depth of the water was measured every hour on the hour. At what time did the fleet leave?

4. The sailing yacht *Albatross* left its home berth in Los Angeles on a trip to Puerto Vallarta, traveling at 12 nautical miles per hour. After 3 hours it developed engine trouble and had to return home at half speed. At what time did the *Albatross* arrive in Los Angeles?

5. A research ship is surveying the ocean floor. During the first hour the ship travels 8 miles due north. During the next hour it drifts 3 miles due south.
   a. If the ship continues in this way, how many miles will it have traveled in all after 7 hours?
   b. After 7 hours where will the ship be in relation to its starting point?

6. There is a monument of rocks near the Reyos dock. The rocks are stacked in the shape of a square pyramid with 100 rocks in the bottom layer, 81 rocks in the second layer, and so on to the top layer of 1 rock.
   a. How many rocks are there in one face of the monument?
   b. How many rocks are there in the entire monument?

424

7. A fishing boat has just come back to port with its catch. In one 3-hour period, the people caught twice as many sea trout as striped bass. They caught 1 less flounder than sea trout and 4 times as many bluefish as flounder. They caught 12 bluefish. How many of each kind of fish did they catch?

8. When she returned to the dock, Marcy sold her day's catch to the local cannery. She then paid $8.00 for her bait. She spent half of what she had left on a new rod, half of what was then left on a new reel, and then bought 6 lead sinkers for 20¢ each. She had $24.20 left. How much did she sell her catch for?

9. Each of the 14 boats in a fishing fleet communicates with each of the other boats once every hour. How many times do all the boats communicate with one another in one hour?

10. Jill has $3.00 in change to make a ship-to-shore telephone call. The cost for a call is 75¢ for the first 3 minutes and 18¢ for each additional minute. How many minutes can Jill talk?

★ 11. Jeff, Stacey, and Lisa collected shells on the beach. They divided the shells equally. Each person then gave away 6 shells. The *total* number of shells left then was the same as the number each person had after the shells were divided equally. How many shells did they start with altogether?

★ 12. The fishing schooner *Sailfish* departed from the dock at 11:00 A.M. It headed due east at 15 nautical miles per hour. At the same time the schooner *Bluefish* departed from the same dock and headed due north at 20 nautical miles per hour. How far apart will the vessels be after traveling 3 hours?

Name the additive and multiplicative inverses of each. pages 406–407

1. 4

2. $\frac{3}{4}$

3. $\frac{-1}{8}$

4. $\frac{-6}{5}$

5. $1\frac{1}{2}$

6. $^-2$

Name the property illustrated. pages 406–407

7. $5 + {}^-5 = 0$

8. $1 \cdot \frac{-5}{4} = \frac{-5}{4}$

9. $\frac{1}{3} \cdot \frac{3}{4} = \frac{3}{4} \cdot \frac{1}{3}$

10. $^-4 + 0 = {}^-4$

11. $\frac{-1}{6} \cdot {}^-6 = 1$

12. $\frac{1}{5}({}^-2 + 6) = \left(\frac{1}{5} \cdot {}^-2\right) + \left(\frac{1}{5} \cdot 6\right)$

Solve and check. pages 408–411, 416–419

13. $x + 9 = 7$

14. $^-6 = y - {}^-4$

15. $^-4n = {}^-16$

16. $\frac{x}{3} = 5$

17. $2n + 1 = 21$

18. $\frac{y}{4} - 1 = {}^-3$

19. $2y + 3 = {}^-7$

20. $4n - n = 21$

21. $^-10 = 8y - 3y$

22. $7y - 5y = 8$

23. $^-n + {}^-3 = 4$

24. $^-3y = 18$

Write an equation or an inequality for each. Then solve. pages 408–413, 416–419

25. Five more than a number n is $^-7$.

26. The product of $^-2$ and a number y, minus 5 is 9.

27. The product of 7 and a number n is less than or equal to $^-21$.

28. Four times a number y, decreased by two times the same number is $^-6$.

Solve. Graph the solution on the number line. pages 412–413, 420–423

29. $5x = {}^-10$

30. $y + 6 > 9$

31. $\frac{n}{3} < 2$

32. $5y - 2y \le 6$

33. $4x - 1 \ge 11$

34. $5y - 9y = 28$

35. $6x - 1 < 5$

36. $n + {}^-3 > {}^-4$

37. $7x - 3x \le {}^-8$

Solve. pages 414–415, 424–425

38. Seven friends each had a cabin on an ocean liner. Each friend visited every other person's cabin. How many visits were made?

39. Peri sold a seascape for $\frac{3}{2}$ of its original price. She sold the painting for $180. What was the original price? Write an equation. Then solve it.

CHAPTER TEST

Name the additive and multiplicative inverses of each.

1. 3

2. $-\frac{1}{4}$

3. $\frac{5}{3}$

4. $^-6$

Solve and check.

5. $x + 9 = 8$

6. $^-5 = n - {}^-3$

7. $\frac{y}{4} = 3$

8. $^-3n = {}^-21$

9. $3y + 1 = 19$

10. $^-2n + 6 = {}^-14$

11. $\frac{x}{3} - 1 = {}^-2$

12. $6n - 2n = 12$

13. $^-4 = 5x - x$

Write an equation or an inequality for each. Then solve.

14. Three times a number x plus 4 times the same number is $^-14$.

15. The product of 3 and a number n is greater than $^-12$.

16. Five minus three times a number t is equal to $^-4$.

17. Ten plus a number y is less than or equal to $^-8$.

Solve. Graph the solution on a number line.

18. $x + 4 \geq 7$

19. $2n = {}^-8$

20. $3n - 1 \leq 11$

21. $5y - y > 8$

22. $7 - 2t = {}^-3$

23. $\frac{m}{11} < {}^-3$

Solve.

24. There are eight towns that form an octagon. There is a road connecting each town with every other town. How many roads are there?

25. The greatest depth of the Mediterranean Sea is about 2,600 ft more than twice the greatest depth of the Red Sea. The depth of the Mediterranean Sea is about 17,000 ft. About how deep is the Red Sea? Write an equation and solve it.

Solve over the integers. List the first three solutions.
$$\frac{^-3}{5} \div \frac{6}{25} \geq \frac{1}{2}n - \frac{3}{4}n - \frac{^-5}{2} + \frac{1}{3} + \frac{2}{3}n$$

SOLVING EQUATIONS

You can use a calculator to solve any equation.

For $n + {}^-6 = {}^-2$, ${}^-2 + 6 = n$.

Press $\boxed{2}\ \boxed{+/-}\ \boxed{+}\ \boxed{6}\ \boxed{=}$ ▭ 4.

So $n = 4$.

For $\frac{x}{4} = {}^-5$, ${}^-5 \cdot 4 = x$.

Press $\boxed{5}\ \boxed{+/-}\ \boxed{\times}\ \boxed{4}\ \boxed{=}$ ▭ - 20.

So $x = {}^-20$.

For $2n - 7 = {}^-3$, $({}^-3 + 7) \cdot \frac{1}{2} = n$.

Press $\boxed{3}\ \boxed{+/-}\ \boxed{+}\ \boxed{7}\ \boxed{\times}\ \boxed{.}\ \boxed{5}\ \boxed{=}$ ▭ 2. ← arithmetic operations

Press $\boxed{(}\ \boxed{3}\ \boxed{+/-}\ \boxed{+}\ \boxed{7}\ \boxed{)}\ \boxed{\times}\ \boxed{.}\ \boxed{5}\ \boxed{=}$ ▭ 2. ← algebraic operations

So $x = 2$.

For $\frac{n}{-3} + 4 = {}^-2$, $({}^-2 + {}^-4) \cdot {}^-3 = n$.

Press $\boxed{2}\ \boxed{+/-}\ \boxed{+}\ \boxed{4}\ \boxed{+/-}\ \boxed{\times}\ \boxed{3}\ \boxed{+/-}\ \boxed{=}$ ▭ 18. ← arithmetic operations

Press $\boxed{(}\ \boxed{2}\ \boxed{+/-}\ \boxed{+}\ \boxed{4}\ \boxed{+/-}\ \boxed{)}\ \boxed{\times}\ \boxed{3}\ \boxed{+/-}\ \boxed{=}$ ▭ 18. ← algebraic operations

So $x = 18$.

Use a calculator to solve each equation. Check each solution.

1. $x + 34 = {}^-45$

2. $n - 27 = 68$

3. $16n = {}^-192$

4. $\frac{d}{15} = {}^-25$

5. ${}^-28w = 1{,}008$

6. $56 - x = {}^-119$

7. $2n + 14 = 62$

8. $3y - 15 = 72$

9. $\frac{n}{5} + 17 = 54$

10. $36 - 8x = {}^-68$

11. $25 = {}^-51 + \frac{w}{9}$

12. ${}^-117 = {}^-62 + 22n$

13. ${}^-3.2n + 6 = 7.6$

14. $40 = 2y - 17$

15. $4t + 2.5 = 15$

16. $\frac{5}{2}n - 6 = {}^-4$

17. $\frac{-1}{4} - \frac{3}{4}x = 5$

18. $3w - 28 = {}^-30$

SOLVING INEQUALITIES

Each inequality below has been multiplied by $^-1$. Notice that the direction of the inequality symbols is reversed.

Inequality	$4 < 5$	$^-2 > ^-3$	$^-2 < 1$
Multiplied by $^-1$	$^-4 > ^-5$	$2 < 3$	$2 > ^-1$

▶When both sides of an inequality are multiplied by the same negative number, the direction of the inequality symbol is always reversed.

Examples

a. Solve $^-3x > 15$.

$$^-3x > 15$$

$$-\tfrac{1}{3} \cdot {}^-3x < -\tfrac{1}{3} \cdot 15 \quad \boxed{\text{Direction reversed}}$$

$$\left(-\tfrac{1}{3} \cdot {}^-3\right)x < {}^-5$$

$$x < {}^-5$$

b. Solve $^-4y \le ^-28$.

$$^-4y \le {}^-28$$

$$-\tfrac{1}{4} \cdot {}^-4y \ge -\tfrac{1}{4} \cdot {}^-28$$

$$\left(-\tfrac{1}{4} \cdot {}^-4\right)y \ge 7$$

$$y \ge 7$$

Solve.

1. $\quad ^-5y > ^-15$

$\quad \square \cdot {}^-5y \; \bullet \; \square \cdot {}^-15$

$\quad\quad y \; \bullet \; 3$

2. $\quad ^-2x \le 6$

$\quad \square \cdot {}^-2x \; \bullet \; \square \cdot 6$

$\quad\quad x \; \bullet \; {}^-3$

3. $^-4x < 12$

4. $^-8y \ge ^-48$

5. $^-20 \le ^-5x$

6. $^-5r - 2 \le ^-12$

7. $7 - 4b < 19$

8. $^-7n - 3 > 25$

9. $\dfrac{x}{^-3} \ge ^-11$

10. $^-4a - 2a < 24$

11. $4 - (3 + x) > 9$

MAINTAINING SKILLS

Choose the correct answers. Write A, B, C, or D.

1. What is 3.096 to the nearest hundredth?

    A 4.0   **C** 3.1

    B 3.09   **D** not given

2. Solve. $x - 14 = 21$

    A $x = 35$ **C** $x = 5$

    B $x = 7$ **D** not given

3. $\frac{3}{5} \div 3\frac{3}{4}$

    A $3\frac{2}{3}$ **C** $\frac{4}{25}$

    B $6\frac{1}{4}$ **D** not given

4. What is $33\frac{1}{3}\%$ of 216?

    A 648   **C** 144

    B 72   **D** not given

5. $53 - {}^{-}12$

    A 65   **C** $^{-}41$

    B 41   **D** not given

6. Why are the triangles congruent?

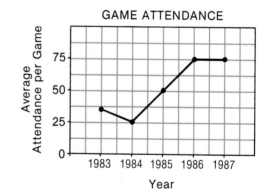

    A ASA   **C** SSS

    B SAS   **D** not given

7. What is the volume?

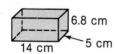

6.8 cm   5 cm   14 cm

    A 476 cm^3 **C** 95.2 cm^2

    B 25.8 cm^3 **D** not given

8. 3.05×10^{-3}

    A 0.00305   **C** 0.305

    B 3,050   **D** not given

9. What is the reciprocal of $^{-}\frac{2}{3}$?

    A $\frac{2}{3}$ **C** 0

    B $^{-}\frac{3}{2}$ **D** not given

10. Solve. $^{-}8 = x - 5$

    A $x = {}^{-}3$ **C** $x = 13$

    B $x = {}^{-}13$ **D** not given

11. $x + 3 > 5$ Which is true?

    A $x > 5$ **C** $x > 2$

    B $x < 3$ **D** not given

Use the graph to solve **12** and **13**. Sponsors of the local soccer league are planning for next year's attendance.

GAME ATTENDANCE

Average Attendance per Game

75, 50, 25, 0

1983 1984 1985 1986 1987

Year

12. If the attendance increases the same amount as it did from 1985 to 1986, how many people can they expect per game in 1988?

    A 60   **C** 100

    B 125   **D** not given

13. The attendance per game in 1981 was half that of 1985. What was the attendance in 1981?

    A 4   **C** 36

    B 25   **D** not given

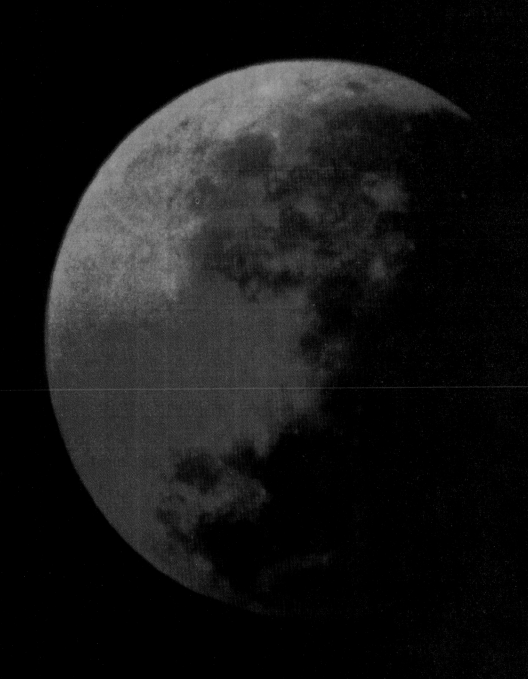

Functions

lithograph by Honoré Daumier—
*M. Babinet prevenu par sa
portière de la Visite de la
Comète*

There are at least 2 million comets speeding through space. The comet that has come closest to the earth is Lexell's Comet. It passed the earth in the year 1770, traveling 24 miles per second.

The distance traveled by the comet is related to the length of time it travels. The graph shows part of this relation.

▶A **relation** is a group of ordered pairs (x, y). The **domain** of the relation is all the values of x. The **range** of the relation is all the values of y.

For the relation shown in the graph, each value of x is the travel time. Each value of y is the distance traveled in that time.

The ordered pairs shown on the graph are
(0, 0), (1, 24), (2, 48), (3, 72), (4, 96), (5, 120).

▶A **function** is a relation in which each value of x is paired only once with a value of y. That is, each value of x occurs only once.

Relations that are functions   **a.** (1, ⁻1), (2, ⁻2), (3, ⁻3)   **b.** (1, 3), (2, 3), (3, 3), (4, 3)

Relations that are not functions **c.** (1, 1), (1, 2), (1, 3), (1, 4) **d.** (⁻5, 0), (3, 0), (7, 7), (3, ⁻2)

CLASSWORK

**Which relations are functions? For 1, write the domain
and range and graph the ordered pairs.**

1. (1, 2), (3, 4), (5, 8), (7, 7)   **2.** (1, 2), (1, 3), (1, 5)   **3.** (1, 6), (⁻1, 6), (0, 5), (⁻4, 4)

Use the following to answer 1–15.

A: (2, ⁻2), (1, ⁻1), (0, 0), (⁻1, 1), (⁻2, 2), (⁻3, 3)

B: (4, 3), (4, 2), (4, 1), (3, 2), (3, 1), (2, 1)

C: (2, 4), (1, 1), (0, ⁻2), (⁻1, ⁻5), (⁻2, ⁻8)

D: (5, 6), (5, 7), (7, 8), (8, 10)

E: (3, 3), (4, 3), (5, 3), (0, 3), (⁻1, 3), (⁻2, 3)

F: (2, ⁻2), (5, ⁻2), (5, 4), (⁻2, 4), (⁻2, 2)

G: (⁻1, 10), (⁻3, 10), (0, 5), (4, 6)

Graph the ordered pairs of each.

1. A 2. B 3. C 4. E 5. F

Which are functions?

6. A 7. B 8. C 9. D 10. E 11. F 12. G

Give the values for each.

13. What is the domain of A?   14. What is the range of C?   15. What is the range of E?

Write the ordered pairs for each graph. Which are functions?

★ 16.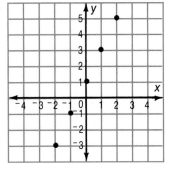

★ 17.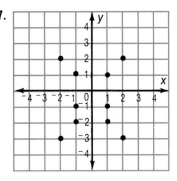

★ 18.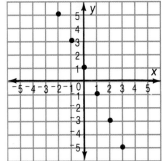

APPLICATION

19. Halley's Comet passed the earth in 1985, traveling toward the sun at a speed of about 20 miles per second. Graph the relation between time and distance traveled for each of 5 seconds. Is this relation a function?

20. Before they entered the spaceship, the 7 travelers met in the lounge. Each traveler shook hands with each of the other travelers. How many handshakes were there altogether?

Graphing Equations

The weight of an object depends on the gravitational pull of the planet or moon it is on. In space an astronaut is practically weightless. On the earth the astronaut is 6 times as heavy as he would be on the moon.

An equation can describe this relation.

$e = 6m$

The graph of the equation is all the points whose coordinates are solutions of the equation. To graph the equation, follow these steps.

Step 1 Make a table of values for m and e. Choose a value for m. Then find the corresponding value for e that makes the sentence true.

m	e = 6m	(m, e)
1	6	(1, 6)
2	12	(2, 12)
3	18	(3, 18)

Step 2 Graph the points for the ordered pairs (m, e) from the table.

Step 3 Draw a line connecting the points. The line is the graph of the equation.

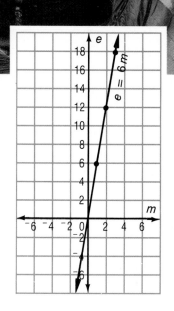

The coordinates (m, e) of any point on the line will be a solution of the equation $e = 6m$. $(^-1, ^-6)$ is a point on the line. $^-6 = 6 \cdot {}^-1$
$(^-1, ^-6)$ is a solution of $e = 6m$.

CLASSWORK

Complete each chart. Then graph each equation.

1. $y = x + 3$

x	y
4	
2	
0	
^-2	
^-4	

2. $y = x - 1$

x	y
4	
3	
2	
1	
0	

3. $y = 2x$

x	y
3	
2	
1	
0	
^-1	

4. $y = 2x - 3$

x	y
4	
2	
0	
^-2	
^-4	

434

Complete each chart. Graph each equation.

1. $y = x + 4$

x	y
3	
2	
1	
0	
⁻1	

2. $y = \frac{1}{2}x$

x	y
4	
2	
0	
⁻2	
⁻4	

3. $y = 2x - 1$

x	y
2	
1	
0	
⁻1	
⁻2	

4. $y = ⁻3x + 1$

x	y
2	
1	
0	
⁻1	
⁻2	

5. $y = x + 2$

6. $y = 2x - 5$

7. $y = x$

8. $y = -x$

9. $y = ⁻3x + 2$

10. $y = \frac{3}{2}x - 1$

★ **11.** $y = 4 - x$

★ **12.** $y = 1 - 2x$

Use the graph of $y = 3x - 1$ to answer 13–17.

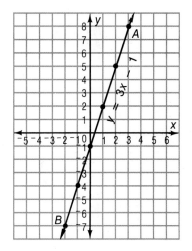

13. What is the value of x when $y = ⁻4$?

14. What are the coordinates of point A?

15. What are the coordinates of point B?

16. Give two other solutions of $y = 3x - 1$.

★ **17.** How many solutions for the equation $y = 3x - 1$ are there?

APPLICATION

18. On Mercury a rock would weigh almost $\frac{1}{2}$ as much as on Earth. Graph the equation $m = \frac{1}{2}e$. Write two ordered pairs that are solutions.

★ **19.** A person can jump 6 times as far on the moon as on Earth. Express this as an equation. Graph the equation for distances from 0 to 9 meters on Earth.

CALCULATOR

Not only does the gravitational pull of planets vary. The length of time it takes to circle the sun varies from planet to planet. This table shows the length of a year on other planets in our solar system. Selina is 10 years old on Earth. How old would she be on each other planet? Give your answers in years, months, or weeks, as appropriate. Round to the nearest one.

Planet	Length of year (earth time)
Mercury	88 days
Venus	225 days
Mars	687 days
Jupiter	11.9 years
Saturn	29.5 years
Uranus	84 years
Neptune	164.8 years
Pluto	248.4 years

Slope

The tilt of the earth's axis is shown in the picture at the right.

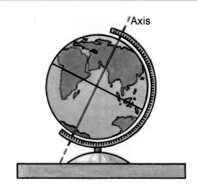

▶The steepness of a line is called its **slope**. The slope of a line can be expressed as a ratio, using any two points on the line.

$$\text{Slope} = \frac{\text{change in } y\text{-value}}{\text{change in } x\text{-value}}$$

Use the points $A(3, 7)$ and $B(6, 14)$ to find the slope of the earth's axis (m).

Change in y-value $= 14 - 7 = 7$
Change in x-value $= 6 - 3 = 3$

$m = \frac{7}{3}$ For every change of 3 units along the x-axis, there is a change of 7 units along the y-axis.

The slope of the earth's axis is $\frac{7}{3}$.

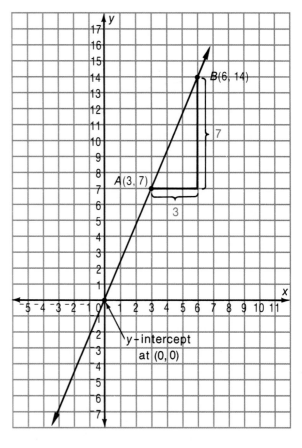

▶The **y-intercept** of a line is the y-value at the point where the line crosses the y-axis.

The slope (m) and the y-intercept (b) of a line can be used to write the equation for that line.

For any line, $y = mx + b$.

For the equation for the earth's axis, $m = \frac{7}{3}$ and $b = 0$.

So $y = \frac{7}{3}x + 0$, or $y = \frac{7}{3}x$.

CLASSWORK

Give the slope and the y-intercept of each line.

1. $y = 3x + 1$

2. $y = 2x - 3$

3. $y = {}^{-}4x + 2$

Write the equation of the line with the given slope and y-intercept.

4. $m = 2; b = 3$

5. $m = \frac{1}{2}; b = {}^{-}2$

6. $m = {}^{-}1; b = 1$

Find the slope of the line containing each pair of points.

7. $(2, 5), (1, 3)$

8. $(3, 1), (4, 2)$

9. $(0, {}^{-}3), (2, 0)$

436

PRACTICE

Give the slope and the *y*-intercept of each line.

1. $y = 3x - 1$ **2.** $y = x - 5$ **3.** $y = 5x - 3$ **4.** $y = {}^-4x + 7$

5. $y = -x - 2$ **6.** $y = \frac{2}{3}x + 6$ **7.** $y = \frac{1}{2}x - 2$ ★**8.** $y = \frac{x}{4}$

Write the equation of the line with the given slope and *y*-intercept.

	slope	y-intercept
9.	2	$^-1$
10.	3	2
11.	$\frac{3}{4}$	8

	slope	y-intercept
12.	$^-6$	$^-5$
13.	7	0
★**14.**	0	11

Find the slope of the line containing each pair of points.

15. (3, 7), (2, 6)   **16.** (2, 5), (1, 2)   **17.** (5, 3), (4, 2)   **18.** (4, $^-7$), (2, $^-3$)

19. (5, $^-10$), (6, $^-4$)   **20.** (17, 6), (15, 6)   **21.** ($^-5$, 1), (5, 3)   **22.** (1, 5), ($^-6$, 13)

Find the slope and *y*-intercept of each line. Then write the equation for each.

★**23.**

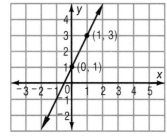

★**24.**

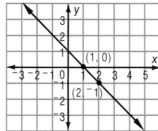

★**25.**

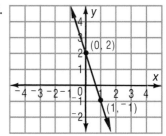

APPLICATION

26. Find the slope of the line of ascent of the space shuttle shown below. Write the answer in lowest terms.

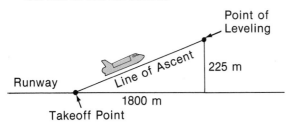

★**27.** A photograph from space showed two hills on the moon. Which hill is easier for an astronaut to climb? Explain why.

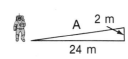

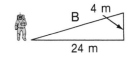

Graphing Inequalities

To graph the inequality $y > 2x$, follow these steps.

Step 1   Graph the equation $y = 2x$. Use a dashed line to show that the graph of $y = 2x$ is not part of the graph of the inequality $y > 2x$.

Step 2   Choose 2 points, one above and one below the line.
$A(1, 3)$ lies above the line.
$B(2, {}^{-}2)$ lies below the line.

Step 3   Find the point that satisfies the inequality $y > 2x$.

For $A(1, 3)$ For $B(2, {}^{-}2)$
3 ⬭ 2 · 1 ${}^{-}2$ ⬭ 2 · 2
$3 > 2$ ${}^{-}2 < 4$

$A(1, 3)$ satisfies the inequality.

Step 4   Shade the graph on the same side of the line as the point that satisfies the inequality. Since $A(1, 3)$ satisfies the inequality, shade above the line.

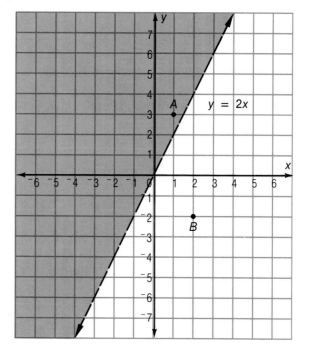

More Examples

a. Graph $y \le 2x$.

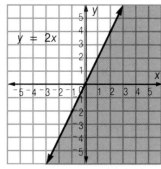

A solid line shows that $y = 2x$ is part of the inequality.

A dashed line shows that $y = x + 1$ is not part of the inequality.

b. Graph $y < x + 1$.

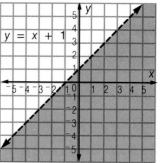

CLASSWORK

Graph each inequality.

1. $y > x$ **2.** $y \le x + 2$ **3.** $y \ge 2x - 1$ **4.** $y < 3x - 2$

PRACTICE

Graph each inequality.

1. $y \leq x$ 2. $y > x - 1$ 3. $y \geq 2x - 3$

4. $y < 2x + 2$ 5. $y > {}^-3x$ 6. $y \geq -x + 2$

7. $y > \frac{1}{3}x$ 8. $y < \frac{1}{2}x - 1$ 9. $y > {}^-2x - 2$

10. $x < {}^-5$ 11. $y \geq 4x$ 12. $y \leq x + 4$

13. $y < -x - 5$ 14. $y \geq \frac{1}{2}x$ 15. $x \geq 3$

16. $y \leq 4$ ★17. $x + y \leq 6$ ★18. $2x - y > 5$

Write an inequality for each graph.

★19.
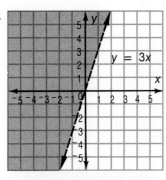

★20.
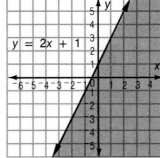

★21.
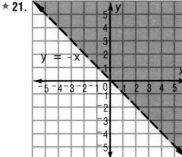

★22.
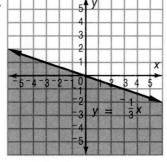

APPLICATION

23. In his astronomy class, Zack drew the graph of the line $y = x$ on his star map. The line divides the map into three sets of stars. Write a mathematical sentence that describes each of the following: the set of stars on the line; the set of stars above the line; the set of stars below the line.

★24. Suppose Zack divides the star map by drawing the graph of any line, $y = mx + b$. Write a mathematical sentence that describes each of the following: the set of stars on or above the line; the set of stars on or below the line.

1. $^-4 + {}^-8$

2. $^-6 + 8$

3. $1.2 \div {}^-0.2$

4. $\frac{3}{4} + \frac{^-1}{8}$

5. $^-12 \cdot {}^-5$

6. $^-2 - {}^-11$

7. $\frac{1}{3} \cdot \frac{^-5}{7}$

8. $^-26 \div 5$

9. $7 - {}^-9$

10. $^-18 - {}^-6$

11. $10^{-6} \cdot 10^4$

12. $10^{-8} \cdot 10^{-4}$

13. $10^9 \cdot 10^{-5}$

14. $10^5 \div 10^3$

15. $10^{-2} \div 10^2$

16. $10^5 \div 10^{-5}$

Write in scientific notation.

17. 0.003

18. 0.0035

19. 0.0102

20. 0.000008

439

Systems of Equations

The first astronauts were professional pilots. Today NASA recruits scientists as well as pilots. One astronaut-training course with 18 people had twice as many scientists as pilots. How many pilots and how many scientists were there?

Write equations for the given information.

$$p + s = 18 \qquad 2p = s$$

The two equations form a **system of equations.**

A graph can be used to solve a system of equations. Graph both equations in the same coordinate plane.

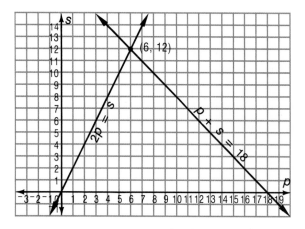

Find the point where the graphs intersect. (6, 12) is the intersection of the graphs. Since (6, 12) is a point on both graphs, it is a solution of both equations. Therefore, it is the solution of the system of equations.

Check Substitute (6, 12) in each equation.

$$2p = s \qquad\qquad p + s = 18$$
$$2(6) = 12 \qquad\qquad 6 + 12 = 18$$

There were 6 pilots and 12 scientists.

CLASSWORK

Solve each system of equations by graphing. Check your solutions.

1. $y = x - 1$
   $y = 2x - 5$

2. $y = 4x - 3$
   $y = x + 3$

3. $y = -x + 3$
   $y = x - 1$

Solve each system of equations by graphing. Check your solutions.

1. $y = 2x + 3$
   $y = x + 4$

2. $y = -x + 6$
   $y = x + 4$

3. $y = {}^-2x$
   $y = -x + 3$

4. $y = 3x - 1$
   $y = x + 3$

5. $y = {}^-3x$
   $y = 2x$

6. $y = x + 5$
   $y = 2$

7. $y = -x - 6$
   $y = x + 2$

8. $y = x - 4$
   $y = -x - 4$

★ **9.** $x + y = 5$
   $x - y = 1$

Use the graph to find the solution for each system of equations.

10. $y = x + 1$
   $x + y = 5$

11. $x + y = 5$
   $y = {}^-3$

12. $y = x + 1$
   $y = {}^-3$

13. $y = x + 1$
   $y = 0$

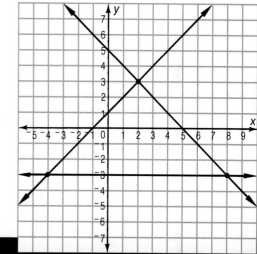

★ **14.** Give the equation of a line that will never have a solution in common with $y = {}^-3$.

Graph each system of equations. What is the relationship between the two lines?

★ **15.** $y = x + 3$
   $y = x - 2$

★ **16.** $y = 2x - 1$
   $y = \frac{-1}{2}x + 2$

APPLICATION

Write systems of equations for 17–19. Solve the systems by graphing.

17. The astronauts spent 20 hours in training. They spent 6 more hours in the classroom than they did in the flight simulator. How long did they spend in each?

18. The mission control room is rectangular. The room is twice as long as it is wide. Its perimeter is 48 meters. Find the dimensions of the room.

★ **19.** The souvenir shop at the space center sold 210 posters one day. A large poster costs $4, and a small poster costs $2. If the total amount collected for posters was $540, how many of each size were sold?

441

Problem Solving

ALTERNATE SOLUTIONS

A problem can often be solved in more than one way. But whichever way it is solved, the answer is always the same. It is often helpful to look back at a problem, using an alternate solution to check your answer.

At 9:00 A.M. EST a Concorde left Washington, D.C., for Paris, France. One hour later another Concorde left Paris for Washington, D.C., flying along the same route. Both planes were traveling at 1,200 mph. The distance from Washington, D.C., to Paris is 4,000 miles. At what time did the planes pass each other?

This problem can be solved by using guess and test or by using simulation.

Method 1—Guess and test

Let A be the Concorde traveling from Washington, D.C., to Paris. Let B be the Concorde traveling from Paris to Washington, D.C. At the point where they passed, the two planes together had traveled 4,000 miles—the distance from Washington, D.C., to Paris. Use the formula $D = rt$ to find the distance each plane had traveled.

Guess	Time	Distance (in mi) Traveled by A	Distance (in mi) Traveled by B	Total Distance (in mi) Traveled by A and B	
1	11:00 A.M.	$1,200 \times 2 = 2,400$	$1,200 \times 1 = 1,200$	$2,400 + 1,200 = 3,600$	← too few
2	12:00 noon	$1,200 \times 3 = 3,600$	$1,200 \times 2 = 2,400$	$3,600 + 2,400 = 6,000$	← too many
3	11:10 A.M.	$1,200 \times 2\frac{1}{6} = 2,600$	$1,200 \times 1\frac{1}{6} = 1,400$	$2,600 + 1,400 = 4,000$	← correct

The planes passed each other at 11:10 A.M. EST.

Method 2—Simulation

Draw a time line to show how far each plane traveled each ho
Traveling at 1,200 mph, the planes took $3\frac{1}{3}$ h to go 4,000 mi. ⟶ $4,000 \div 1,200 = 3\frac{1}{3}$

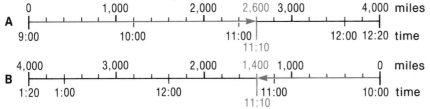

The planes passed each other at 11:10 A.M. EST.

Are both answers the same?

Show two methods to solve each problem. Compare the answers. They should be the same.

1. A sample population of 1,200 eighth-grade students was asked to name the first United States astronaut to walk on the moon. The students who remembered that it was Neil Armstrong numbered twice as many as those who did not remember. How many students remembered that it was Neil Armstrong?

2. Suppose a telephone call sent by satellite cost $5.25 for the first 3 minutes and $.58 for each additional minute. Alexandra paid $9.31 for one call. How long was the call?

3. The Topeka Building opens every morning at 8:00 A.M. The elevator starts on the ground floor. By 8:05 A.M. one day, it was on floor 42. It had made 7 trips: up 36 floors, up 28 floors, down 18 floors, up 12 floors, down 42 floors, up 37 floors, and one more trip. How far did it go on the last trip?

In 2012 the crew on the space shuttle *Xavier* is visiting Space Station XXII.

4. There are 24 space-patrol vehicles in a hangar. Some of the vehicles carry 3 crew members. The others carry 4 crew members. All 86 crew members are at a briefing. How many vehicles carry 3 crew members?

5. The *Xavier* leaves Space Station XXII to visit 4 more stations. The voyage begins with 100 passengers. At each station, passengers get off and on as follows: Station X—10 off, 25 on; Station IV—35 off, 18 on; Station XIV—40 off, 22 on; Station XIX—65 off, 82 on. The *Xavier* then returns to Station XXII. How many passengers are there on the return flight?

6. The return trip to Station XXII is 25,000 mi. The *Xavier* travels at 6,250 mph. At what time must it leave the last stop (Station XIX) to arrive at Station XXII at 3:00 P.M.?

7. The crew of *Xavier* has been assigned to repair satellites 1, 2, 3, and 4. The satellites can be repaired in any order. In how many different orders can the satellites be repaired?

CREATE YOUR OWN PROBLEM

Use the facts to write a problem that can be solved in more than one way. Have a classmate solve it in two ways.

SPACECRAFT LAUNCHED	
Year	Number of Spacecraft
1	31
2	38
3	46
4	55

Tessellations and Transformations

You have probably seen floor tiles, wallpaper, or decorative designs that repeat a single shape to cover a surface without any gaps or overlapping. To tessellate a plane, you can move a basic shape, using slides, turns, or flips. These moves are called **transformations.** Shown below are several examples of basic shapes that tessellate a plane.

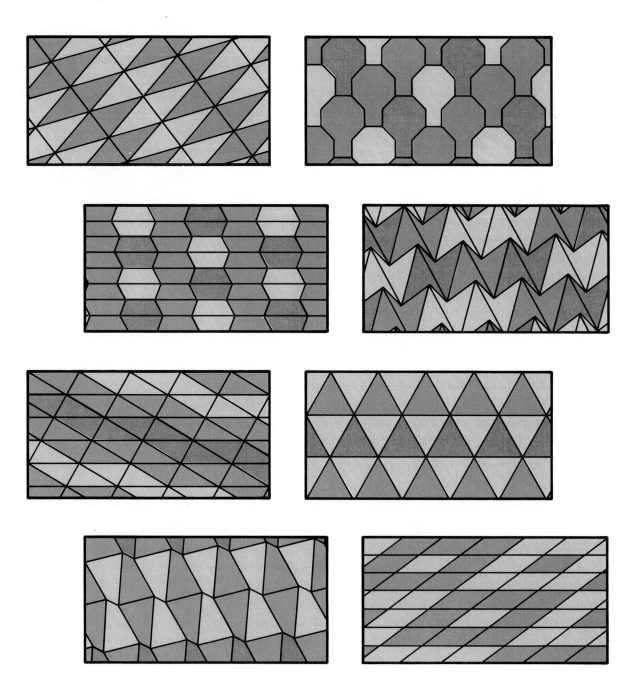

WORKING TOGETHER

Work with a partner. You will need stiff paper or tagboard, scissors, and a straightedge.

1. Look at the tessellation examples. Name or describe the special shapes in each figure.

2. Pick a basic shape in each figure. Then slide, flip, or turn that shape to the other positions in the figure.

3. Draw a triangle on stiff paper and cut it out carefully. Use the shape as a pattern to draw a tessellation of the plane.

4. Draw a quadrilateral on stiff paper. Use the quadrilateral shape the same way you did the triangle to make a different tessellation.

SHARING YOUR THINKING

Discuss your tessellations with your partner.

1. What transformations did you use in creating your tessellation design?

2. Figure out whether you could have made a different pattern with your triangular shape.

3. Did anyone find a shape that would not tessellate the plane?

THINKING IT THROUGH

1. Discuss whether it is possible to use any triangle or quadrilateral to tessellate the plane.

2. Look at a tessellation based on a triangular shape. What combination of six angles meet at every vertex?

3. Look at a tessellation based on a quadrilateral shape. What combination of angles seem to meet at a point?

4. How can you relate the previous two questions to the sum of the interior angles of a triangle and quadrilateral? Explain.

5. Experiment to see if you can tessellate the plane, using regular pentagons. Describe any problems you encounter.

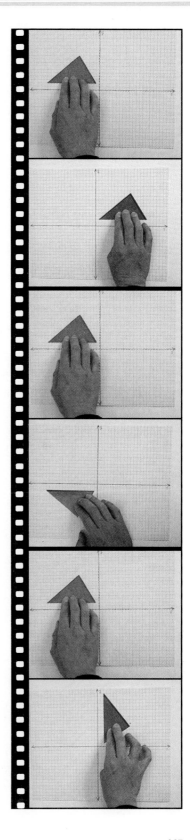

Exploring Transformations

Work in a small group. Use grid paper. Graph triangle *ABC* as shown. As you perform the transformations below, keep a record of the coordinates of *A*, *B*, and *C*, and of the coordinates of the transformation, *A′*, *B′*, and *C′*.

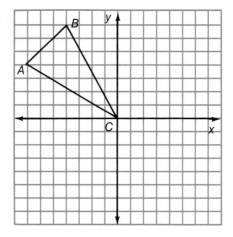

1. Slide triangle *ABC* any number of units
   - horizontally.
   - vertically.
   - both horizontally and vertically.

2. Reflect triangle *ABC*
   - using the *y*-axis as the line of reflection.
   - using the *x*-axis as the line of reflection.

3. Rotate triangle *ABC*, using the origin as a center of rotation.
   - Rotate counterclockwise 90°.
   - Rotate counterclockwise 180°.

1. Examine the records you kept of the slides you made with triangle *ABC*.

   - How did the *x*- and *y*-coordinates change?
   - Can you find a pattern when the triangle slides both horizontally and vertically?

2. Look at the reflections of triangle *ABC*.

   - How would you describe the changes in the coordinates for corresponding vertices? Check your ideas by reflecting other triangles about these axes.
   - Must one vertex be at the origin for your ideas to work?

3. Look at the triangles that resulted from the counterclockwise rotations of triangle *ABC*.

   - How do the coordinates of the vertices of the image through a 90° rotation compare with those of triangle *ABC*?
   - How do those of the 180° rotation compare?
   - Can you predict the coordinates of the vertices for a rotation of 270°?

THINKING IT THROUGH

1. To show your understanding of translations, predict the position of a figure with vertices at $(-5, 2)$, $(3, 3)$, and $(1, -1)$ after it is translated 5 units to the right and 4 units down. How can you verify your prediction?

2. To show your understanding of reflections, predict the coordinates of the reflections about the *x*-axis and about the *y*-axis of a figure with vertices at $(12, 8)$, $(10, 8)$, $(2, 2)$, and $(8, 2)$. How can you verify your prediction?

3. How do you know when you have rotated a figure 90°?

4. Choose a center of rotation other than the origin. Experiment to find the image of a figure through a 90° rotation counterclockwise; 180° rotation. Do the same rules hold as for a rotation about the origin?

5. Draw a figure with several vertices anywhere on a coordinate plane. Use transformations to draw your design in other positions.

447

Problem Solving

SKILLS AND STRATEGIES REVIEW

Solve. Use the sign below to answer 3–4.

1. The next space launch will take place on the twelfth of the month. The month has five Mondays, three of which have even-numbered dates. For which day of the week is the launch scheduled?

2. The following month there are two launches scheduled for two consecutive days. The product of the dates of those days is 812. What are the dates on which the two launches will take place?

3. Rona is halfway between the launch area and the hospital. Can she reach the laboratory in one hour if she drives an average of 50 km per h?

4. Pedro has traveled 20 km from the launch area to the hospital. How far is he from the laboratory?

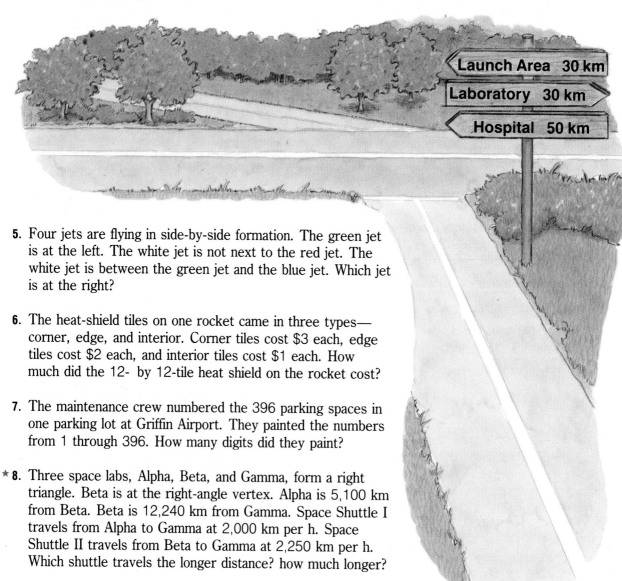

5. Four jets are flying in side-by-side formation. The green jet is at the left. The white jet is not next to the red jet. The white jet is between the green jet and the blue jet. Which jet is at the right?

6. The heat-shield tiles on one rocket came in three types— corner, edge, and interior. Corner tiles cost $3 each, edge tiles cost $2 each, and interior tiles cost $1 each. How much did the 12- by 12-tile heat shield on the rocket cost?

7. The maintenance crew numbered the 396 parking spaces in one parking lot at Griffin Airport. They painted the numbers from 1 through 396. How many digits did they paint?

★8. Three space labs, Alpha, Beta, and Gamma, form a right triangle. Beta is at the right-angle vertex. Alpha is 5,100 km from Beta. Beta is 12,240 km from Gamma. Space Shuttle I travels from Alpha to Gamma at 2,000 km per h. Space Shuttle II travels from Beta to Gamma at 2,250 km per h. Which shuttle travels the longer distance? how much longer?

Firsts in Aviation

This table lists five aircraft that were "firsts" in aviation history.

Aircraft	Year Service Began
Douglas DC-3	1936
De Havilland Comet	1952
Boeing 707	1958
Boeing 747	1970
Concorde	1976

1. The first plane built specifically for passenger service was the twin-engine Douglas DC-3. The first jet airliner was the De Havilland Comet. How many years after the Douglas DC-3 began service did jetliner service begin?

2. A Douglas DC-3 is 20 m long and has a wingspan of 30 m. A De Havilland Comet is 34 m long and has a wingspan of 35 m. Which is longer, a Douglas DC-3 or a De Havilland Comet? how much longer?

3. The first jumbo jet was the Boeing 747. It is $3\frac{1}{2}$ times as long as a Douglas DC-3. Its wingspan is twice that of a Douglas DC-3. What are the length and the wingspan of a Boeing 747?

4. The De Havilland Comet was built by the British. The Boeing 707 was the first jetliner built in the United States. A De Havilland Comet can fly nearly 800 km per h. Which jet flies faster?

5. The first supersonic transport (SST) to go into passenger service, the Concorde, was built by the United Kingdom and France. How many years after jetliner service began did SST service begin?

6. A Concorde is 62 m long. A Boeing 707 is 45 m long. Which of the five aircraft listed in the table is the longest?

7. A Concorde has a 25-m wingspan. Which of the five aircraft listed in the table has the smallest wingspan?

8. A Douglas DC-3 can carry about 20 passengers. A Boeing 747 can carry nearly 500 passengers. How many times as many passengers can a Boeing 747 carry?

9. A Concorde can fly 2,400 km per h. How many times as fast as the first jetliner, the De Havilland Comet, can a Concorde fly?

10. A Boeing 747 can fly 9,700 km nonstop. Between which two cities listed in this table can the Boeing 747 *not* fly without stopping?

Routes	Distance (in km)
New York to Tokyo	10,872
Paris to New York	5,850
Los Angeles to Melbourne	12,761
Rio de Janeiro to Chicago	8,499
Caracas to Honolulu	9,688
Vienna to Singapore	9,710

Which relations are functions? pages 432–433

1. (3, 3), (3, 2), (3, 1), (5, 3), (5, 2), (5, 1)　　**2.** (2, ⁻4), (1, ⁻2), (0, 0), (⁻1, 2), (⁻2, 4)

3. (1, 0), (2, 0), (3, 0), (4, 0)　　**4.** (1, 6), (5, 6), (⁻5, 4), (0, 4)

Graph each equation. pages 434–435

5. $y = x + 2$　　**6.** $y = 3x - 4$

Give the slope and the *y*-intercept of each line. pages 436–437

7. $y = 2x + 5$　　**8.** $y = {}^-3x + 6$　　**9.** $y = \frac{1}{2}x - 1$

Find the slope of the line containing each pair of points. pages 436–437

10. (1, 2), (3, 4)　　**11.** (0, 4), (2, 0)

Write the equation of the line with the given slope and *y*-intercept. pages 436–437

12. $m = 3; b = 2$　　**13.** $m = {}^-2; b = {}^-4$

Graph each inequality. pages 438–439

14. $y > x$　　**15.** $y < x + 2$

Solve each system of equations by graphing. pages 440–441

16. $y = x + 2; y = -x + 4$　　**17.** $y = x - 6; y = {}^-2x$

Name each transformation. pages 446–447

18. 　　**19.** 　　**20.**

Copy the figure. Draw each transformation on the same set of axes. Write the coordinates of each new point. pages 446–447

21. Translate *ABCD* 7 units to the left.　　**22.** Reflect *ABCD* over the *x*-axis.

Solve. pages 442–443, 448–449

23. The crew members of a space shuttle are eating lunch. If there are 3 meats and 4 vegetables on the menu, how many possible combinations of meat and vegetable are there?

24. In a given hour there were twice as many takeoffs as landings at an airport. If there were 15 flights altogether, how many takeoffs and how many landings were there?

Which relations are functions?

1. (1, 2), (2, 4), (3, 6), (4, 8), (5, 10)

2. (5, 0), ($^-$5, 0), (4, 1), (4, 1), (0, 0)

3. (7, 8), (9, 10), (11, 12)

Graph each equation.

4. $y = 2x + 1$

5. $y = x - 2$

Give the slope and the y-intercept of each line.

6. $y = 3x + 4$

7. $y = {}^-4x + 2$

8. $y = \frac{1}{2}x - 1$

Find the slope of the line containing each pair of points.

9. (0, $^-$2), (1, 1)

10. ($^-$2, 5), (0, 1)

Write the equation of the line with the given slope and y-intercept.

11. $m = {}^-1; b = 5$

12. $m = \frac{1}{2}; b = 7$

Graph each inequality.

13. $y < -x + 1$

14. $x \geq 2$

Solve each system of equations by graphing.

15. $y = x + 2; y = 2$

16. $y = -x + 5; y = x + 1$

Choose the next transformation.

17.

a.

b.

c.

Copy the figure. Draw each transformation on the same set of axes.

18. Translate △ABC 5 units up.

19. Reflect △ABC about the y-axis.

Solve.

20. Suppose a package sent airmail cost $7.50 for the first 10 oz and $.57 for each additional ounce. If Janet spent $10.92, how heavy was the package?

Solve by graphing.

$y = 7 - x$ $x - y = 3$

ROCKET HUNT

The Space Scouts of Alphaville are having a rocket hunt. The figure below is a map showing a portion of the town. The blocks are all square and all the same size.

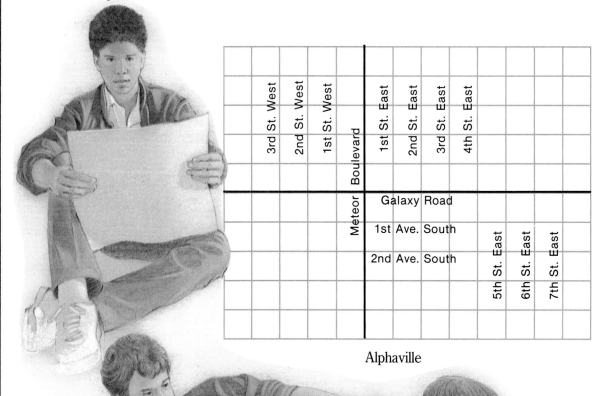

Alphaville

The instructions for the hunt are as follows: Draw two lines. One line goes through the intersection of Galaxy Road and Meteor Boulevard and through the intersection of 20th Street East and 10th Avenue North. The second line goes through the intersection of Galaxy Road and 35th Street East and through the intersection of 40th Street East and 15th Avenue North. The rocket is in the silver building at the intersection of these two lines.

One of the Space Scouts was well prepared and brought graph paper. By extending the map above, show the drawing the scouts used, and tell where the rocket is located.

PARABOLAS

The equation $y = x^2$ defines a function. The graph of the function is the **parabola** shown at the right. This parabola is a symmetric figure with the y-axis as its line of symmetry. Study the table of values for $y = x^2$.

For any value of x, the value of y is the same at x and at $-x$.

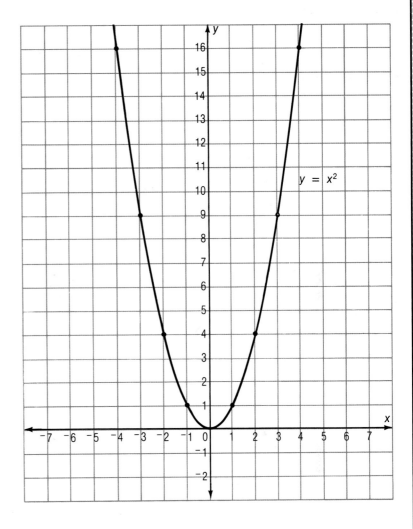

x	y
$^-3$	9
$^-2$	4
$^-1$	1
0	0
1	1
2	4
3	9

For the function $y = x^2$, the value of x can be any real number. Therefore, the domain of the function is all real numbers. Since x^2 must be positive or 0, all the values for y must be positive or 0. Therefore, the range of the function consists of all nonnegative numbers ($y \geq 0$).

Graph each parabola. What is the line of symmetry for each?

1. $y = 2x^2$ **2.** $y = 3x^2$ **3.** $y = \frac{1}{2}x^2$ **4.** $y = -x^2$

5. What are the domain and the range of the function $y = -x^2$? Under what kind of transformation is the graph of $y = -x^2$ the image of the graph of $y = x^2$?

6. Graph the parabola $x = y^2$.

SYSTEMS OF EQUATIONS

The solutions of many systems of equations cannot be determined easily by graphing. Approximate solutions can be found by *combing* an interval along the *x*-axis to see when the corresponding *y*-values are nearly equal.

$$y = \frac{-3}{5}x + 3 \qquad\qquad y = x - 3$$

As *x* gets closer to the point of intersection, the *y*-values get closer together.

Portion of Babbage's Difference Engine

In the program below, the computer is told to test progressively larger values of *x* until it finds the one that gives the closest approximation of the correct solution.

PROGRAM

Test all values of *x* from 0 to 5 in increments, or steps, of 0.01 →

The *y*-value for the first equation is Y1. →

The *y*-value for the second equation is Y2. →

ABS(*n*) means absolute value of *n*. The difference between the *y*-values should be quite small. →

Round *x* and *y* to the nearest hundredth. →

```
10 REM SYSTEMS OF EQUATIONS
20 FOR X = 0 TO 5 STEP 0.01
30 LET Y1 = -3/5 * X + 3
40 LET Y2 = X - 3
50 IF ABS(Y1 - Y2) < 0.005 THEN GOTO 90
60 NEXT X
70 PRINT "NO SOLUTION IN THE INTERVAL"
80 GOTO 130
90 LET X = INT(X * 100 + 0.5)/100
100 LET Y = INT(Y1 * 100 + 0.5)/100
110 PRINT "APPROXIMATE SOLUTION AT"
120 PRINT "X = ";X; " AND Y = ";Y
130 END
```

Use the program on page 454 to answer each question.

1. Why does graphing a system of equations not always give an exact solution?

2. How would graphing each system before running the program help in finding a solution?

3. How is the value 0.005 in line 50 related to the STEP value in line 20?

4. How could a *closer* approximation be found?

Graph each system to determine an appropriate interval to comb.

5. $y = 3x - 1$
   $y = x + 4$

6. $y = x + 1$
   $y = -x + 2$

7. $y = \frac{-1}{2}x + 3$
   $y = \frac{1}{3}x - 1$

8. $y = 2x - 3$
   $y = {}^-3x + 4$

9. $y = {}^-3x - 4$
   $y = 2x + 2$

10. $y = \frac{1}{3}x - 2$
    $y = \frac{-1}{3}x + 5$

11. $y = \frac{3}{2}x - 2$
    $y = -x - 5$

12. $y = \frac{-1}{3}x + 1$
    $y = x - 6$

Rewrite the program to allow each change.

13. Make the increments smaller.

★ 14. Allow the user to *input* the two equations.

★ 15. Allow the user to *input* the interval to be combed and select the size of the increments.

AT THE COMPUTER

1. Run the program on page 454 to find an approximate solution for each system in **5–12** above.

Run the program with smaller increments to find an approximate solution for each system.

2. $y = 3x - 4$
   $y = \frac{2}{3}x + 1$

3. $y = 5x + 6$
   $y = {}^-3x + 1$

4. $y = \frac{2}{3}x + 4$
   $y = {}^-2x + 1$

★ 5. $y = \frac{-3}{4}x - 1$
   $y = \frac{1}{3}x + 2$

FINAL REVIEW

Choose the correct answers. Write A, B, C, or D.

1. What is 5,463,921 rounded to the nearest million?

A 6,000,000 C 5,500,000
B 5,000,000 D not given

2. 7,008 − 4,526

A 2,482 C 3,582
B 3,522 D not given

3. What is 6^3 in standard form?

A 18 C 36
B 216 D not given

4. What is the value of 4 in 6.045?

A 400 C 0.04
B 0.4 D not given

5. 0.32 + 3.2 + 30.002

A 33.522 C 36.402
B 30.266 D not given

6. 0.36 × 0.008

A 0.0288 C 0.00248
B 288 D not given

7. 0.0315 ÷ 0.63

A 0.05 C 20
B 0.005 D not given

8. Complete. 8,340 m = ___ km

A 0.834 C 8.34
B 83.4 D not given

9. Complete. 32.4 g = ___ mg

A 3.24 C 3,240
B 0.324 D not given

10. What is the GPE for 3.4 m?

A 0.05 m C 0.4 m
B 0.5 m D not given

11. What is 1636 in 12-hour time?

A 4:36 A.M. C 6:36 P.M.
B 4:36 P.M. D not given

12. Complete. $(8 \times 2) + (3 \times 8) = \square(2 + 3)$

A 5 C 8
B 16 D not given

13. 50 − (2 × 10)

A 480 C 80
B 30 D not given

14. If $b = 3$ and $c = 5$, what is $(c - b) \times 3$?

A 24 C 10
B 6 D not given

15. $x + 8.3 = 11$

A $x = 2.7$ C $x = 3.3$
B $x = 19.3$ D not given

16. What is the GCF of 21 and 12?

A 4 C 3
B 12 D not given

Choose the correct answers. Write A, B, C, or D.

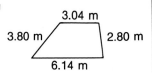

17. What is the prime factorization of 40?

   A $2^2 \times 5$ **C** 5×8
   B $2^3 \times 5$ **D** not given

24. What is the perimeter?

   A 15.78 m   **C** 12.74 m
   B 17.192 m   **D** not given

18. What is the LCM of 36 and 18?

   A 9   **C** 36
   B 3   **D** not given

25. What is the area?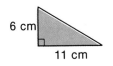

   A 29.5 cm   **C** 33 cm^2
   B 68.75 cm^2 **D** not given

19. What is $6\frac{4}{5}$ as an improper fraction?

   A $\frac{34}{5}$ **C** $\frac{22}{5}$
   B $\frac{32}{5}$ **D** not given

26. $\frac{6}{9} = \frac{9}{n}$

   A $n = 2$ **C** $n = 13.5$
   B $n = 12$ **D** not given

20. $12\frac{5}{6} + 3\frac{1}{6}$

   A 16   **C** $9\frac{2}{3}$
   B 15   **D** not given

27. What is the unit price of 5 for $4.22?

   A $4.00   **C** $.86
   B $.83   **D** not given

21. $5\frac{3}{8} - 2\frac{3}{4}$

   A $8\frac{1}{8}$ **C** $3\frac{5}{8}$
   B $3\frac{3}{8}$ **D** not given

28. What ratio is 125%?

   A $\frac{1}{4}$ **C** $\frac{5}{4}$
   B $\frac{7}{4}$ **D** not given

22. $16 \div 1\frac{1}{3}$

   A 12   **C** $21\frac{2}{3}$
   B $\frac{1}{12}$ **D** not given

29. What is 4.5% of 17?

   A 0.765   **C** $377.\overline{7}$
   B 76.5   **D** not given

23. What kind of angle is this?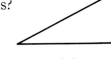

   A acute   **C** right
   B obtuse   **D** not given

30. What is the sale price?
    original price = $165.00
    rate of discount = 20%

   A $33.00   **C** $132.00
   B $198.00   **D** not given

FINAL REVIEW

Choose the correct answers. Write A, B, C, or D.

31. $^-16 + ^-8$

    A 24   **C** $^-8$

    B $^-24$ **D** not given

32. $^-3 - 4$

    A $^-7$ **C** $^-1$

    B 1   **D** not given

33. $18 \cdot ^-5$

    A 90   **C** 23

    B 13   **D** not given

34. What is the median of 18, 12, 14, 6, 23?

    A 14   **C** 17

    B 14.6   **D** not given

35. What is the probability of choosing *fall* from a box holding 1 label for each season?

    A $\frac{1}{12}$ **C** $\frac{3}{4}$

    B $\frac{1}{4}$ **D** not given

36. What is the surface area of a cube 1 in. on a side?

    A 4 in.^{2} **C** 6 in.^{2}

    B 1 in.^{2} **D** not given

37. What is the volume of a cylinder with a radius of 7 ft and a height of 30 ft? $\left(\pi \approx \frac{22}{7}\right)$

    A 4,620 ft^3 **C** 147 ft^3

    B 154 ft^3 **D** not given

38. Complete. 300 mL = ___ cm^3

    A 30   **C** 300

    B 0.3   **D** not given

39. $^-2\frac{2}{3} - \frac{1}{3}$

    A $^-3$ **C** 2

    B $^-2\frac{1}{3}$ **D** not given

40. What is 140.6 in scientific notation?

    A 1.406×10^3 **C** 1.406×10^2

    B $14.06 \times ^-1$ **D** not given

41. What is $^-\sqrt{49}$?

    A 7   **C** 14

    B $^-7$ **D** not given

42. Solve. $4 = y + ^-10$

    A $y = ^-6$ **C** $y = 14$

    B $y = 6$ **D** not given

43. Which illustrates the inverse property of addition?

    A $7 + ^-7 = 0$ **C** $\frac{4}{3} + 0 = \frac{4}{3}$

    B $\frac{2}{3} \cdot \frac{3}{2} = 1$ **D** not given

44. Solve. $\frac{n}{2} \leq 10$

    A $n \leq 20$ **C** $n \leq 5$

    B $n > 5$ **D** not given

45. What is the solution of this system of equations? $y = x + 3; y = 2x$

    A (2, 1)   **C** (1, 4)

    B (3, 6)   **D** not given

46. What is the slope of $y = 4x - 6$?

    A 6   **C** $^-6$

    B 4   **D** not given

CHAPTER RESOURCE

FINAL REVIEW

Choose the correct answers. Write A, B, C, or D.

Solve.

The Chang family attended the air show at Central Airport. The show began at 10:30 A.M. It ended at 3:30 P.M. The travel time from their home to the airport was 1 h 15 min.

47. What time would the Chang family have left home if they stopped $\frac{1}{2}$ hour for breakfast on the way?

   A 8:45 A.M.   **C** 9:15 A.M.
   B 8:30 A.M.   **D** not given

48. About how many trucks did the children count on the way home if they averaged 18 every 15 minutes?

   A 72   **C** 90
   B 22   **D** not given

Solve.

49. Alan Running Fox is building a model of a traditional totem pole. It will have 15 sections, each 10 in. long. The top, or crown, will be equal to 3 sections. If the diameter of each section is 5 in., how high will the totem pole stand?

   A $86\frac{1}{4}$ in.   **C** 18 in.
   B 180 in.   **D** not given

Complete the pattern to solve each.

50. 7, 7, 14, 42, 168,＿＿

   A 210   **C** 336
   B 840   **D** not given

51. 81, ＿＿, 9, 3, 1

   A 36   **C** 27
   B 18   **D** not given

Solve.

The local Booster Club was selling raffle tickets to raise money.

52. For each ticket sold at $2.00, the merchants contributed $.25. If 425 tickets were sold, how much money did the club raise?

   A $106.25   **C** $956.25
   B $425.00   **D** not given

53. If the profit on each ticket before the merchants' contribution was $1.00, how much total profit was made after the merchants' contribution?

   A $400.00   **C** $106.25
   B $531.25   **D** not given

Solve.

54. Linda planted a new dogwood sapling in her yard 5 years ago. At that time it had 3 branches. Each branch grew 2 new branches that first year. This continued until today. How many branches will Linda's tree have at the end of this year?

   A 32   **C** 48
   B 100   **D** not given

55. During a steeplechase a horse ran 0.5 mi south from the starting point. Then it ran 1.4 mi east and 0.5 mi north. It finally ran 0.6 mi west before reaching the last obstacle. What was the remaining distance from the last obstacle to the starting point?

   A 0.6 mi north   **C** 0.8 mi west
   B 3 mi east   **D** not given

Choose the correct answers. Write **A**, **B**, **C**, or **D**.

Use the table to solve 56 and 57.

Squares	2	4	6	8
Triangles	4	8	12	16

56. Katie is making a quilt based on a colonial design using triangles and squares. The table shows how many of each shape she will need. If she uses 6 squares, how many triangles will she need?

   A 6   **C** 16
   B 4   **D** not given

57. If she uses 24 triangles, how many squares will she need?

   A 12   **C** 15
   B 10   **D** not given

Make a list to solve 58 and 59.

58. Danny is placing the silverware on the buffet table. He has knives, forks, teaspoons, and soup spoons. How many different ways can he arrange them so that the soup spoons are first and the knives are last?

   A 1   **C** 4
   B 2   **D** not given

59. The doorbell and telephone ring together at 1:00 P.M. The doorbell rings every 7 minutes and the telephone rings every 8 minutes. What time will they both ring together again?

   A 1:15 P.M.   **C** 1:56 P.M.
   B 2:00 P.M.   **D** not given

Choose the statement that must be true from the statements given.

60. Eighth-grade students study mathematics. Thelma is an eighth-grade student. Thelma is ___.

   A carrying school books   **C** 13 years old
   B studying mathematics   **D** not given

61. All rectangles are parallelograms. ABCD is a rectangle. ABCD ___.

   A has only 3 sides   **C** is a square
   B has 2 pairs of parallel   **D** not given
     sides

Solve.

62. Randy bought a ticket for a concert. The artist received $\frac{1}{4}$ of the cost and $\frac{1}{10}$ of the cost went to the state, for taxes. Printing the ticket cost $1.00. The remaining $12.00 went to the concert promoter. How much did the ticket cost?

   A $8.00   **C** $20.00
   B $12.00   **D** not given

63. Some people bought tickets at the door. Four times as many people bought tickets in advance. If 1,200 tickets were sold, how many were bought in advance?

   A 1,000   **C** 240
   B 960   **D** not given

SET 1 Write each number in standard form.

pages 4–5

1. seventeen million, twenty-five   **2.** 10^7 **3.** 8×10^3

4. $(9 \times 10^{11}) + (3 \times 10^{10}) + (6 \times 10^8) + (1 \times 10^7) + (4 \times 10^4) + (6 \times 10^3) + (3 \times 1)$

Give the value of the digit 9. Then write in expanded form using exponents.

5. 69,012   **6.** 78,029   **7.** 150,960   **8.** 9,300,286

9. 37,095,016   **10.** 1,213,769,008   **11.** 2,932,006,048,318

Round each number to the nearest thousand, the nearest ten thousand, and the nearest million.

12. 369,357   **13.** 706,935   **14.** 5,861,406

SET 2 Estimate each sum, difference, or product.

pages 6–7; 12–13

1. 764
 + 42

2. 685
 − 241

3. $1,254
 + 381

4. $620.59
 + 75.02

5. 2,584
 − 1,937

6. $29.10 + $3.15   **7.** 41,832 − 34,450   **8.** $429.83 − $345.89

9. $83.10
 × 44

10. $65.82
 × 28

11. $45,000
 × 625

12. $400.17
 × 714

13. 50,425
 × 3,813

14. 85 × $62.37   **15.** 605 × 850   **16.** 2,503 × 39,067

SET 3 Add or subtract. Estimate to be sure your answer makes sense.

pages 8–9

1. 5,602
 − 688

2. $6,649
 + 6,075

3. 726,039
 − 38,185

4. $141.02
 265.45
 + 852.25

5. 95,330
 19,578
 + 46,347

6. $38.43 + $12.21 + $5.04   **7.** 7,645 + 3,924 + 28   **8.** 96,100 − 63,805

9. 75,899 + 47,412   **10.** 398,820 − 27,140   **11.** $225.90 − $37.91

SET 4 Multiply. Estimate to be sure your answer makes sense.

pages 14–15

1. 576
 × 926

2. $94.99
 × 12

3. $8,641
 × 458

4. 8,399
 × 3,043

5. 41,061
 × 8,602

6. 51 × 27   **7.** 83 × 539   **8.** 83 × 5,390   **9.** 35 × $401.02

10. 51 × 270   **11.** 209 × $398.65   **12.** 867.2 × 2.016

SET 1   Rename using exponents.   pages 16–17

1. $5 \times 5 \times 5$ 2. 6×6 3. $17 \times 17 \times 17 \times 17$ 4. 15

Write as a product of factors. Then write the number in standard form.

5. 7^2 6. 11^2 7. 5^5 8. 1^6 9. 12^3 10. 3^8

SET 2   Divide. Check your answers by multiplying or by estimating.   pages 18–19

1. $23\overline{)1,198}$ 2. $12\overline{)1,109}$ 3. $32\overline{)6,510}$ 4. $58\overline{)47,360}$

5. $80\overline{)31,573}$ 6. $54\overline{)\$171.18}$ 7. $425\overline{)12,400}$ 8. $357\overline{)\$289.17}$

9. $72\overline{)21,931}$ 10. $403\overline{)7,033}$ 11. $82\overline{)109,051}$ 12. $251\overline{)792,204}$

13. $\$12.24 \div 34$ 14. $26,181 \div 143$ 15. $908,704 \div 778$

16. $\$185.50 \div 50$ 17. $96,490 \div 501$ 18. $980,050 \div 909$

SET 3   Write the decimal for each. Then give the value of the digit 5.   pages 30–31

1. twenty and five hundredths   2. $(9 \times 1) + (5 \times 0.1) + (8 \times 0.01)$ 3. $\frac{35}{1,000}$

4. forty-eight and five hundred seventy-two thousandths   5. $\left(2 \times \frac{1}{100}\right) + \left(5 \times \frac{1}{10,000}\right)$

6. $(2 \times 1) + (5 \times 0.1) +$ (9×0.001) 7. $90 + 9 + \frac{1}{100} + \frac{5}{10,000}$ 8. $1 + \frac{5}{100} + \frac{8}{1,000}$

Round to the nearest one, the nearest hundredth, and the nearest ten-thousandth.

9. 0.35088 10. 0.00675 11. 2.45097 12. 1.92535 13. 27.260009

SET 4   Replace each ● with <, >, or =.   pages 32–33

1. 0.75 ● 0.77 2. 0.81 ● 0.801 3. 2.82 ● 2.820

4. 3.294 ● 3.249 5. 13.045 ● 13.0405 6. 0.6351 ● 0.6531

7. 0.0296 ● 0.02960 8. 40.56 ● 400.056 9. 0.0726 ● 0.1

10. 4.810 ● 4.180 11. 69.803 ● 6.9803 12. 0.60 ● 0.5888

SET 1   Estimate.

pages 36–37; 42–43

1. 10.5341
    − 2.4821

2. 83.75
    + 5.849

3. $21.54
    − 1.75

4. $54.63
    × 6.04

5. 6.86
    × 7.6

6. $38.52
    42.15
    70.90
    + 98.90

7. 5.289
    3.906
    1.023
    + 0.962

8. 0.395
    0.486
    1.032
    + 0.998

9. $1.45
    1.05
    3.75
    + 2.10

10. 39.16
    62.88
    85.13
    + 50.92

11. 15 − 5.108

12. 3.09 × 36

13. 0.652 + 0.90 + 2.08

SET 2   Add or subtract. Check each answer.

pages 38–39

1. 2.4936
    − 0.524

2. 4.078
    + 1.947

3. 1.6832
    − 0.503

4. 0.002
    − 0.00176

5. 25
    − 14.82

6. 10.063
    − 7.981

7. 23.909
    − 14.961

8. $65.82
    − 9.99

9. 35.06
    49.88
    14.33
    + 90.90

10. 0.891
    11.538
    6.789
    + 14.118

11. $11.87 + $2.70 + $35.75

12. 5.63 − 0.706

13. 43.86 + 54.512 + 7.901

14. 320.7 + 46 + 73.04

15. 15 − 5.108

16. 0.652 + 0.90 + 2.08

SET 3   Multiply. Estimate to be sure each answer makes sense.
Round 2 and 7 to the nearest cent.

pages 44–51

1. 8.75
    × 0.5

2. $32.43
    × 12.1

3. 2.192
    × 0.68

4. 17.03
    × 2.78

5. 5.685
    × 0.708

6. 0.3 × 7.82

7. 3.4 × $91.25

8. 0.992 × 45.4

Divide. Round to the nearest hundredth.

9. $8\overline{)17.35}$

10. $32\overline{)6.704}$

11. $0.2\overline{)0.1856}$

12. $2.8\overline{)7.084}$

13. $\frac{7}{6}$

14. $\frac{1.296}{32.4}$

15. $\frac{14.35}{15}$

16. 85.2 ÷ 67

17. 0.072 ÷ 0.5

SET 4   Find each product or quotient.

pages 52–53

1. 792 × 10

2. 67.3×10^3

3. 0.183 ÷ 100

4. 8.41×10^5

5. $5,350 \div 10^3$

6. 314.8 × 10,000

Write in scientific notation.

7. 98,300

8. 704,600

9. 5,210,000

10. 432,700,000

EXTRA PRACTICE

pages 62–65

SET 1 **Complete.**

1. 9 cm = ___ mm
2. ___ m = 2,000 mm
3. 17,000 m = ___ km
4. 715 cm = ___ m 15 cm
5. ___ mm = 1 m
6. 5 m 41 cm = ___ cm
7. 500 m = ___ km
8. 13 hm = ___ m
9. ___ dm = 0.5 km
10. ___ dam = 8 km
11. 3 m = ___ hm
12. 75 dm = ___ km
13. 1.35 km = ___ m
14. 1,350 m = ___ cm
15. 13.5 cm = ___ mm

SET 2 **Complete.**

pages 66–71

1. 3 g = ___ mg
2. ___ t = 9,000 kg
3. 61,000 g = ___ kg
4. 4,000 mL = ___ L
5. 7 kL = ___ L
6. 79 L = ___ mL
7. 19 daL = 1.9 ___
8. 0.35 kg = ___ g
9. 2,000 L = ___ hL
10. ___ L = 47.5 kL
11. 4.01 hg = ___ g
12. 0.072 kg = ___ mg

SET 3 **For each measurement and precision give the greatest possible error.**

pages 72–73

1. 17 m; 1 m
2. 10 L; 10 L
3. 2.50 cm; 0.01 cm
4. 9.75 kg; 0.01 kg
5. 312 mL; 1 mL
6. 9.35 L; 0.01 L
7. 3,200 kg; 100 kg
8. 2.36 dm; 0.01 dm
9. 701 km; 1 km
10. 21.0 m; 0.1 m
11. 0.002 km; 0.001 km
12. 200 mL; 100 mL

SET 4 **Add, subtract, or multiply.**

pages 76–79

1. 57 min 14 s
   − 12 min 20 s

2. 3 d 8 h
   ×   7

3. 9 wk
   − 1 wk 3 d

4. 3 yr 10 wk 2 d
   + 1 yr 45 wk 6 d

5. 138 min
   − 42 min 8 s

6. 6 d 7 h 42 min
   + 3 d 2 h 16 min

7. 7 wk 2 d
   ×   4

8. 1 yr 2 mo 3 wk
   ×   10

Find the elapsed time between the given times.

9. 5:00 A.M. and 8:15 A.M.
10. 7:30 P.M. and 12:15 A.M.
11. 10:38 P.M. and 7:05 A.M.
12. 2:18 P.M. and 9:48 P.M.

Find each to the nearest tenth.

13. 82 h = ___ d
14. 7.5 h = ___ min
15. 235 s = ___ min

SET 1   Name the property illustrated.   pages 94–95

1. $5 \times 8 = 8 \times 5$

2. $42 \times 1 = 42$

3. $71 + 0 = 71$

4. $0 \times 35 = 0$

5. $9 + (2 + 10) = (9 + 2) + 10$

6. $2 \times (5 + 6) = (2 \times 5) + (2 \times 6)$

7. $35 + 7 = 7 + 35$

8. $304 \times 0 = 0$

9. $1 \times 95 = 95$

SET 2   Find the value of each expression.   pages 96–99

1. $7 - 5 + 4$

2. $9 \div 3 + 15$

3. $\frac{6 + 2}{4} \times (10 + 2)$

4. $25 \times (2 + 5) \div 5$

5. $(12 + 5 - 3) \div 2$

6. $(9^2 + 4) \div 5$

Evaluate each expression. Let $a = 16$, $b = 2$, $c = 6$, and $d = 3$.

7. $c + 9$

8. $6 \times d$

9. $5b - 7$

10. d^2

11. $22 - 2c$

12. $bd + 5$

13. $\frac{3c - d}{3}$

14. $(a - 8) \times d$

15. $\frac{c^2 - a}{4}$

16. $50 - 2(a + b)$

17. $b(c + 4d) - 5$

18. $d + c(a - 10)$

19. $\frac{4(c - b)}{b^2}$

20. $3d(b + c) \div 2$

21. $c^2 - b\left(\frac{a - b}{2}\right)$

22. $a \div 2(c - b^2)$

SET 3   Write an equation for each.   pages 100–101; 104–105

1. A number b plus six is ten.

2. Ten less than a number x is five.

3. Seven less than the product of six and a number f is eleven.

4. A number y divided by ten equals ten.

Name the inverse of each operation.

5. decrease by 2

6. add 10

7. triple a number

8. divide by 6

SET 4   First tell what must be done to both sides of the equation.   pages 106–109
Then solve it. Check each solution.

1. $x + 2 = 13$

2. $y - 9 = 30$

3. $14 + x = 26$

4. $c - 9 = 27$

5. $18 + y = 18$

6. $53 = c + 20$

7. $58 = r - 12$

8. $w - 8 = 78$

9. $9n = 90$

10. $12 = \frac{x}{9}$

11. $80 = 8b$

12. $98 = a \times 49$

13. $20 = \frac{x}{8}$

14. $y \div 6 = 12$

15. $c \times 5 = 95$

16. $110 = 5t$

EXTRA PRACTICE

SET 1 First tell what must be done to both sides of the equation. Then solve it. Check each solution.

pages 106–109

1. $a + 9.1 = 14.8$

2. $b - 5.6 = 2.1$

3. $y \times 4.1 = 20.5$

4. $t - 4.8 = 7.6$

5. $\frac{x}{2.1} = 30$

6. $2.5 + c = 8.3$

7. $3 = \frac{c}{4.2}$

8. $3.8 \times r = 19$

9. $x - 4.9 = 1.5$

10. $15.2 = n + 9.8$

11. $3.9 \times t = 35.1$

12. $\frac{a}{5} = 7.8$

SET 2 Write the common factors. Then find each GCF.

pages 118–121

1. 20, 66

2. 15, 30

3. 12, 52

4. 19, 25

5. 15, 35

6. 14, 84

7. 81, 90

8. 45, 99

Write the prime factorization for each. Use exponents.

9. 30

10. 99

11. 80

12. 65

13. 150

14. 405

15. 208

16. 189

17. 256

18. 525

19. 756

20. 1,080

SET 3 Find the GCF and the LCM for each.

pages 122–125

1. 8, 20

2. 7, 13

3. 17, 34

4. 15, 25

5. 14, 18

6. 9, 48

7. 6, 20

8. 14, 42

9. 57, 76

10. 3, 4, 6

11. 2, 4, 16

12. 2, 5, 6

13. 4, 10, 12

14. 2, 3, 5

15. 3, 12, 36

16. 8, 16, 20

SET 4 Replace each ⬤ with = or ≠.

pages 128–131

1. $\frac{3}{9}$ ⬤ $\frac{7}{21}$

2. $\frac{2}{5}$ ⬤ $\frac{12}{30}$

3. $\frac{5}{7}$ ⬤ $\frac{30}{49}$

4. $\frac{7}{8}$ ⬤ $\frac{21}{24}$

5. $\frac{8}{9}$ ⬤ $\frac{9}{10}$

6. $\frac{12}{20}$ ⬤ $\frac{5}{3}$

7. $\frac{9}{10}$ ⬤ $\frac{45}{50}$

8. $\frac{7}{15}$ ⬤ $\frac{28}{45}$

Write each as a mixed number or a whole number.

9. $\frac{6}{5}$

10. $\frac{54}{3}$

11. $\frac{22}{8}$

12. $\frac{61}{9}$

13. $\frac{72}{7}$

14. $\frac{18}{6}$

15. $\frac{50}{4}$

16. $\frac{52}{3}$

17. $\frac{45}{21}$

18. $\frac{65}{10}$

19. $\frac{82}{14}$

20. $\frac{48}{5}$

21. $\frac{87}{11}$

22. $\frac{68}{24}$

SET 1 Write as like fractions.

pages 132–133

1. $\frac{2}{3}, \frac{6}{5}$
2. $\frac{1}{2}, \frac{5}{8}$
3. $\frac{7}{9}, \frac{5}{12}$
4. $\frac{4}{5}, \frac{1}{7}$
5. $\frac{1}{3}, \frac{3}{14}$

6. $\frac{5}{12}, \frac{7}{15}$
7. $\frac{2}{7}, \frac{1}{4}$
8. $\frac{9}{4}, \frac{5}{6}$
9. $\frac{1}{4}, \frac{1}{5}, \frac{1}{10}$
10. $\frac{1}{3}, \frac{2}{5}, \frac{5}{6}$

Compare. Use <, >, or = for each ⬭.

11. $\frac{5}{9}$ ⬭ $\frac{4}{9}$
12. $\frac{1}{6}$ ⬭ $\frac{2}{12}$
13. $\frac{3}{5}$ ⬭ $\frac{2}{8}$
14. $\frac{3}{10}$ ⬭ $\frac{1}{2}$
15. $\frac{7}{9}$ ⬭ $\frac{5}{7}$

16. $\frac{6}{9}$ ⬭ $\frac{2}{3}$
17. $\frac{2}{5}$ ⬭ $\frac{7}{12}$
18. $\frac{9}{6}$ ⬭ $\frac{9}{5}$
19. $9\frac{1}{5}$ ⬭ $8\frac{4}{5}$
20. $4\frac{1}{7}$ ⬭ $4\frac{1}{5}$

SET 2 Write each as a decimal.

pages 134–135

1. $\frac{3}{10}$
2. $\frac{3}{6}$
3. $\frac{2}{3}$
4. $\frac{1}{12}$
5. $\frac{5}{8}$
6. $\frac{3}{5}$

7. $\frac{10}{4}$
8. $\frac{9}{20}$
9. $\frac{7}{16}$
10. $\frac{2}{9}$
11. $\frac{8}{30}$
12. $\frac{6}{25}$

13. $2\frac{7}{10}$
14. $8\frac{4}{5}$
15. $9\frac{3}{4}$
16. $3\frac{11}{50}$
17. $1\frac{5}{6}$
18. $7\frac{11}{12}$

19. $6\frac{3}{5}$
20. $4\frac{7}{8}$
21. $11\frac{4}{5}$
22. $17\frac{13}{40}$
23. $12\frac{5}{11}$
24. $14\frac{17}{22}$

SET 3 Add or subtract. Write each answer in simplest form.

pages 146–151

1. $\frac{8}{9} - \frac{2}{9}$
2. $\frac{5}{12} + \frac{5}{12}$
3. $\frac{2}{5} + \frac{3}{10}$
4. $\frac{1}{4} + \frac{3}{10}$
5. $\frac{7}{12} - \frac{3}{8}$

6. $7 + 1\frac{5}{6}$
7. $8\frac{3}{8} - 4\frac{1}{4}$
8. $3\frac{1}{2} - 2\frac{3}{8}$
9. $2\frac{5}{6} + 5\frac{2}{3}$
10. $6 - 4\frac{2}{5}$

11. $\frac{7}{8} + \frac{3}{12}$
12. $\frac{9}{10} - \frac{3}{5}$
13. $4\frac{5}{6} - 3\frac{7}{12}$
14. $9\frac{7}{10} - 3\frac{5}{6}$

15. $5\frac{1}{2} + 1\frac{11}{12}$
16. $6 - 3\frac{4}{9}$
17. $10\frac{1}{4} + 4\frac{1}{6}$
18. $15\frac{3}{7} - 4\frac{1}{2}$

19. $11\frac{2}{3} - 10\frac{3}{4}$
20. $18\frac{4}{7} + 7\frac{2}{3}$
21. $8\frac{1}{4} - 5\frac{2}{5}$
22. $10\frac{1}{4} - 6\frac{6}{9}$

EXTRA PRACTICE

SET 1 Multiply or divide. Write each answer in simplest form. pages 152–157

1. $\frac{3}{10} \times \frac{3}{4}$

2. $\frac{7}{8} \times \frac{1}{2}$

3. $8 \times \frac{4}{5}$

4. $\frac{2}{3} \times 6$

5. $\frac{3}{4} \div \frac{7}{4}$

6. $\frac{4}{5} \div \frac{3}{5}$

7. $\frac{4}{9} \div \frac{1}{12}$

8. $25 \div \frac{5}{8}$

9. $3\frac{2}{3} \times 2\frac{2}{5}$

10. $4\frac{3}{8} \times 2$

11. $8\frac{1}{4} \div 3\frac{2}{3}$

12. $6\frac{1}{8} \times 2\frac{1}{7}$

13. $10 \div 2\frac{1}{7}$

14. $7\frac{1}{12} \times 1\frac{3}{5}$

15. $1\frac{7}{8} \div 5$

16. $7\frac{1}{5} \times 6\frac{2}{3}$

17. $4\frac{2}{5} \div 1\frac{5}{6}$

18. $1\frac{1}{16} \times 3\frac{5}{9}$

19. $4\frac{9}{10} \div \frac{7}{30}$

20. $6\frac{4}{7} \times 4\frac{2}{3}$

SET 2 Write each as a fraction or mixed number in simplest form. pages 160–161

1. 0.70

2. 0.32

3. $0.83\frac{1}{3}$

4. 4.6

5. 0.4375

6. 7.25

7. $0.33\frac{1}{3}$

8. 5.45

9. 6.875

10. 4.05

11. 9.72

12. 8.375

13. $0.66\frac{2}{3}$

14. 5.625

15. 7.34

16. 10.425

SET 3 Estimate each answer. pages 162–163

1. $6\frac{11}{12}$ $+ 2\frac{2}{5}$

2. $\frac{5}{8}$ $- \frac{1}{6}$

3. $7\frac{8}{9}$ $+ 3\frac{3}{4}$

4. $5\frac{9}{11}$ $- \frac{7}{8}$

5. $1\frac{4}{5}$ $+ 8\frac{3}{7}$

6. $6 \times 2\frac{1}{7}$

7. $10\frac{4}{9} \div 2\frac{1}{3}$

8. $4\frac{2}{7} \times 3\frac{5}{6}$

9. $8\frac{1}{4} \div 1\frac{11}{12}$

10. $8 + 1\frac{3}{9}$

11. $5\frac{1}{4} \times 4\frac{7}{10}$

12. $9\frac{7}{15} - 6\frac{9}{16}$

13. $8\frac{5}{6} \div 3\frac{2}{9}$

14. $7\frac{5}{13} \times 2\frac{4}{11}$

15. $2\frac{7}{12} \times 1\frac{8}{15}$

16. $11\frac{7}{8} \div 6\frac{11}{23}$

17. $5\frac{4}{7} - 4\frac{7}{12}$

SET 4 Solve and check. pages 164–165

1. $x + \frac{2}{5} = \frac{4}{5}$

2. $y - \frac{2}{3} = \frac{2}{3}$

3. $\frac{3}{4} + n = \frac{5}{4}$

4. $x - \frac{5}{12} = \frac{5}{12}$

5. $\frac{1}{8}x = 2$

6. $y \div \frac{1}{3} = 5$

7. $n \div \frac{4}{5} = 5$

8. $\frac{2}{3}y = 10$

9. $2\frac{1}{2} \times n = 1\frac{1}{4}$

10. $\frac{3}{5} + x = \frac{2}{3}$

11. $y \div \frac{7}{12} = 1\frac{5}{7}$

12. $x - \frac{1}{4} = \frac{1}{3}$

SET 1   Complete.

pages 166–169

1. 60 in. = ___ ft

2. $2\frac{1}{4}$ lb = ___ oz

3. $8\frac{1}{3}$ yd = ___ ft

4. 4,218 lb = ___ t ___ lb

5. 13,200 ft = ___ mi

6. 30 qt = ___ gal ___ qt

7. 144 in. = ___ yd

8. 16 qt = ___ pt

9. 17 c = ___ qt ___ c

Add, subtract, or multiply.

10.   1 ft 4 in.
   +   9 in.

11.   6 gal 2 qt
   − 2 gal 3 qt

12.   4 lb   2 oz
   + 1 lb 15 oz

13.   9 yd
   − 4 yd 1 ft

14.   10 oz
   ×   4

15.   3 ft 5 in.
   ×   3

16.   3 lb 2 oz
   ×   3

17.   2 qt
   × 5

SET 2   Write *true* or *false*.

pages 178–181

1. An acute angle measures more than 90°.

2. A straight angle measures 180°.

3. Two angles are complementary if the measure of their sum is 180°.

4. If m∠A = 65° and m∠B = 25°, they are complementary angles.

5. If m∠C = 155°, it is an obtuse angle.

6. If m∠D = 90°, it is a straight angle.

7. If m∠A = 129° and m∠B = 51°, they are supplementary angles.

8. If the length of $\overline{AC}$ is 3 cm, and the length of $\overline{DE}$ is 3 cm, the line segments are congruent.

SET 3   Complete. In the figure to the right $\overleftrightarrow{BD} \parallel \overleftrightarrow{EG}$, and m∠ACD = 120°.

pages 182–185

1. ∠ACB is ___ to ∠BCF.

2. ∠DCF and ∠___ are alternate interior angles.

3. ∠EFC measures ___ degrees.

4. ∠ACD and ∠CFG are ___ angles.

5. ∠EFC and ∠GFH are ___ angles.

6. ∠ACB and ∠___ are alternate exterior angles.

7. ∠EFH and ∠HFG are ___.

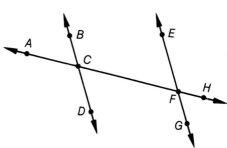

EXTRA PRACTICE

pages 186–189

SET 1 For each *regular* polygon named below give the measure of one angle.

1. triangle
2. quadrilateral
3. pentagon
4. hexagon

Complete.

5. In a regular polygon all sides are ___ in length and all angles have ___ measurement.

6. The sum of all angles in a pentagon is ___.

7. A ___ triangle has no sides congruent.

8. A right triangle contains one angle with a measure of ___.

9. In $\triangle ABC$, $m\angle A = 45°$, $m\angle B = 45°$, $m\angle C = 90°$. $\triangle ABC$ is a ___ triangle.

10. In $\triangle ABC$, $m\angle A = 27°$, $m\angle B = 72°$, $m\angle C = $ ___.

11. In $\triangle ABC$, $m\angle A = 95°$, $m\angle B = 43°$, $m\angle C = $ ___.

SET 2 Complete.

pages 190–191

1. Four examples of quadrilaterals are ___, ___, ___, ___.

2. A ___ has exactly one pair of opposite sides that are parallel.

3. A ___ has both pairs of opposite sides parallel and congruent.

4. A ___ is a parallelogram with all sides congruent.

5. A ___ is a parallelogram with four right angles.

6. A ___ is a rectangle with all sides congruent.

The figure to the right is a parallelogram.

7. $\overline{AD}$ is parallel to ___.

8. $\overline{AB}$ is parallel to ___.

9. $m\angle C = $ ___

10. $m\angle B = $ ___

The figure to the right is a parallelogram.

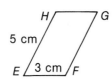

11. $\overline{HG}$ is ___ in length.

12. $\overline{GF}$ is ___ in length.

13. $\angle E$ is congruent to ___.

SET 1 Find the perimeter. pages 194–195

1. a regular pentagon 25 m on a side

2. a square 5.6 cm on a side

3. an equilateral triangle 8.6 m on a side

4. a rectangle 5.6 cm on one side and 6.4 cm on the other

5. a regular hexagon 18.5 cm on a side

6. a regular heptagon 19.3 cm on a side

7. a regular octagon 9.72 cm on a side

SET 2 Find the area. pages 196–199

1. a triangle having a base 12 cm and height 3 cm

2. a triangle having a base 15.3 cm and height 4 cm

3. a triangle having a base 24.7 cm and height 6 cm

4. a trapezoid with base 1.5 cm, base 2.3 cm, and height 12 cm

5. a trapezoid: $h = 10$ m, $b_1 = 6.5$ m, $b_2 = 8.4$ m

6. a triangle: $b = 8.7$ m and $h = 10.2$ m

7. a trapezoid: $h = 14.4$ cm, $b_1 = 15.5$ cm, $b_2 = 20.1$ cm

8. a trapezoid: $h = 9.8$ m, $b_1 = 7.6$ m, $b_2 = 5.3$ m

SET 3 Find the circumference to the nearest one. Use 3.14 for π. pages 200–201

1. $d = 20$ cm **2.** $r = 5$ cm **3.** $d = 15.6$ m

4. $r = 3.2$ m **5.** $r = 15$ cm **6.** $d = 24.5$ m

7. $r = 7.5$ cm **8.** $d = 21$ cm **9.** $r = 6.5$ cm

Find the area to the nearest one. Use 3.14 for π.

10. $r = 10$ cm **11.** $r = 2.5$ cm **12.** $r = 7.8$ m

13. $d = 6.4$ m **14.** $d = 21$ m **15.** $d = 12$ cm

SET 1 Write a fraction for each ratio or comparison. pages 214–217

1. 4 cucumbers for $1.00

2. 2 cans for $1.89

3. 5 revolutions per minute

4. $475 per month

5. 6 blouses to 4 shorts

6. 7 typewriters for 7 students

Write three more equal ratios for each.

7. $\frac{1}{3}, \frac{2}{6}, \frac{3}{9}$

8. $\frac{2}{5}, \frac{4}{10}, \frac{6}{15}$

9. $\frac{1.5}{3}, \frac{3}{6}, \frac{4.5}{9}$

Replace each ⬤ with = or ≠.

10. $\frac{3}{4}$ ⬤ $\frac{45}{60}$

11. $\frac{7}{8}$ ⬤ $\frac{26}{30}$

12. $\frac{3.2}{9}$ ⬤ $\frac{19.2}{54}$

Solve. Check each answer.

13. $\frac{7}{9} = \frac{n}{27}$

14. $\frac{5}{3} = \frac{120}{n}$

15. $\frac{n}{15} = \frac{138}{345}$

16. $\frac{23}{n} = \frac{57.5}{17.5}$

17. $\frac{5}{7} = \frac{n}{35}$

18. $\frac{7}{n} = \frac{17.5}{7.5}$

19. $\frac{n}{13} = \frac{3}{2.6}$

20. $\frac{8}{21} = \frac{2}{n}$

Write a proportion for each. Then solve to find the answer.

21. 4 for 98¢
    24 for how much?

22. 9 in 30
    How many in 63?

SET 2 Find the unit price. Round to the nearest cent. pages 218–219

1. 5 erasers for 98¢

2. 4 cans for 89¢

3. a dozen oranges for $1.89

4. 4 stickers for 50¢

5. 3 rolls for $2.50

6. 7 cans for $1.00

Which is the better buy?

7. shampoo
   a. 7.5 oz for $1.98
   b. 10 oz for $2.50

8. peanut butter
   a. 28 oz for $2.69
   b. 16 oz for $1.98

SET 3 Complete. pages 220–221

1. scale: 1 cm to 25 cm
   drawing: 6 cm
   actual: ____

2. scale: 1 cm to 1.5 km
   drawing: 15 cm
   actual: ____

3. scale: 1 mm to 7 cm
   drawing: ____
   actual: 56 mm

4. scale: 1 mm to 5 km
   drawing: 1.5 mm
   actual: ____

5. scale: ____
   drawing: 135 mm
   actual: 135 m

6. scale: 1 cm to 15 km
   map: 5 cm
   distance: ____

SET 1 Complete.

pages 222–223

1. 780 km in 4 h
d km in 9 h
d = ___

2. 360 km in 3 h
d km in 7 h
d = ___

3. 424 km in 4 h
d km in 1 h
d = ___

4. 16 m in 16 min
1 m in *t* min
t = ___

5. 500 km in 6 h
2,200 km in *t* h
t = ___

6. 12 m in 6 min
1 m in *t* min
t = ___

7. 2,550 km in 5 h
d km in 7 h

8. 207 m in 9 min
d m in 4 min

9. 220 km per h
330 km in *t* h

SET 2 For each pair of similar polygons, complete the proportion. Then name the congruent angles.

pages 226–229

1. $\triangle ABC \sim \triangle DEF$

$\dfrac{AB}{DE} = \dfrac{\Box}{\Box} = \dfrac{\Box}{\Box}$

2. $MNOP \sim RSTU$

$\dfrac{MN}{RS} = \dfrac{\Box}{\Box} = \dfrac{\Box}{\Box} = \dfrac{\Box}{\Box}$

3. $DEFHI \sim JKLMN$

$\dfrac{DE}{JK} = \dfrac{\Box}{\Box} = \dfrac{\Box}{\Box} = \dfrac{\Box}{\Box} = \dfrac{\Box}{\Box}$

4. $\triangle CAT \sim \triangle DOG$

$\dfrac{CA}{DO} = \dfrac{\Box}{\Box} = \dfrac{\Box}{\Box}$

Find each. $\triangle MOT \sim \triangle DEF$

5. $\dfrac{MO}{DE} = \dfrac{OT}{\Box}$

6. $m\angle M = 60°$
$m\angle D =$ ___

SET 3 Use the table on page 497 to find each.

pages 230–231

1. tan 26° **2.** tan 55° **3.** tan 33° **4.** tan 74°

Use the table on page 497 to find the measure of ∠A.

5. tan m∠A = 0.1944 **6.** tan m∠A = 0.6009 **7.** tan m∠A = 1.5399 **8.** tan m∠A = 7.1154

9. tan m∠A = 0.5543 **10.** tan m∠A = 2.9042 **11.** tan m∠A = 0.0524 **12.** tan m∠A = 2.0503

SET 4 Write each percent as a ratio in its simplest form and each ratio as a percent.

pages 240–245

1. 18% **2.** 29% **3.** 55% **4.** 72% **5.** $\frac{35}{100}$ **6.** $\frac{3}{5}$ **7.** $\frac{4}{25}$

Write each percent as a decimal and each decimal as a percent.

8. 38% **9.** 72.5% **10.** 2.4% **11.** $17\frac{1}{2}$% **12.** 0.7% **13.** 13.2% **14.** 0.002

Write as a ratio or a percent. Simplify if possible.

15. 330% **16.** 0.75% **17.** 150% **18.** 560% **19.** $\frac{1}{200}$ **20.** $\frac{225}{100}$ **21.** $\frac{6}{5}$

EXTRA PRACTICE

SET 1 Find the percent of each number.   pages 246–249

1. 5% of 275 **2.** $33\frac{1}{3}$% of 210 **3.** $37\frac{1}{2}$% of 400 **4.** 18% of 25 **5.** 56% of 90 **6.** 22% of 562

Find each percent.

7. What percent of 21 is 7? **8.** What percent of 36 is 9? **9.** What percent of 200 is 155?

10. 15 is what percent of 10? **11.** 80 is what percent of 120? **12.** 75 is what percent of 60?

SET 2 Find n to the nearest one.   pages 250–255

1. 25% of n is 40. **2.** 30% of n is 33. **3.** 5% of n is 24. **4.** 40% of n is 32.

5. 12% of n is 1.86. **6.** 7.7% of n is 2,000. **7.** $33\frac{1}{3}$% of n is 120. **8.** $62\frac{1}{2}$% of n is 270.

Find an estimate for n.

9. 23% of 100 is n. **10.** 52% of 60 is n. **11.** 77% of 12 is n. **12.** 67% of 210 is n.

SET 3 Complete each chart.   pages 256–259

Find the percent of increase or decrease and so indicate.

	Original	New	Percent
1.	50	60	
2.	24	20	
3.	275	250	
4.	72	24	

Find the discount and the sale price.

	Regular Price	Rate of Discount	Discount	Sale Price
5.	$125	15%		
6.	$24.50	20%		
7.	$130	$12\frac{1}{2}$%		
8.	$1,220	30%		

SET 4 Complete each chart.   pages 260–263

Find the amount of markup and the selling price.

	Cost	% of Markup	Amount of Markup	Selling Price
1.	$85	25%		
2.	$13	15%		
3.	$60	17%		
4.	$22.50	30%		

Find the interest.

	Principal	Rate of Interest	Time	Interest
5.	$500	6.5%	2 yr	
6.	$280	10%	9 mo	
7.	$1,550	5.5%	1 yr	
8.	$668	6%	3 yr	

SET 1 Replace each ● with >, <, or =. pages 274–277

1. $^-8$ ● $^+2$

2. $^+11$ ● $^+42$

3. $^-105$ ● 0

4. $^-62$ ● $^-98$

5. $|^-10|$ ● $|^+10|$

6. $|^-43|$ ● $|^+36|$

7. $|^+71|$ ● $|^-77|$

8. $|^+18|$ ● $|^-17|$

9. $^+11 + {}^+8$ ● $^+14$

10. $^-21 + {}^-17$ ● $^-28$

11. $^-12 + {}^-16$ ● $^-18 + {}^-4$

Add.

12. $^+13 + {}^+8$

13. $^-22 + {}^-43$

14. $^+106 + {}^+58$

15. $^-110 + {}^-77$

16. $^-52 + {}^-19$

17. $^+19 + {}^+39$

18. $^-82 + {}^-31$

19. $^+96 + {}^+5$

SET 2 Add or subtract. pages 278–281

1. $^+11 + {}^-8$

2. $^-18 + {}^+12$

3. $^+9 + {}^-14$

4. $^-6 + {}^+30$

5. $^-22 + {}^+13$

6. $^+62 + {}^-75$

7. $^-48 + {}^+55$

8. $^+77 + {}^-31$

9. $^+16 - {}^+14$

10. $^+26 - {}^-12$

11. $^-21 - {}^+8$

12. $^-14 - {}^-11$

13. $^+13 - {}^+19$

14. $^-9 - {}^+21$

15. $^+10 - {}^-32$

16. $^-21 - {}^-28$

SET 3 Multiply or divide. pages 284–287

1. $8 \cdot 7$

2. $11 \cdot {}^-2$

3. $^-9 \cdot 5$

4. $^-7 \cdot {}^-6$

5. $^-20 \cdot {}^-3$

6. $14 \cdot {}^-2$

7. $^-5 \cdot 12$

8. $^-8 \cdot {}^-12$

9. $^-81 \div 9$

10. $^-144 \div {}^-12$

11. $0 \div {}^-56$

12. $^-34 \div {}^-17$

13. $121 \div {}^-11$

14. $16 \div {}^-16$

15. $^-36 \div 18$

16. $^-108 \div {}^-12$

SET 4 Write the coordinates of each point, or name the point for each of the given coordinates. pages 288–291

1. *A*

2. *B*

3. *C*

4. *D*

5. *E*

6. *F*

7. $(^-5, {}^-3)$

8. $(5, {}^-2)$

9. $(5, 5)$

10. $(4, {}^-1)$

11. $(^-1, {}^-1)$

12. $(1, {}^-5)$

13. $(0, 0)$

14. *E, H,* and *I* are in quadrant _____.

15. *A* and *G* are in quadrant _____.

16. *B* and *C* are in quadrant _____.

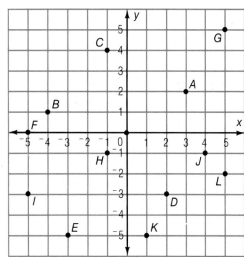

EXTRA PRACTICE

SET 1   Solve the problems from the frequency table.   pages 300–305

1. Which 4 countries have the highest population density? What is their mean density?

POPULATION DENSITIES IN AFRICA (persons per sq mi)					
Algeria	22	Burundi	409	Chad	9
Angola	14	Cameroon	48	Congo	12
Benin	85	Kenya	80	Egypt	116
Botswana	4	Mali	15	Zaire	33

2. What is the range of the population densities?

3. What is the mean density of the 4 countries having the smallest population density?

4. What is the median of this data?

American Immigration Figures for 1860–1940
1861–1870—2,314,000;   1871–1880—2,812,000;   1881–1890—5,246,000;
1891–1900—3,687,000;   1901–1910—8,795,000;   1911–1920—5,735,000;
1921–1930—4,107,000;   1931–1940—528,000

5. What is the median?

6. What is the mean?

7. Which decade had the greatest number of immigrants?

8. Determine the range.

SET 2   Using the spinner, give the probability of the following: pages 322–325

1. P (animal that eats only plants)

2. P (animal that eats meat or fish)

3. P (animal that flies or swims)

4. P (animal that lives only in the water)

5. P (animal that flies and swims)

6. P (animal that has four legs)

7. P (animal that has feathers)

8. P (animal that flies)

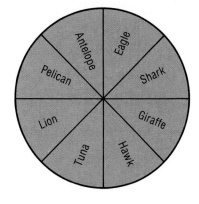

SET 3   Two of the cards below are picked at random. The first draw is replaced before the second card is chosen. Find each probability, $P(A$ and $B)$.   pages 328–329

1. A: Pick a T; B: Pick an R.

2. A: Pick an S; B: Pick a T.

3. A: Pick an R; B: Pick a vowel.

4. A: Pick a consonant; B: Pick an E.

Two of these cards are drawn at random. The first draw is not replaced. Find each probability.

5. P (T and R)

6. P (S and T)

7. P (R and vowel)

8. P (consonant and E)

476 COMPUTATION

SET 1 Using a straightedge, draw a line segment of the given length. Then, using a straightedge and compass, construct a perpendicular bisector for each.

pages 342–347

1. 85 mm   **2.** 9 cm   **3.** 60 mm   **4.** 21 cm   **5.** 12 cm

SET 2 Trace the figure at the right.

1. Construct a line parallel to $\overleftrightarrow{MN}$ through P.

2. Construct a line perpendicular to $\overleftrightarrow{MN}$ through R.

Draw an angle with the given measure. Then construct an angle congruent to the given angle. Then construct the angle bisector.

3. 60°   **4.** 35°   **5.** 115°   **6.** 95°   **7.** 156°

SET 3 Find the surface area and the volume of each prism.

pages 352–355

1. rectangular prism
$l = 2$ cm
$w = 3$ cm
$h = 4$ cm
$A = $ ___
$V = $ ___

2. cube with side 4 cm
$A = $ ___
$V = $ ___

3.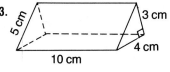
$A = $ ___
$V = $ ___

4. cube with side 6.8 dm
$A = $ ___
$V = $ ___

5. rectangular prism
$l = 7.5$ m
$w = 4.2$ m
$h = 11.8$ m
$A = $ ___
$V = $ ___

6.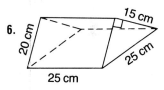
$A = $ ___
$V = $ ___

SET 4 Find the equivalent measures.

pages 362–363

7. 3 mL = ___ cm³

8. 1.8 L = ___ dm³

9. 0.5 dm³ = ___ L

10. 8,000 cm³ = ___ mL

11. 25 mL = ___ cm³

12. 80 cm³ = ___ mL

13. 120 dm³ = ___ L

14. 4,800 cm³ = ___ mL

15. 4,000 L = ___ dm³

16. 8 cm³ = ___ mL

17. 18 L = ___ dm³

18. 40,000 L = ___ dm³

19. 77 cm³ of water weighs ___ g.

20. 9 L of water weighs ___ kg.

21. 56 mL of water weighs ___ g.

22. 90 dm³ of water weighs ___ kg.

EXTRA PRACTICE

SET 1 Solve. pages 372–377

1. $\dfrac{-2}{3} + \dfrac{-1}{3}$ 2. $-1\dfrac{3}{7} + \dfrac{6}{7}$ 3. $\dfrac{1}{5} - \dfrac{4}{5}$ 4. $\dfrac{1}{2} - \dfrac{-1}{3}$ 5. $1\dfrac{1}{3} + \dfrac{-3}{4}$

6. $4.1 + {}^{-}3.6$ 7. $^{-}0.3 - 1.2$ 8. $^{-}0.34 \cdot 0.4$ 9. $^{-}19.2 \div 6$

SET 2 Write as a single power of 10. pages 380–383

1. $10^4 \cdot 10^1$ 2. $10^{-5} \div 10^7$ 3. $10^{-8} \cdot 10^{-3}$ 4. $10^8 \div 10^{-2}$ 5. $10^{-6} \cdot 10^4$

Write in scientific notation.

6. 0.0003 7. 0.0000006 8. 0.0000083 9. 0.0000547 10. 0.0000009041

Write in standard form.

11. 5×10^{-5} 12. 4.9×10^{-8} 13. 2.37×10^{-6} 14. 3.093×10^{-4} 15. 7.6518×10^{-7}

SET 3 Write a real number between each pair of real numbers. pages 384–389

1. 1 and 2   2. $^{-}1$ and $^{-}2$ 3. 0 and 1   4. $^{-}1$ and 0   5. 1.1 and 1.11

Find each square.

6. 4^2 7. 16^2 8. 28^2 9. 53^2 10. 61^2

Use the divide-and-average method to find each square root
to the nearest tenth.

11. $\sqrt{5}$ 12. $\sqrt{121}$ 13. $^{-}\sqrt{52}$ 14. $\sqrt{91}$ 15. $^{-}\sqrt{15}$

SET 4 Tell whether a triangle with the given sides is a right triangle. pages 390–393

1. 3 m, 4 m,   2. 9 km, 12 km,   3. 4 cm, 6 cm,   4. 6 km, 8 km,   5. 3 m, 2 m,
   7 m   15 km   8 cm   10 km   5 m

Find the missing measure of each right triangle to the nearest tenth.

6. $a = 2$ cm   7. $a = 9$ m   8. $a = $ ____   9. $a = 4$ m   10. $a = 1$ cm
   $b = 3$ cm $b = $ ____ $b = 40$ km $b = 4$ m $b = $ ____
   $c = $ ____ $c = 15$ m $c = 41$ km $c = $ ____ $c = 5.1$ cm

SET 5 Draw a coordinate system. Graph and label these points. pages 394–395

1. $A(2, 3)$ 2. $B(^{-}3, {}^{-}2)$ 3. $C\left(\dfrac{-3}{2}, {}^{-}6\right)$ 4. $D\left(\dfrac{1}{2}, \dfrac{-5}{4}\right)$ 5. $E(9, \sqrt{2})$

478 COMPUTATION

SET 1   Solve and check.
pages 408–411

1. $x + 10 = 23$
2. $y - {}^-13 = 7$
3. $16 + y = {}^-34$
4. $42 = n - {}^-15$

5. $5y = 45$
6. ${}^-6y = 48$
7. ${}^-81 = {}^-9x$
8. ${}^-63 = 3n$

9. $x + \frac{{}^-2}{3} = 4$
10. $n - 1\frac{2}{5} = \frac{{}^-3}{5}$
11. $\frac{1}{3}x = {}^-33$
12. $21 = \frac{{}^-7}{8}x$

13. $36 = {}^-22 + n$
14. $x - {}^-9 = 5$
15. $y - 4 = {}^-17$
16. $n + \frac{5}{6} = {}^-22$

SET 2   Solve over the integers and check. List the first three solutions.
pages 412–413, 420–421

1. $x + 7 > 15$
2. $y - 11 < 18$
3. $4n \geq 28$

4. $w + {}^-2 \geq 12$
5. $\frac{b}{6} < 5$
6. ${}^-4 + a > 0$

Solve these inequalities.

7. $2x + 3 < 9$
8. $5y - 1 \leq 19$
9. $6x - 3 \geq 27$

10. $10y - 6y \geq 36$
11. $4n + 7n < {}^-22$
12. $8a - 3a > 45$

13. ${}^-3b + 4b \geq {}^-14$
14. $2x - 5 \leq 21$
15. $5y - 14 \leq {}^-9$

SET 3   Solve and check.
pages 416–417

1. $4x + 2 = 10$
2. $3y - 5 = 7$
3. $2n + 2 = 12$
4. $6 - 3a = 3$

5. $5b + 4 = {}^-11$
6. $4 = {}^-4 + 4w$
7. ${}^-5 = 1 - 2x$
8. ${}^-3y + 1 = 16$

9. $\frac{n}{2} + 1 = 5$
10. $2a + 1 = 2$
11. $\frac{{}^-5}{4}b - 3 = {}^-13$
12. $6 = 0.6a + 3$

13. $\frac{{}^-2}{3}x + 5 = {}^-4$
14. $4y = {}^-8\frac{4}{5}$
15. $\frac{3}{4}z + 2 = 1$
16. ${}^-7 = \frac{7}{9}a - 8$

SET 4   Solve and check.
pages 418–419; 422–423

1. $8w + 2w = 20$
2. $11x - 5x = 24$
3. $2n + 5n = {}^-35$
4. ${}^-y + 3y = 2$

5. $7a - a = {}^-48$
6. ${}^-9b - b = {}^-30$
7. $x + 3x = 5$
8. $3.3y + 2.1y = 10.8$

Solve. Graph the solutions on the number line.

9. $4n = {}^-12$
10. $2a + 2 \leq 10$
11. $4w - 6 = {}^-2$
12. $8y - 2y + 15 > 27$

EXTRA PRACTICE

SET 1 Solve each problem.

pages 432–433

1. Write the ordered pairs for this relation.

2. Write the domain of this relation.

3. Write the range of this relation.

x	0	1	2	3
y	0	5	10	15

4. Write *relation* or *function* for each.
   a. (1, 2) (2, 4) (3, 6) (4, 8)
   b. (2, 20) (2, 10) (4, 5) (10, 2)
   c. (10, ⁻1), (8, ⁻1), (6, ⁻1), (4, ⁻1)

SET 2 Complete each table of values. Then graph each equation.

pages 434–435

1. $y = x - 3$

x	y
2	
1	
0	
⁻1	
⁻2	

2. $y = 3x$

x	y
2	
1	
0	
⁻1	
⁻2	

3. $y = 2x + 2$

x	y
2	
1	
0	
⁻1	
⁻2	

4. $y = 3x - 2$

x	y
2	
1	
0	
⁻1	
⁻2	

Graph each equation.

5. $y = x + 3$

6. $y = 3x - 4$

7. $y = 5x$

8. $y = {}^-2x$

9. $y = {}^-2x + 1$

10. $y = 3x + 2$

11. $y = 3x - 1$

12. $y = x + 1$

SET 3 Give the slope (*m*) and y-intercept (*b*) of each line.

pages 436–437

1. $y = 3x + 2$

2. $y = 2x - 4$

3. $y = x + 1$

4. $y = x - 7$

5. $y = {}^-5x + 1$

6. $y = 3x + 2$

7. $y = {}^-x - 6$

8. $y = \frac{3}{4}x + 5$

Write the equation of each line.

9. $m = 4, b = 3$

10. $m = \frac{1}{3}, b = 2$

11. $m = {}^-2, b = 5$

12. $m = 1, b = {}^-3$

SET 4 Solve each system of equations by graphing. Check your solutions.

pages 440–441

1. $y = 2x + 2$
    $y = x - 2$

2. $y = 4x - 4$
    $y = x + 2$

3. $y = -x - 3$
    $y = x + 1$

4. $y = x + 2$
    $y = 2x$

5. $y = {}^-x - 1$
    $y = {}^-2x$

6. $y = x - 2$
    $y = 2x + 1$

7. $y = x - 2$
    $y = 2x - 1$

8. $y = 3x - 1$
    $y = x + 1$

9. $y = 4x$
    $y = x + 3$

10. $y = 2x - 2$
    $y = x - 4$

11. $y = x + 5$
    $y = 5 - x$

12. $y = 3x - 4$
    $y = x - 6$

480 COMPUTATION

pages 10–11

SET 1   Use this copy of Ted's catalog order to answer the questions.

Stock No.	Color	Size	How Many	Description	Price Each	Total Price
134	tan	M	1	sports cap	$ 9.50	$ 9 50
416	navy	30	1	belt	$10.00	$10 00
172	brown	M	2	hiking socks	$ 4.00	$ 8 00

Shipping and Handling Charges		
$26 and under add $3.25	Item total	
$26.01 to $51 add $3.75		
$51.01 to $75 add $4.50	Shipping/Handling	
Over $75 add $5.00	TOTAL	

1. How much is Ted spending on socks?

2. What costs $9.50?

3. What is the item total of Ted's order?

4. What must Ted add for Shipping/Handling?

5. What is the total cost of Ted's order?

SET 2   Use the table at the right to answer these.

pages 20–21

1. How much admission would you have to pay for a day at Funpark?

2. What is the admission cost for Mr. and Mrs. Nguyen and their children, ages 2 and 5?

3. Find the admission cost for two adults and two teenagers after 6:00 P.M.

4. If Funpark is open for 12 hours each day, what is an adult admission worth per hour?

FUNPARK ADMISSION FEES	
Regular Admission (Ages 10–64)	$15.00
Junior Admission (Ages 4–9)	$12.00
Children (Age 3 or under)	FREE
Senior Citizens (Age 65 or over)	$8.00
SUNSET PLAN (5:00 P.M. to Closing)	
Regular $12.00 Junior $9.50	

SET 3   Solve each problem, if possible. Tell what facts are missing, if any. Tell what facts are extra, if any.

pages 40–41

1. Pánfilo de Narváez explored Florida in 1528. Fifteen years earlier, Florida had been discovered by Ponce de León. What was the year of Florida's discovery?

2. Robert E. Peary first explored Greenland in 1886 at age 30. He attempted to reach the North Pole in 1893 but did not succeed until 1909. How old was he when he reached the North Pole?

3. Christopher Columbus made 4 voyages from 1492 to 1502. He sailed with 90 men in 1492, 17 ships and 1,500 men in 1494, 6 ships in 1498, and 135 men in 1502. How many men sailed on the 4 voyages?

4. In 1806, Arctic explorer William Scoresby traveled north of Spitsbergen to 81° 30′. In 1607, Henry Hudson had journeyed north of Spitsbergen to 80° 23′. How far apart are the two latitudes?

SET 1   Read the table and solve each problem.   pages 54–55

1. How much faster is the cheetah than the Thomson's gazelle?

2. What is the average speed of the elk, lion, and pronghorn antelope?

3. Which animal runs 4 mph faster than the greyhound?

4. Which animal is fastest? How much faster is it than the slowest animal?

SPEEDS OF ANIMALS	
ANIMAL	SPEED (MPH)
Cheetah	70
Coyote	43
Elk	45
Gray fox	42
Greyhound	39
Hyena	40
Lion	50
Pronghorn antelope	61
Thomson's gazelle	50

SET 2   Use simulation to solve each problem.   pages 74–75

1. In a parade, 15 persons will ride in 5 cars. Two cars hold only 2 persons each. No car holds more than 4. No one will ride alone. How many ride in each car?

2. A student at Cedar Lake Junior High outlined letters on a white notebook cover. In how many ways can she color the letters using at least one of the colors orange and blue?

At a football game, 42 students will each hold up an orange or a blue card. The orange cards will form the letters C F and the blue cards will form the background and border.

3. If there are 6 rows with 7 cards in a row, how many cards will be orange?

4. To make the letters twice as high, how many students with cards would have to be added to the card section?

SET 3   Solve each problem. Tell what facts are missing, if any.   pages 80–81

1. On the world's longest rink, Eric skated 1.45 km, which is $\frac{1}{5}$ of its length. How long is the rink?

2. Rushing River is 4.75 km south of Longbow. Eric drives 3.5 km west and 1.25 km south to get to Longbow. How far does he travel?

3. Eric drove from Rushing River to Lake Arrowhead. His odometer readings were 60,021.9 and 60,207.5. He drove 8.4 km out of his way to buy gasoline. How far is the lake from the river?

4. It took Eric 45 minutes to drive around the lake. When he returned, the odometer read 60,234.5. What was his average speed for the trip around the lake?

5. Eric caught 3 fish on each of the first and second days, and 4 fish on each of the third and fourth days. How many fish will he catch in 7 days?

SET 1 Complete each pattern. pages 102–103

1. 13, 13.5, 14.5, 16, 18, ___, ___

2. 4, 7, 13, 25, 49, ___, ___

3. 100, 99, 97, 94, 90, ___, ___

4. 480, 240, 120, 60, ___, ___

5.
	6	12	14		22
2	8		16	18	

6.
1	2	3	4	5	6
2	5			14	

7.

8.

SET 2 The Green Sox play 3 days in a row and then have a day off. Their first game is on Monday, May 1. pages 102–103

1. When will the Green Sox play again on a Monday?

2. If the Green Sox play all their scheduled games through May 31, how many games will they play in May?

3. There are 6 adults and 10 children in the Forest Booster Club. The club paid $104.00 for tickets to a game. All tickets cost the same amount. How much was each ticket?

4. The club will eat in the picnic area before the game. Box suppers cost $6.00 for adults and $4.50 for children. How much will the club pay for supper?

5. All the children and one half the adults bought popcorn. How much money did the popcorn vendor collect?

6. In the game, the Green Sox scored 2 runs in each even-numbered inning. The visiting team, the Bears, scored 1 run each inning from the third through the ninth inning. What was the final score?

SET 3 Use the table to solve each problem. pages 126–127

1. Gary bought 3 packages of Caribbean Blend and 2 packages of Tropical Fruit Mix. What did he pay?

2. Ricardo had $7.50 to buy 5 packages of Nutty Delight. Did he have enough money?

3. Yolanda bought 4 packages of Nutty Delight. Samantha bought 5 packages of Wilderness Pack. Who paid more? How much more?

4. The Warren County Hiking Club bought a box of 24 packages of Carob Munch for $30.00. How much did they save per package?

Trail Mixes	5 oz package
California Mix	$1.29
Caribbean Blend	$1.25
Carob Munch	$1.39
Nutty Delight	$1.49
Tropical Fruit Mix	$1.29
Wilderness Pack	$1.19

SET 1 Wednesday Linda parked in the garage at 9:30 A.M. She
left the garage at 3:15 P.M.

pages 136–137

1. She was charged for how many hours?

2. What was her total parking fee?

3. What would Linda have paid to park the
   same amount of time on a Saturday?

4. If Linda had not left until 5:15 P.M.
   Wednesday, what would she have paid?

5. Linda and her family parked from 7:00 P.M.
   to 10:30 P.M. on Friday while at the circus.
   What did they pay for parking?

DOWNTOWN PARKING GARAGE		
Hours	**Monday–Friday**	**Cost**
7 A.M. to 6 P.M.	First Hour or Part	$3.50
	Each Additional Hour or Part	$1.50
	Daily Maximum	$12.00
6 P.M. to Midnight	Each Hour or Part	$1.75
	Maximum to Closing	$7.50
Saturday & Sunday		
8 A.M. to Midnight	Each hour or part	$2.00
	Daily Maximum	$11.00

SET 2 Kathi is buying metal panels that can be connected to make
the sides, shelves, and top of a bookcase. The panels, each 12 in.
wide, come in 4 lengths: 24 in., 30 in., 36 in., and 48 in.

pages 158–159

1. Kathi's bookcase will be 4 ft high, 3 ft
   wide, and 1 ft deep. How many panels of
   what size should she buy for the vertical
   sides of her bookcase?

2. The bookcase will have shelves about 12
   in. apart from top to bottom. How many
   panels of what size should she buy for the
   horizontal shelves?

3. Later Kathi may attach additional panels to
   make the bookcase 5 ft wide. How many
   panels of what size would she need for the
   vertical sides of her bookcase?

4. If Kathi put shelves 8 in. apart in the new
   section, how many panels of what size
   would she need?

SET 3 Use the graph to answer the questions.

pages 170–171

1. For which quizzes were the scores the same?

2. What was the difference between Tom's
   highest and lowest scores?

3. To the nearest whole number, what was
   Tom's average score for the 7 quizzes?

4. If the highest and lowest scores are not
   included, how will this affect Tom's quiz
   average?

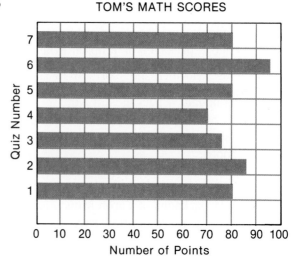

TOM'S MATH SCORES

SET 1 Mrs. Lewis is planning to cover a rectangular floor with square tiles. The table shows the plan for her design. Copy and complete the table.

pages 192–193

1. How many tiles are in each row?

2. How many white tiles are in row 5?

3. How many green tiles will she need?

4. How many white tiles will she need?

5. Make a drawing of the pattern of tiles.

Row	1	2	3	4	5	6	7	8	9
White Tiles	13	6	5	4	3	4		6	
Green Tiles	0	1	3	5	7	5		1	0
White Tiles	0	6	5				5		0

SET 2 Anna is making a quilt. She is piecing together stars to put on 9-inch squares. The quilt will have 9 rows of squares, 6 squares per row. The drawing shows the pattern of the squares and colors of the stars.

pages 202–203

1. How many squares will Anna have to make?

2. What are the dimensions of the quilt?

3. Anna wants to cut the squares from a piece of fabric 48 in. wide and 3 yd long. Is there enough fabric?

4. How many of each color star will Anna need?

5. Anna will put a border strip 4 in. wide on all 4 sides. What will be the dimensions of the quilt with its border?

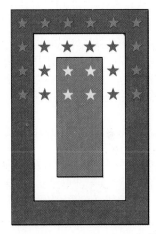

SET 3 Solve each problem.

pages 224–225

1. There are 5 TV programs on Channel 16 from 5:30 P.M. to 11:00 P.M. The news and cooking shows last 30 min each; the nature show lasts 60 min; the sports show lasts 90 min; and the movie is 2 h long. Use the given clues. Tell when each program begins.
   a. The sports show is on between the nature show and the movie.
   b. The last program is the movie.
   c. The news begins at 6:00.

2. The high temperatures on July 1 for six cities were 70°F, 75°F, 79°F, 84°F, 96°F, and 100°F. Use the given clues. Tell which city recorded which temperature.
   a. San Diego had the second highest temperature.
   b. Los Angeles had a higher temperature than Spokane.
   c. Seattle had the lowest temperature.
   d. Seattle's temperature was 5° lower than Portland's.
   e. Spokane's temperature was 5° higher than San Francisco's.

EXTRA PRACTICE

SET 1   Solve each problem.

pages 232–233

1. A notebook cover measures 29.5 cm by 22 cm. Tell the dimensions of the largest square photograph that will fit on the cover.

2. A chart measuring 36.8 cm by 27.5 cm is reduced to $\frac{4}{5}$ of its size. Will the reduced copy fit on the notebook cover?

3. Liz is covering the lid of a square box with rectangular stickers. Each sticker is 2.5 cm by 5 cm. The perimeter of the lid is 82 cm. What is the greatest number of stickers that she can put on the lid with no overlapping?

4. Liz has put as many stickers on the lid as she can with no overlapping. How much area of the lid is not covered with stickers?

SET 2   Use an organized list to help you solve each problem.

pages 252–253

1. Last year (not leap year), Maggie jogged every day for 3 consecutive months. How many different numbers of days might this be? What are they?

2. If Maggie jogged for 91 days in three months, what are the months she might have jogged?

3. Tickets cost $11 and $9 for one play, $8 and $6 for the second, and $12 and $10 for the third. If Scott buys 1 ticket for each play, how many different combinations of ticket prices are possible?

4. Scott spent $27 for tickets to the 3 plays. What combinations are possible?

SET 3   Solve each problem.

pages 264–265

1. An issue of *News Magazine* costs $1.95 on the newsstand and $1.11 by subscription. An issue of *Them Magazine* costs $1.50 on the newsstand and $.99 by subscription. About what percent off the newsstand price is saved by subscribing to each magazine?

2. Joe made punch. His recipe was 1 part lime juice, 4 parts grapefruit juice, and 5 parts grape juice. He used 16 cups of grapefruit juice. How many cups of grape juice did he use?

3. Dues for the Outdoor Club are $23.50 this year. Lifetime dues are $150. Dues will increase $1.00 per year. After how many years will the total paid in yearly dues exceed the lifetime dues?

4. In a baseball lineup, Bobby bats directly between Sam and Chris. Jackie bats after Sam. Who bats first?

5. Four photos of pets and their owners were in the newspaper. The pets were a cat, dog, canary, and goldfish. The pet owners were Cindy, Ruth, Manuel, and Quan. Use the clues at the right to tell which pet belongs to which owner.

CLUES
a. Manuel's pet does not purr.
b. Cindy's pet makes no noise.
c. Quan and Manuel have pets with fur.

SET 1 Solve each problem. pages 282–283

1. Wright's Clothing Store had 37 T-shirts on sale. Seven shirts were white and 6 were black. There were an equal number of red, blue, and green shirts. How many shirts of each of these three colors were there?

2. On each day of the sale, the current price of the shirts was reduced 10%. On the third day, the price was $10.21. What was the original price?

3. Mrs. Horn bought 2 of the shirts on the third day. She also bought 6 pairs of socks. Her total bill was $26.90. What was the cost of one pair of socks?

4. At the conclusion of the sale, $\frac{1}{3}$ of the shirts left were size Small. One half were size Medium. The remaining 3 were size Large. How many shirts were unsold?

SET 2 Solve each problem. pages 292–293

1. Paul earns $3.65 per hour stocking shelves in a supermarket. He also works part-time at a gas station for $4.35 per hour. Last week he worked 8 hours at the supermarket. His total earnings were $77.05. How many hours did he work at the gas station?

2. Anita works in the supermarket after school. She works Monday through Thursday and earns $4.00 per hour. Each day she works one more hour than the previous day. What are her weekly earnings?

3. Jim, John, and Jane each play a musical instrument. The instruments are flute, violin, and guitar. Use the given clues. Tell which person plays which instrument.
   a. Jim's and Jane's instruments have strings.
   b. Jim plays his instrument with a bow.

4. Complete the pattern.

   $10\frac{2}{3}$, $5\frac{1}{3}$, $2\frac{2}{3}$, $1\frac{1}{3}$, —, —

SET 3 Determine whether the conclusion following each pair of statements is correct. Answer yes or no. pages 314–315

1. The nation's oldest zoo is in Pennsylvania. Brookfield Zoo is in Illinois.
   Conclusion: Brookfield is not the oldest zoo.

2. Dubuque is on the Mississippi River. Parts of the Mississippi flow through Minnesota.
   Conclusion: Dubuque is in Minnesota.

3. All ferns are plants. All palms are plants.
   Conclusion: All ferns are palms.

4. All fish have gills. All eels are fish.
   Conclusion: All eels have gills.

If possible, draw a conclusion from each pair of statements.

5. If you use Plush hair conditioner, then you will be popular.
   Stephanie is popular.

6. All cats have 4 legs.
   Polly has 2 legs.

EXTRA PRACTICE

SET 1   Solve each problem.

pages 314–315

1. Five events took place at the Mt. Pine Winter Carnival. The first 3 events were outside, and started with men's alpine skiing. After the figure skating, the ice hockey game was played in the same arena. The women's speed skating took place before bobsledding. Tell the order of the events.

2. Michael is making 7 diamond-shaped signs. He will put black tape around each sign's perimeter. Will 50 feet of tape be enough?

3. Three figure skaters—Megan, Kitty, and Peter—performed at a workshop. In how many different ways could the skaters have been scheduled to perform?

4. There were 6 finalists in the snow sculpture contest. In how many ways could sculptures win first place and second place?

SET 2   Solve each problem.

pages 350–351

1. Josh has a collection of 208 postcards. He has 3 times as many U.S. cards as foreign cards. How many of each kind does he have?

2. Steve keeps 103 seashells in 3 boxes. Box A has 8 fewer shells than Box B. Box C has 6 more shells than Box B. How many shells are in each box?

3. Maria displays her 42 rocks on 3 shelves. There are twice as many rocks on the third shelf as on the first. There are 6 more rocks on the second shelf than on the first. How many rocks are on each shelf?

4. Lena's 56 owls are made of glass, plastic, and wood. There are twice as many glass owls as plastic ones. There are twice as many plastic owls as wood ones. How many of each kind of owl are there?

5. Joan has 70 quarters, dimes, and nickels in a jar. There are four times as many nickels as quarters and half as many dimes as nickels. Find the value of her coins.

6. Mrs. Young's spoon collection fills 2 spoon racks. One rack holds 50% more than the other. If Mrs. Young has 30 spoons, how many are in each rack?

SET 3   Solve each problem.

pages 364–365

1. Nick is trimming the top edge of an octagonal basket with silver ribbon. Will a yard of ribbon be enough to trim the perimeter?

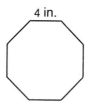

2. Pam's kitchen has a square window. How many square feet of wallpaper will cover the wall area surrounding the window?

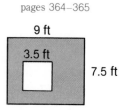

3. Tickets to a ski movie cost $2.50 for children, $3.00 for senior citizens, and $4.00 for adults. One day the theater sold twice as many children's tickets as adult tickets and $\frac{1}{5}$ as many senior tickets as adult tickets. If 400 tickets were sold, what were the total receipts for the day?

SET 1   The graph shows the number of volunteers at Dewey Library.   pages 378–379

1. How many volunteers did the library have in 1984?

2. In which year was the number of volunteers the least?

3. What was the increase in the number of volunteers between 1983 and 1986?

4. In what year was there the greatest increase in the number of volunteers from the previous year?

5. What was the average number of volunteers per year over the 5 years? Answer to the nearest whole number.

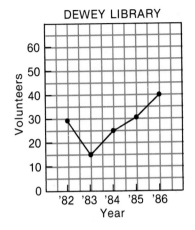

SET 2   Solve each problem.   pages 396–397

1. Henry and Kevin sold a total of 51 tickets to the Community Concert series. If Henry sold 7 more tickets than Kevin, how many tickets did each sell?

2. Liz sold $\frac{3}{4}$ of her Community Concert tickets to her friends. She sold $\frac{1}{3}$ of the remainder to a neighbor. The 2 tickets she had left she sold to her aunt. How many tickets did Liz sell?

3. A member of Best Video Club pays a $5 fee to join, and rents video cassettes for $3 each. A nonmember pays $4 to rent a video cassette. How many cassettes will a member rent before the two costs are equal?

4. Yesterday, Joanne ran 2.5 times as many miles as Sara. Sara ran 3 times as many miles as Ron. How many miles did each run?

5. Alice, Helena, Mako, and Scott climbed a mountain. Helena reached the top before Mako and after Scott. Scott reached the top after his sister. In what order did they reach the top?

6. A bank adds 10% interest on the amount that remains in an account for 1 year. Therese puts $100 in such an account and does not add more or withdraw anything. How much is in the account after 7 years?

SET 3   Solve each problem.   pages 414–415

1. Eleven soccer players practice kicking. Each player kicks the ball to each of the other players. How many times is the ball kicked?

2. Five contestants played checkers. Each player played 3 games with each other player. How many games were played in all?

3. Seven pianists play duets with each other. Each person plays with each of the others. How many duets are played altogether?

4. Each day Mr. Pease bicycled 2 km farther than the day before. He rode 1 km on Monday. What was the total distance he had ridden by the end of the next Saturday?

SET 1 Solve each problem.

pages 424–425

1. Alex had $15 to spend on light bulbs. He bought a pack of 2 floodlight bulbs for $7. He spent the rest on 4-bulb packs at $3 per pack. How many bulbs did he buy?

2. Sylvia packed 124 sandwiches in 5 bags. Each bag had twice as many sandwiches as the ones before it. How many sandwiches were in each bag?

Dorothy is knitting a scarf. The first day she knits 11 rows. The next day she unravels 5 rows and reknits 4 rows. On the third day, she knits 11 rows like the first day. On the fourth day, she repeats what she did on the second day.

3. If Dorothy continues in this way, how many rows will she have knitted in 8 days?

4. How many rows of the scarf will be completed after 8 days?

SET 2 Solve each problem in more than one way, if possible. Check that your answers are the same.

pages 442–443

1. In 1984, 5.7 million people visited the Lincoln and Jefferson Memorials. Twice as many visited the Lincoln Memorial as visited the Jefferson Memorial. How many visited each memorial?

2. A tourist bus with 60 passengers stopped for lunch. One third of the passengers ordered ham sandwiches, $\frac{1}{4}$ cheese, and $\frac{1}{5}$ club. The rest of the group ate salads. How many of each were eaten?

3. A bus with 45 passengers leaves the Washington Monument and stops 4 times. At the first stop, 16 people get off and 3 get on. At the second stop, 12 people get off and 18 get on. At the third stop, 24 people get off and 26 get on. At the last stop, 3 get off and 1 gets on. How many passengers are on the bus that returns to the Washington Monument?

4. Cal spent $9.69 in a museum shop. He bought a wall calendar for $4.95 and pocket calendars for $.79 each. How many calendars did he buy?

5. Two hundred people board 14 tourist vans. Some vans have 12 seats and the rest have 16 seats. If all seats are occupied, how many 16-seat vans are there?

SET 3 Solve each problem.

pages 448–449

1. Jim's birthday in March is the day after John's birthday. If the product of their birthdays is 812, what are their birthdays?

2. Two out of 5 students in a class cannot type. Twenty-one students know how to type. How many students are in the class?

3. There are 4 typewriters on a table. The black typewriter is on the right. The red typewriter is between the tan typewriter and the gray typewriter. The black typewriter and the gray typewriter are not next to each other. Which typewriter is on the left?

4. A game board is 15 squares wide by 15 squares long. A third of the squares in rows 1, 5, 10, and 15 are worth 40 points each. A third of the squares in the remaining even-numbered rows are worth 50 points each. A third of the squares in the remaining odd-numbered rows are worth 60 points each. What are the total points for the squares?

Glossary

absolute value   The distance an integer is from 0 on the number line.

acute angle   An angle with a measure less than 90°.

acute triangle   A triangle with three acute angles.

additive inverses   Two numbers whose sum is zero. *Example:* $^+3$ and $^-3$ are additive inverses.

adjacent angles   Angles that have a common ray and a common vertex between them.

altitude   The height of a triangle or parallelogram.

angle   Two rays with a common endpoint called the vertex.

arc   A part of the circumference of a circle.

area   The number of square units needed to cover a region.

associative property of addition   The way that addends are grouped does not change the sum. *Example:* $(a + b) + c = a + (b + c)$

associative property of multiplication   The way that factors are grouped does not change the product.

base (of a polygon)   base

base (of a space figure)   base

BASIC   A computer language.

basic counting principle   If a first event has n outcomes and a second event has m outcomes, then the first event followed by the second event has $n \times m$ outcomes.

binary   A numeration system that uses the number two as its base.

bisect   To divide into two congruent parts.

central angle   An angle that has its vertex at the center of a circle.

central processing unit (CPU)   The part of a computer where calculations are performed.

chord   A line segment with both endpoints on the circle.

circle   A plane closed figure with all points the same distance from a point called the center.

circumference   The distance around a circle.

common factor   A factor that is the same for two or more numbers.

common multiple   A multiple that is the same for two or more numbers.

commutative property of addition   The order of the addends does not change the sum.

commutative property of multiplication   The order of the factors does not change the product.

complementary angles   Two angles the sum of whose measures is 90°.

complex fraction   A fraction having one or more fractions in the numerator, denominator, or both.

composite number   A whole number greater than 1 with more than two factors.

cone   A space figure with a circular base and one vertex.

congruent figures   Figures that have the same size and shape.

coordinate plane   The plane determined by a horizontal number line, called the x-axis, and a vertical number line, called the y-axis, intersecting at a point called the origin. Each point of the plane corresponds to an ordered pair of numbers.

cosine   The ratio of the length of the side adjacent to an acute angle to the length of the hypotenuse in a right triangle.

cross products   Products obtained by multiplying the numerator of one fraction by the denominator of a second fraction, and the denominator of the first fraction by the numerator of the second fraction. *Example:* $\frac{2}{3} = \frac{4}{6}$ $2 \times 6 = 3 \times 4$

cube   A rectangular prism whose faces are all congruent square regions.

cylinder   A space figure with two parallel bases that are congruent circles.

data   Information that is gathered.

decimal   A number with one or more places to the right of a decimal point.

degree   A unit for measuring angles.

degree Celsius (°C)   A unit for measuring temperature in the metric system.

degree Fahrenheit (°F)   A unit for measuring temperature in the customary measurement system.

density property Between any two real numbers, there is always another real number.

diagonal A segment joining any two nonadjacent vertices in a polygon.

diameter A line segment that passes through the center of a circle and has both endpoints on the circle.

discount The amount that a regular price is reduced.

distributive property of multiplication over addition If one factor is a sum, multiplying each addend before adding does not change the product.

divisible A number is divisible by another number if the remainder is zero after dividing.

domain All the values of x in a relation.

edge The segment formed where two faces of a space figure meet.

END The last line in a BASIC computer program.

endpoint A point at the end of a segment or ray.

ENTER The key that causes a computer to accept and process information. It is also called RETURN key.

equal ratios Ratios that describe the same rate or make the same comparison.

equally likely outcomes Outcomes that have the same chance of occurring.

equation A number sentence with an equal (=) sign.

equilateral triangle A triangle with all sides congruent.

equivalent fractions Fractions that name the same number.

estimate To give an approximate rather than an exact answer.

even number A whole number that is divisible by 2.

event One or more outcomes of an experiment.

expanded form A number written as the sum of the values of its digits.

exponent A number that tells how many times the base is used as a factor.

expression A mathematical phrase made up of a variable or combination of variables, and/or numbers, and operations.
Examples: $5n$; $4x - 7$; $(5 \times 2) - (6 \div 3)$

factors The numbers that are multiplied to give a product.
Example: $3 \times 8 = 24$ The factors are 3 and 8.

flowchart A diagram that shows the steps used to solve a problem.

formula An equation that states a fact or rule.

FOR . . . NEXT Statements in a BASIC computer program that create a loop or sequence of commands that are repeated.

fraction A number in the form $\frac{a}{b}$. It names part of a region or part of a group. The number below the fraction bar is the denominator. The number above the fraction bar is the numerator.

frequency The number of times a given item occurs in a set of data.

frequency table A listing of data together with the number of times an item occurs.

function A relation in which each value of x is paired only once with a value of y.

GOTO A statement in a BASIC computer program that tells the computer to go to another line in the program.

graph A drawing used to present data. Some types are bar graphs, line graphs, and circle graphs.

greatest common factor (GCF) The greatest number that is a factor of each of two or more numbers.

greatest possible error (GPE) In any measurement, one half the precision of the measurement.

hardware The machinery of a computer system.

height (of a parallelogram) A segment that joins opposite sides and is perpendicular to the base.
Example:

height (of a triangle) A segment drawn perpendicular to the base of a triangle from a vertex of the triangle.

heptagon A polygon with seven sides.

hexagon A polygon with six sides.

histogram A bar graph that represents frequency data.

hypotenuse The side opposite the right angle in a right triangle.

identity property of addition The sum of any number and 0 is that number.
Example: $0 + a = a$

identity property of multiplication The product of any number and 1 is that number.
Example: $1 \times a = a$

IF . . . THEN A statement in a BASIC computer program that is used to test a certain condition and then to act on the results.

improper fraction A fraction in which the numerator is greater than or equal to the denominator.

inequality A mathematical sentence that uses one of the symbols $<$, $\leq$, $>$, $\geq$, or $\neq$.

input The numbers and commands entered in a calculator or computer.

integer The numbers . . . $^-3$, $^-2$, $^-1$, 0, $^+1$, $^+2$, . . .

interest The charge for borrowing money or the amount paid for the use of money.

intersecting lines Lines that cross at one point.

inverse operations Two operations that are opposite in effect. Addition and subtraction are inverse operations. Multiplication and division are inverse operations.

irrational number Any number that cannot be expressed as a quotient of two integers. In decimal form an irrational number is nonrepeating and nonterminating.

isosceles triangle A triangle with two congruent sides.

least common multiple (LCM) The least nonzero number that is a multiple of each of two or more numbers.

LET A statement in a BASIC computer program that assigns a value to a memory location named by a letter.

line The collection of points along a straight path. It has no endpoints.

line segment A part of a line having two endpoints.

lowest-terms fraction A fraction is in lowest terms, or simplest form, when the GCF of the numerator and the denominator is 1.

mean In a collection of data, the sum of all the data divided by the number of data.

median The middle number or average of the two middle numbers in a collection of data when the data are arranged in order.

memory The part of a computer system that stores all information and instructions.

midpoint A point that divides a segment into two congruent segments.

mixed number A number written as a whole number and a fraction.

mode The number that occurs most often in a collection of data.

multiple The product of a whole number and any other whole number.

mutually exclusive events Events that cannot occur at the same time.

negative integers The numbers less than zero that are opposites of natural numbers.

obtuse angle An angle with a measure greater than 90° but less than 180°.

obtuse triangle A triangle with one obtuse angle.

octagon A polygon with eight sides.

opposite integers Two integers that are the same distance from zero on the number line.
Example: 3 and $^-3$ are opposite integers.

ordered pair A pair of numbers used to locate a point in the coordinate plane.

origin The point of intersection of the x-axis and y-axis in a coordinate plane.

outcome A possible result in a probability experiment.

output The answer given by a computer or a calculator.

parallel lines Lines in the same plane that never intersect.

parallelogram A quadrilateral with opposite sides parallel. Each pair of opposite sides and angles is congruent.

pentagon A polygon with five sides.

percent A ratio whose second term is 100. Percent means parts per hundred. The symbol % is used for percent.

perimeter The distance around a polygon.

permutations An ordered selection of a group of objects from a given set.
Example: There are 6 permutations of 2 letters from the letters *A*, *B*, and *C*. The permutations are *AB*, *BA*, *AC*, *CA*, *BC*, and *CB*.

perpendicular lines Two lines that intersect to form right angles.

pi (π) The ratio of the circumference of a circle to its diameter. The ratio is the same for all circles.
$\pi \approx 3.14$ or $\frac{22}{7}$.

plane A flat surface extending endlessly in all directions.

point An exact location in space.

polygon A closed plane figure made up of line segments.

polyhedron A space figure whose surfaces, or faces, are all flat.

positive integer A whole number greater than zero.

precision of measurement A property of measurement that depends on the unit of measure used. The smaller the unit of measure, the more precise the measurement.

prime factorization Writing a number as the product of prime factors.
Example: $24 = 2 \times 2 \times 2 \times 3$

prime number A whole number greater than 1 with only two factors, itself and 1.

PRINT A command to the computer to show information on the monitor.

prism A polyhedron with two parallel, congruent faces called bases.

probability The ratio of favorable outcomes to possible outcomes of an experiment.

product The answer in multiplication.

program A list of instructions for the computer.

proper fraction A fraction in which the numerator is less than the denominator.

property of one Any number multiplied by 1 will equal the number.

proportion A sentence that states that two ratios are equal.

protractor An instrument used to measure angles.

pyramid A space figure whose base is a polygon and whose faces are triangles with a common vertex.

Pythagorean rule In a right triangle the square of the hypotenuse (*c*) equals the sum of the squares of the legs (*a* and *b*). That is, $c^2 = a^2 + b^2$.

quadrilateral A polygon with four sides and four angles whose sum is 360°.

quotient The answer in division.

radius A line segment with one endpoint at the center of a circle and the other endpoint on the circle.

range (function) All the values of *y* in a relation.

range (statistics) The difference between the greatest and the least numbers in a collection of data.

rate A ratio that compares different kinds of units.

rate of discount The percent by which a regular price is reduced.

ratio A pair of numbers that describes a rate or compares two quantities.

rational number Any number that can be expressed as a quotient of integers where the divisor is not 0. In decimal form a rational number is either repeating or terminating.

ray A part of a line that has one endpoint and extends endlessly in one direction.

real numbers All rational and irrational numbers.

reciprocals Two fractions whose product is 1.
Example: $\frac{3}{4} \times \frac{4}{3} = 1$

rectangle A parallelogram with four right angles.

reflection The mirror image of a figure.

regular polygon A polygon with all sides congruent and all angles congruent.

relation A group of ordered pairs (*x*, *y*).

relatively prime Two numbers whose GCF is 1.

REM A remark for the computer programmer, which is ignored by the computer.

repeating decimal A decimal in which a digit or group of digits repeats unendingly in a pattern.

rhombus A parallelogram with all sides congruent.

right angle   An angle that measures 90°.

right triangle   A triangle with one right angle.

rotation   A transformation obtained by rotating a figure a given turn angle about a point.

rounding   Expressing a number to the nearest ten, hundred, thousand, and so on.

RUN   An instruction that tells the computer to follow instructions one line at a time.

sample space   All the possible results, or outcomes, for an experiment.

scale drawing   A drawing that is a reduction or an enlargement of an object or distance.

scalene triangle   A triangle that has no congruent sides.

scientific notation   A product of two factors. The first factor is a number from 1 to 10. The second factor is a power of 10 in exponent form.

significant digits   In a measurement the digits that tell the number of times the unit of measure is used.

similar   Having the same shape but not necessarily the same size.

sine   The ratio of the length of the side opposite an acute angle to the length of the hypotenuse in a right triangle.

skew lines   Lines that do not intersect, and are not in the same plane.

slope   The steepness of a line. The slope of a line can be expressed as a ratio, using any two points on the line.

$$\text{slope} = \frac{\text{change in } y\text{-value}}{\text{change in } x\text{-value}}$$

solution   The value of a variable that makes a number sentence true.

solve   To find all the solutions of an equation.

space figure   A geometric figure whose points are in more than one plane.

sphere   A space figure with all points an equal distance from the center.

square (in geometry)   A rectangle with all sides congruent.

square (in numeration)   To multiply a number by itself.
Example: The square of 7 is $7 \times 7 = 7^2 = 49$.

square root   The square root of a, written $\sqrt{a}$, is the number whose square is a.
Example: The square root of 36, $\sqrt{36}$, is 6, since $6^2 = 36$.

statistics   The science of collecting, organizing, and analyzing data.

straight angle   An angle that measures 180°.

supplementary angles   Two angles, the sum of whose measures is 180°.

surface area   The sum of the areas of all the faces of a space figure.

symmetric   A plane figure is symmetric about a line if it can be folded into two congruent parts that match exactly.

tangent (tan)   The ratio of the length of the side opposite an acute angle to the length of the side adjacent to that angle in a right triangle.

terminating decimal   A decimal that ends or terminates.
Example: 0.75 is a terminating decimal.

transformation   A rigid motion of a figure in a plane.

translation   The slide image of a figure.

transversal   A line that intersects two or more lines.

trapezoid   A quadrilateral with exactly one pair of opposite sides parallel.

tree diagram   A diagram used to find outcomes of an experiment.

triangle   A polygon with three sides.

unit price   The ratio: price per unit of measure.

variable   A letter used to stand for a number in an expression or equation.

vertex   The point where two rays meet. The point of intersection of two sides of a polygon. The point of intersection of three edges of a space figure.

vertical angles   Two pairs of congruent angles formed when two lines intersect.

volume   The number of cubic units needed to fill a space figure.

y-intercept   The y value at the point where the line crosses the y-axis.

zero property of multiplication   The product of any number and 0 is 0.

Squares and Square Roots

N	N²	√N
1	1	1.00
2	4	1.41
3	9	1.73
4	16	2.00
5	25	2.24
6	36	2.45
7	49	2.65
8	64	2.83
9	81	3.00
10	100	3.16
11	121	3.32
12	144	3.46
13	169	3.61
14	196	3.74
15	225	3.87
16	256	4.00
17	289	4.12
18	324	4.24
19	361	4.36
20	400	4.47
21	441	4.58
22	484	4.69
23	529	4.80
24	576	4.90
25	625	5.00
26	676	5.10
27	729	5.20
28	784	5.29
29	841	5.39
30	900	5.48
31	961	5.57
32	1,024	5.66
33	1,089	5.74
34	1,156	5.83
35	1,225	5.92
36	1,296	6.00
37	1,369	6.08
38	1,444	6.16
39	1,521	6.24
40	1,600	6.32
41	1,681	6.40
42	1,764	6.48
43	1,849	6.56
44	1,936	6.63
45	2,025	6.71
46	2,116	6.78
47	2,209	6.86
48	2,304	6.93
49	2,401	7.00
50	2,500	7.07

N	N²	√N
51	2,601	7.14
52	2,704	7.21
53	2,809	7.28
54	2,916	7.35
55	3,025	7.42
56	3,136	7.48
57	3,249	7.55
58	3,364	7.62
59	3,481	7.68
60	3,600	7.75
61	3,721	7.81
62	3,844	7.87
63	3,969	7.94
64	4,096	8.00
65	4,225	8.06
66	4,356	8.12
67	4,489	8.19
68	4,624	8.25
69	4,761	8.31
70	4,900	8.37
71	5,041	8.43
72	5,184	8.49
73	5,329	8.54
74	5,476	8.60
75	5,625	8.66
76	5,776	8.72
77	5,929	8.77
78	6,084	8.83
79	6,241	8.89
80	6,400	8.94
81	6,561	9.00
82	6,724	9.06
83	6,889	9.11
84	7,056	9.17
85	7,225	9.22
86	7,396	9.27
87	7,569	9.33
88	7,744	9.38
89	7,921	9.43
90	8,100	9.49
91	8,281	9.54
92	8,464	9.59
93	8,649	9.64
94	8,836	9.70
95	9,025	9.75
96	9,216	9.80
97	9,409	9.85
98	9,604	9.90
99	9,801	9.95
100	10,000	10.00

N	N²	√N
101	10,201	10.05
102	10,404	10.10
103	10,609	10.15
104	10,816	10.20
105	11,025	10.25
106	11,236	10.30
107	11,449	10.34
108	11,664	10.39
109	11,881	10.44
110	12,100	10.49
111	12,321	10.54
112	12,544	10.58
113	12,769	10.63
114	12,996	10.68
115	13,225	10.72
116	13,456	10.77
117	13,689	10.82
118	13,924	10.86
119	14,161	10.91
120	14,400	10.95
121	14,641	11.00
122	14,884	11.05
123	15,129	11.09
124	15,376	11.14
125	15,625	11.18
126	15,876	11.22
127	16,129	11.27
128	16,384	11.31
129	16,641	11.36
130	16,900	11.40
131	17,161	11.45
132	17,424	11.49
133	17,689	11.53
134	17,956	11.58
135	18,225	11.62
136	18,496	11.66
137	18,769	11.70
138	19,044	11.75
139	19,321	11.79
140	19,600	11.83
141	19,881	11.87
142	20,164	11.92
143	20,449	11.96
144	20,736	12.00
145	21,025	12.04
146	21,316	12.08
147	21,609	12.12
148	21,904	12.17
149	22,201	12.21
150	22,500	12.25

Sines, Cosines, and Tangents

Degrees	Sin	Cos	Tan	Degrees	Sin	Cos	Tan
1	0.0175	0.9998	0.0175	46	0.7193	0.6947	1.0355
2	0.0349	0.9994	0.0349	47	0.7314	0.6820	1.0724
3	0.0523	0.9986	0.0524	48	0.7431	0.6691	1.1106
4	0.0698	0.9976	0.0699	49	0.7547	0.6561	1.1504
5	0.0872	0.9962	0.0875	50	0.7660	0.6428	1.1918
6	0.1045	0.9945	0.1051	51	0.7771	0.6293	1.2349
7	0.1219	0.9925	0.1228	52	0.7880	0.6157	1.2799
8	0.1392	0.9903	0.1405	53	0.7986	0.6018	1.3270
9	0.1564	0.9877	0.1584	54	0.8090	0.5878	1.3764
10	0.1736	0.9848	0.1763	55	0.8192	0.5736	1.4281
11	0.1908	0.9816	0.1944	56	0.8290	0.5592	1.4826
12	0.2079	0.9781	0.2126	57	0.8387	0.5446	1.5399
13	0.2250	0.9744	0.2309	58	0.8480	0.5299	1.6003
14	0.2419	0.9703	0.2493	59	0.8572	0.5150	1.6643
15	0.2588	0.9659	0.2679	60	0.8660	0.5000	1.7321
16	0.2756	0.9613	0.2867	61	0.8746	0.4848	1.8040
17	0.2924	0.9563	0.3057	62	0.8829	0.4695	1.8807
18	0.3090	0.9511	0.3249	63	0.8910	0.4540	1.9626
19	0.3256	0.9455	0.3443	64	0.8988	0.4384	2.0503
20	0.3420	0.9397	0.3640	65	0.9063	0.4226	2.1445
21	0.3584	0.9336	0.3839	66	0.9135	0.4067	2.2460
22	0.3746	0.9272	0.4040	67	0.9205	0.3907	2.3559
23	0.3907	0.9205	0.4245	68	0.9272	0.3746	2.4751
24	0.4067	0.9135	0.4452	69	0.9336	0.3584	2.6051
25	0.4226	0.9063	0.4663	70	0.9397	0.3420	2.7475
26	0.4384	0.8988	0.4877	71	0.9455	0.3256	2.9042
27	0.4540	0.8910	0.5095	72	0.9511	0.3090	3.0777
28	0.4695	0.8829	0.5317	73	0.9563	0.2924	3.2709
29	0.4848	0.8746	0.5543	74	0.9613	0.2756	3.4874
30	0.5000	0.8660	0.5774	75	0.9659	0.2588	3.7321
31	0.5150	0.8572	0.6009	76	0.9703	0.2419	4.0108
32	0.5299	0.8480	0.6249	77	0.9744	0.2250	4.3315
33	0.5446	0.8387	0.6494	78	0.9781	0.2079	4.7046
34	0.5592	0.8290	0.6745	79	0.9816	0.1908	5.1446
35	0.5736	0.8192	0.7002	80	0.9848	0.1736	5.6713
36	0.5878	0.8090	0.7265	81	0.9877	0.1564	6.3138
37	0.6018	0.7986	0.7536	82	0.9903	0.1392	7.1154
38	0.6157	0.7880	0.7813	83	0.9925	0.1219	8.1443
39	0.6293	0.7771	0.8098	84	0.9945	0.1045	9.5144
40	0.6428	0.7660	0.8391	85	0.9962	0.0872	11.4301
41	0.6561	0.7547	0.8693	86	0.9976	0.0698	14.3007
42	0.6691	0.7431	0.9004	87	0.9986	0.0523	19.0811
43	0.6820	0.7314	0.9325	88	0.9994	0.0349	28.6363
44	0.6947	0.7193	0.9657	89	0.9998	0.0175	57.2900
45	0.7071	0.7071	1.0000	90	1.0000	0.0000	—

TABLE OF MEASURES

METRIC

LENGTH
1 millimeter (mm) = 0.001 meter (m)
1 centimeter (cm) = 0.01 meter
1 decimeter (dm) = 0.1 meter
1 dekameter (dam) = 10 meters
1 hectometer (hm) = 100 meters
1 kilometer (km) = 1,000 meters

MASS/WEIGHT
1 milligram (mg) = 0.001 gram (g)
1 centigram (cg) = 0.01 gram
1 decigram (dg) = 0.1 gram
1 dekagram (dag) = 10 grams
1 hectogram (hg) = 100 grams
1 kilogram (kg) = 1,000 grams
1 metric ton (t) = 1,000 kilograms

CAPACITY
1 milliliter (mL) = 0.001 liter (L)
1 centiliter (cL) = 0.01 liter
1 deciliter (dL) = 0.1 liter
1 dekaliter (daL) = 10 liters
1 hectoliter (hL) = 100 liters
1 kiloliter (kL) = 1,000 liters

AREA
1 square centimeter (cm²) = 100 square millimeters (mm²)
1 square meter (m²) = 10,000 square centimeters
1 hectare (ha) = 10,000 square meters
1 square kilometer (km²) = 1,000,000 square meters

CUSTOMARY

LENGTH
1 foot (ft) = 12 inches (in.)
1 yard (yd) = 36 inches
1 yard = 3 feet
1 mile (mi) = 5,280 feet
1 mile = 1,760 yards

WEIGHT
1 pound (lb) = 16 ounces (oz)
1 ton (T) = 2,000 pounds

CAPACITY
1 cup (c) = 8 fluid ounces (fl oz)
1 pint (pt) = 2 cups
1 quart (qt) = 2 pints
1 quart = 4 cups
1 gallon (gal) = 4 quarts

AREA
1 square foot (ft²) = 144 square inches (in.²)
1 square yard (yd²) = 9 square feet
1 acre = 43,560 square feet
1 square mile (mi²) = 640 acres

TIME
1 minute (min) = 60 seconds (s)
1 hour (h) = 60 minutes
1 day (d) = 24 hours
1 week (wk) = 7 days
1 year (yr) = 12 months (mo)
1 year = 52 weeks
1 year = 365 days
1 century (c) = 100 years

FORMULAS

$P = 2(l + w)$ — Perimeter of a rectangle
$P = 4s$ — Perimeter of a square
$P = ns$ — Perimeter of a regular polygon
n = number of sides
$A = lw$ — Area of a rectangle
$A = s^2$ — Area of a square
$A = bh$ — Area of a parallelogram
$A = \frac{1}{2}bh$ — Area of a triangle
$A = \frac{1}{2}h(b_1 + b_2)$ — Area of a trapezoid
$C = \pi d$, or $2\pi r$ — Circumference of a circle
$A = \pi r^2$ — Area of a circle

$V = lwh$ — Volume of a rectangular prism
$V = Bh$ — Volume of any prism
$V = \pi r^2 h$ — Volume of a cylinder
$V = \frac{1}{3}Bh$ — Volume of a pyramid
$V = \frac{1}{3}\pi r^2 h$ — Volume of a cone
$SA = 2\pi r^2 + \pi dh$ — Surface area of a cylinder
$a^2 + b^2 = c^2$ — Pythagorean Theorem
$I = prt$ — Simple interest
$d = rt$ — Distance

SYMBOLS

$=$	is equal to
$\neq$	is not equal to
$>$	is greater than
$<$	is less than
$\geq$	is greater than or equal to
$\leq$	is less than or equal to
$\approx$	is approximately equal to
$\cong$	is congruent to
$\sim$	is similar to
. . .	continues without end
$1.\overline{3}$	repeating decimal 1.333 . . .
%	percent
π	pi (approximately 3.14)
°	degree
°C	degree Celsius
°F	degree Fahrenheit
$\overleftrightarrow{AB}$	line AB
$\overline{AB}$	line segment AB
$\overrightarrow{AB}$	ray AB
$\angle ABC$	angle ABC
m$\angle ABC$	measure of angle ABC
$\triangle ABC$	triangle ABC
$\overarc{AB}$	arc AB
$\parallel$	is parallel to
$\perp$	is perpendicular to
2:5	ratio of 2 to 5
10^2	ten to the second power
$\sqrt{\ }$	square root
$^+4$	positive 4
$^-4$	negative 4
$\lvert^-4\rvert$	absolute value of $^-4$
$(3, ^-4)$	ordered pair 3, $^-4$
$P(E)$	probability of event E
sin 45°	sine of 45°
cos 45°	cosine of 45°
tan 45°	tangent of 45°

Index

CREDITS

Design by Silver Burdett & Ginn

Contributing design by Taurens Associates

Cover: Computer Art/Ron Morecraft and Nancy Moore

Photographs and illustrations by Silver Burdett & Ginn except as noted below

All line art by BurMar unless otherwise noted.

Chapter 1 1: Julie Habel/West Light. 2,3: Lane Yerkes. 4: Focus on Sports. 5: *t.l.*, *b.l.* ©Gerard Vandystadt/Photo Researchers, Inc.; *t.r.* Sally Schaedler; *b.r.* Jerry Wachter/Focus on Sports. 6: Martin Rogers/Stock, Boston. 8: Art Resource/Scala/Bildarchiv Foto Marburg. 10: Steven Schindler. 11: *t.*, *m.* Kathie Kelleher; *b.* Suzanne Clee. 12: Lane Yerkes. 16: Blanche Sims. 18: Len Ebert. 19: ©Danny Brass/Photo Researchers, Inc. 20: Jeremy Guitar. 21: *t.* Jeremy Guitar; *b.* David Reinbold. 23: *r.* Eulala Conner. 24: *t.* Peter Krempasky. 25: Tom Powers. 28: Kathie Kelleher.

Chapter 2 29: Owen Franken/Stock, Boston. 30: *t.* Flag Research Center; *b.* Al Fenn for Silver Burdett & Ginn, photo courtesy Time Inc. 31: Peter Krempasky. 32: *l.* Peter Krempasky; *r.* Flag Research Center. 33: Leo deWys, Inc. 34: *t.* Flag Research Center; *m.* Peter Krempasky; *b.* Richard Pilling/Focus on Sports. 35: ©1984 Topps Chewing Gum, Inc. 36: *l.* Peter Krempasky; *t.r.*, *t.m.r.* Flag Research Center; *m.*, *b.m.r.*, *b.r.* Dan De Wilde for Silver Burdett & Ginn. 37: Peter Krempasky. 38: *t.r.* Flag Research Center; *b.* Lane Yerkes. 39: Peter Krempasky. 40,41: Kathie Kelleher. 42: *t.* Flag Research Center; *b.* Nancy Schill. 43: Lane Yerkes. 44: *l.* Culver Pictures; *r.* Flag Research Center. 46: *t.*, *b.* Flag Research Center. 46–47: Nancy Schill. 48: *l.* Peter Krempasky; *r.* Flag Research Center; *b.r.* Phil Degginger. 50: *t.* Flag Research Center; *m.*, *b.* Focus on Sports. 52: *l.* Peter Krempasky; *r.* Flag Research Center; *b.* E.R. Degginger. 54: Jeremy Guitar. 55: *t.* Bradley Clark; *b.* Kathie Kelleher. 58–59: Peter Krempasky.

Chapter 3 61: Focus on Sports. 62: *t.* Lane Yerkes; *b.* Peter Krempasky. 63: NASA. 64: *b.* ©Robert Goldstein/Photo Researchers, Inc. 65: Herman Vestal. 66: Gary Undercuffler. 67: *b.* Courtesy, Bausch & Lomb. 68: *m.* Dan De Wilde for Silver Burdett & Ginn; *b.* ©Porterfield-Chickering/Photo Researchers, Inc. 69: Peter Krempasky. 70–71: Focus on Sports. 72: *l.* Peter Krempasky; *r.* Lane Yerkes. 74: *t.* Konrad Hack; *b.* Steven Schindler. 75: *t.* Focus on Sports; *b.* Bradley Clark. 76: Lane Yerkes. 77: Ken Lax/The Stock Shop. 78–79: Bradley Clark. 80: Konrad Hack. 81: David Madison/Duomo. 84: Pat Traub.

Chapter 4 89: ©George Hall/Woodfin Camp & Associates. 90,91: Les Gray. 92,93: Peter Krempasky. 94: Eulala Conner. 96: Konrad Hack. 98: E.R. Degginger. 100: *t.* Robert Jackson; *b.* courtesy of the Montana Historical Society. 101: North Dakota Department of Parks and Recreation. 104: *l.* Michelle Epstein; *r.* Hans Huber/The Stock Shop. 105: IMAGERY. 106: Don Dyen. 107: ©Southern Living/Photo Researchers, Inc. 108: Phil Degginger/Bruce Coleman. 111: *r.* Michelle Epstein. 113: *t.* Dennis O'Brien; *b.* S. Vidler/Leo deWys, Inc. 116: Suzanne Clee.

Chapter 5 117: Jim Holland/Stock, Boston. 118–119: Stephen Marchesi. 120: *t.* Victoria Beller-Smith for Silver Burdett & Ginn. 122: Matchbox/Lesney Products. 124: Russell Dian for Silver Burdett & Ginn. 125: Eulala Conner. 126: Kathie Kelleher. 127: *m.* Kathie Kelleher. 128: *t.* Paul Kuhn/Tom Stack & Associates; *b.* Michal Heron. 129: Eulala Conner. 130: Stephen Marchesi. 131: Victoria Beller-Smith for Silver Burdett & Ginn. 132: R.W. Tignor/Virginia Community College System. 134: *t.* Eulala Conner; *b.* Everett C. Johnson/Leo deWys, Inc. 135: Laird/Leo deWys, Inc. 136: *t.* Konrad Hack. 137: Lyle Miller. 140–141: Dennis O'Brien.

Chapter 6 145: ©Russ Kinne/Photo Researchers, Inc.; *inset* Eric Carle/Shostal Associates. 146: *t.* Peter Krempasky; *b.* Tom Leonard. 148: *t.r.* Michal Heron for Silver Burdett & Ginn; *t.l.* Peter Krempasky. 149: Gary Undercuffler. 150: Jackie Rogers. 152: Konrad Hack. 153: Stock Thode/International Stock Photo. 154–155: Don Dyen. 156: *l.* Michal Heron for Silver Burdett & Ginn; *r.* Gary Undercuffler. 157: Gary Undercuffler. 158: Steven Schindler. 159: *t.* Eulala Conner; *b.* Suzanne Clee. 160: Stephanie Maze. 161: Laura Riley/Bruce Coleman. 162–163: Floyd Cooper. 164: Samantha Smith. 165: E.R. Degginger/Bruce Coleman. 166: Kathie Kelleher. 167: *t.* Peter Krempasky; *b.* Don Dyen. 169: Suzanne Clee. 170: *l.* Kathie Kelleher; *r.* Lyle Miller. 171: Kathie Kelleher. 173: Michelle Epstein. 174: Kirby Harrison. 175: Suzanne Clee.

Chapter 7 177: Charles Moore/Black Star; *inset* ©Alan Carey/Photo Researchers, Inc. 178: *overlay* Allison Fazio; *b.* Suzanne Clee. 180: *t.* E.R. Degginger; *b.* Norman Owen Tomalin/Bruce Coleman. 182–183: E.R. Degginger. 184: Ed Cooper. 185: Steven Schindler. 186: *t.* Eulala Conner. 189: *t.l.* E.R. Degginger; *t.r.*, *b.l.* Mike Mazzachi/Stock, Boston; *b.r.* Philip Jon Bailey/Taurus Photos. 190: *l.* Chris Newbert/Bruce Coleman; *m.t.* Jeffrey Rotman/Peter Arnold, Inc.; *m.b.* Manfred Kage/Peter Arnold, Inc. 192: Eulala Conner. 193: Steven Schindler. 194–195: Leslie Dunlap. 196: *t.* J. Howard/Stock, Boston. 198: *t.* ©Georg Gerster/Photo Researchers, Inc. 200: *t.*, *r.* ©Georg Gerster/Photo Researchers, Inc. 201: *m.* ©Georg Gerster/Photo Researchers, Inc. 202: *t.* Leslie Dunlap. 203: Stephen Marchesi. 208: *t.* Dan De Wilde for Silver Burdett & Ginn. 209: *t.* Michal Heron for Silver Burdett & Ginn; *m.* Michael Anderson/Folio; *b.* Walter Hodges/West Stock.

Chapter 8 213: ©Lucasfilm Ltd. (LFL) 1980. All rights reserved.; *inset* ©Lucasfilm Ltd. (LFL) 1983. All rights reserved. Courtesy of Lucasfilm Ltd. 214: *b.* Al Fenn for Silver Burdett & Ginn, photo courtesy Time Inc. 215: Lane Yerkes. 216: The Granger Collection. 218: Courtesy Fitzgerald Sporting Goods, Morristown, N.J. 220–221: Tom Powers. 222: NASA/Johnson Space Center. 223: Len Ebert. 224: Steve Moore. 228: *t.* John Hamberger. 229: *b.* John Hamberger. 230: *t.* Rick Del Rossi. 231: *b.* Tony Arruza/Bruce Coleman. 232: ©Lawrence Migdale/Photo Researchers, Inc. 233: *t.* Leslie Dunlap; *b.r.* Steven Schindler. 236: *l.* The Louvre, Art Resource.

Chapter 9 239: Murray Greenberg/Shostal Associates. 240: Larry Lee/West Light. 241: Suzanne Clee. 242: Steve Ross/Photo Unique. 244–245: E.R. Degginger. 246: Victoria Beller-Smith for Silver Burdett & Ginn. 248–249: Stephen Marchesi. 250–251: Gerald Corsi/Tom Stack & Associates. 252: James Watling. 253: *b.* Tom Powers. 254: *t.* Suzanne Clee; *b.* Michal Heron for Silver Burdett & Ginn. 255: Michal Heron for Silver Burdett & Ginn. 256: Lane Yerkes. 258: *t.* Suzanne Clee; *b.* IMAGERY. 259: *b.r.* Stephen Marchesi. 260: Courtesy M. Epstein. 262–263: Stephen Marchesi. 264: John Hamberger. 267: Lane Yerkes. 268: *t.* Dennis O'Brien; *b.* Stephen Marchesi. 270: Walter Hodges/West Stock.

Chapter 10 273: Robert McKenzie/Tom Stack & Associates. 274: *t.* Steven C. Kaufman/Peter Arnold, Inc. 274: *b.* IMAGERY. 275: A Hirai/Shostal Associates. 276: Samantha Smith. 278: The Granger Collection. 279: Suzanne Clee. 280: Samantha Smith. 282: *t.* Ondre Pettingill; *b.* Michal Heron for Silver Burdett & Ginn. 283: J. Michael McCormick. 284: Suzanne Clee. 285: Phil Degginger. 286: *l.* Keith Gunnar/Bruce Coleman; *r.* Spencer Swanger/Tom Stack & Associates. 288: *t.r.* Dennis O'Brien. 290: *t.r.* Dennis O'Brien. 290–291: Charles Varner. 292: Keith Gunnar/Bruce Coleman. 293: *r.* John Weeks. 296: *b.* Ondre Pettingill.

505

CREDITS

Chapter 11 299: E.R. Degginger. 302: *l.* J. Michael McCormick; *r.* Michal Heron. 303: ©1987 George Hall/Woodfin Camp & Associates. 304–305: Austrian National Tourist Office. 308: C. Henneghien/Bruce Coleman. 310: Jerry Wachter/Focus on Sports; *inset* Culver Pictures. 312: *l.* Dan De Wilde for Silver Burdett & Ginn. 313: Bill Colrus. 314: Wendell Metzen/Bruce Coleman. 316: Lane Yerkes. 317: *t.* Peter Krempasky. 318–319: ©1986 by Dale Seymour. 320–321: Lane Yerkes. 322: The Granger Collection. 323: Novosti from Sovfoto. 324: *t.* S. Dudhediya/Shostal Associates. 326: *l.* Sally Schaedler. 330: *t.* ©1987 John Estcott YVA Momatiuk/Woodfin Camp & Associates. 332: *m.* Sally Schaedler. 333: *m.* Sally Schaedler. 335: *t.l., b.r.* Sally Schaedler. 336: *t.* Michal Heron.

Chapter 12 341: Werner Miller/Peter Arnold, Inc. 342: The Bettmann Archive. 345: Art Resource. 344–347: ©1988 by Dale Seymour. 348: *r.* Norman Owen Tomalin/Bruce Coleman. 350,351: Lawrence Migdale. 354: *t.* Stacy Pick/Stock, Boston. 355: *b.* D. Brewster/Bruce Coleman. 358: ©Earl Roberge/Photo Researchers, Inc. 360: *t.r.* Bob Burch/Photo Unique. 362: *t.r.* Steve Moore. 363: *b.* J.P. Nacivet/Leo deWys, Inc. 365: *t.* ©Brian Blake/Photo Researchers, Inc. 369: *t.* Eberhard Streichan/Shostal Associates: *b.* Gene Ahrens/Shostal Associates.

Chapter 13 371: Erich Lessing/Magnum; *inset* Historical Picture Service. 372: *t.* Smithsonian Institution; *b.* Chuck Yeager/Wide World Photos. 374: NASA. 375: *t.* Suzanne Clee. 376: Courtesy, U.S. Navy. 377: Dick Hufnagle/Monkmeyer Press. 378: *t.* Steve Moore. 380–381: ©M. Serraillier/Photo Researchers, Inc. 381: Bill Stanton/International Stock Photo. 382: The Bettmann Archive. 387: Lane Yerkes. 390: Egyptian Expedition of The Metropolitan Museum of Art, Rogers Fund, 1930. 392: *t.* Rene Pauli/Shostal Associates. 393: *r.* NASA. 394: *b.r.* IMAGERY for Silver Burdett & Ginn. 396: *t.* Tom Powers; *b.* ©Joyce Photographics/Photo Researchers, Inc. 397: Lane Yerkes. 400: Tom Powers; *inset* Smithsonian Institution. 403: Michal Heron.

Chapter 14 405: Susan Van Etten/Picture Cube. 406, 407: J. Michael McCormick. 408, 409: E.R. Degginger. 410–411: John Hamberger. 412: E.R. Degginger. 414: Leslie Dunlap. 415: *b.* Don Dyen. 416–417: *b.* Painting by Michele Sanok. 418–419: John Hamberger. 420: *t.* Alastair Black/Focus on Sports; *b.* Lane Yerkes. 421: *t.* Gary Undercuffler; *b.* Al Grotell. 423: *t.* Ginger Chih/Peter Arnold, Inc. 424, 425: E.R. Degginger.

Chapter 15 431: ©Dr. Fred Espenale/Photo Researchers, Inc. 432: *t.* Lithograph by Honore Daumier, courtesy, Museum of Fine Arts, Boston. 433: *t.* E.R. Degginger. 434: *t.* NASA. 436: *t.* Kathie Kelleher. 440: *r.* NASA. 441: *b.* NASA/Johnson Space Center. 442: Steve Vidler/Leo deWys, Inc. 443: NASA. 446,447: ©M.C. Escher %Cordon Art-Baarn-Holland. 448: Leslie Dunlap. 449: National Air and Space Museum, Washington, D.C. 452: *t.l.,b.r.* Steve Moore. 454: *l.* Don Dyen; *m., r.* The Granger Collection.

ABCDEFGHIJ—RRD—96 95 94 93 92 91 90 89 88